Practical
Knowledge for All

Our Colour Plates

(1) ON THE OCEAN FLOOR

Here is such a scene as a diver might observe on a bank of sea moss off one of the West Indian islands. Top left is a flat Angel fish ; next comes a pair of Sea-Horses, and then a school of Blennies. Below is a red Sea Fan (colony of coral) ; and, below that, a hideous Gurnard. On the right are Sea Anemones, and bottom left a Sea Urchin and a Mushroom Coral.

(2) BUILDERS OF CORAL ISLANDS

In our second plate are illustrated a number of types of coral. Top left is Rhipidogorgia flabellum, or Venus's Fan, as it is popularly called. Below it, in descending order, are Isis hippuris, Heliopora coerulea, or Blue Coral, and Tubipora musica, or Organ-Pipe Coral. Clearly recognizable in the centre is Diploria cerebriformis, or Brain Coral, beneath which is Leptogorgia sarmentosa. Then on the right are Corallium nobile, Plexaurella vermiculata and Equisetella gregorii, while at the bottom of the picture may be seen some tufts of Moseleya latistellata.

ZOOLOGY 36

PRACTICAL KNOWLEDGE FOR ALL

Sir John Hammerton

Comprising Easy Courses in Literature Language History Geography the Arts and Sciences Written by Experts and Arranged for Home Study

NEWLY REVISED EDITION

In Six Handy Volumes with over 360 Special
Plates including Twelve in Full Colours
and about 1300 other Illustrations

SIXTH VOLUME

LONDON
THE WAVERLEY BOOK COMPANY LTD.

Printed in Great Britain by The Amalgamated Press, Ltd., London

LITERARY CONTENTS

OF VOLUME VI

COMPLETE LIST OF COURSES

ACCOUNTANCY	ECONOMICS	LATIN
AERONAUTICS	ENGINEERING	MATHEMATICS
ART & ARCHITECTURE	ENGLISH LANGUAGE	MODERN HISTORY
ASTRONOMY	ENGLISH LITERATURE	PHILOSOPHY
BIOLOGY	FRENCH	PHYSICS
BOTANY	GEOGRAPHY	PHYSIOGRAPHY
BRITISH HISTORY	GEOLOGY	PHYSIOLOGY
CHEMISTRY	GERMAN	SHORTHAND
DRAWING & DESIGN	HISTORY : ANCIENT &	SPANISH
ECONOMIC GEOGRAPHY	MEDIEVAL	ZOOLOGY

LIST OF SPECIAL PLATES
IN VOLUME VI

Frontispieces in Colour :
On the Ocean Floor ; Builders of Coral Islands

Maps and Plans in the Text

LESSON 19

More About the Balance Sheet

LIABILITIES may be divided into two classes, short- and long-term. Short-term liabilities are obligations which must be met either immediately or within a short space of time, while long-term liabilities are more in the nature of an investment of capital. Economically, a loan for a period of, say, ten years is an investment of capital just as much as the purchase of shares in a limited company. In both cases funds which can be used for general business purposes are acquired, and in both cases there is freedom from the anxiety of any sudden demand for repayment. Legally, of course, a loan is distinct from a subscription to capital and must be separately stated in the Balance Sheet. In estimating the financial position of a concern, however, long-term loans and capital may be conveniently classed together. Long-term liabilities may take the form of mortgages and debentures ; short-term liabilities consist of credit balances on bought ledger accounts (trade creditors), bills payable, and expenses accrued.

The Balance Sheet is an interesting and sometimes complicated document. If it is badly drafted, it may be completely impossible to form a correct estimate of the true position of the undertaking, and even if it is properly drawn up it may require close study before an intelligent opinion can be formed. It is not sufficient to observe the figure on the Profit and Loss Account. In the first place, the correctness of that figure depends, as we have seen, upon the values that are placed upon the assets. The basis upon which the assets are valued should therefore be closely scrutinized. Secondly, the existence of a credit balance upon Profit and Loss Account is not proof, in itself, that the business is in a sound position. It is of vital importance to ascertain the amount of the *working capital*. The word " capital " is used, unfortunately, in a number of different senses ; it is used to denote the proprietors' capital account, or, in the case of a company, the Share Capital Account, and it is also used to denote the assets which represent the original investment of capital, together with undistributed profits.

Working capital denotes that proportion of original capital, plus undistributed profits, which is represented by floating, as distinct from fixed assets. In precise terms, working capital may be defined as the excess of floating assets over current liabilities, that is, the amount by which the assets which will in the near future be converted into cash exceed the claims of creditors which will fall due in the near future. If the current liabilities exceed the value of the assets which will, in the ordinary course of business, be converted into cash, the undertaking is clearly in a dangerous position ; it has no working capital. If, on the other hand, floating assets exceed current liabilities, the business is in a position to meet its obligations as they fall due, and the amount of the working capital is a measure of the strength of the concern.

It is quite possible for a business to be short of working capital, even if there is a large credit balance upon the Profit and Loss Account. An excessive volume of funds may have been injudiciously invested in acquiring new fixed assets, and many businesses have literally been ruined by success. Large profits have sometimes led to an over-rapid expansion and the excessive purchasing of new equipment, with the result that liquid funds are insufficient for immediate liabilities.

Long-term liabilities may be secured or unsecured. A secured creditor is one who has priority as to repayment over unsecured creditors. Certain assets may be legitimately earmarked against a loan, even though considerable amounts are due to trade creditors. In the event of the business being wound up, the proceeds of the earmarked assets would be first applied to paying the secured creditors in full, before the unsecured creditors can claim a penny.

Long-term loans usually take the form of an issue of debentures. A debenture is a loan evidenced by a certain document, analogous to a share certificate, which is evidence of the ownership of shares. Like shares, debentures are usually divided into amounts of fixed denominations. Debentures may be issued at their nominal value, at a discount or at a premium. The book-keeping entries are similar to those necessary to record the issue of shares.

Classes of Debentures. Debentures may be of three classes : naked, specific or floating A naked debenture is simply an unsecured loan, and is seldom found in practice. Specific and floating debentures are both secured loans, the security in each case being different in nature.

MORE ABOUT THE BALANCE SHEET

A specific debenture is one which is secured by the mortgage (or, in ordinary language, the earmarking) of certain specific and usually fixed assets. The company may continue to use, for business purposes, the fixed assets which have been mortgaged, but it is not at liberty to dispose of them.

A floating debenture is one which is secured by some or all of the assets of the company, present and future. Under a floating charge, the company may do as it likes with its assets; it may buy and sell, and continually change their nature. If the floating charge covers, as it invariably does, floating assets, this provision is clearly necessary, since a continual change in the constitution of the floating assets must inevitably take place if the business is to be carried on. Debtors pay their debts, and cash takes the place of book-debts; stock is sold, and book-debts take the place of stock; stock is purchased, and so on.

A floating charge is said to crystallize when a specified event happens. The specified event, in practice, is the insolvency of the company, or, at least, grave danger of insolvency. When a floating charge crystallizes the control of the company over the assets ceases; it can no longer dispose of the assets, or change their nature in any way. Control normally passes to a receiver, who is the agent of the debenture-holders, and whose duty it is to realize the assets, so that the debenture-holders may be repaid out of the proceeds.

A floating charge is generally wider than a specific or fixed charge, since it usually covers a larger volume of assets, but it carries with it the disadvantage that the company is not restricted as to the use it makes of the assets, and the value of the security therefore depends upon the general position of the company. Furthermore, specific mortgages of certain assets may be created subsequent to the floating charge, and ranking prior to it (as to the assets specifically mortgaged), even though the floating charge is expressed as covering all assets, present and future. Thus, from some points of view, a specific debenture is preferable to a floating debenture.

The conditions of an issue of debentures are usually set out in a document termed the debenture trust deed. If the proceeds of the secured assets are insufficient to meet the claims of the debenture-holder, he may claim for the balance on the same level with the unsecured creditors. All debentures must be registered with the Registrar of Joint-Stock Companies at Somerset House.

LESSON 20

Balance Sheets and the Companies Act

I T is not proposed here to attempt a survey of Company Law. A very brief outline of the legal procedure in the formation of a limited company is set out in Lesson 15 (Volume 5, page 20). Since, however, Lessons 18 and 19 have been devoted to the examination of the Balance Sheet, it is appropriate to review the provisions of the 1929 Act which are relevant. The general policy guiding the drafting of the Act was the insistence upon the need for the disclosure of fuller information in the published accounts of limited companies. Such a reform was by no means premature, and it is very possible that the law, particularly with regard to holding companies, will be strengthened.

The following information must appear on the Balance Sheet :

(1) A summary of the authorized and of the issued Share Capital.

(2) A summary of liabilities and assets.

(3) Fixed assets must be distinguished from floating assets ; it is illegal to group any fixed and floating assets in one composite item.

(4) The basis of valuation of fixed assets must be stated.

(5) The following must be stated under separate headings :
   (a) Preliminary expenses.
   (b) Expenses in connexion with the issue of shares and debentures, in so far as they are not written off.
   (c) Goodwill, patents and trade-marks.

(6) If any liability of the company is secured by a charge on any of the assets, this fact must be stated, although it is not necessary to disclose the nature of the security.

(7) Any loans to directors must be separately stated in the Balance Sheet, including any loans repaid during the period of the accounts ; e.g. suppose on Jan. 1 £1,000 is due from a director to the company. On December 30 £950 is repaid. The balance of £50 would be set out in the Balance Sheet as follows :

Loans to Directors.

As at January 1	£1,000
Less Repayments	950
As at December 31	£50

It would otherwise be possible for the director to borrow the £950 again on January 1 in the next period, to repay it on the following December 30, and thus to remain almost permanently in possession of £1,000 without the fact being disclosed in the Balance Sheet.

(8) The total remuneration of the directors must be separately stated in the Profit and Loss Account, with the exception of the managing director's salary.

(9) It is illegal for a company to purchase, either directly or indirectly, its own shares, except by way of loan to employees or to trustees for employees, in order to enable the employees or their trustees to acquire fully-paid shares. Any such loans must be separately stated in the Balance Sheet.

(10) There are certain provisions governing the Balance Sheets of holding companies which will be dealt with in later Lessons.

The provisions governing the issue of Redeemable Preference Shares will now be described. Prior to the 1929 Act it was illegal for a company to purchase its own shares, or to redeem any of its share capital by repayment to shareholders. Under the 1929 Act it has become possible for a company to issue Redeemable Preference Shares.

The conditions are :

(1) Such shares can be redeemed only when fully paid.

(2) They can be redeemed only (a) out of profits, or (b) out of the proceeds of a new issue of capital.

If the shares are redeemed out of profits, an amount equal to the sum applied in redemption must be transferred from Profit and Loss Account (or from General Reserve) to the credit of an account termed ' Capital Redemption Reserve Fund." The amount of this fund cannot be written back to the Profit and Loss Account, or used for paying dividends In this way a part of the company's profits takes the place of Preference Share Capital which has been redeemed and the assets representing these profits take the place of the assets representing the capital, in so far as they cannot be used for dividends In this way the general principle that the capital fund available for creditors may not be deliberately reduced (except in special circumstances) remains unimpaired.

For the purpose of illustration we may suppose that a limited company had issued 40,000 Redeemable Preference Shares, redeemable at a premium of one shilling per share. The Directors decide to redeem the whole issue out of general reserve, which stands at £70,000. The entries will be as follow :

Redeemable Preference Shares Account.

To Sundry Share-				
holders..	£40,000	By Balance	£40,000

General Reserve.

To Capital Redemp-		By Balance	£70,000
tion Reserve Fund	£40,000		
To Sundry Share-			
holders (Premium			
on redemption) ..	2,000		
To Balance	28,000		
	£70,000		£70,000
		By Balance	£28,000

Capital Redemption Reserve Fund.

	By General Reserve..	£40,000

Sundry Shareholders.

To Cash	£42,000	By Redeemable Pre-	
		ference Shares Ac-	
		count	£40,000
		By General Reserve..	2,000
	£42,000		£42,000

It will be noticed that the premium on the redemption is provided for out of the undistributed profits, and that an amount equal to the original balance of the Redeemable Preference Shares Account is capitalized in the Capital Redemption Reserve Fund.

Reduction of Capital. The law has always stressed the importance of preserving the capital of limited companies intact. Such a requirement must logically accompany the privilege of limited liability, since, if creditors have no claim upon the private property of members, it is only fair that they should be assured of the integrity of the capital that has been subscribed. Under certain circumstances, however, reduction of capital is permissible. Reduction may take any one of the following forms : (1) Cancellation of unissued capital. (2) Forfeiture of shares. (3) Cancellation of uncalled liability. (4) Return of cash to shareholders. (5) Writing off capital on account of losses, or permanent decline in asset values.

In the first two cases there are no formalities. A cancellation of unissued capital affects nobody ; forfeiture of shares is only possible on the default of the shareholder. In the remaining three cases, however, a general meeting of the company must be called and the reduction sanctioned by a special resolution ; furthermore, the consent of the court is required. In cases (3) and (4), the cancellation of uncalled liability, and a return of cash to shareholders. the fund available for creditors is reduced, and before sanctioning the reduction the court will order an inquiry into the liabilities of the company, *and all* the creditors must either consent to the reduction or be paid in full before the reduction can take effect.

" Writing Off " Procedure. The fifth is the usual form of reduction. In this case, as the fund available for creditors is not affected, the court makes no inquiry into the liabilities of the company. The transaction is purely a book-keeping one. If assets have permanently depreciated in value, or if a large debit balance exists on the Profit and Loss Account, the procedure is simply to credit the appropriate asset accounts. or the debit balance on the Profit and Loss Account, thus reducing or eliminating them, and debiting Share Capital Account. The gain from such a procedure may not, at first sight, be apparent, but a little reflection will show that the step is a logical one. Part of the original capital has, in fact, been lost, and it is therefore desirable to bring the accounts into line with the facts. If a company has passed through a bad time, and entered upon a period of prosperity, the continued existence of a debit balance upon Profit and Loss, or the slow writing off of assets that have lost a large part of their value, gives a false colour to the accounts.

LESSON 21

Depreciation in Modern Accounting

I T is the purpose of this Lesson to examine four of the more important methods by which depreciation is dealt with. The first of these is known as the Straight Line Method, by which the cost of the fixed asset (less any residual scrap value) is charged to Profit and Loss Account by equal annual instalments throughout the life of the asset. This method is certainly the most straightforward, and is in many respects the best, for reasons which will become apparent as the other methods are considered.

The second method is the Diminishing Balance Method, by which a fixed percentage, not of the original cost of the asset, but of the balance brought forward from the preceding year, is written off annually. The advantage of this method is its simplicity. Theoretically, however, it is indefensible, since its effect is to charge the Profit and Loss Accounts of the earlier years with an unduly heavy proportion of the cost of the asset. For example, take an asset costing £100, and assume the rate of depreciation to be 10 %. In the first year £10 is written off, leaving a balance of £90 ; in the second year £9 is written off, and £81 is carried forward ; in the third year £8 2s. od. is written off ; in the fourth year £7 5s. 9d., and so on. It is clearly absurd to spread the cost in such an uneven manner. Each year derives a similar benefit from the asset, and each year should bear an equal charge. This method is, however, sometimes employed in practice, since the Straight Line Method involves a separate calculation for each machine or individual asset.

The third method is known as the Annuity Method. Under this system the asset account is debited at the end of each financial year with interest on the balance brought forward at the commencement, and this interest is credited to Profit and Loss Account. It must not be thought that this interest is received in cash, or that it represents a transaction with any outside individual ; it is purely a matter of book-keeping. Secondly, the asset account is credited with a *fixed amount* of depreciation each year, and Profit and Loss Account is debited. Now, since

(16)

the balance of the asset account diminishes from year to year, the interest which is debited thereto and credited to Profit and Loss Account will diminish also, since this interest is calculated on the value of the balance at the commencement of the year ; and since the depreciation charge which is debited to Profit and Loss Account is fixed and does not diminish, it follows that the *net debit* to Profit and Loss Account (i.e. the fixed debit for depreciation minus the diminishing credit for interest) must increase each year. The fixed amount of depreciation is so calculated that the asset account will be closed at the end of the life of the asset ; interest on the balance brought forward at the commencement of the last year of the asset's life will bring the asset account up to a figure which exactly equals the fixed amount of depreciation to be written off. The mathematics by which the annual instalment of depreciation is calculated do not concern us here.

This method may be made clear by a very simple illustration. Take the case of a two years' lease dating from January 1, 1932, costing £205. (This unusually short period is assumed for clarity of exposition.) Interest is to be calculated at 5% per annum. The accounts will be as follow :

Lease Account.

1932				1932			
Jan. 1				Dec. 31			
To Cash				By Depreciation (to			
Dec. 31	..	£205	0 0	P. & L.) ..	..£110	5	0
To Interest							
(to P. & L.)	..	10	5 0	„ „ Balance	.. 105	0	0
		£215	5 0		£215	5	0
1933				1933			
Jan. 1				Dec. 31			
To Balance		£105	0 0	By Depreciation ..£110	5	0
Dec. 31							
To Interest	..	5	5 0				
		£110	5 0		£110	5	0

Thus, in 1932, Profit and Loss Account is debited

with ..	..	..	..	..	..	..£110 5 0
And credited with		..	..	..	..	.. 10 5 0

NET DEBIT £100 0 0

In 1933, Profit and Loss Account is debited with ..£110 5 0
And credited with 5 5 0

NET DEBIT £105 0 0

At first sight it seems inequitable that the depreciation charge should increase with each successive year. The theory of the Annuity Method is this : As depreciation is written off, the capital invested in the asset is gradually recovered. For instance, if a profit of £1,000, calculated before charging depreciation, is earned, it follows that the net assets of the business have also been increased by £1,000. If a depreciation charge of £200 is debited to Profit and Loss Account, the net profit is reduced to £800, but the increase in assets (other than the fixed assets which have been depreciated) is still £1,000. Now the fixed asset has been reduced in book value by £200 ; the net profit is £800 ; the increase in other assets is £1,000. Of this £1,000, £800 represents the profit, and £200 part of the capital previously invested in fixed assets.

It is argued that, since the later years obtain the benefit of the increase in working capital, they should bear a higher share of the depreciation charge than the earlier years, because, if the capital that is recovered were invested outside the business in, say, Government securities, interest would be earned, and received in cash. This gradually increasing cash income would offset the increasing net debit for depreciation, and the *real* charge to Profit and Loss Account would, in fact, be equalized. The fact that, in some cases, the capital recovered is allowed to remain inside the business is immaterial. If it remains as increased working capital, it is presumably needed, and if such a source of supply were not available, it might be necessary to borrow on overdraft and pay interest to the bank. In other words, the *real* expenses of the business would, in fact, be increasing, and the Annuity Method reflects the true state of affairs.

The fourth method is the Sinking Fund Method. This is used where it is necessary to provide a liquid fund to replace the asset at the end of its working life.

Profit and Loss Account is debited each year with a fixed sum for depreciation, which is not, however, credited to the asset account, but to a Sinking Fund Account. Each year an amount equal to this fixed sum is invested in some gilt-edged

Lease Account.

1932		£	1933		£
Jan. 1	To Cash	.. 205	Dec. 31	By Sinking Fund	205

Sinking Fund Account.

1933		£	1932		£
Dec. 3	To Lease		Dec. 31	By Profit and Loss	
	Account	 205		Account	 100
			1933		
			Dec. 31	By Interest (5%)	5
			Dec. 31	By Profit and Loss	
				Account ..	 100
		£205			£205

Investment Account.

1932		£	1934		£
Dec. 31	To Cash	.. 100	Jan. 1	By Cash (proceeds	
1933				of Sale of Investment)	205
Dec. 31					
	To Interest ..	.. 5			
	„ Cash ..	.. 100			
		£205			£205

security. The interest on this investment is re-invested in the same security ; the investment account is therefore debited with the interest, and the Sinking Fund Account is credited. The fixed sum is so calculated that, at the end of the working life of the asset, the value of the investment and the credit balance on Sinking Fund Account are exactly equal to the cost price of the asset. The asset account is transferred to the debit of the Sinking Fund Account, both accounts (since they are equal) being closed. The investment is realized, and the proceeds used to purchase a new asset.

Taking the same simplified figures that were used in the example of the Annuity Method, the accounts would appear as set out in the previous page.

It will be seen that the process by which Sinking Fund is credited, and the asset account transferred thereto at the end of the life of the asset, is not in principle different from the process by which the asset account is directly credited with depreciation. The final result is the same in both cases.

It must be emphasized that there is no *direct* connexion between the credit to Sinking Fund and the purchase of the investment for cash. The purchase of the investment could be made, even if the ordinary direct method of depreciation were employed. The purpose of showing the asset at cost price and the Sinking Fund on the liabilities side is to make it clear that the investment is earmarked, and that it cannot be used for general purposes.

A Sinking Fund may be created for the redemption of a liability (e.g. debentures). The entries are similar : (1) Debit Profit and Loss Account and Credit Sinking Fund ; (2) Credit cash and Debit Investment Account. Interest is treated as before. When the debentures are to be repaid, the investment is realized, and cash is then credited and the Debenture Account debited. The Sinking Fund Account, in this case, *remains in the books*, and is transferred to General Reserve. The reason for this important difference is that the depreciation of a fixed asset is a charge against profits, while the repayment of a liability cannot be a charge against profits. The credit to the Sinking Fund in the latter case is an appropriation of profits.

LESSON 22

Company Profits and Reserves

IT is a ruling principle of company law that limited companies may not use their capital for the purpose of paying dividends. The capital of the company must, as far as possible, be preserved intact for the protection of creditors. It is not always easy to determine whether or not a company may legally declare a dividend, since the law on the subject is very confusing, and some of the decided cases appear to be almost contradictory. The following general principles can, however, be laid down :

(1). A company may distribute current profits without making good past losses. Thus, the existence of a debit balance on Profit and Loss Account, representing the losses of past years, does not prevent a company from declaring a dividend, if the Profit and Loss Account of the current year shows a surplus. It has been held that if a part of the capital has in the past been sunk and lost, then it can be no more used in paying dividends than in paying debts. Therefore a dividend declared on the basis of current profits is not paid out of capital, although it is true that the past losses have not been made good. But the omission to replace capital that has been sunk and lost is a very different thing from using capital to repay dividends.

That is the theory. But it should be noticed that it rests upon the assumption that the Profit and Loss Account is not a continuous account. If a Profit and Loss Account were prepared, say, once in five years, it is clear that if a loss of, say, £1,000 occurred in the first four years, while a profit of £300 was earned in the fifth year, the Profit and Loss Account for the five-year period would show a loss of £700, and no dividend could be declared. The rule that has been stated above, therefore, depends entirely upon what is, after all, a more or less arbitrary division of time into distinct and separable periods.

(2). Before arriving at such current profit, it is necessary to provide for depreciation of floating assets, held with a view to conversion into cash, and also for depreciation of fixed assets which require replacement. The last clause is very important.

Its effect is that it is not legally necessary to provide for depreciation of fixed assets that do not require replacement.

(3). It should be noted that it is possible for profits to be of a capital nature. For example, if a freehold building is sold at a price above its original cost, such an exceptional profit must be distinguished from a normal profit on trading. Capital profits are available for dividend, but only when they have been realized in cash, and provided that any capital losses are fairly offset, and that the results of the year as a whole are taken into account.

(4). Finally, whatever the circumstances, a dividend can never be paid if it leaves a company unable to pay its debts.

The term " Reserve " is a somewhat loose one, and is used in several senses. A reserve may be created to provide for expenses accruing, or for the depreciation of an asset. Examples are reserves for outstanding expenses (suspense creditors) and reserves for bad and doubtful debts. In some cases the depreciation of fixed assets is dealt with by crediting a " Depreciation Reserve " account, instead of crediting the asset account directly ; the asset account is closed off to the reserve account at the end of the working life of the asset. This procedure is similar to the method by which a sinking fund is created, but in this case no corresponding investment is made.

Reserves of this type are all in the nature of provision for revenue expenditure, and are known as specific reserves. Such reserves will appear in the Balance Sheet as liabilities (suspense creditors) or on the asset side as deductions from assets ; a reserve for Bad and Doubtful Debts is a deduction from Sundry Debtors ; a depreciation reserve should be deducted from the appropriate fixed asset. It will be observed that the effect of the creation of specific reserves is to reduce the value of the net assets ; this is quite correct, since revenue expenses must necessarily be accompanied by a decrease of assets or an increase of liabilities.

Secondly, reserves may be appropriations of profits. General reserves are simply undistributed profits. Reserves for redemption of liabilities, though apparently of a different nature, are nevertheless similar. When a liability is repaid, cash is credited, and the liability account is debited. Such a transaction clearly involves neither profit nor loss. If, however, a reserve is created (by transfer from the appropriation account) in connexion with the repayment of a liability, the purpose of this transfer is to indicate that part of the assets representing the profits may not be used for dividend purposes, but must be set aside in order to provide a fund for redeeming the liability. In the same way a general reserve is created in order to make it clear that it is proposed to increase the working capital of the business by retaining part of the increase in assets which have been produced by the profits.

Thirdly, we must examine the nature of secret reserves. A secret reserve exists when assets are understated or liabilities are overstated in the Balance Sheet. It is clear that, if net assets are shown in the Balance Sheet at less than their true value, the balance of undistributed profits must also be shown at less than its true figure.

The following are examples of methods by which secret reserves may be created : 1. Excessive depreciation of fixed assets. 2. Undervaluation of stock 3. Excessive provision for bad debts. 4. Merging General Reserves with Sundry Creditors, in the Balance Sheet. 5. Reserves for remote contingencies 6. Writing down goodwill.

It will be asked what are the objects of creating secret reserves ? Can their use be justified ? The principal object of creating secret reserves is to enable the directors of a company to tone down fluctuations in profit by decreasing the amount of the reserves in bad times, and increasing them in good times. The creation of a reserve has the effect of diminishing the apparent profit ; on the other hand, if asset values are increased, the apparent profit is also increased. Thus the manipulation of asset values makes it possible to show an apparent profit that is greater or less than the profit actually earned.

It is undeniably true that the modification of fluctuations in earnings is an important factor in the maintenance of confidence. Many a business has averted a panic in an exceptionally bad year by drawing on its secret reserves. The most efficiently managed concern may at times suffer reverses, but its reputation might suffer severely if the fact were known. The utilization of secret reserves is unquestionably a very useful means of averting a loss of confidence that might have consequences entirely out of proportion to the extent of the losses actually incurred. It should be noted that in no case does the Balance Sheet overstate the true position. The real value of the assets is understated to a greater extent at some times than at others.

On the other hand, there is always the danger that secret reserves may be used for improper purposes. It is the duty of the auditors to see that this is not done. Were it not for the fact that, under the Companies Act, the Balance Sheet must be audited and certified by an independent auditor, it would be within the power of unscrupulous directors to manipulate the accounts, and therefore the market value of a company's shares, to their own advantage. Hence the responsibility of an auditor to shareholders and the public is a very grave one.

Whatever may be the justification for the proper use of secret reserves, the fact remains that, when they exist, the Balance Sheet does not disclose fully the actual position of the company. It has been laid down in the case of Newton v. The Birmingham Small Arms Company that "the purpose of the Balance Sheet is primarily to show that the financial position of the Company is *at least as good as* there stated, and not to show that it is not, or may not be, better." The auditor always has the power to draw attention in his report to the existence of secret reserves, and he must be satisfied that their existence is for the benefit of the company as a whole.

LESSON 23

Amalgamations and Holding Companies

ONE of the most distinctive features of the post-war years has been the marked growth in the size of the business unit. The process of integration takes many forms, but the most typical are : amalgamations of two or more companies ; absorption of small by large undertakings ; and the creation of "holding companies," which own either the whole or the greater part of the shares of other companies, termed subsidiaries.

The accounting aspect of a case of absorption will be first considered. The accountancy of amalgamations is almost identical with that of absorptions, since in the former case a new company is usually formed to take over the assets and liabilities of the amalgamating companies. The entries in the books of the companies that are taken over are analogous to the entries for a dissolution of partnership since the old companies are wound up.

As an illustration of the accounting necessary in such circumstances, let us suppose that X Ltd. agrees to absorb the undertaking of Y Ltd. The condensed Balance Sheets of the two companies are as follow :

X Limited.

	£		£
Ordinary Share		Sundry Assets ..	370,000
Capital ..	200,000	Cash at Bank ..	80,000
5% Debentures ..	50,000		
Sundry Creditors..	160,000		
Profit and Loss			
Account	40,000		
	£450,000		£450,000

Y Limited.

	£		£
Ordinary Share		Sundry Assets ..	140,000
Capital	100,000	Profit and Loss	
Preference Share		Account	50,000
Capital	25,000	Goodwill	10,000
5% Debentures ..	40,000		
Overdraft at			
Bankers	5,000		
Sundry Creditors ..	30,000		
	£200,000		£200,000

The directors of X Ltd. agree to pay off the debenture-holders of Y, and to pay a further £95,000 for the assets, to be discharged as to £30,000 in cash, and as to the balance by the issue of 65,000 fully paid ordinary shares of £1 each in X Ltd. The creditors are to be paid out of the proceeds of the sale of the undertaking. and, with the exception of the bank, agree to accept 16s. 8d. in the £ in full settlement.

The preference shareholders agree to accept 3 shares in X for every 5 shares in Y, and the ordinary shareholders agree to accept 1 share in X for every 2 shares in Y.

The market value of the shares of X is assumed to be equal to their nominal value. The entries in the books of Y will be as follow :

Realization Account.

To—	£	By—	£
Sundry Assets ..	140,000	5% Debentures ..	40,000
Goodwill ..	10,000	X Ltd.	95,000
Profit and Loss		Discount on	
Account ..	50,000	Creditors ..	5,000
		Sundry Share-	
		holders :	
		Preference ..	10,000
		Ordinary ..	50,000
	£200,000		£200,000

X Limited.

To—	£	By—	£
Realization		Cash	30,000
Account.. ..	95,000	Shares in X at par	65,000
	£95,000		£95,000

Five per cent Debentures Account.

To—	£	By—	£
Realization		Balance	40,000
Account (taken			
over by X Ltd.)	40,000		

Sundry Creditors (including Bank Overdraft).

To—	£	By—	£
Realization		Balance	35,000
Account (dis-			
count)	5,000		
Cash	30,000		
	£35,000		£35,000

Preference Share Capital Account.

To—	£	By—	£
Preference Shareholders	25,000	Balance	25,000

Ordinary Share Capital Account.

To—	£	By—	£
Ordinary Shareholders	100,000	Balance	100,000

Preference Shareholders.

To—	£	By—	£
Realization Account ..	10,000	Preference Share Capital Account	25,000
Shares in X Ltd.	15,000		
	£25,000		£25,000

Ordinary Shareholders.

To—	£	By—	£
Realization Account.. ..	50,000	Ordinary Share Capital Account..	100,000
Shares in X ..	50,000		
	£100,000		£100,000

Shares in X.

To—	£	By—	£
X Ltd.	65,000	Preference Shareholders ..	15,000
		Ordinary Shareholders ..	50,000
	£65,000		£65,000

All assets (including debit balance on Profit and Loss Account) are transferred to the Realization Account, which is credited with the proceeds (in total, £135,000), since the assumption by

X Ltd. of the debentures is equivalent to a cash payment to Y, because Y Ltd. would have been bound to discharge this liability. The Realization Account is also credited with the discount on creditors, leaving a balance of £60,000 to be written off. In a partnership, this amount would be debited to partners' capital accounts ; in the case of a limited company, the share capital accounts must, first, be transferred in total to the shareholders' accounts, and the loss is then debited to these accounts. The proceeds (shares in X Ltd.) are distributed to the shareholders, and this is recorded by crediting the Shares in X account and debiting the shareholders' accounts.

The entries in the books of X Ltd. are simple. The assets acquired from Y Ltd. are debited to the appropriate accounts at purchase price, i.e. £135,000. Thus goodwill disappears, and the assets which formerly stood in the books of Y at £140,000 will be reduced to £135,000. This double entry will be completed by credits to cash £70,000 (including discharge of Debentures) and to Share Capital £65,000.

The Balance Sheet of X Ltd., after these transactions, will appear as follows :

X Limited.

	£			£
Share Capital ..	265,000	Sundry Assets	..	505,000
5% Debentures ..	50,000	Cash at Bank	..	10,000
Sundry Creditors ..	160,000			
Profit and Loss				
Account ..	40,000			
	£515,000			£515,000

Holding Companies. There is no definition of a holding company in the Companies Act of 1929. A subsidiary company is, however, defined by Sect. 127. If the assets of one company consist in whole or in part of the assets of another company, and the holding company owns more than 50% of the issued share capital *or* controls more than 50% of the voting power *or* has power to appoint a majority of the directors, that other company is deemed to be a subsidiary company.

The Balance Sheet of the holding company must contain the following particulars relating to its interest in the subsidiaries :

(1) Shares in subsidiaries must be set out in the Balance Sheet separately from all other assets, though it is not necessary to distinguish between the shares of different subsidiaries ; (2) the aggregate amount owing by subsidiaries to the holding company must be separately stated ; (3) the aggregate amount owing by the holding company to the subsidiaries must also be stated separately ; (4) a statement must be annexed to the Balance Sheet, showing how profits and losses of subsidiaries have been dealt with in the accounts of the holding company, and, in particular, what provision, if any, has been made for losses incurred by subsidiaries.

Shares in subsidiaries may be shown in the Balance Sheet of the holding company at cost, even though they may have depreciated in value. The statement to be annexed to the Balance Sheet may be in very general terms ; it is not necessary, under the Act, to state the amounts of the profits and losses of subsidiaries. It is clear that the accounts and Balance Sheet of the holding company may, while complying with these regulations, fail to give a correct view of the position of the combined undertaking. Thus dividends from prosperous subsidiaries may be credited to the Profit and Loss Account, while no provision is made for the losses of another.

Accountants are agreed that the legal Balance Sheet is unsatisfactory, and they have attempted to meet the difficulty by the construction of Consolidated Balance Sheets. The principle is simply to substitute for the item in the Balance Sheet of the holding company " Shares in Subsidiaries," the assets and liabilities representing these shares. The following is a simple illustration of a Consolidated Balance Sheet :

Holding Company.

	£				£
Share Capital	200,000	Cash			5,000
General Reserve	40,000	Stock			110,000
Sundry Creditors	250,000	Debtors			135,000
Profit & Loss Account	10,000	Fixed Assets			150,000
		Shares in Subsidiary (at cost)			100,000
	£500,000				£500,000

Subsidiary Company.

	£				£
Share Capital	..	100,000	Cash ..	..	2,000
Debentures ..	..	50,000	Stock ..	..	48,000
Sundry Creditors	..	150,000	Debtors	..	110,000
			Fixed Assets ..	..	140,000
		£300,000			£300,000

Consolidated Balance Sheet.

	£				£
Share Capital	..	200,000	Cash ..	..	7,000
Debentures ..	..	50,000	Stock ..	..	158,000
General Reserve	..	40,000	Debtors	..	245,000
Sundry Creditors	..	400,000	Fixed Assets ..	..	290,000
Profit & Loss Account	10,000			
		£700,000			£700,000

It will be observed that the Share Capital of the subsidiary cancels out with Shares in Subsidiary on the assets side of the holding company's Balance Sheet.

This is the Consolidated Balance Sheet in its simplest form. If the cost price of the shares of the subsidiary is not equal to their nominal value, or if the holding company does not own all the shares, the construction of a Consolidated Balance Sheet becomes a much more complicated matter.

LESSON 24

Foreign Currencies in Accounts

I N times of currency stability the complications that arise when the transactions of a single firm are conducted in more than one national currency are of minor importance. If exchange rates fluctuate within very narrow limits round established parities, all entries can be made in the books in terms of the home currency, items in foreign currencies being converted at par. Any inaccuracies arising from divergences between actual rates and par rates of exchange will, under such conditions, be trivial. These conditions do not obtain today. For many years exchange rates have fluctuated violently, and it is impossible to predict the character of future movements. The study of the accountancy problems arising from exchange instability is therefore a subject of very great practical importance.

A distinction must be drawn between two types of foreign dealing. Some concerns have transactions with foreigners, without maintaining any permanent establishment abroad. Other firms set up foreign branches. The accountancy of buying and selling in terms of foreign currencies, where no foreign branch is maintained, will first be considered.

The personal accounts of foreign customers and suppliers are ruled with two columns on each side, one for the foreign currency and one for sterling. The first principle which must be clearly understood is that the currency columns are purely memorandum. The sterling columns form part of the double-entry system.

When goods are bought in terms of foreign currencies, the personal account is credited in the currency column and the price is converted into sterling at the rate of exchange ruling when the transaction takes place, and the sterling value so ascertained is entered in the second column on the credit side, and Purchases Account is debited. When the account is settled, the currency column is debited with the amount of the draft, in terms of currency, while the sterling cost of the draft is debited in the sterling column of the personal account. If the rate of exchange ruling on the date of payment is different from the rate ruling on the date when the goods were purchased, it is evident that, although the currency columns of the personal account will be closed, the sterling columns will not agree. Such a difference is a profit or loss on exchange, and must be written off to a Profit and Loss on Exchange Account.

The following are the transactions of a firm with American customers and suppliers for the month of January:

					$
Jan. 5—Goods sold to	A:	..	..	..	.. 500.00
„ 10— „ „	B:	..	..	..	.. 300.00
„ 15— „ „	C:	..	..	..	.. 1200.00
„ 8—Purchased from D:	..	..	..	.. 1000.00
„ 12— „ „	E:	..	..	..	.. 900.00

The rates of exchange were as follow :

Jan. 1 to 8 : $5 to £1.
Jan. 9 to 15 : $4.50 to £1.

On January 20, A pays in full, the remittance realizing £95 ; on the 22nd, B pays in full, £65 being realized ; on the 25th D is paid in full, the draft costing £50. The accounts will appear as in the table below.

The goods sold to A were worth £100 when they were sold, but

A

	$	£				$	£	
Jan. 5. To Goods	500.00	100	0	0	Jan. 20. By Cash	500.00	95	0 0
					„ Loss on Exchange		5	0 0
	$500.00	£100	0	0		$500.00	£100	0 0

B

	$	£				$	£	
Jan. 10. To Goods	300.00	66	13	4	Jan. 22. By Cash	300.00	65	0 0
					„ Loss on Exchange		1	13 4
	$300.00	£66	13	4		$300.00	£66	13 4

C

	$	£		
Jan. 15. To Goods	1200.00	266	13	4

D

	$	£				$	£	
Jan. 25. To Cash	1000.00	180	0	0	Jan. 8. By Goods	1000.00	200	0 0
To Profit on Exchange		20	0	0				
	$1000.00	£200	0	0		$1000.00	£200	0 0

E

						$	£	
					Jan. 12. By Goods	900.00	200	0 0

Purchases.

	£	
To D	£200	0 0
„ E	200	0 0
	£400	0 0

Sales.

	£	
By A	100	0 0
„ B	66	13 4
„ C	266	13 4
	£433	6 8

Profit and Loss on Exchange.

	£			£	
To A	£5	0 0	By D	£20	0 0
„ B	£1	13 4			

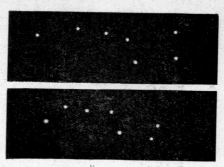

MOTION OF THE 'PLOUGH.' The stars have not only an apparent but a "proper" motion. Thus the familiar constellation of the "Plough" or "Great Bear," seen as it is today in the upper diagram, will have changed in 50,000 years from now to the shape shown in the lower diagram. ASTRONOMY 34

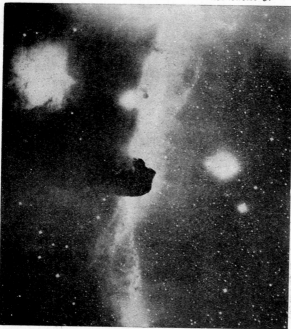

DARK NEBULA. The inconceivably vast space between the stars is occupied by opaque nebulous matter which over a large area is illuminated; the intervention of a dark non-illuminated region is strikingly shown in this photo of the so-called horse's head in the Orion nebula. ASTRONOMY 36

Mount Wilson Observatory

A STARRY MAZE. This photograph is of M.13 in Hercules, which is so far removed from us in space that Sirius, the apparently brightest star in the heavens, would be quite invisible to us if it were situated at the same distance. Each one of the stars in the cluster must, therefore, have an actual luminosity immensely greater than that of Sirius.

ASTRONOMY 35
Courtesy of Royal Astronomical Society

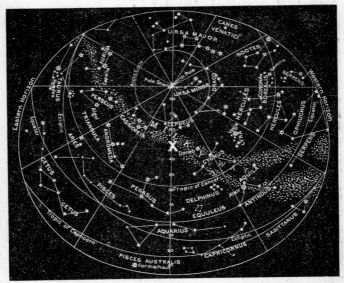

MAPS OF THE HEAVENS. The above map and that in Plate 3 show the relative positions of the principal stars in spring (left) and autumn evenings (right) in Great Britain. The cross marks the point in the sky immediately above the observer. The maps may be compared with those in Vol. 1, plate 14, which show

Plate 2   *Volume VI*

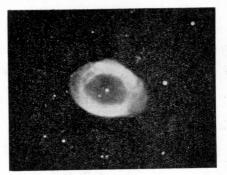

PLANETARY NEBULA. Planetary, ring, or disk nebulae apparently consist of vast luminous atmospheres, surrounding a comparatively faint star. This photo is of the nebula in Lyra, one of the best known of the 150 ring nebulae so far observed
ASTRONOMY 36

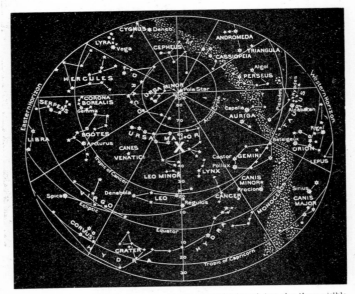

not only the stars visible in January at twelve hours' interval, but also those visible on winter evenings (right-hand map) and on summer evenings (left-hand map). In all four maps the stars of each constellation have been joined by lines in order to facilitate recognition. The dotted band represents the Milky Way. ASTRONOMY 34

ANDROMEDA NEBULA. This great spiral nebula is so immensely distant that its light takes a million years to reach us. Some idea of its size may be gathered from the fact that compared with Andromeda our sun is as a speck of dust in a sunbeam compared to the earth. ASTRONOMY 37

Courtesy of the Royal Astronomical Society

Plate 4   *Volume VI*

in fact only £95 was realized, and the fall in value is regarded as a loss on exchange, since it is due solely to the movement in the rate of exchange.

If January 31 were the end of an accounting period, it would become necessary to value the balances due to and from the Americans. The accepted principle is that floating assets and

C

	$	£			$	£
Jan. 15. To Goods	1200.00	266 13 4	Jan. 31. By Balance	1200.00	200 0 0	
			,, Loss on Exchange		66 13 4	
	$1200.00	£266 13 4			$1200.00	£266 13 4
	$	£			$	£
Feb. 1. To Balance	1200.00	200 0 0				

E

	$	£			$	£
Jan. 31. To Balance	900.00	150 0 0	Jan. 12. By Goods	900.00	200 0 0	
,, Profit on Exchange		50 0 0				
	$900.00	£200 0 0		$900.00	£200 0 0	

current liabilities in foreign currencies should be converted into sterling at the rate of exchange ruling on the date of the Balance Sheet. In other words, liabilities in terms of foreign currencies should be shown at the sum which it will cost to discharge them, while debtors should be shown at the amount they are expected to produce when the sterling remittance is received.

In the above illustration, if the rate of exchange on January 31 were $6 to the £1, the balance on C's account would be equivalent to £200, while the amount due to E would be equivalent

Profit and Loss on Exchange Account.

		£			£
To A		5 0 0	By D		20 0 0
,, B		1 13 4	,, E		50 0 0
,, C		66 13 4	,, Balance, being net loss on exchange, transferred to Profit and Loss Account		3 6 8
		£73 6 8			£73 6 8

to £150. These balances, converted on this basis, would be brought down and the difference written off to Profit and Loss on Exchange, as shown above.

The Profit and Loss on Exchange Account in its final form will be as shown above.

B6

A more difficult problem arises if a firm has a **foreign branch**. If the branch is self-contained, it will keep its own complete set of books in terms of the foreign currency, and will prepare a trial balance at the end of the firm's accounting period. This trial balance must be converted into sterling, and incorporated into the final accounts of the head office.

The rules for converting a branch trial balance from a foreign currency into sterling are as follow :

1. Convert fixed assets at the rate ruling when purchased.

2. Convert floating assets and current liabilities at the rate ruling on the date to which the accounts are made up.

3. Convert Profit and Loss items at the average rate for the period of the accounts.

4. Convert remittances between the branch and the head office at the actual rate at which the remittances were made.

The two sides of the branch trial balance will now show different totals. The amount of the difference is profit or loss on exchange.

The foregoing rules are in no way arbitrary. They are simply the application of normal accountancy principles to a special case. It is a normal rule that fixed assets are valued at cost (less depreciation at an appropriate rate), and the rate ruling at the date of the purchase must be applied if the fixed assets of foreign branches are to be shown in the Balance Sheet of the head office on this basis. Similarly, floating assets are valued with regard to the amount they are expected to produce, which, in the case of floating assets in foreign currencies, is in part determined by the current rate of exchange.

In order to arrive at the correct measure of any profit or loss on exchange, each revenue item should be converted at the rate ruling on the day when the individual transaction took place. The theory is that the value of a profit is the value of the asset representing that profit. if the value of the asset representing the profit subsequently declines from unusual causes (such as the fall in the value of a currency) such a loss should be distinguished from profits and losses on trading. Now the profit on trading transactions pure and simple is determined by the value of the assets acquired as and when the profit accrues. For example, if goods are sold at a profit of $20 at a time when the rate of exchange is $4 to the £1, the value of the profit is £5. If the rate subsequently falls to $5 to the £1, the value of the cash representing the profit falls to £4—a loss on exchange of £1.

If all revenue items are converted at an average rate, the sterling figures will approximately represent what the value of the profits would have been, if the net proceeds of trading had been immediately remitted to the Head Office, as and when earned. The value of the floating assets representing this profit, since they are converted at a different rate of exchange, will be greater or less than the apparent value of the profit itself. This increase or decrease in value is the profit or loss on exchange, and is properly distinguished from profits and losses on trading.

LESSON 25

Accounting Aspect of Income Tax

INCOME Tax is a difficult and complex subject, and in this Course it will be considered only in relation to business profits. It is not proposed to attempt any survey of the whole field, but an examination of the main principles upon which profits are taxed should prove instructive. For convenience of administration, the income or profit arising in any year is deemed, for Income Tax purposes, to be the income of the following year. It would be impossible to levy tax during the course of any year upon the profits of that year, since the amount of the profit is not known until the year is ended. Assessments, then, are based upon the preceding year's profits.

The fiscal year runs from April 6 to April 5. Since it rarely happens that business accounts are made up to the same date, it becomes necessary to base the assessment, in practice, upon the profits arising during the accountancy period ending within the preceding year. Thus, the profits for the accountancy year ending on December 31, 1932, become the basis of assessment for the fiscal year April, 1933, to April, 1934. The tax is paid, by individuals and partners, in two instalments, on January 1, in the year of assessment, and on July 1 in the following *fiscal* year (i.e. six months later). Thus the actual profit for the calendar year 1932 becomes the statutory profit for 1933–34, and the tax on this profit is paid on January 1 and July 1, 1934. Limited companies are required to pay the whole of the tax on January 1 of the year of assessment.

For accounting purposes, Income Tax is regarded as accruing due by equal instalments during the *fiscal* year to which it relates.

For example, the profit for the year to December 31, 1932, is the statutory income for the year 1933-34, and Income Tax on this statutory income is deemed to accrue during the period April, 1933, to April, 1934. Thus, when the accounts for the year ending December 31, 1933, are made up, approximately three-quarters of the Income Tax liability for the year 1933-34 is deemed to have accrued due, although payment does not fall to be made until January and July, 1934. Three-quarters of the tax payable for 1933-34 is reserved on December 31, 1933, and appears in the Balance Sheet for that date as a liability.

For purposes of illustration we assume that the profits of a company are as follow

Year to December 31, 1931 £4,000
Ditto 1932 £6,400
Assessment for 1932-33 is £4,000
Ditto 1933-34 is £6,400
Tax Payable for 1932-33 (at 5s. in the £) is £1,000
Ditto 1933-34 Ditto is £1,600

In the accounts for the year to December 31, 1932, it is necessary to reserve three-quarters of the tax for 1932-33, that is, £750. This sum is debited to Income Tax Account, and brought down as a credit balance, and appears in the Balance Sheet as a liability. During 1933 the whole of the £1,000 is paid, and debited to Income Tax Account. On December 31, 1933, three-quarters of the liability for 1933-34, £1,200, must be reserved.

If we assume that the general meeting of the company was held on March 31, 1933, and a dividend of £4,000 was declared, out of the profit of £6,400 earned during 1932, Income Tax Account will be credited on that date with £1,000, leaving only £450 to be charged to the Appropriation Account at December 31, 1933.

It will be seen that the amount written off to appropriation account is equal to one-quarter of the 1932-33 liability (£250) plus three-quarters of the 1933-34 liability (£1,200) minus tax deducted from a dividend declared and paid during 1933.

It is only fair that losses should be offset against profits, in computing Income Tax liability. There are three important clauses under which relief may be claimed for losses.

1. Rule 13, Cases 1 and 2, Schedule D (Income Tax Act, 1918), by which a person who carries on, or is a partner in, more than

one business may offset a statutory loss in one business against a statutory profit for the same year in the other business.

2. Section 34 (Income Tax Act, 1918), by which a person may offset an *actual* loss in any one year against any statutory income for that year. Thus, if a business showed a profit of £500 for the accounting year to December 31, 1931, this would be the statutory profit for 1932–33. If the accounts to December 31, 1932, showed a loss of £400, this loss could be offset against the statutory income of £500, and tax on £100 only would be payable for 1932–33.

3. Section 33, Finance Act, 1926, by which business losses, for which relief has not been claimed under either of the preceding clauses, may be offset against the profits of subsequent years. Losses cannot, however, be carried forward for more than six years ; thus, if a statutory loss for the year 1927–28 were greater than the total of the statutory profits for the years 1928–29 to 1933–34, the excess could not be set off against any profit for 1934–35, and such a profit would be liable to tax in full.

In Lesson 17 (Volume 5, p. 29) the procedure by which Income Tax is deducted from dividends was explained. The same method is applied to annual interest and other charges. such as ground rent. Any person making such a payment deducts Income Tax from the gross amount due. Thus, if the ground rent on a leasehold house is £8, and Income Tax is 5s. in the £, the landlord receives only £6 in cash. His position is, for tax purposes, the same as the shareholder who receives a dividend less tax, in that he is not called upon to pay any further tax on that income. The person making the payment must. however, account to the revenue authorities for the full amount of the tax he has deducted.

The position is complicated by the fact that annual interest and charges are allowed as deductions from gross income in the calculation of taxable income. Thus. if the net profit of a company. before charging debenture interest, is £1,000, and if the interest is £100 gross, the income of the company is £900. The company must also, however, hand over to the revenue authorities the £25 tax deducted from the gross amount of the debenture interest, since the debenture holders only received £75 in cash. In order to avoid making two assessments, the £25 is collected not by a separate assessment, but by " adding back " the £100 to the £900 net profit of the company, thus making the statutory profit of the company £1,000. The letter of the law is to the effect that charges from which tax has been deducted are not allowable as deductions from profits.

Assuming the above figures, the statutory profit of the company is £1,000, upon which £250 Income Tax is paid. In reality, the profit of the company is £900, tax upon which is £225; in addition, the company hands over the £25 deducted in paying interest.

INCOME TAX ACCOUNT.

1933			1933		
Jan. 1 To Cash	..	£1,000	Jan. 1 By Reserve	..	£750
Dec 31 „ Reserve	..	1,200	(¾ of 1932–33 liability)		
(¾ of 1933-34 liability)			Mar. 31 „ Dividend	..	1,000
			Dec. 31 „ Profit & Loss Account (Appropriation Section)	..	450
		£2,200			£2,200
			1934		
			Jan. 1 By Balance	..	£1,200

The procedure works well enough when the profits are sufficient to cover the charges. Supposing the Profit and Loss Account of the company to be as follows :

PROFIT AND LOSS ACCOUNT.

To—		By—			
Debenture Interest ..	£100	Balance ..	..	..	£20
		Net Loss	..	..	80
	£100				£100

Under the normal method of assessment, the statutory profit is :

Net Loss per Accounts	..	..	..	..	..	£80
Less Debenture Interest	..	..	..	..	..	100
Adjusted Profit	..	..	..	..	..	£20

Now it is clear that, if the company only paid tax on £20, it would not be handing over to the revenue the full amount of the tax deducted from the debenture interest. In order that the tax on the £100 may be recovered, Rule 21 of the General Rules (Income Tax Act, 1918) makes provision for additional assessments in such cases. In this illustration there would be a Rule 21 assessment on £80. Thus, the company would pay tax on £20 (viz. £5) under Schedule " D," and on £80 (viz. £20) under Rule 21. Any assessment made under Rule 21 may, however, be carried forward in the same way as losses under Section 33 (Finance Act, 1926). This is clearly equitable, since the true loss of the company is £80.

The profit shown by the Profit and Loss Account is not necessarily the statutory profit for Income Tax purposes. We have seen that interest and charges from which tax has been deducted are not allowable as deductions from profits, but, if debited in the Profit and Loss Account, must be added back. Profit, for Income Tax purposes, is ascertained according to certain well defined rules, by which certain specific expenses are not allowed as deductions from profits while other deductions and allowances may be claimed, whether they are debited in the accounts of the business or not. Some of the more important " deductions not allowed " are :

(1) Reserve for bad and doubtful debts. (But specific accounts written off are allowed.) (2) Royalties. (3) Premiums paid for leases. (4) Company preliminary expenses (5) Discounts on issue of shares or debentures. (6) Underwriting commission. (7) Certain type of legal charges. (8) Any losses not connected with or arising out of the trade, such as the loss on a sale of investments. (9) Income Tax. (10) Depreciation.

On the other hand, in lieu of depreciation, a " wear and tear " allowance is granted on plant and machinery. The amount of the allowance is based on an official schedule of rates, which are not always adequate. Furthermore, wear and tear allowances are calculated on the diminishing balance method. This deficiency is partly supplied by an obsolescence allowance. The amount of this allowance is equal to the original cost of the asset, less total wear and tear already allowed, and is granted when plant and machinery become unsuitable to its original purpose," and only when the asset is replaced. The obsolescence allowance does not cover all cases in which plant and machinery are scrapped. If a new invention renders an old machine unsuitable, the allowance will usually be granted ; but in cases where an old machine is scrapped while still serviceable, and a new one of a similar type is introduced in order to secure greater speed or efficiency, the allowance will usually not be granted. In the event of particular types of production being discontinued, no claim can be made in respect of the plant that thereby becomes redundant. It by no means always follows that the full cost of plant and machinery will, even in the long run, be allowed as a charge against profits, for Income Tax purposes.

LESSON 26

Technique of Cost Accounting

I T would be possible to ascertain the net profit of a business from a statement of its assets and liabilities at the commencement and at the end of a period, since a profit is represented by an increase in assets. The management of a modern business is, however, concerned to know, not only what the profit is, but also how it has been earned. The Profit and Loss Account shows this to some extent.

For example, the net profit may be the same for two periods, although the manner in which it has been earned may vary. A decline in sales or gross profit percentage may have been offset by economies in expenses. The total expenses for two years may have been identical, though the fact might conceal economies in certain directions, offset by wasteful expenditure in others. In order that intelligent control may be exercised, it is necessary to have information on these and similar points of detail.

The Trading and Profit and Loss Account, however, under modern large-scale conditions, is inadequate. It classifies expenditure according to the nature of the expenses, but not according to the nature of the transactions. The net profit is the outcome of all the transactions for the period, and the Trading and Profit and Loss Account is, after all, nothing more than a highly condensed summary of a large number of transactions which may differ from each other in every way.

In a departmental stores, the expenses and sales of each department are recorded separately, and a separate Profit and Loss Account is prepared for each. In this way a far more intelligent management of the business is made possible. If the final accounts were merged, it might be possible for profits on some departments to cover losses on others without anyone being the wiser. By preparing separate departmental accounts, the management knows which departments are more profitable, and can concentrate its attention on improving the position of the less profitable sections.

In the same way, a modern factory may produce hundreds of different types and grades of articles. Some will cost more to produce than others, but it is impossible to discover this from the financial accounts. The Trading and Profit and Loss Account may conceal many anomalies ; profitable activities may be paying for losses ; efficiency in some directions may conceal waste and bad management in others. It is the purpose of cost accounting to remedy this deficiency, to extend and amplify the information disclosed in the financial accounts ; to show which products and which types are being sold at a profit, and which are un-profitable ; to examine in detail the component parts of the cost of each article, and to measure these costs against predetermined standards of efficiency. Until this has been done, the manage-ment cannot know where its profit is, or how it has been earned ; it cannot decide in what proportions each type of output con-tributes to the final result ; it cannot be sure that expenses have been reduced to a minimum, and that the maximum profits have been earned ; selling prices cannot be intelligently adjusted.

The technique of cost accounting consists in analysing ex-penditure according to the type of product in respect of which it is incurred. If the total expenditure of a manufacturing business were correctly analysed in this way, it would be found that the total of all the cost accounts would be equal to the total expenditure as shown by the financial accounts ; the difference is that the expenditure is analysed in a different way. If it is asked : '' What proportion of the total expenditure consists of factory wages or rent ? '' the financial accounts supply the answer. But if it is asked : '' What proportion of the total expenditure has been incurred in the production of a particular article ? '' cost accounts supply the answer. Every distinctive unit of output may be considered in relation to the expenses for which it is responsible.

Cost accounting technique divides the expenses of the factory into three main sections : (1) Direct Material Cost ; (2) Direct

Labour Cost; (3) Overhead Expenses or Oncost. Direct material cost consists of the cost of the physical materials which enter into the composition of the finished output. Direct labour cost consists of the wages of the factory operatives who are directly engaged on productive processes. Thus the wages of foremen and timekeepers are not a part of the direct labour cost. Oncost consists of all the overhead expenses, indirect wages, rent, rates, lighting and heating, power and fuel, depreciation of machinery, and so on.

In order to find the cost of the material content of each article or batch of articles, it is essential that the storekeeper should only issue materials to the factory upon the production of a requisition note signed by a foreman or responsible official. This document states the amount of material to be issued, and the distinctive number of the job for which it is required. The requisition notes are summarized by cost clerks at the end of every week or month. and the storekeeper endeavours to check the accuracy of these records by testing his stocks of materials. The storekeeper will usually keep a detailed classified record of all materials received and issued. Issues are recorded by the requisition notes. and if these are correct. the storekeeper should be able to confirm the fact by a physical stocktaking of one or two types of material. A complete stocktaking cannot, of course, take place every week or month.

A separate ledger sheet or card is kept for each job, which is the term given to the production of each batch of articles . from the summary of the requisition notes the total material cost of each job can be entered upon the cost sheet. Similar records must be kept for wages Each worker is obliged to keep a record of how his time has been spent, indicating the number of hours devoted to each job. The workers time sheets are summarized at the end of each week or month, and the total time taken on each job can be found. This time can be priced by reference to the rates of wages in force. In this way, the total direct wages cost is split up between the different types of production, and each job is charged with its appropriate share.

The allocation of oncost or overhead expenses is a more difficult matter in theory, though, once the basis of allocation has been settled, the subsequent practical work is not great. What determines the overhead expenses of the factory ? The cost of the materials consumed may or may not be a guide. It is certainly not always so, since some types of heavy work make relatively large demands upon factory space, while other types of work may be performed in a much smaller compass, although the value of the materials used may be much higher. In other words, bulk certainly does not vary according to value.

The level of the overhead expenses is determined by many factors—the extent of space, the degree of supervision required, the nature of the machinery used, and, above all, the length of time necessary for production. No system which does not take the time factor into account can possibly be of any value. It is clear, other things being equal, that, if the time taken in the production of one class of goods is twice as long as the time taken in the production of a second class of goods, then the factory necessary for the manufacture of the first type of goods will have to be twice as big, and therefore twice as expensive, as the factory in which a similar quantity of the second type can be produced.

The length of the productive process is therefore in all cases a factor determining the demands made by each type of output upon the services of the factory, and must in every case be taken into account in the allocation of the cost of providing those services.

In factories where the bulk of the work is done by machinery, the usual basis of allocation is the machine. By this system, all factory overhead expenses are distributed over the machines. The space occupied by each machine determines the proportion of rent, rates, lighting and heating to be charged to it. The cost of the machine, given its working life, determines the cost of depreciation. Horse-power is a rough index of the power consumed by each machine; the total cost of providing power is therefore divided up between the machines according to the capacity of each machine. The scope of this Lesson does not permit a more detailed examination of the allocation of expenses to the individual machine, but the principle should be clear. It is reasonable to regard each machine as responsible for a part of factory oncost, and to allocate the expenditure fairly.

Having found the total oncost applicable to each machine, the next step is to allocate this oncost to individual jobs or units of output.

Divide the oncost allocated to each machine by the total number of hours for which the machine is expected to be in operation ; this figure is termed the machine-hour rate. As each job is performed, a record is made of the number of hours for which each machine used in the process has been worked ; the number of machine-hours, multiplied by the appropriate machine-hour rate, gives the oncost to be charged to the job.

The total oncost seldom exactly equals the actual factory overhead for a given period, since this system requires two estimates which, of their very nature, cannot be expected to be absolutely correct. The calculation of the machine-hour rate requires an estimate of the total oncost for a period, and also of the total number of hours for which each machine will be in operation. It is impossible to defer the calculation until the end of the accounting period, because, under modern conditions, cost figures must be produced with the least possible delay. It is clear that, if the factory works for a smaller number of hours than estimated, the oncost charge will be insufficient. Oncost rates can, however, be revised from time to time, as the extent to which the factory is used changes. The rates should not be altered for seasonal changes, but a yearly average should be taken. Alterations in rates should only be made for changes in the volume of output over a full year.

Cost accounting is one of the most important branches of accounting science. It is recognized that the financial accounts do not produce all the information which is necessary for the proper understanding of business operations. The whole trend of accounting technique is to extend and improve costing methods, and to remodel the form of the financial accounts upon costing classifications.

Books Recommended for Further Study. " Higher Book-Keeping and Accounts," Cropper (Macdonald and Evans) ; " Principles of Auditing," de Paula (Pitman) ; " Principles of Modern Book-Keeping," Hamilton (Jeeves).

This Lesson concludes our Course in Accountancy.

LESSON 34

Reading the Map of the Heavens

(See plates 1–3)

So as to facilitate the recognition of any particular star or constellation, the apparent sphere of the sky is divided by imaginary lines of right ascension and declination, corresponding respectively to terrestrial meridians and parallels of longitude and latitude. The imaginary lines of right ascension —great circles or meridians—pass through the imaginary celestial sphere's two poles. These poles are situated where the axis of the earth, if indefinitely prolonged in both directions, would intersect the celestial sphere, and so they occupy the *zenith of the terrestrial poles*—'' zenith '' being the astronomical term for the point vertically above the observer's head. The *celestial equator* is a great circle drawn round the imaginary sphere midway between the poles, and is situated above the earth's equator.

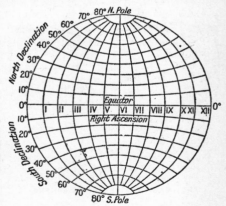

STELLAR MEASUREMENTS

Every place has its own celestial meridian circle, and the rotation of the earth causes this meridian to make a complete revolution of the sky in 24 hours. In the course of this revolution it passes over every visible star, but it is usual to speak of the stars as '' crossing the meridian.'' This occurs when they are due south of the North Celestial Pole (as seen from these latitudes), and are therefore at their highest altitude above the horizon. The horizon is usually regarded as the limit of our vision at any particular place, but astronomically it consists of the great circle 90° distant from the zenith of the observer; consequently observers at different latitudes on earth are bounded by different celestial horizons. The farther south the latitude, the higher the altitude attained by the stars, and therefore the greater the number to come within observation. A star's altitude, then, depends upon the observer's standpoint on the earth and also upon the time of observation.

There is one star upon which the time of observation makes very little difference—the Pole Star, which is nearly above the terrestrial pole and always remains almost at the same altitude according to the latitude of the observer. It is always practically in the same position, since it revolves in a small circle round the exact celestial pole at a distance of only 1° 3½′ from it. All the other stars will be seen to bear a permanent relationship to this

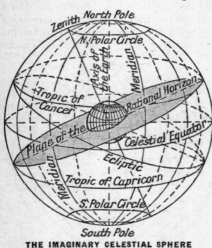

star, and only differ relatively to the horizon and the observer on account of their diurnal revolution and annual progression westward. But those stars which are *circumpolar* and revolve north of the zenith point are within the *circle of perpetual apparition.*

THE IMAGINARY CELESTIAL SPHERE

The most famous and familiar of these are the seven bright stars of Ursa Major, known popularly as the Plough or Charles's Wain. Two of these stars, α and β, will be seen to point almost directly to the Pole Star or *Polaris*—hence their name of the Pointers. Five of these stars, β, γ, δ, ε and ζ, together with several smaller ones, constitute a group of suns which are all travelling in the same direction in space, apparently more or less toward Arcturus; on the other hand, α and η are travelling in different directions, with the result that in 50,000 years' time the familiar figure of the Plough will have changed.

The Plough is about overhead in the spring evenings and low down in the north below the Pole Star in the autumn

On the opposite side of the Pole Star to the Plough are the five familiar stars of Cassiopeia, arranged somewhat in the form of a W, which, with a fainter sixth star κ added constitute the popular Cassiopeia's Chair. While these constellations occupy two quadrants of this circumpolar area, two very bright stars, together with several easily remembered of lesser brilliance, comprise the constellations of Auriga and Lyra. The brilliant Capella and β Aurigae of the former are almost overhead in the winter evenings, and Vega and the two stars β and γ Lyrae below it are nearly overhead late in the summer evenings. On the other hand, Vega is low down in the north in winter evenings, while Capella occupies this position in summer evenings.

Among the less prominent stars is the constellation of Draco, the celestial Dragon, which is between the zenith and the Pole Star on summer evenings. Cepheus is in this position on autumn evenings, with the brilliant Deneb of Cygnus, the Swan, but popularly known as the Northern Cross, nearly overhead. Deneb is also within the circle of perpetual visibility, although the " Cross " is not ; it is a sun of exceptional intrinsic brilliance, radiating 10,000 times the light of our sun, but from a distance 41,140,000 times as great, and possessing an absolute magnitude of — 5.2. It is the most brilliant sun of the northern heavens and probably the greatest, though owing to its distance it does not appear as bright as Vega.

As if they were swinging round the north celestial pole are the seven stars of Ursa Minor, the Little Bear. These remotely resemble in arrangement the seven stars of Ursa Major, but only Polaris and the " Leaders " are bright—Polaris at the tip of the Bear's tail, β and γ between it and the " Plough Handle." They are north of Polaris in winter evenings, east in spring, south in summer, and west in autumn.

Procession of the Stars. Apart from these circumpolar, always visible stars, most of the starry host appear to pass before us as a diurnal procession from east to west between the zenith and the southern horizon all, that is, except those perpetually hidden because they encircle the south celestial pole.

As the earth's rotation successively brings into view all these stars in 24 hours, it would be possible to see the entire concourse were it not that the sunlight obscures about one-half of them during daylight hours. As the earth revolves, however, in its annual orbit, the other half of the starry heavens comes into view. In the sky stars appear as if projected upon a dome, but star-maps, such as those in Volume 1, plate 14 and those accompanying this Lesson, present them on a flat surface with resultant distortion of relative positions.

In the star-maps in Plates 2 and 3 the lines of right ascension have to appear as if radiating from the pole in straight lines instead of arcs of great circles. Those of declination are indicated by the degrees close to the central meridian.

The right ascension of a star is the angular distance between the great circle which passes through that star and the pole, and another great circle passing through the pole and a fixed point on the celestial equator known as the vernal equinox or the First Point of Aries. Right ascension is always reckoned from this equinox in an easterly direction round the equator, which is divided into 360°. As the celestial sphere appears to make one complete revolution in 24 hours, a meridian passes over 15° in every hour. It is usual, therefore, to reckon right ascension not in degrees but in hours, minutes and seconds. One hour of time or right ascension is equal to 15°, one minute of time to 15 minutes of angular measurement, and one second of time to 15 seconds of angular measurement. This is expressed in symbols thus: 1 hr. = 15°, 1 min. = 15′, 1 sec. = 15″. As the position of a geographical place is stated as being situated in, say, latitude 51° 30′ and longitude 10° 15′, so the position of a star—Sirius, e.g.—is stated as right ascension 6 h. 40 m. 42 sec., and declination — 16° 35′ (the minus sign indicates south declination, and + north declination).

LESSON 35

Salient Details of Star Clusters

(See plates 2 and 3)

STAR clusters are those aggregations in which groups of stars are physically associated, and are quite distinct from artificially grouped constellations (see Lesson 26, Volume 4, page 105). They are divided into *open clusters* and *globular clusters*. The first variety, of which about 200 are known, consists of clusters in which large numbers of stars are apparently massed together in an irregular manner with many outlying members, as in the cases of the well-known Pleiades and Hyades clusters, which are two of the few open clusters visible to the naked eye. It is usual for the members of the cluster to possess a similar proper motion and to average about the same distance from the earth. Thus it comes about that in some cases there are numbers of bright stars apparently not close together, or clustered, which nevertheless are found to form a cluster; the individual members appear far apart on account of their comparative nearness to our planet. Nearly all the stars of Orion and most of those in the " Plough " area of Ursa Major thus form two open clusters, while our sun is found to be a member of a cluster of which Sirius, Procyon, Alpha Centauri, Altair and many lesser luminaries are members.

We see, therefore, that the thousands of millions of stars composing our universe are not distributed evenly or at haphazard throughout the heavens, but are arranged in obvious groups—in clustered masses like eddies in a vast swirl of waters.

Though apparently massed together, the stars are nevertheless separated from each other by distances usually to be measured in light-years and approximating to the distances of the nearest stars to the sun in our cluster.

The Hyades is the nearest of these open clusters and averages about 40 parsecs distant. In this are calculated to be about 100 stars, 40 of them larger and brighter than our sun. The whole forms a cluster between 30 and 40 light-years in diameter, and all travelling in a similar direction, towards the east, as observed from our latitudes. This cluster, therefore, contains approximately a similar number of stars as is contained in the same cubic space of our solar cluster. Some of the stars—for instance, Aldebaran—lie between us and the Hyades, while many faint ones are beyond it; stars which are not members of the cluster may usually be distinguished by their different parallax and proper motion.

The Pleiades is the best known open cluster and is interesting as a sight test. Seven stars are to be perceived by sharp eyes. These were known to the ancients under the names of Alcyone, the brightest, of 3rd magnitude; Electra and Atlas, of the 4th; Merope, Maia and Taygeta, of the 5th; and Pleione, of the 6th magnitude; very good sight could perceive Asterope and also glimpse its companion, Celaeno, under very favourable conditions. A field-glass will increase the number to between 30 and 40, while a powerful telescope will reveal over 2,000 stars in this field, a large number of which are members of the Pleiades cluster. Its average distance is about 100 parsecs, a singular feature being the radiant nebulosity surrounding the brighter stars, which are of the B Class. This nebulous matter apparently fills most of the space between the stars ; it is now believed that its radiance is derived from the intense luminosity of these helium suns. A similar state of things exists in the Orion cluster, which approximates to an average distance of 200 parsecs.

The Praesepe is another cluster appearing to the unaided eye as a faint luminous area in the constellation of Cancer. An opera-glass will resolve it into stars, between 30 and 40 being observed, the number increasing with higher powers. These stars are mostly of the A Class, and at a distance of about 180 parsecs.

The greater the distance of these known agglomerations of stars the more they help us to gain some idea of the structure of the universe. Many of these open clusters are between 2,000 and 3,000 parsecs distant. The density of the stars in the various clusters differs immensely, but it is usually much greater toward the centre. In some cases the number of stars is a thousand times greater than in our solar cluster.

Spectroscopic examination of the members of star clusters shows that every type of star is represented, but in some clusters certain types predominate. For instance, in the Hyades and Praesepe the A Class predominates in the brighter stars , in the Pleiades and Orion clusters the B Class stars are by far the most numerous and brightest.

Numerous nebulous patches of light in various regions of the heavens are found on telescopic examination to be composed of innumerable stars ; two such are in Perseus, and known as H.VI.33,34, but in this famous double cluster many of the stars are revealed by field-glasses. Other impressive areas, most of them much more extensive, require powerful telescopes to resolve them into stars , they are then found to amount to many millions, and are usually designated *star-clouds* Thus the subject of these star-clusters merges into the far greater one of the galaxy as presented to us in what is popularly known as the Milky Way.

The nomenclature adopted is that of the following generally accepted Catalogues The first and most famous was that of Messier, made in 1784. This contained nomenclature for all the brighter objects then observable, and is still most generally used for those objects, which included nebulae as well as star clusters, the essential differences between the two being then unknown ; altogether 103 items were catalogued, and they are now referred to as, for instance, M.44 for the Praesepe, or M.35 for the splendid cluster in Gemini. Subsequently, Sir John Herschel compiled some lists which were gathered into a General Catalogue. Thus the above double cluster in Perseus has come to be known as H.VI.33,34. By the year 1887 Dreyer's New General Catalogue, containing 7,840 objects, was produced ; in this, for example, the Praesepe M.44 becomes N.G.C.2632. Dreyer's catalogue refers mostly to the fainter objects, chiefly nebulae which had been revealed by the higher powers of the telescope, and a supplement is the Index Catalogue, I.C., which adds about 6,000 more objects, chiefly faint nebulae.

Globular Clusters. The Globular Clusters, included in the above catalogue nomenclature, are totally different from open clusters ; about 70 are known, and they constitute most remarkable agglomerations of suns into what would seem to be small island universes apart. The number of stars each cluster contains must average at least 50,000, probably many more, since, owing to their great distance, suns the size of ours would not be perceptible. Moreover, toward the centre these clusters appear so condensed that individual stars are indistinguishable.

Every type of star ranging from Class B to Class M is present, the latter being obviously the largest. They contain numerous variable stars, proved by taking photographs at short intervals ; thus both short-period Cepheids and long-period variables are revealed. The presence of Cepheids has proved to be a valuable aid for estimating the distances of these clusters. This has been ascertained by means of the period-luminosity curve, which provides mathematically the absolute magnitude of the particular star. The difference between the absolute and the apparent magnitude gives the distance, by the same method as already described in Lesson 27 (Volume 4, page 110) as applied to the stars. The distance of the clusters being thus obtained, their size is but a matter of calculation, and so it is found that the diameters of these clusters must approximate to at least 30 parsecs. The condensation of stars toward the centre will therefore be very great ; there must be over a thousand stars in some cubic regions of these clusters, where there is but one in a similar cube of space in our part of the universe.

In appearance, globular clusters all very much resemble the

photograph of M.13 in Hercules in Plate 2, which, by the way, is the only one perceptible to the unaided eye from our latitudes. Seen thus it appears as a very faint hazy star, but it requires a telescope of at least 6 inches aperture to see it partially resolved into some of the 50,000 stars believed to compose it. One of the most powerful telescopes is necessary to show it as represented here. Close inspection of the photograph will reveal innumerable fainter stars as a background to the brighter ones, which compare with Betelgeuse and Antares in magnitude, the whole spectacle being at a distance of about 11,000 parsecs.

The nearest of all these clusters is the still grander spectacle of ω Centauri, in the southern hemisphere and invisible from northern latitudes. It was so titled because to the eye without telescopic aid it appears as a hazy 4th magnitude star and its true character was not then known. Now it is seen to be a still vaster cluster than M.13 and about 6,500 parsecs away. The farthest of these clusters is upwards of 70,000 parsecs distant.

The arrangement of these singular clusters in space takes the form of an ellipsoidal area some 75,000 parsecs in diameter, according to the exhaustive researches of Shapley. The solar system is situated on one side of this vast area, thus accounting for the clusters being almost exclusively found in the half of the celestial sphere that is within 90° of the constellation of Sagittarius, which is regarded by many as the centre of " our universe."

LESSON 36

Principal Types of Nebulae

(See plates 1, 3 and 4)

NEBULAE are faint ill-defined areas of light usually of small apparent extent and resembling wisps of luminous mist. They present every conceivable form and are generalized into four classes : (1) irregular nebulae ; (2) planetary nebulae ; (3) dark nebulae ; (4) spiral nebulae. Between 2,000,000 and 3,000,000 such areas are now known, most of them through the application of long-exposure photography, in conjunction with very high telescopic powers.

Some of these hazy spots of light having been revealed by increases in the powers of the telescope as clusters of stars, the opinion was formed that all were simply star-clusters so far away that their light merged into the impression of nebulous light as does that of the Milky Way. This assumption was destroyed by the spectroscope, which distinguishes with certainty between the light sent to us from a solid star and that emitted by a gas. When this instrument was applied to the nebulae it showed that, whereas some were composed of groups of stars, others were, beyond doubt, masses of luminous gas. The so-called nebulae were therefore divided into two groups, the gaseous and non-gaseous.

It was soon noticed that whereas the gaseous variety shone with a bluish light, the other radiated a white light, this being due to the above differences in their sources. Fortunately there are a few examples of both types just perceptible to the naked eye.

Irregular Nebulae. These are essentially gaseous, bluish in tint and occasionally associated with highly incandescent stars of very great temperatures. Such, for example, is the great nebula of Orion, which may be perceived on any dark and clear night below the " belt " of Orion, and extending for a considerable apparent distance from the multiple star θ Orionis. Various portions of this nebula are in motion in different directions, amounting to as much as 6 or 7 miles a second, and suggesting a rotary motion which indicates a period of about 300,000 years. Actually this nebula extends as a diffuse nebulosity for about 45° to 30° over an area much larger than the constellation of Orion, and enveloping most of its stars, including the three stars of the " belt."

Other nebulae of this first class visible in the low powers of the telescope are the " dumb-bell " nebula in Vulpecula and the " crab " nebula in Taurus (so named by Lord Rosse. who first observed that its extending filaments resembled legs), which has also been found to have a rotary motion with an observed tendency to expansion. The extensive nebulosities surrounding many of the Pleiades are also of the irregular class, while there are numerous areas in Scorpius, Sagittarius and Cygnus ; the " looped " nebula in Dorado is, however, the largest known irregular nebula, with a diameter calculated by Shapley at 130 light-years.

The spectra of these irregular nebulae consist of a faint continuous spectrum upon which is superimposed a line emission spectrum ; lines of hydrogen and helium are pronounced, together with two green lines, supposed to be derived from an element unidentified at present and named *nebulium*.

The densities of these nebulae are exceedingly low, estimated to be many billions of times less than the earth's atmosphere —therefore far less than can be attained in an artificial vacuum. For such rarefied matter in space to be incandescent and produce the spectra of hydrogen and helium seems out of the question.

Now since these gases in a state of incandescence are most prominent in the stars which are enveloped or associated with these vast areas of diffuse nebulae, it appears, according to Hubble, that these stars cause the luminosity observed in the nebulae. This circumstance is singularly well displayed in the way in which the Pleiades light up the surrounding nebulous masses. These masses are obviously in motion and the light has been observed to change with the movement. When we come to consider dark nebulae this solution would appear to be true.

Planetary Nebulae. In this second class the nebulae are smaller than in the first ; they are also denser, more massive, and appear approximately regular in outline, presenting under low magnification a disk which looks somewhat like that of a planet seen out of focus. From this they derive their name.

Though a few of these nebulae have a diameter approaching 12′, most of them are much smaller. About 150 are known, and of these the " owl " nebula in Ursa Major—so named from the fancied resemblance of its disk to the face of an owl—known astronomically as N.G.C.3587, is one of the most easily observed. Another is the so-called " ring " nebula in Lyra—N.G.C.6720 in the Catalogue nomenclature, which is the same as for star clusters (*see* Lesson 35, page 48). This nebula is situated almost midway between β and γ Lyrae, and has an apparent diameter of 1′ 23″ at its widest ; it appears as a ring under low magnification, but, photographed with high telescopic powers, it is seen to be filled with nebulous detail together with a star in the centre. Most of the disks of planetary nebulae are found, when photographed through powerful telescopes, to exhibit a mass of detail which suggests the rotation of the whole round a central star, nucleus or condensation. This rotation may take from 5,000 to 15,000 years to complete, according to various examples tested, the rate being from 1 to 12 miles a second.

Other noteworthy examples are N.G.C.7662 in Andromeda, H.IV.27 in Hydra, and, largest of all, N.G.C.7293 in Aquarius, which, with a diameter of 12′, is at a distance of about 80 light-years and is the nearest known planetary nebula. These nebulae are more numerous in the neighbourhood of the Milky Way, especially in the region of Sagittarius, and are as a rule apparently smaller than those in regions distant from the Milky Way. This is explained as due to the fact that those situated near the galactic plane (the central line of the Milky Way) are farthest from the earth.

The spectra of this class of nebulae are similar to those of the class O and Wolf-Rayet stars. Some of these so strikingly resemble planetary nebulae that it might be inferred that many of them represent one-time novae, which in distant ages blazed up and have been left in nebulous condition, slowly to die down into star again.

Dark Nebulae. These were first suspected to exist as many dark patches in the heavens, conspicuous for being destitute of distant stars, in regions—such as certain parts of the Milky Way—where the adjoining areas are dense with stellar luminosity. At one time it was thought that these dark areas were regions destitute of stars : but since Cowper Ranyard drew attention to their singular shape in many of the smaller patches revealed in the early days of celestial photography, it has been found that they are due to the intervention of opaque cosmic material. Barnard catalogued nearly 200 of these remarkable objects : more have been added by the continued application of photography, particularly in the vicinity of the luminous nebulae, one of the most impressive being the mass of dark nebulous material which encroaches upon the bright portions of the Orion nebula below ζ Orionis, the easternmost star of the famous " belt " illustrated in Plate 1. These are doubtless dark portions of the nebula itself which more or less obscure the illuminated regions.

Other remarkable examples are the " coal sack " in Crux (the Southern Cross), and the dark nebulae in Ophiuchus. Scorpius. Taurus and Cygnus. Their distances are found to vary from 100 parsecs to the limits of the Milky Way . they are also associated with many of the open clusters, e.g. the Pleiades and Orion.

The great cleft in Cygnus, perceptible on any dark night in summer and autumn, extends through Aquila to Ophiuchus. It is undoubtedly caused by the intervention of a belt of opaque nebulous matter which obscures part of the Milky Way with its numerous stars beyond, while only those which are between us and the obscuring clouds are perceived. The material is believed to consist of cosmic particles which may be, in size, anything from a molecule to a planetoid, and spread through areas to be measured by hundreds or even thousands of parsecs, as we shall see when the fourth class, the spiral nebulae, is considered in our next Lesson.

LESSON 37

Problems of the Cosmos

(See plate 4)

SPIRAL nebulae were at one time regarded as masses of gaseous nebulosity which ultimately evolved into suns and solar systems ; but spectroscopic analysis of their light, together with photography applied with greatly increased powers of the telescope, has revealed them to be of stellar composition, only slightly gaseous, possessing many features which distinguish them entirely from every other class of celestial object, and nebulae only in appearance. Though more numerous than the true or galactic nebulae, these so-called nebulae are spread over the sky on a totally different plan, their numbers apparently increasing toward the *galactic poles*, particularly the northern, and there being only very few within 20° of the *galactic equator*, that is, the median line of the Milky Way.

The spectroscope, with the aid of long exposure photographs, shows the spectra of spiral nebulae to be continuous and crossed by numbers of dark absorption lines—just such spectra as are obtained from the sun and the stars. Thus it has been ascertained that these so-called nebulae are actually composed of suns more or less similar to our own, and since lines of nebulium are also present in certain localized areas, gaseous nebulae are also present as in our *galactic system*.

The fact is therefore revealed that they are galaxies apart from the galaxy or universe of which the solar system is a constituent. They are in consequence often referred to as extra-galactic nebulae, or more picturesquely as " island universes," a term sometimes applied to globular clusters of stars, which are, however not extra-galactic, but an integral part of our galaxy, whereas it has been proved that the extra-galactic are far beyond it.

Photographs taken by long exposure for several hours have revealed the dim patches of misty light (which is all that even telescopes exhibit to the eye) to be composed of star-clouds, clustered masses of suns, the larger of which are individually perceived in the nearer of the "nebulae." The whole usually appears arranged as a vast spiral, the arm composed of streaming star-clouds intermingled with nebulosity and frequently more bluish at the outer than the central regions. In some cases there are belts of dark nebulous matter, generally extending round the outer regions of the spiral, which partially hide the stellar radiance beyond, as in our galaxy. The centre of a typical spiral consists of a massed condensation of stellar radiance in which the individual suns appear clustered and require still higher powers of the telescope to resolve.

The spirals exhibit every variety of form; variations are increased by perspective and the angle from which they are viewed. They appear to be more or less flattened lens-shaped agglomerations of thousands of millions of suns and doubtless numerous worlds, together with star-clusters and nebulae proper, such as enter into the composition of our galaxy. In a small proportion the spiral form is less obvious owing to various irregular star-clouds and streams of nebulosity disguising the structure; these are known as *irregular spirals*. Others are so distant, or in such an early stage, that the spiral form is not obvious.

In the larger and nearer of the so-called spiral nebulae both variable stars, particularly Cepheids, and novae are found. The Cepheids have proved to be most important as a means for calculating the distance and immensity of the extra-galactic nebulae. For since it was possible to estimate the absolute magnitude of the Cepheid variables from the period-luminosity curve, their distance could be calculated from the difference between their absolute and apparent magnitudes. These extra-galactic universes are the most distant objects known.

One of the nearest is the great nebula of Andromeda, at a distance of about 270,000 parsecs, and therefore far beyond the extreme limits of our galaxy, which are probably from 20,000 to 50,000 parsecs distant. This grand spiral, shown almost edge-wise in the photograph given in Plate 4, may be seen with the naked eye almost overhead in the autumn evenings, when it appears as an oval area of faint misty light somewhat greater than the moon's apparent width.

The study of this far-off galaxy has proved instructive, and we have gained therefrom some conception of what our own galaxy appears like *from the outside*, as it were. Considerations such as the arrangement of the star-clouds of the Milky Way, spectroscopic parallaxes and Cepheid distances, have combined to give experts fairly accurate grounds for the hypothesis that our galaxy has the form of a spiral and that the solar system is situated somewhere within it, at about 10,000 parsecs from one side and between 20,000 and 50,000 parsecs from the farther and vaguer side. The centre of the system is estimated to be in the dense star-clouds of Sagittarius and Scorpius at approximately some 10,000 parsecs distant, and the greatest diameter of the whole galactic system is between 40,000 and 60,000 parsecs. Owing to the obvious difficulty of estimating the *depth* of the star-clouds, considerable latitude must be allowed in estimates. Professor Kapteyn, the late leading expert authority upon the galaxy, considered the diameter of this lens-shaped spiral system to be about five times its thickness; this is well in accord with the observed proportions of many extra-galactic universes. Kapteyn estimated our galaxy to contain a total of about 47,000,000,000 stars; Seares and Van Rhijn, about 30,000,000,000. Of these about 2,000,000,000 may be regarded as dimly observable, the others being hidden in the star-clouds of the Milky Way.

There are two other galactic systems that are known to be nearer than the great nebula of Andromeda, but they are only to be seen from more southern latitudes. Visible to the naked eye as large, faintly luminous areas, resembling detached portions of the Milky Way, they are popularly known as the Magellanic Clouds, but astronomically as Nebecula Major and Nebecula Minor. They are far apart, the former chiefly in Dorado, the latter in Toucan. Belonging to the irregular class of spirals, they are of great interest, since they represent small galaxies adjacent to our own. Nebecula Minor was found by Shapley to be at a distance of about 32,000 parsecs, and Nebecula Major about 34,500.

The total number of these extra-galactic universes represented by these spiral nebulae approaches 2,000,000, and it is certain that further increase of telescopic power will add to the number. The speed at which they are travelling relative to our galaxy is terrific, and ranging from 200 to 1,000 miles a second. Now, a most remarkable circumstance of supreme importance to our conception of the Cosmos is the fact that about 80 per cent of these galaxies appear to be receding from our galaxy. From this it is inferred by certain authorities, particularly those who accept the mathematical concepts of Relativity, that the Cosmos or entire " Universe of Galaxies " is expanding.

Relativity of Space and Time. Our galaxy is doubtless travelling at a speed comparable with the above, and in a direction which has no meaning except one *relative* to the others. The time taken has likewise no meaning except that it is *relative* to the speeds of other objects through what we call space. When mathematically considered as an essential part of the Cosmos, space and time are found to be indissolubly linked ; thus the mathematical investigation, begun by Lorentz and elaborated by Minkowski, may be summed up in the latter's words :

" The views of space and time which I have set forth have their foundation in experimental physics. . . From henceforth space in itself and time in itself sink into mere shadows, and only a kind of union of the two preserves an independent existence."

Moreover, none of these extra-galactic universes is where it appears to be ; neither are the stellar denizens of our own galaxy ; so we never see the universe as it is or as it was at any particular moment of time. It is impossible to do so, since the *space* separating us from each member, and the *time* that light takes in transit across those spaces, vary with the different distances. Indeed, it has even been conceived that a galaxy which now appears in one region of the heavens may actually be in the opposite region, owing to the lapse of time the light has taken to reach us, 140 million light-years being taken by the light of the farthest known.

Dr. Albert Einstein carried on the work of his predecessors and, in particular, corrected and adapted the famous laws of Newton adequately to explain by mathematical formulae certain observed phenomena in physics, optics and astronomy. This he presented in his Special Theory of Relativity in 1905.

Einstein's General Theory of Relativity (1915) chiefly deals with optical and electrical phenomena and accelerated motion, even to the extent of predicting certain results. These were, first, the forward motion of the perihelion of Mercury, which amounts to 40".1 per century ; Einstein's hypothesis requires it to advance 42".9 per century and is the only adequate explanation. The second was the bending of light rays when passing near a large gravitational mass such as our sun ; this was proved to occur by the Greenwich Eclipse Expedition to Brazil in 1919, when the photographs, taken with great precision, showed that the light from certain stars passing near the sun at the time of total eclipse was bent toward it to the observed extent of 1".98, whereas Einstein predicted 1".75. A subsequent expedition to the Australian total eclipse of 1922 gave the observed bending as 1".78 ; thus, after allowing for unavoidable observational errors, Einstein was proved correct. The third was the displacement of spectral lines so that they shift toward the red end of the spectrum, as the result of the vibrations becoming slower when the light is emitted from the sun or any other massive body ; this was also finally proved to occur in the case of the massive companion to Sirius.

Already, however, Einstein's concept of a cosmic universe of fixed and limited extent has had to give place to one conceived by Dr. de Sitter, in 1917, which presents an expanding cosmic universe. This at present is most in accord with the observed receding galaxies. Other concepts are : warped space in gravitational fields ; the possibility of curved space and a spherical cosmos in which light travels in a curved path and may return upon itself, as does the surface of a sphere ; even gravitation as a force is questioned by the new theories. These are largely subjects of mathematical discussion, in which the names of Dr. de Sitter, Sir James Jeans, Sir Arthur Eddington, Professor E. A. Milne, and the Abbé G. Lemaitre are to the forefront. Their writings should be referred to for a presentation of the various aspects of the problems. Meanwhile, this outstanding fact remains beyond question : that there is no known limit to *that which is*, i.e. existence, in either time, space or space-time ; therefore we must infer its infinity and eternity.

Bibliography. Jeans' " Universe Around Us." and " Stars in their Courses " (Cambridge University Press) ; H. S. Jones' " General Astronomy " (Arnold).

This Lesson concludes our Course in Astronomy.

Neo-Lamarckism in Biology

Two different theories have been presented to the reader in Lessons 32 and 33 (Volume 5, pages 80 and 83), each of which seeks to explain how evolution has occurred. " The innate tendency of organisms to evolve towards greater complexity," which is Lamarck's theory, has been adopted and elaborated by the Neo-Lamarckians. Bergson's " Élan Vital," or theory of a life force, regards the effort, which Lamarck supposed each individual to make, as an expression of a force or upward urge which permeates all living matter, and which uses each organism as a vehicle for its expression. Variations are merely manifestations of this force, which urges an organism to acquire characters suitable for its environment and which, presumably, ensures the inheritance of these characters.

This, termed the vitalist theory, raises further points for consideration. Is the urge, which Shaw has called a life force, aiming at some definite goal ? Is its aim merely to enable the individual organism to live successfully in its environment, or is there some greater end in view, some final stage in evolution, to attain which the life force is urging all creation ? Is the life force, in fact, purposive or purposeless ?

There are many difficulties in adopting the purposive view. If the life force has aimed, throughout the course of evolution, at a definite goal, what explanation is to be given of the numberless species which palaeontological records prove to have evolved and become extinct ? Does the life force work by the method of trial and error ? Why has the life force taken such a long and roundabout path to attain its end ? Again, most living organisms have their parasites, some of which are beneficial to their host, while others are harmful and even lethal. In the first case, in which the host benefits from its parasite, we have to imagine a life force which produces one organism, the host, so unfitted to its environment that a second organism is needed to safeguard its life. In the second case, it is difficult to reconcile the idea of a purposive life force with the fact that the host is often injured and sometimes killed by the parasite. If both host and lethal parasite are the productions of a purposive life force, its action in the production of the host appears to be at cross purposes with its action in producing a parasite which kills it.

The theory of a blind, purposeless life force need not be considered here ; it is, in effect, the sort of theory, or lack of a theory, which the Darwinian interpretation of the facts of evolution suggests.

Those who are attracted by the idea of a purposive life force as a cause of evolution are recommended to study the works of Samuel Butler. In his book " Unconscious Memory," Butler extends Lamarck's theory of the inheritance of acquired characters to include memory. He points out that the first untaught actions of a baby—its breathing, eating and drinking, digestion and crying—are all complicated and difficult processes, and are only performed so successfully by the infant because it has inherited an unconscious memory of the same performances by its forbears through the generations.

The title of Butler's book " Luck or Cunning ? " is a condensation of the two opposing theories of evolution. " Cunning " is Butler's term for Lamarck's idea of characters being acquired by the efforts of the parent, while he stigmatizes the Darwinian theory of the survival by natural selection of the fitter variations as " luck." He asks : " Do animals and plants grow into conformity with their surroundings because they and their fathers and mothers take pains, or because their uncles and aunts go away ? " In his " Life and Habit," Butler contends that heredity is a " mode of memory," and we must conclude, therefore, that Butler would consider that the evolution of an eye is due to the descendant's remembrance of the efforts to see made by its eyeless ancestors.

Butler was not primarily a scientist, but the reader who is prepared to accept as evidence the inspired suggestions of a man of genius, supported by the most cogent reasoning, will find it difficult to dismiss his theory too lightly. On the other hand, it may be suggested that, since evolution has culminated in the production of Man, it is, no doubt, a temptation for Mankind to believe that there has been purpose in evolution : but Man has always shown this tendency to invoke some occult agency to account for phenomena beyond his understanding.

NEO-LAMARCKISM IN BIOLOGY

For the scientist the Neo-Lamarckian theory of a purposive life force has two weak points :

(1) It cannot be proved by experiment that there is, or is not, a life force at work.

(2) The theory depends on the inheritance of acquired characters of which also we have no experimental proof.

An acceptance of Darwin's mechanistic theory involves a denial of purpose in evolution. The infinite number of variations that have occurred, and are occurring, in Nature do so, as far as is known, at random. Experiments on the banana-fly prove that many variations arise through mutations of the genes, or through the breaking and recombining of chromosomes, and that these mutations can be induced by subjecting the fly to X-rays. There is further evidence that more mutations appear in these flies when they are bred in an area where earth radiation is greater than when they live in an area of smaller earth radiation.

It has been conjectured, to account for this fact, that genes are molecules differing from those of the inorganic world only by their greater complexity of structure, and that these molecules are composed of atoms, just as a molecule of water is composed of two atoms of hydrogen and one of oxygen. Modern physics find the atom to be a centre of electric force (proton) with negative charges of electricity (electrons) revolving round it. These revolving electrons are sensitive to bombardment The suggestion is, then, that the mutations which are the basis of evolution are the results of the chance bombardment of the molecules which are genes by the waves of earth radiation If this is right, the whole evolutionary process is an accident, and it is only an accident that Mankind happens to be the dominant phylum.

The evidence of palaeontology and embryology corroborates this mechanistic theory of the cause of evolution, and it is, therefore, on the whole, the most generally accepted theory among modern scientists. Man has now, however, begun to interfere with the course of evolution He is busily creating an artificial environment, and finds himself with his primitive set of genes maladjusted both physically and mentally to his new surroundings. But it is not fantastic to suggest that he has almost within his grasp the power to decide whether the future course of his evolution shall continue to be accidental In the science of genetics lies the clue to solving the problem of breeding a race of men more at harmony with the modern world and with each other.

Some Practical Uses of Biology

THE first attempts at agriculture by prehistoric Man included wheat growing. Wheat grains have been found in the rubbish heaps left by the lake-dwellers of Italy and Switzerland, and in the bricks of an Egyptian pyramid which was erected about 3359 B.C. All the ancient civilizations used wheat as a staple food, the Greeks and Romans considering it to be a gift from the gods. Quite recently the wild wheat, from which all modern varieties have descended, has been found growing on the slopes of Mount Hermon. The Roman agriculturist experienced the same difficulty as that which beset our own farmers up to the present century, namely, that cultivated wheat was liable to be attacked by rust, a fungus disease. On April 25 every year the Romans held a feast to propitiate the rust-god Robigus, burning the entrails of a red dog upon his altar.

As soon as the significance of Mendel's laws was realized, one of the first practical applications was the endeavour to improve the quality of wheat. The ideal wheat was to be glutinous, hard, high-yielding, and rust-resisting. Sir Rowland Biffen crossed a low-yielding, rust-resisting wheat with a high-yielding variety which was not immune from the disease. The experiment turned out in accordance with the Mendelian table shown in the diagram in Lesson 15 (Volume 2, page 82). All F_1 were infected, but in F_2 some plants were homozygous both from rust-resisting and high yield ; that is, in the general re-shuffling of genes by the self-fertilizatilon of F_1, a double dose of rust-resisting and high-yielding genes met in some plants, and these alone were selected for future propagation. The result has been a high-yielding wheat immune from rust, and this today forms one-third of the world's crop.

Canada has its special problems in wheat growing. A wheat that ripens five or six days earlier than other varieties may enable the farmer to make a profit instead of a heavy loss. The harvest escapes the frost, which in the northern districts sets in about August 20, and the farmer has a few days to clear the land

FERNS OF THE BRITISH COUNTRYSIDE. Top, spleenwort (Asplenium trichomanes). Centre, royal fern (Osmunda regalis) and hart's-tongue (Scolopendrium vulgare). Bottom, hard fern (Blechnum spicant) and male fern (Aspidium filix-mas). BOTANY 34

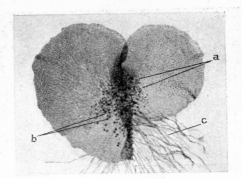

PROTHALLUS produced from a fern spore; a, archegonia : b, antheridia ; c, rhizoids (× about 8).
BOTANY 34
J. J. Ward

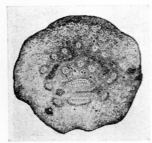

SALVINIA. This small water-fern is a native of southern Europe. Down hanging leaves take the place of roots
BOTANY 34

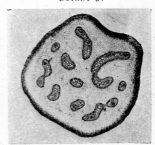

FERN STRUCTURE. Top, left, transverse section of rhizome of Pteris aquilina, a polystelic stem (× about 3). Bottom, left, transverse section of petiole of Osmunda regalis, showing large stele (× 4). Right, transverse section of petiole of Pteris aquilina, showing steles in ground tissue (× 5).
BOTANY 34
H. S. Cheavin

Plate 6   *Volume VI*

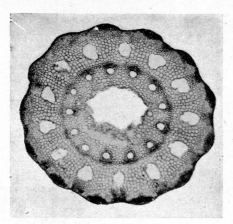

HORSETAIL STEM. Photomicrograph of a transverse section showing the vascular bundles arranged in a circle ; × 16 approx. BOTANY 35

H. S. Cheavin

HORSETAIL AND CLUB MOSSES. Top, left, fertile and barren stems of the horsetail. Right, quillwort (Isoetes). Bottom, left, Lycopodium clavatum, showing the spore-bearing cones. BOTANY 35

GEORGE III (1738–1820). Succeeding his grandfather, George II, in 1760, he determined to be the real ruler of the State, but the attempt ended in the disasters of the American war and in the king's insanity. Recovering his reason at intervals he interfered, generally for the worse, in public affairs, but in 1811 he became finally incapacitated. This engraving by W. Holl is from the portrait by Sir Thomas Lawrence.
BRITISH HISTORY 19

CHARLES JAMES FOX (1749–1806). Elected M.P. in 1769 he led the Whigs for many years, and in 1782 and 1806 was secretary of state.
BRITISH HISTORY 20

WILLIAM PITT THE YOUNGER (1759–1806). Younger son of William Pitt, 1st earl of Chatham, he entered Parliament in 1781, became chancellor of the exchequer in 1782, and prime minister in 1783. Resigning in 1801, he was again premier from 1804 until his death. BRITISH HISTORY 20
After Gainsborough; Iveagh Bequest; photo, Pullman

Plate 8   *Volume VI*

before the " freeze up." Further, the heavy storms to which the wheat lands of Canada are subjected make it desirable for the wheat to have a stout, pliant straw and an ear from which the grains are not easily shattered The " Marquis " wheat, which most nearly fulfils these conditions, is now grown with great success over vast areas in America and Asia By crossing this variety with many others, a Russian geneticist has succeeded in identifying the six pairs of genes which produce the distinctive characters, the peculiar broad-shaped grains and glumes, of the " Marquis " wheat.

A frequent occurrence in the reproduction of plants is the duplication of entire sets of chromosomes. In Lesson 16 (Volume 3, page 109) the normal cell was described as diploid—that is to say, it has a double set of chromosomes—but after meiosis has taken place the gametic cells are usually haploid, having only a single set. It occasionally happens in plants, but less frequently in animals, that for some reason not yet known the cell division stops half-way, and, instead of two haploid gametic cells, the original gametic cell remains with a double number of chromosomes. If the plant is self-fertilizing, the progeny also has a double number of chromosomes. In the result all the characters are affected ; the cells are much enlarged, and the plant, although identical in character with its parent, is itself larger. The extra growth of many of our cultivated garden plants is due to the fact that they are tetraploids , that is to say, each somatic cell, instead of a double set, has four sets of chromosomes The common evening primrose has 14 chromosomes, while the giant variety has 28 in each somatic cell. Many garden roses and flowering bulbs are tetraploid.

A third type of plant (triploid) is produced by crossing a diploid with a tetraploid. If a gamete from a tetraploid is fertilized by a gamete from a diploid, there will be a fusion of two sets of chromosomes from the tetraploid plant with one set from the diploid ; the result is a triploid individual with three sets. Most of these triploid plants are sterile, since odd numbers of sets of chromosomes form gametes with unequal numbers of chromosomes and complete pairing is impossible.

Triploid varieties of roses can, however, be propagated by grafting and by cuttings, and triploid bulbs by offsets. Japanese cherries are sterile triploids grown from cuttings and grafts, and many dahlias, roses, lilies, tulips and daffodils are triploid or tetraploid. Wild wheat has 14 chromosomes, while many of the best-yielding cultivated varieties have 42. Hexaploid and octoploid plants can be formed by further crossing. A fertile octoploid wheat was created in 1926, and a hexaploid variety in 1930.

Science of Genetics. Animals have been bred for so long by practical breeders that the empirical art of breeding is in advance of the science of genetics. The science of genetics has only recently become a full-grown science, and has been limited so far to the experimental study of the genetics of inexpensive, quick-maturing and highly fecund types, such as fruit-flies, moths, rabbits, guinea-pigs, mice and rats. Moreover, the science of genetics is faced with a much more difficult problem in dealing with the animal world than that which is presented by plants. This problem arises from the fact that there is no self-fertilizing animal, and pure line experimental breeding is therefore impossible. Nor can useful but sterile hybrids such as the mule be perpetuated by grafting, as is done in the case of plants. Nevertheless, much analytical work has been done which explains the difficulties and disappointments of the practical breeder, even if it does not yet show him how to overcome them. For example, the knowledge of Mendelian inheritance explains why there cannot be a tortoiseshell tom cat which is fertile. The science of genetics has also cleared away the many superstitions that impeded the art of practical breeding.

Determining Sex Ratio. Much work has been done in investigating the sex ratio—the proportion of males to females—which is a very important matter for poultry farmers, etc. It has been discovered that the sex ratio varies with the season of conception, and also that the characteristic of male-producing or female-producing can be made a feature of a breed by judicious breeding. It may be conjectured that, as the technique of genetics becomes more perfect, the point will be reached when the chromosomes and even the gene can be manipulated directly, so that, instead of breeding a generation from which many members must be rejected, we may be sure in advance that all the off-spring of a single mating will have all the characters required.

Books bearing upon the subject are : " Animal Genetics," Crew (Oliver and Boyd) ; " Science of Life," Book IV, pp. 363–375, Wells, Huxley and Wells (Amalgamated Press).

Dysgenic Factors in Modern Society

THE study of the evolution of life in the past prompts the consideration of its course in the future. The student has been shown a picture of Nature in a continual state of flux. Great and widespread phyla of plants and animals have flourished, become dominant, and then faded out, to be replaced by a more plastic and usually a more complex, type of organism. In the more recent eras brain capacity has been the characteristic which has led to the advance of a species, and it is owing to the possession of a reasoning mind that Man appears to be the dominant phylum today.

Among the many races of Man those that have been the most backward in developing brain power are dying out. The Australian aboriginal population is dwindling year by year, and the still more primitive Tasmanian is already extinct. What of the future ? Evolution, it is clear, points to the fact that a phylum must progress or regress. What, then, of ourselves ? Is the brain capacity of civilized communities growing or deteriorating ? Comparing the output of original thought of the Athenian population of 2,000 years ago with that of the much larger civilized population of today, it would be difficult to assert with confidence that the intellectual capacity of Man is increasing. Science has equipped us with powers and riches undreamt of by the ancient Greeks, but we cannot yet refrain from using some of these powers to exterminate our fellow men, and we find our riches so embarrassing to handle that men in one area may be badly in need of goods which are being destroyed in another area, where there is a plethora.

Mental ability is transmitted by heredity ; that is to say, a man's mental equipment depends on the relevant genes which were contributed by his father and mother. Feeble-mindedness, for example, behaves as a Mendelian recessive. In the table in Lesson 15 (Volume 2, page 84) it was shown that when a recessive character, such as feeble-mindedness, is present in a double dose, the individual is homozygous for, and exhibits, feeble-mindedness. Thus, Goddard records that 477 were feeble-minded out of 482 children born of feeble-minded parents, and the records of 41 marriages of feeble-minded members of the Kallilak family show that of 224 children born only two were normal.

A still more disastrous union is that in which one parent is feeble-minded and the other an epileptic. Twenty-seven such marriages, of which records have been kept, produced 43 epileptic, 58 feeble-minded, 1 insane and 8 neurotic offspring. It is a disturbing fact that there is no bar to such marriages, unless the bride or bridegroom is certifiable. Apart from the cost to the community of the care of the defective children born of such parents, it is obvious that the mental power of the nation is lowered by every such child who lives, marries and spreads his defective genes.

Intelligence Tests. Dr. Cyril Burt has carried out a series of intelligence tests on children attending two London schools. Those attending one of the schools lived in a good neighbourhood and their parents were among the most well-to-do of those who send their children to a primary school. The other school was in a slum area. The tests were devised to indicate powers of intelligence and memory. In these tests a child who is more successful than the average is given a " mental " age higher than his chronological age. Thus, a child of seven who can pass tests which previous experiments have shown to be suitable for the average child of nine would be given a " mental " age of nine.

INTELLIGENCE OF CHILDREN IN TWO CONTRASTED SCHOOLS.

Chrono-logical age	Average No. of tests passed		Average mental age	
	Superior school	Poor school	Superior school	Poor school
7	44·5	31·2	8·99	6·1
8	48·5	36·3	10·1	7·2
9	51·0	42·6	10·6	8·4
10	54·3	46·8	11·5	9·6
11	56·2	50·4	12·1	10·3
12	57·5	52·9	12·8	11·0
13	59·3	55·2	13·7	11·7
14	60·5	54·8	14·2	11·6

DYSGENIC FACTORS IN MODERN SOCIETY

The slightly lower performance of the older children in the better school is due to the school being " creamed " of its best scholars, who, at the age of eleven, leave to go to a secondary school. It should be noted that large groups of children are tested, and, although there are many bright exceptions in the poor school and many dull ones in the better school, the average mental age in the former is from one to two years lower than that in the latter school.

No doubt the difference of environment accounts for some of the marked differences shown in the table, but the history of identical twins given in Lesson 35 (Volume 5, page 89) shows that heredity is a far more potent factor than environment in determining mental capacity. The qualities by which men usually succeed in the world are ambition, foresight, prudence, self-control, judgement and brain power. Lacking these, men tend to gravitate to lower and lower strata of society, and since like seeks like, they marry their intellectual equals. If the children born of this type of parent were heavily outnumbered by children born of the higher type of parent, the future of the race of mankind would not be jeopardised to any great extent by this perpetuation of individuals who are homozygous for defective genes ; but the second table of statistics collected by Dr. Burt gives still more disquieting facts.

	Best school	Poorest school
Average number of children living at home	2·9	5·2
Average number of rooms in home	4·7	2·3

Thus the lower type of child is being born at almost double the rate of the better type.

Many forces are at work to account for this modern tendency of the lower types to breed at the expense of the higher. The ambitious and prudent delay marriage until they have advanced some way in their career. Professional men—teachers, doctors, architects, lawyers, etc.—have not only to pass severe examinations, but subsequently they must wait to establish their position before marrying, and these delayed marriages tend to smaller families. Moreover, in order to make proper provision for the education of their children, parents today often deliberately restrict their number. (Some high-grade types are even penalized if they marry. Many authorities dismiss a woman teacher if she marries, and, in so far as dismissal is a deterrent, valuable potential racial recruits are lost. Further wastage of good racial material is caused by modern warfare, which takes a huge toll of the biologically fit. War is a racial as well as an economic disaster.)

The unskilled labourer, on the other hand, is earning his maximum wage at 20-25 years of age, and the greater his lack of brain power, ambition, foresight, etc., the less likely is he to delay marriage or restrict the number of his children. Thus the population of most civilized countries is being recruited largely from below.

McDowell estimates that one in every fourteen of the normal-minded population carries the gene for feeble-mindedness, although, since like seeks like, the proportion is much higher than this among the lower-grade classes and much lower in the professional and higher classes. Inmates of special schools and asylums are increasing both in England and America and, as the foregoing tables show, defective germ plasm is spreading.

LESSON 39

Sterilization and Birth Control

THE study of Biology, reinforced by the statistics cited in the preceding Lesson, leads to the conviction that Man must guide the future evolution of his race, if it is to persist. Unfortunately, the eugenist does not obtain the attention he deserves, because the measures he advocates are largely for the benefit of posterity, while the modern statesman is so occupied in commending himself to the approval of the present generation that he cannot spare thought for those yet to come. Moreover, any advocacy of restriction or regulation of marriage and birth raises a storm of criticism. G. K. Chesterton, for example, in " Eugenics and Other Evils," says that the eugenist would have prevented the birth of R. L. Stevenson, and would exterminate the whole of the Cratchit family because of Tiny

Tim. No biologist will agree, however, that it is necessary to be unhealthy to be a genius, and common sense tells us that, had Tiny Tim been healthy and had fewer brothers and sisters, Bob Cratchit with his weekly 15s. would have " kept the pot aboiling " more cheerfully because more easily.

Humanity now does its best to thwart natural selection and to keep the Tiny Tims alive, but every child born into a very poor household reduces the opportunities and standard of living of its brothers and sisters. Moreover, when pregnancies quickly succeed each other, the mother's health is menaced and the resulting children are less strong. The day may come, therefore, when the government of a civilized country will have a population department which will regulate the birth rate. Already a number of local authorities in this country give advice to those who seek it on the subject of birth control.

Whatever opinions may be held as to the morality of birth control—which is legal in England, sterilization being illegal, while in the United States birth control is illegal in all States and sterilization legal in twenty-nine of the States—the fact must be faced that it is likely to exert an immense influence over the evolution of Mankind—an influence, too, which will be far greater in the future. Birth control has, so far, however, been practised almost entirely by those classes of society from which it is desirable that the race should be recruited, while, owing to ignorance of its method or indifference as to the future, limitation of family is largely neglected by the lower types of society, whose contribution to the population is proved by statistics to be inferior both mentally and physically.

Birth control, then, at present, is mainly dysgenic in its effect. To remedy this the eugenist advocates that the knowledge of contraceptive methods should be spread among the lower strata of society. It is probable, however, that even in this event the intelligent would use, and the less intelligent neglect, such knowledge. Seemingly, then, something beyond voluntary control is needed.

Eugenic Suggestions. One suggestion that has been made is that the number of children in all families receiving public assistance should be recorded and, in cases where the parents are so physically or mentally defective as to have no prospect of earning a living, warning should be given that, if any more children are born, public assistance would be withdrawn.

Another suggestion made by eugenists is that men and women contemplating marriage should seek expert advice. It would be an economically sound act on the part of any government to furnish such advice free. The contracting parties would each furnish records of the incidence of consumption, insanity, feeble-mindedness, etc., in their family history, and an expert eugenist would, after examining the records and the prospective bride and bridegroom, express his opinion as to the advisability of their having a family. As the family pedigree, recorded and handed down, would give in succeeding generations particulars of grandfathers and grandmothers, the expert's advice would become more definite in the second and succeeding generations.

On the positive side the eugenist urges that the more intelligent types—the professional classes, for example, and those who can produce evidence of enterprise, prudence and foresight—should be encouraged to have larger families. Such encouragement might take the form of a substantial relief in income tax for every child under 16 or, in cases where income tax is not paid, a direct bonus for each child might be offered, as in France.

Sterilization and Compulsion. The eugenist is on more dangerous ground when he advocates compulsory sterilization. In the first place, the cry of " the right to parenthood " is raised. But this slogan, although it appeals to an important instinct, ignores the right of the unborn child to have healthy parents, who can equip him with brains and health and who are sufficiently intelligent to bring him up in proper surroundings.

A real danger is that sterilization might be used not only as a biological safeguard, but as a political weapon. The Nazi party in Germany has advocated, under the guise of eugenic measures, not only compulsory checks to the breeding of alien or non-German inhabitants, but state restriction of the reproduction of various types of defective, and their term for defective—*minderwertig*—specifically includes *those who do not share the political opinions of the dominant party*. Both from the economic and biological standpoint, however, a civilized state cannot afford to continue to allow certain types to reproduce. More research is needed before we are in a position to say which types, but certain kinds of feeble-mindedness and at least one kind of cancer—glioma—are definitely inheritable.

From the economic view only, the government of the U.S.A. would have saved on arrests, trials, and public assistance over two million dollars had, for example, the founders of the notorious Jukes family been sterilized. In 1874 many Jukes were found in state gaols. The family history was traced back to two brother Jukes, who married two sisters and settled in an isolated valley. Of 162 women 52 were prostitutes ; of 535 children 106 were illegitimate, and 23 per cent of the family had received state relief. There had been 50 convicted criminals and over 250 arrests and trials. In 1916, out of 654 persons of this name, 323 were either unable or unwilling to work and 255 were un-skilled labourers. This slightly better record is due to less intermarriage, but it also means a wider spread of defective genes.

The biologist claims that Man has already the knowledge (which is being rapidly augmented) to enable him to control his destiny. The eugenist urges that he shall acquire the wisdom and have the courage to use this knowledge.

In " Last and First Men," by Olaf Stapledon (Methuen) a forecast is given of the possibilities of the controlled evolution of mankind. Millions of years hence a race of men evolves with strong, healthy bodies, whose normal lifetime is two thousand years. Their minds, free from material cares and worry, are in telepathic communication with each other, and are able to project themselves into the past and live at will in any previous epoch. At intervals the minds of all living human beings join to form a communal mind, participating in which each shares the experiences of others—in short, a race of men is pictured entirely in harmony with their environment and with each other. This book is recommended to all interested in biology, and for further study of Eugenics the student should read : " Eugenic Reform," L. Darwin (Murray) ; " Studies in Evolution and Eugenics," Holmes (Harcourt Brace & Co.) ; "What is Eugenics? " L. Darwin (Watts).

This Lesson concludes our Course in Biology.

LESSON 34

Some Familiar and Unfamiliar Ferns

(See plates 5 and 6)

A CLASS of plants far more highly organized than any of the *Bryophyta* as regards their vegetative structure is called the *Pteridophyta*, and includes the ferns, the horsetails and the club-mosses. The ferns are a vast group, including about 150 genera and over 6,000 species. In the British flora seventeen genera and about forty species are represented, but the hot, damp forests of tropical and sub-tropical regions may be regarded as the headquarters of the fern group. In parts of the southern hemisphere—notably Australia, New Zealand and Ceylon— some ferns grow to the size of trees, and may even make up forests. They somewhat resemble palms in appearance, with their long, bare trunks, bearing crowns of feathery leaves.

A fern plant of the kind familiar in England generally consists of an underground stem (rhizome), which may creep horizontally at some distance below the surface, as in bracken (*Pteris aquilina*), or may be obliquely embedded in it, as in male fern (*Aspidium filixmas*). The stems of other species are attached to the bark of trees, or find a home in the crevices of walls or rocks. Brown branching roots grow out from the stem and serve, as usual, the double purpose of fixation and absorption of a part of the food. The leaves or fronds grow in the contrary direction into the air and light, and do the same work as in seed-plants. They are sometimes broad and unbranched, as in the hart's-tongue (*Scolopendrium*), but their shape is commonly more or less feather-like. Young fern fronds are rolled up in the shape of a bishop's crosier, and are thus enabled to force their way up through the soil without getting damaged.

Internal Structure. If a transverse section of a fern rhizome is examined under the microscope it will be seen to consist of a large number of vascular strands or *steles* embedded in thin-walled tissue whose cells are filled with starch grains. The steles consist chiefly of the xylem cells almost surrounded by a ring of phloem. Among the steles are seen bands or groups of thick-walled fibres, which are additional strengthening tissue.

Other strengthening cells appear near the epidermis, which is thick-walled and bears characteristic brown membranous scales.

Such a stem is described as *polystelic* and is found in most, though not all, ferns. Some, regarded as the most primitive members, have a single stele in the mature stem, and this ancestral character is usually found in the very young stems of the polystelic forms.

The leaf stalks show very much the same structure as do the underground stems, though usually there is less development of extra strengthening fibres. Here, again, there is variation in the internal structure, and some members of this group possess only a single (often horseshoe-shaped) stele in the petiole.

The roots and leaves show the same general structure as do those organs of the flowering plants. The roots of most ferns have but two xylem groups, and owe their wiry character to an extremely thick-walled fibrous cortex.

The life cycle of a fern consists of two distinct alternating phases, sporophyte and gametophyte, as described in Lesson 33 (Volume 5, page 112) for the *Bryophyta*. In the fern, however, each phase is a separate self-supporting plant. The sporophyte is the familiar fern plant, often of large size, with highly organized internal structure. This plant produces the asexual spores which, on germination, give rise to the very small, inconspicuous gametophyte phase.

Spore Production. Probably everyone has noticed regularly arranged brown patches on the backs of fern fronds. Each of these is termed a *sorus*, and species differ considerably according to the shape of sori and their manner of distribution. In bracken they are close to the edges of the frond, and follow its outline ; in hart's-tongue they are long streaks diverging from the middle of the leaf, and in polypody (*Polypodium*), so common on tree-trunks, and male fern, they are round patches. A sorus may have no special investment, as in polypody, or it may be covered by a membrane (*indusium*), as in male fern. In some cases there are special fertile fronds of different shape from the others, upon which the sori are borne, e.g. the hard fern and royal fern, the latter being our largest native species.

Examination of a sorus under the microscope shows that it is made up of a number of stalked sporangia, in which are contained a quantity of angular brown spores. A sporangium is of biconvex shape, with a thickened ring (*annulus*) running round the greater part of its margin. This band is in a state of tension, and when the spores are ripe it tears open the sporangium and scatters them.

Germination of Spores. The spores are cells of simple structure and are not, like a seed, the result of a process of fertilization, but are asexually produced. Should one reach a damp spot it at once germinates. Its firm coats split, and two outgrowths make their appearance—a delicate, colourless rhizoid which grows down, and a green thread that makes its way upward. But few spores are able to effect their work of continuing the species. It has been calculated that, on the average, only one spore per plant succeeds in doing this each season. The germinating spore gives rise to a small heart-shaped green expansion, the *prothallus*, attached to the soil by numerous rhizoids. Prothalli may often be seen in quantity in greenhouses, growing on the soil in which ferns have been planted. The artificial conditions are very favourable to their production. This prothallus is the gametophyte plant.

Upon the under side of the prothallus, in its central region (the cushion), which is thicker than its edges, will be found a

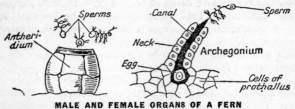

MALE AND FEMALE ORGANS OF A FERN

group of archegonia, each of which consists of a basal part embedded in the prothallus and containing an egg-cell, and a projecting neck. Scattered about on the same side of the prothallus, but restricted to its thinner part, are a number of very minute hemispherical projections, the antheridia, in each of which are produced many very small spermatozoids.

Fertilization. Within the mature egg-organ a sort of slime is produced, which swells up and forces apart the cells making up the neck, so as to leave a passage down to the egg-cell. Meanwhile, the ripe antheridia have been burst open in similar fashion, and the liberated spermatozoids swim actively about by means of their numerous cilia. The slime which oozes from the archegonia exerts a chemical attraction upon them and should a sperm succeed in making its way down to an egg-cell it fuses with it.

As soon as this happens, the fertilized egg-cell begins to divide, and soon gives rise to a young fern-plant (sporophyte), which remains attached to the prothallus, but ultimately takes root in the ground. The prothallus now perishes.

We see, therefore, that the life history of the fern includes two alternating stages : (1) the ordinary fern plant, which produces spores asexually, and (2) the prothallus possessing archegonia and antheridia. We may call these two stages the *sporophyte generation* and the *gametophyte generation*.

This remarkable phenomenon is known as " alternation of generations," and is typically seen in fern-like plants, mosses, etc., and many lower forms of plants, particularly some red and brown seaweeds. It is also characteristic of seed-plants in a somewhat modified form.

The small, rather uncommon British ferns, the adder's-tongue and moonwort, differ in several ways from their allies just described, for they possess but a single leaf which divides into a sterile and fertile part, while each sporangium develops from a group of cells, and not from a single one as is the case in an ordinary fern. In the adder's-tongue (*Ophioglossum*) the sterile part of the leaf has a simple outline, while the elongated fertile portion is practically a mass of closely crowded sporangia. But in moonwort both parts of the leaf are branched in a feather-like manner.

Water-Ferns. The water-ferns make up a small but interesting group of little plants which are either purely aquatic or grow, with some exceptions, in ground of a swampy character. All the water-ferns have sporangia of two kinds, which respectively contain small spores and large spores, and, having regard to the fate of these, we may call the leaves which produce them *male spore-leaves* and *female spore-leaves*. For a small spore germinates to produce a minute male prothallus with a single antheridium, while a female spore gives rise to a rather larger female prothallus, which bears a few archegonia. One member of this group is *Salvinia*, a small aquatic plant, native to south Europe. It is entirely devoid of roots, and consists of a stem bearing two kinds of leaves, some being oval and floating on the surface, while the others are finely divided and submerged. The latter play the part of roots, and they are also fertile, rounded sori at their bases, containing large and small sporangia.

Growing in marshy ground, *Marsilea* is represented by European and Australian species. There is a creeping stem, from the under side of which roots are given off. The long-stalked leaves fork into a sterile and a fertile portion, the former terminating in a blade which is divided into four parts, and somewhat suggests wood-sorrel in general appearance. The fertile section ends in a hard, bean-shaped structure, which may be called the *spore-fruit,* and contains a number of sporangia, of which some enclose large and others small spores. When these are ripe, part of the internal tissue of the fruit is converted into mucilage, which swells up and splits open the firm investments along one side. The spores now germinate to give rise to the two kinds of prothallus, and the fertilized egg-cells grow into new plants.

The pillwort (*Pilularia*) grows in the same kind of places as the last-named plant, and is a European species occurring in Britain. It possesses a creeping stem with roots, and narrow leaves. Parts of their bases are modified into rounded, brown spore-fruits, the shape of which has suggested the popular and scientific names. These contain a number of sporangia of both kinds, which are liberated by the swelling up of mucilage that bursts open the fruit in a valvular fashion.

LESSON 35

Horsetails and Club Mosses

(See plate 7.)

THE horsetails are not now a very important group, for there is only one living genus, *Equisetum,* containing about twenty-five species. Although today in reduced circumstances, the family is a very ancient one and, from the study of fossil botany, is known to have played an important part in the formation of coal. In those early geological times when the coal-beds were being formed the horsetail family was in the height of its glory, and was represented by a number of very diverse forms, many of which grew into trees. Most existing species are of comparatively small size. One tropical one (*E. giganteum*), however, reaches the height of over thirty feet, and one of our native forms (*E. maximum*) may be six feet in length.

Several species of horsetail are natives of England, and some are very common, e.g. the field horsetail (*Equisetum arvense*), which abounds in damp waste places and is very difficult to eradicate. They all bear a strong family likeness to one another in general appearance, all having stiff, upright, jointed green stems, with whorls of little tooth-like leaves, those of each whorl being united to form a sheath round the stem. If the stem is branched, the branches are also in whorls, and the whole plant has a very formal and regular appearance. The spores are borne in cone-shaped fructifications, each cone being produced at the end of an upright stem or of a branch. In some species, e.g. *E. arvense*, there are special fertile stems which only bear the cones, but do not branch, and are not green. In others, the cones are borne on the ordinary green vegetative stems. Underground, the plants have much-branched rhizomes which penetrate to a great depth

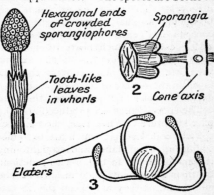

HORSETAIL (Equisetum); Organs of reproduction. **1.** Part of fertile branch bearing unripe cone; slightly reduced. **2.** Single sporangiophore; × 5. **3.** Mature spore in dry condition: highly magnified.

in the soil, perpetually giving rise to new aerial shoots and bearing numerous slender adventitious roots.

Internal Structure. If a cross section of an aerial stem of a horsetail is examined under the microscope it will be seen to contain a number of vascular bundles arranged in a ring—an arrangement typical of the bundle-system in the stem of a dicotyledonous flowering plant. Large intercellular spaces are present both in the cortex and on the inner side of the vascular bundles. The stems are ridged, and each ridge is occupied by a strand of fibres giving mechanical support to the aerial shoot on the principle of girder construction. Additional bands of fibres also occupy the outer part of the cortex between the projecting ridges. Now in plants whose leaf system is little developed, the function of carbon assimilation must be undertaken by the stems. This is rendered possible by the presence of stomata in the epidermis which connect through to bands of chlorophyll-containing cells in the cortex. Both the underground rhizomes and the fertile shoots are somewhat modified in structure, though the arrangement of the vascular bundles remains constant and approaches nearer to the simple gymnosperm and dicotyledons than does the anatomy of any other living Cryptogam.

Alternation of Generations. The horsetails resemble the ferns in having a sharply-marked alternation of generations in their life cycle. The plant, as we see it, is the asexual sporophyte, producing asexual spores in the terminal cones. Each cone consists of a central axis round which are borne densely-packed scales, each of which bears from five to ten sporangia. Each scale (*sporangiophore*) has its end expanded into a flat disk, and these are in such close contact that they appear as hexagonal areas on the surface of the cone. The sporangia are borne on these expanded disks and lie between them and the cone axis.

The spores which are produced are all alike, and of rather complex structure. When ripe, the outer spore coat splits into four spirally coiled strips, which are extremely sensitive to moisture, coiling up when damp and straightening out when dry. There is some doubt as to the precise function of these strips (*elaters*) ; by their movements they may cause the rupture of the sporangium wall, or they may keep the liberated spores entangled and thus ensure that they germinate in groups. This is important in the horsetails, as the male and female organs are usually produced on distinct gametophyte plants.

The product of germination of the asexual spore is, as in the ferns, a minute green prothallus attached to the ground by rhizoids. The prothalli are the gametophyte generation and produce antheridia (male organs) or archegonia (female organs) according to conditions of nutrition. The poorly nourished become males and remain much smaller than the well-nourished females. A similar state of affairs may be seen in ferns, for when the prothalli grow densely crowded they often bear antheridia only, although unisexuality with them is the exception rather than the rule.

It is a remarkable fact that while a horsetail plant bears no resemblance whatever to a fern plant, the prothallus and sexual organs are very much alike in both. The conditions of life of the minute gametophytes are simple and uniform compared with those to which the asexual sporophytes are exposed, so that the former have less need for varied structural adaptations. Consequently, we often find that at the gametophyte stage there is much in common between families which, so far as their sporophytes are concerned, have lost all traces of relationship.

Fertilization occurs by the union of a motile spermatozoid with the egg cell in the archegonium, and the development of the sporophyte is again initiated.

Varieties in Club Mosses. Club mosses are today represented mainly by the two genera *Lycopodium* and *Selaginella*, most species of which inhabit the damp forests of tropical countries. A few may be found growing in this country on boggy moors or in mountainous districts. They are all that is left of a group which was dominant in the days when the Coal Measures were being formed, at which time many of them were large forest trees. The quillwort (*Isoetes lacustris*), which occurs submerged in mountain tarns, is a peculiar member of this group, differing markedly from the two other genera in habit, yet revealing many features in common with the fossil club mosses of the Coal Measures.

The small spirally arranged leaves of *Lycopodium* densely clothe the stems, which may be erect, as in the fir club moss (*L. selago*), or creeping, except for the fertile shoots, as in the stag's horn club moss (*L. clavatum*). Adventitious roots are produced from the stems, both stems and roots displaying forked branching. Some of the stem branches end in elongated cones comparable to those of the horsetails. The cone axis bears closely-packed leaves similar to the ordinary foliage leaves, except that each has a single large sporangium on its upper surface, near the base. Each sporangium contains numerous uniform yellow dust-like spores. These spores constitute the inflammable yellow powder known as " lycopodium powder." On being shed, they germinate to give rise to peculiar fleshy prothalli, which in most species grow underground as saprophytes, obtaining their food with the help of a symbiotic fungus (mycorrhiza) from the humus. Both male and female sexual organs are borne on the same prothallus, and its life cycle resembles those of ordinary ferns and horsetails, showing a well-marked alternation of generations.

In *Selaginella* and *Isoetes* we come to club mosses which produce two different kinds of sporangia, large and small, and two different kinds of spore. This same phenomenon was described for the water-ferns in Lesson 34. Plants which produce spores of two different kinds are said to be *heterosporous*, while those whose spores are all alike are *homosporous*. The large spores, usually termed *megaspores*, produce the female prothalli, while the small spores, known as *microspores*, produce the male gametophyte. The horsetails and most ordinary ferns are homosporous plants, though conditions of nutrition may affect the occurrence of sexual organs on the resulting prothalli.

The quillwort has the appearance at first sight of a stoutly-built grass, but, if examined during the summer, large and smaller sporangia will be found on the inner sides of the bases of its leaves. The spores produce minute female and male prothalli, and the usual type of life cycle is shown.

LESSON 36

On the Borderline of Flowerless and Flowering

AMONG the flowerless plants *Selaginella* is one which in its general course of development and reproduction comes as near to the flowering plants as any other cryptogam now living. This makes it of special interest to the student of botany, as its reproductive processes illustrate the relation between these two main subdivisions of the vegetable kingdom. The genus is a large one containing about five hundred species, most of which inhabit the damp forests of tropical countries. Only one species (*S. spinosa*) is found in Britain, though several members of the genus are commonly cultivated in greenhouses.

The general habit is like that of *Lycopodium* (*see* Lesson 35), the long, usually creeping stems being thickly clothed with small leaves. These are arranged in four rows, two rows of small leaves on the upper side of the stem and two rows of larger ones on the lower side. The British *S. spinosa* has erect stems and, like other species with the erect habit, possesses leaves that are all alike. Each leaf bears on its upper surface, close to the base, a small membranous outgrowth, the *ligule*, which is characteristic of the whole genus *Selaginella*, and also of the related *Isoetes*. The function of the ligule is quite obscure, but it is a very ancient character and is found in a large family of fossil plants of the coal period.

From the stems slender leafless branches are given off, from whose tips true roots arise and penetrate the soil.

Reproductive Process. The reproductive organs are borne in upright cones as in *Lycopodium*. Each sporangium is borne on the upper side at the base of a cone leaf. *Selaginella* is a heterosporous plant bearing sporangia of two kinds in its cones. The microsporangia usually occupy the upper part and the megasporangia the lower part of the cone. For a time the development of the two kinds of sporangia is identical, but at maturity the microsporangia contain numerous small spores, while the megasporangia possess but four large spores each. In every respect the microsporangium throughout its development closely resembles a pollen sac of a flowering plant, while the microspores, in their structure and mode of origin, correspond to the pollen grains.

The microspores are liberated from the ripe sporangium by its dehiscence and, if falling on damp ground, germinate to give rise to minute colourless male prothalli. These consist almost entirely of a small group of antheridia from which the motile spermatozoids are liberated in wet weather. The germination of the microspores thus differs from that of the pollen grains of flowering plants : the differences are connected with the various means by which fertilization is effected—by free-swimming cells in the cryptogams, by passive male cells conveyed by a pollen tube in the phanerogams.

The megaspores of *Selaginella* begin to germinate before they are shed from the sporangium, but do not usually mature till they are liberated and lying on the ground. When ready for fertilization the female prothallus consists of cellular tissue within the spore wall, which is ruptured at one end where the prothallus tissue is consequently exposed. On this exposed part the archegonia are situated, while the rest of the prothallus are stored with food material for the nourishment of the young embryo when fertilization is accomplished. The exposed part of the prothallus turns green and may produce a few rhizoids, but it is obvious that in *Selaginella* both male and female prothalli are very reduced structures compared with the gametophyte generations of the horsetails and ferns.

Following successful fertilization of an egg cell by a swimming spermatozoid, the embryo soon becomes an independent sporophyte plant, ready to repeat the life cycle.

Let us now see how the alternation of generation, which is so marked in the Bryophyta and Pteridophyta, occurs in the life cycle of the flowering plants. In order better to understand the significance of the reduction of the gametophyte, it will not be amiss to say a few words regarding the trend of evolution in the plant world.

There is no doubt that water is the original home of life, and it is only by a long process of evolution that certain groups of animals and plants have become fitted for existence on land. Limiting ourselves to plants, we may say that marshes, swamps and damp places constitute a sort of half-way house between water and land, and play a leading part in the tactics of forms which are endeavouring to abandon their old aquatic home. It is also important to remember that the life history of any particular organism broadly recapitulates the evolutionary history of the group to which it belongs. We shall thus be able to understand the phenomenon of alternation of generations.

If we take, for instance, the life history of a fern, we find a small, relatively insignificant gametophyte (the prothallus) living in very moist surroundings, of which the fertilized egg cells become the relatively large and complex " fern plants " that constitute the sporophyte, and produce spores which germinate into prothalli. The sporophyte, it is true, flourishes best in damp, shady places, but it is far less dependent upon moisture than the prothallus is, and is adapted in many ways to comparatively dry conditions.

We may perhaps look upon the insignificant gametophyte as being the much diminished representative of the remote aquatic ancestor from which the fern has descended, while the " fern plant," the sporophyte, is a special development that has gradually arisen as an adaptation to the conquest of the land. Passing up the scale to seed plants, we find that the gametophyte becomes more and more reduced, and the sporophyte of increasing importance. In the true mosses and liverworts (*see* Lesson 33, Volume 5, page 112) the " plant " is the gametophyte generation, while the sporophyte is a wholly or partially parasitic outgrowth upon it, following fertilization. Comparing the Pteridophyta with this state of affairs, they show clearly the great increase in importance of the sporophyte and reductions of the gametophyte.

All the fern-like plants are more or less thwarted in their attempts to dominate the land, because they still retain in their life history a gametophyte (prothallus) which is very dependent upon moisture, and partly because the motile sperms, essential for the fertilization of the egg cells, have to swim to their destination. But seed plants, though they still retain a gametophyte generation, have reduced it to very small dimensions, and have so arranged matters that they are no longer obliged, for its sake, to live with " one leg in the water." Let us, then, briefly consider the life history of a flowering plant in the light of what has just been said.

The " plant " itself is the sporophyte generation, and its flowers are arrangements for producing spores—in this case of two kinds, large and small. The carpels are spore-leaves

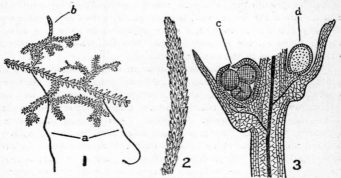

SELAGINELLA. **1.** General view (reduced) of S. kraussiana : a, rhizophore ; b, spike or cone. **2.** Fertile cone of S. spinosa ; natural size approx. **3.** S. helvetica : part of longitudinal section through cone showing two sporangia ; c, megasporangium dehiscing ; d, microsporangium with numerous microspores ; × 11 approx.

giving rise to megaspores (embryo sacs), contained in sporangia (ovules). The stamens are also spore leaves which produce microspores (pollen grains), developed in sporangia (pollen sacs), of which four are embedded in each anther—at least, in the case of angiosperms. The gametophyte generation consists of male and female prothalli. The male prothallus is very much reduced, and represented merely by the contents of the germinating pollen grain. Except in the lowest gymnosperms (*see* Lesson 27, Volume 4, page 163), the male gametes are not motile, but are conveyed to the egg cell by the growth of the pollen tube ; and thus they have dispensed with the necessity for water for fertilization.

The female prothallus of the flowering plants is represented by the contents of the embryo sac, and remains safely sheltered within the ovule on the sporophyte plant. In gymnosperms, such as the Scotch fir, the female prothallus is a tissue of small cells filled with food material and bearing archegonia towards the micropylar end of the ovule. The prothallus of the gymnosperms is often called " endosperm," but it must not be confused with the endosperm of angiosperms, which is formed as a result of, and not before, fertilization (*see* Lesson 18, Volume 3, page 142). The growth and structure of the female prothallus of *Selaginella* exactly corresponds to that in the Scotch fir : the differences are that in *Selaginella* the megaspore is usually shed from the sporophyte, while the mature prothallus may protrude slightly from the spore wall, become partly green and produce a few rhizoids. It is, in fact, a more independent structure, developing freely on the ground, instead of within the closed tissues of the ovule, as in the gymnosperms.

Organs which resemble each other in their development and place in the life history are said to be *homologous* with one another, and it is only by tracing the homology of organs that we can determine the probable relationships of different groups of plants. The homologies between *Selaginella* and a gymnospermous flowering plant are quite clear, and have been indicated above. We have every reason to believe that the flowering plants are descended from heterosporous cryptogams, but it is certain that there is no near affinity between *Selaginella* and the gymnosperms, for fossil evidence tells us that, apart from having spores of two kinds, the actual ancestors of the gymnosperms were quite unlike any existing cryptogam. The lowest gymnosperms (cycads and ginkgo) present a beautiful transition between cryptogamic and phanerogamic methods of fertilization (*see* Lesson 27).

At present we are not in a position to determine either the relation of angiosperms to gymnosperms, nor that of monocotyledons to dicotyledons. We may hope for further light on both these questions from the study of fossil forms ; the first appearance of angiosperms falls within a geological period which abounds in fossil remains. Some light has already been thrown on the subject by the discovery of Mesozoic plants allied to cycads (the *Bennettiteae*) which produced elaborate hermaphrodite " flowers " somewhat comparable to those of the angiosperms.

LESSON 37

Nuclear Division of Plant Cells

W HEN an ordinary vegetative cell, e.g. one from the growing point of a root or stem (*see* Lesson 8, Volume 1, page136), is about to undergo division, marked changes occur in the nucleus. The nucleus of a resting cell appears under the high power of a microscope as if made up of a fine network of threads on which are scattered many small granules. At the approach of division the network resolves itself into a coiled beaded thread, thicker and of far greater staining capacity than the structure in the resting stage. This thread presently breaks up into a number of short pieces called *chromosomes* (Greek, *chrŏma* = colour ; *sŏma* = body). The number of chromosomes which appears during nuclear division of any vegetative cell of a given species of plant (or animal) is constant ; for example, in the cabbage there are eighteen, in the tomato, twenty-four. The numbers vary enormously in different plants, some being much lower than those cited, others as high as over a hundred, but the same number will occur in any vegetative cell of the given plant. Quite often differences in shape and size are shown by the chromosomes of the dividing nucleus, and when they occur the differences are likewise constant, reappearing in each successive division of the species in question.

The chromosomes at first lie scattered irregularly in the nucleus, but soon mass together in the central region and arrange themselves more or less in one plane. By this time the membrane which formerly separated the nucleus from the surrounding protoplasm (cytoplasm) of the cell no longer persists, but in its place are seen numerous fine fibres converging to two points at opposite ends of the parent cell. This mass of fibres is known as the " spindle " and its end points as " poles." The chromosomes range themselves round the equatorial plane of this spindle, and each chromosome can be seen to be a double structure, being longitudinally split down its centre. In all probability this split is present in the earlier thread stages, but is not then so easily observed.

Process of Mitosis. This longitudinal split divides each chromosome into two exactly equal " daughter " halves. The halves of each chromosome separate from one another on the spindle. The chromosomes become attached to the spindle fibres, and, by unknown forces, one set of half chromosomes travels to one pole, the other set to the opposite pole. Having reached their destination, the chromosomes lose their distinct outline and great capacity for staining, and with the formation of a nuclear membrane each " daughter " nucleus passes into a resting state exactly similar to that of the mother nucleus before

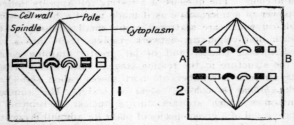

DIAGRAMS ILLUSTRATING MITOSIS. 1. Each chromosome is split longitudinally. **2.** Half chromosomes travelling to opposite poles; AB marks position where new cell wall is later formed.

it began division. A new cell wall is formed by deposition of substance across the equator of the vanishing spindle ; the wall substance ultimately reaches the sides of the mother cell, and thus division into two similar daughter cells is finally accomplished, and the traces of spindle fibres are completely absorbed into the cytoplasm. This mode of nuclear division is called *mitosis*, and obviously secures the equal division of the chromosome material (chromatin) among all the cells making up the adult body.

Students who are also reading the Course in Biology will realize that the behaviour of the chromosomes in mitosis is almost the same in plants as in animals. The differences to be found are : (1) the absence in the higher plants of centrosomes, though these are found in certain lower groups, e.g. fungi ; (2) the method of cell division, by constriction of the cytoplasm, in animal cells and by deposition of a new cell wall in plants.

The fact that there is a constant number of chromosomes for any given species is important, and of special interest in connexion with the formation of the sex cells or gametes, ova and sperms. In sexual reproduction two cells, the male and female gamete, fuse to form the new individual. If the gametes each possessed the number of chromosomes characteristic of the nucleus of a vegetative cell, the zygote would obviously have twice that number, and so on for each generation. This is prevented by a special kind of nuclear division, *meiosis*, or the reduction division, occurring at the formation of the sex cells and preceding the formation of the gametes, the number of chromosomes present in the resultant daughter nuclei being reduced to half the number of the ordinary vegetative cells. This reduction takes place in what are known as the sex " mother cells " of the anther and ovary ; pollen mother cells in the former, and embryo sac mother

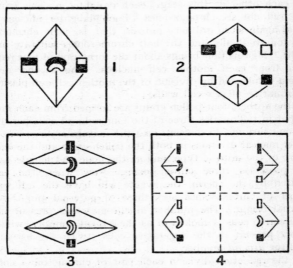

DIAGRAMS ILLUSTRATING MEIOSIS, 1. Chromosomes in pairs. **2.** Whole chromosomes separating. **3.** Chromosomes longitudinally split for the second (mitotic) division. **4.** Chromosomes about to form four reduced nuclei; dotted lines indicate later division of the cytoplasm.

cells in the latter. The result is that all nuclei of the mature pollen grains and all nuclei of the ripe embryo sac contain but half the specific number of chromosomes, and by fusion of male and female gamete the whole number is restored in the zygote.

Let us, for simplicity, take a case where the number of chromosomes in the vegetative cells is only six. When gametes are about to be formed by division of the mother cells, the preliminary nuclear changes leading to the formation of chromosomes appear somewhat the same as in ordinary cells. When the spindle is formed, however, the chromosomes are closely associated side by side in pairs. In cases where there are differences in size and shape among the chromosomes it is clearly seen that similar chromosomes always pair together. One chromosome of each pair is of paternal, the other of maternal origin. These three pairs of chromosomes lie on the equatorial plane of the spindle, and the members of each pair then separate, passing to opposite poles. Since whole chromosomes separate from each other at this stage, each daughter nucleus contains three and not six chromosomes. Each daughter nucleus then divides again as in ordinary mitosis, that is, each chromosome splits longitudinally and the half chromosomes separate on the spindle. Meiosis thus brings about the formation of four reduced nuclei from each mother cell nucleus. The second nuclear division is followed by division of the mother cell cytoplasm and the formation of new cell walls.

In the anthers four pollen grains are formed from each mother cell, but in the ovaries three of the four reduced cells perish and only one survives to develop into the mature embryo sac. All further nuclear divisions in both the pollen grain and the embryo sac are of the mitotic type, and so the male and female gamete each possesses three chromosomes. Now when the egg is fertilized by the sperm, the zygote will have the full specific number of chromosomes (six), three of paternal and three of maternal origin. The number of chromosomes present in the reproductive cells is spoken of as the *haploid* number, while the number present in the vegetative cells (twice the haploid) is called the *diploid* number.

At the reduction division each pair of chromosomes consists of a maternal and a paternal partner. When the chromosomes separate it is apparently a matter of chance which partner goes which way—to this or that daughter cell. This being so, and inasmuch as the number of gametes produced by a plant is very great, chance will decree that all possible distributions of chromosomes shall occur in equal proportions in the gametes.

LESSON 38

Inheritance in the Plant World

IN all the important structural features, and frequently in even most trivial details, offspring resemble their parents, though they always vary from them more or less.

During the present century much research has been made by biologists of all nations with a view to ascertaining how variations are brought about, and the means by which parental characters are transmitted to offspring by those two single cells, the sperm of the male and the egg of the female.

The foundation upon which the whole science of genetics rests is the work of Gregor Mendel (1822–1884), whose biological work is dealt with in Lessons 14 and 15 in Biology. The distinctive and essential feature in Mendel's methods of attacking the problems is that he studied the inheritance of obvious striking characteristics ("unit characters") as separate units. His researches were conducted on the edible pea, a plant very suitable for the purpose in view ; first, because its flowers are normally self-pollinated, but cross-pollination can easily be effected artificially ; secondly, because it exhibits several well-marked varieties, readily distinguishable from one another, e.g. some are tall, some dwarf ; some have seeds with green testas, others with yellow ; some have wrinkled testas, others smooth. Careful records of the inheritance of these unit characters resulted in the establishment of Mendel's Law.

Following Mendel's initiative, others have made similar breeding experiments, and there has now been accumulated abundant evidence to the effect that hereditary characters are transmitted from parents to offspring by means of the chromosomes.

Apart from their scientific interest, the fundamental " laws " of Mendelism are of great practical economic importance. The plant (or animal) breeder is no longer groping in the dark ; in a few generations he can, by appropriate mating, combine together desirable qualities formerly existing only apart in separate breeds, and can be certain that his product will breed true.

Mendel's explanation of the facts of heredity was put forward merely as a working hypothesis. His principles are now recognized as laws for the important reason that the mechanism—that of chromosome reduction and fertilization—can be seen. In several cases of heredity the application of the laws is complicated or even modified out of all direct recognition, but it is known that the same principles must be at work because the same kind of mechanism is observed. When these complications arise the geneticist (plant or animal breeder) must now turn to the cytologist (student of the chromosomes) for an explanation.

In many plants that have been bred extensively and examined under the microscope it is found that there are abnormalities in the number of chromosomes. Instead of the normal diploid number there may be one extra chromosome. Examples of such are found in certain species of evening primrose, stock and tomato ; the plant with the extra chromosome always has a different external appearance from the normal. It is often distinct in leaf, stem, flower and fruit—such is the disturbing effect of the extra chromatin. A striking case of this sort is known in the thorn apple. This plant has twelve pairs of chromosomes, and there are found to be twelve different kinds of plants, each with one extra chromosome. In other cases even the presence of an additional fragment of chromosome is known to affect the external appearance of the individual. There are also many examples known in plants where the chromosome number is a multiple, greater than two, of the ordinary haploid number. This is explained in Lesson 37 in Biology (page 64).

These, and many other important findings of cytologists, show that every part of every chromosome has its own peculiar qualities, and that the hereditary properties of any plant (or animal) depend not only on the presence of those qualities, but on the proportion in which they occur. Since the chromosomes are different from one another they obviously contain materials for the origin of *variations*, and by their study the breeder is enabled to work in the right direction for obtaining and preserving the results likely to be most profitable.

Books Recommended for Further Reading : " Life of Plants," Keeble (Oxford University Press) ; " Introduction to the Study of Plants," Fritsch and Salisbury (Bell) ; " Botany of the Living Plant," Bower (Macmillan) ; " Chromosomes and Plant Breeding," Darlington (Macmillan) ; " Plant Life Through the Ages," Seward (C.U.P.) ; Bentham and Hooker's " Flora " (Reeve).

This Lesson concludes our Course in Botany.

End of the First British Empire
(See plate 8)

FOR nearly thirty years after the Seven Years' War Great Britain took practically no part in continental politics. For ten years after his accession George III was organizing a new monarchy of his own devising, while the mother-country was quarrelling with the American colonies. When his methods had secured his temporary ascendancy in Parliament, the quarrel with America developed into the war by which the old colonies won their independence, rending the British Empire into two parts, whose relations for the next hundred years were seldom friendly. (*See* Lesson 17 in Modern History, Vol. 3, page 544.)

The intervention of hostile European powers materially affected the course of the American struggle and for a short time threatened the British maritime supremacy. The home government imagined that the colonies could easily be forced to yield, being mutually jealous and having no common government, no trained troops, no trained officers, and no navy. But they organized an emergency government and found in George Washington a chief whose infinite patience, perseverance, tact and common sense held them together, while the commanders sent out from England neither desired nor attempted to strike crushing blows. They occupied Boston ; then they evacuated Boston and occupied New York instead. Contradictory orders came from England ; the generals failed to cooperate, and a force coming down from Canada was compelled to surrender at Saratoga (1777). Thereupon the French, who had once again been building up a navy, joined the conflict as allies of the colonies, who had by now declared their independence ; Spain was drawn in their wake, and Holland started a quarrel on her own account.

American Independence. The French fleets in American waters outnumbered the British, blockaded a British force in Yorktown, and forced it to surrender (1781)—the decisive event of the war so far as America was concerned. Britain's tottering sea-power was saved by Rodney's great naval victory in the West Indies over the French, which enabled a peace to be made in 1783 that left England maimed but not shattered. What had been the

" thirteen colonies " became the United States of America ; while Canada, which had refused to join them, remained within the empire, still preponderantly French and Roman Catholic in population, in spite of the influx of " United Empire loyalists " from the lost colonies.

Meanwhile the system built up by George III since his accession broke down. He had at first abandoned the rôle of constitutional king for that of party leader, in order better to crush the Whigs, who, he declared, had ceased to be a constitutional party but had established their power by means of patronage and bribery. The return of members of Parliament and their voting in Parliament was largely though not entirely, controlled by the great Whig families collectively, through a highly developed machinery of corruption to which Pitt had always refused to lend himself. From 1757 to 1761 Pitt had dominated the government by sheer influence of his personality ; but he could rule only as an autocrat, and his autocracy was broken partly by the desertion of some of the Whigs, partly by the influence of the new king and by the revival of the Toryism which, after the conclusive collapse of Jacobitism, could revert to its old-time loyalty to the person of the sovereign.

North's Ministry of " King's Friends." George's policy was to re-create the supremacy of the crown by destroying the popular minister's domination, breaking up the Whig combination, and using their machinery of corruption to build up in Parliament a Court party of the " King's Friends," who would look to him personally as their leader. Public opinion still looked to Pitt, but he could not recover the ascendancy which had been begotten of a crisis in which it had become obvious that he was the one man who could save the country. Though George found himself forced to reinstate him at the head of the ministry in 1766 (when he was made Earl of Chatham), Pitt's health broke down, and the ministry carried on without him with a total disregard for all his principles. By 1770 George had achieved his object ; Lord North became the head of the ministry, and North's one guiding rule was to carry out the king's will.

Affairs in India. While the State had pursued blindly a course which led inevitably to the disruption of the empire in one direction, in another its servants, acting on their own initiative and responsibility, had been consolidating its power. During the Seven Years' War Clive had made the British responsible for the government of Bengal, turning the Company into a territorial power in India by force of arms. In 1765 he had legalized its position by obtaining official sanction for the authority it exercised, from the Mogul, of whose empire Bengal was a province. The home government did not take over this authority from the Company, but, feeling a responsibility for the action of a British company in unprecedented conditions, it devised in North's Regulating Acts an experimental scheme of government in India which proved thoroughly unworkable in the hands of a governor liable to be overridden by a factious majority of his Council. Despite the fact that his hands were thus tied, the Governor, Warren Hastings (*see* Lesson 17 in Modern History, Volume 3, page 544), succeeded in establishing the Company's position among the crowd of rival powers, though driven to employ methods which to orientals were a matter of course but from a western point of view were often unscrupulous—the only alternative being the elimination of the Company. Hastings, returning to England in 1785, found himself not applauded for having saved the position in circumstances of extraordinary difficulty, but faced with impeachment.

The disasters of the American war wrecked North's ministry and, with it, George's system. In 1783, a coalition ministry was in charge of the peace settlement and of a new scheme for the Indian government. Over that scheme the coalition was wrecked, and a general election returned William Pitt, Chatham's younger son, to power, with an enormous Parliamentary majority behind him at the beginning of 1784.

LESSON 20

First Premiership of William Pitt

(See plates 8 and 9)

G EORGE III has been underrated as a ruler and as a man. The publication of his correspondence has revealed the fact that he was by no means the pigheaded, aggravating cause of misunderstandings which some older historians have made him appear. Concerning the events which had led up to the American War of Independence for example, it was the king, not his ministers, who advocated a policy that might quite possibly have averted the breach. As a man he was happily unlike his grandfather and his father, and his Court was a model of propriety. His popularity, however, was largely due to the fact that by birth and by education, as well as by taste, he claimed to be an Englishman. Towards the end of the century the country was profoundly stirred by events in France. There was a large and influential party in England with democratic and revolutionary tendencies, and it is difficult to say what might have happened but for the sympathy and loyalty that were awakened among the people by the aging king's infirmity, which increased rather than lessened his popularity.

Lord Chatham's second son, William Pitt, who at the age of twenty-one had entered Parliament in 1781, took office as Prime Minister in 1783. He accepted the position from the king—who was desirous of freeing himself from the Coalition under Lord North and Charles James Fox—and adopted the established Tory doctrine that ministers were to be selected by the king and not by the House of Commons. He reintroduced, however, the long-forgotten principle of appealing to the constituencies before final decisions could be taken. The Coalition, now in opposition, had members enough in the House of Commons to outvote him ; he refused to resign or dissolve Parliament, however, until he could have his opponents at a disadvantage. His popularity with the nation increased, he possessed the royal support, and members began to change sides, until in 1784 Pitt thought it safe to risk an election. Many of Fox's supporters lost their seats, though he himself was triumphantly returned at the famous Westminster election, when he was supported by the duchess of Devonshire, and continued to lead the opposition.

Pitt's Reforming Measures. Pitt's first administration lasted for seventeen years. During the first nine years he showed great constructive ability, and these years were marked by prosperity and peace in England. Praised as the ablest of financiers, the minister won the complete confidence of the country with his plans for reconstruction after the disasters and mismanagement of the American war, together with the creation of a workable constitution for the British dominion within what was officially the Mogul empire—the attempt to provide which had brought about the fall of the Coalition ministry under Fox and North.

Pitt's successful financial measures were based on the recently propounded doctrines of Adam Smith's " Wealth of Nations." Commerce advanced rapidly, so that it was largely due to the

'**FOX FOR WESTMINSTER!**' This print shows the uproarious crowd in Covent Garden, jostling each other amid waving banners, at the famous Westminster election of 1784, which returned Charles James Fox in opposition to the Tory candidates supported by George III. It was on this occasion that the duchess of Devonshire purchased votes for the Whig candidate with her kisses.   BRITISH HISTORY 20

ARTHUR WELLESLEY, 1st DUKE OF WELLINGTON

(1769–1852). Younger son of the earl of Mornington, his birthplace was probably Dublin. He entered the army in 1787, and first saw active service—in the Netherlands—in 1794. From 1796 to 1805 he held commands in India, and in 1808 he proceeded to Portugal in command of a division. The next year he became C.-in-C. in the Peninsula, and in 1814 brought the war to a successful conclusion. Victor at Waterloo in 1815, he remained in France in command of the army of occupation until 1818, when he returned home and entered politics as a Tory. From 1828 to 1830 he was prime minister, and subsequently held many high offices in the State. He lies buried in St. Paul's. BRITISH HISTORY 21

After Count D'Orsay, in the National Gallery

HORATIO LORD NELSON

(1758–1805). Born at Burnham T h o r pe, Norfolk, he entered the navy in 1770, and became captain in 1779. He greatly distinguished himself in the French war, displaying time and again the " Nelson Touch " until his last and greatest victory at Trafalgar. He was created a viscount in 1801.
BRITISH HISTORY 21

After L. F Abbott, National Portrait Gallery

Plate 10   *Volume VI*

WATERLOO. At La Belle Alliance farm, seen here, Wellington and Blücher met on the evening of their day of triumph. BRITISH HISTORY 21

THE 'PETERLOO MASSACRE.' On August 16, 1819, 60,000 Radicals demonstrated in St. Peter's Field, Manchester. The police, by order of the magistrates, attempted to arrest the popular leader, "Orator" Hunt, and when this proved impossible, the magistrates gave the order for yeomanry to charge and disperse the crowd. In the ensuing mêlée several people were killed and about 500 injured. The memory of Waterloo was still fresh in the public mind, and so the name Peterloo was coined in derision. This drawing by George Cruikshank, published in 1819, is entitled "The Massacre of Peterloo, or Britons Strike Home." BRITISH HISTORY 21

GEORGE IV (1762–1830). Eldest son of George III, he acted as regent during his father's bouts of insanity and succeeded him on the throne in 1820. His relations with his wife, Caroline of Brunswick, gave rise to a public scandal, but there were some who hailed him as " the first gentleman of Europe."

BRITISH HISTORY 21

QUEEN VICTORIA (1819–1901). Granddaughter of George III, she succeeded her uncle, William IV, on the throne of Britain in 1837. She married in 1840 her cousin, Albert of Saxe-Coburg-Gotha (died 1861), and had nine children. After reigning longer than any of her predecessors she died at Osborne on January 22, 1901, and was buried at Frogmore.

BRITISH HISTORY 22

National Portrait Gallery

Plate 12

Volume VI

great wealth gathered in the years of peace that Britain was able to bear far better than any other country the enormous financial strain of the years of war that followed. This development of wealth was furthered, though to the temporary detriment of the manual labouring classes, by the new manufacturing power of which Great Britain had an entire monopoly.

Advent of Machinery. James Watt (1736–1819) took out his first patent for a steam-engine in 1769, thereby inaugurating the new age in industry and in life. Though not the inventor of the steam-engine—the first being made by Thomas Savery in 1698—he discovered how to apply steam power to the driving of machinery on a large scale; the machinery required iron instead of wood; the iron needed furnaces, which required coal. Great Britain had the coal, the iron and the inventors; these between them gave the country the monopoly of large-scale manufacture, turning it into the world's workshop as well as its greatest mart. But the machinery wiped out the domestic hand industries, which to the rural population had meant the difference between decent and abject poverty. They could not live on the land. Some became farm labourers; the rest drifted to the manufacturing areas, ready to take any wages which would keep them alive. The country accumulated wealth, but during the period of adjustment masses of the unemployed starved. Watt himself did not realize the great field open in factory work, or the expansion of the cotton industry that would be made possible by his application of steam to wheels, when in 1781 he patented a method of applying the steam-engine to rotary motion.

Dual Control in India. Pitt's new Act for the government of India was passed in 1784 and, with some modification, remained in force till 1858. It set up in England beside the Company—to which the Government of India was directly responsible—a Parliamentary Board of Control, which might on occasion over-rule the Company. In India it set up an autocratic Governor-General with an advisory Council, who had actual power to act against instructions from home, but did so at his own peril. In his hands was the conduct of the administration on the spot. The Company had its own sepoy army, wholly under British officers, supplemented by regiments of the British army. Its civil administration was in practice, if not in law, confined as regarded the higher grades to British officials. The impeachment (1788–95) of Warren Hastings, though he was ultimately acquitted on every one of the charges brought against him, made it clear that oppression in high places would have to face a stern public opinion at home. And with hardly an exception the governors who were sent out proved worthy to support the tremendous responsibilities laid upon them.

Britain's New Dominion. In 1788 Great Britain entered into possession of a new continent, Australia. The first English seaman to reach it had been William Dampier in 1688, but it was practically deserted until Captain Cook's arrival in 1770. Now, a year before the fall of the Bastille announced the French Revolution, the first English settlement was made at Sydney Cove in New South Wales.

Canada was a French province, with French traditions and customs and a French population, into which had flowed from the old American colonies a British population loyal to British traditions and the empire. Pitt's solution of the otherwise impossible amalgamation of these two elements was the division of Canada into two : the upper part (Ontario) mainly British, the lower (Quebec) mainly French, each having its own appointed governor and elected legislature (1791).

When the beginning of the French Revolution was signalized by the fall of the Bastille, it was viewed at first with a qualified approval in Britain by the democratic party. Fox even went so far as to declare a welcome to it. By the close of 1792, however, public feeling had changed. The September massacres, the fall of the monarchy, the attitude of aggressive interference with other countries adopted by the Republic, and, finally, the open violation of Dutch treaty-rights that had been guaranteed by both France and Great Britain, followed by the execution of Louis XVI, drove Pitt to join the European coalition, with which France was already at war, in February, 1793. In the management and conduct of that war on the Continent there was little enough that was to the credit of the allies ; Great Britain's own share in it was small and ineffectual, but not actually disastrous. This country retained throughout the mastery of the seas, and with it the monopoly of sea-borne commerce ; though threatened for a moment in the Mediterranean, this mastery was saved by the battle of Cape St. Vincent (1797), and turned into an overwhelming supremacy by Nelson's annihilation of Bonaparte's fleet in Aboukir Bay (the battle of the Nile, 1798). In 1801 Britain was left to face the French forces alone ; in that year

Pitt and his ablest colleagues resigned, and next year the Peace of Amiens brought an interval that lasted for fourteen months.

Act of Union. Pitt's last act before his resignation was the accomplishment of the legislative union of Great Britain and Ireland. His resignation was caused by the king's conscientious refusal to sanction, as a part of it, the Catholic Emancipation to which the minister, with many of his colleagues, was pledged up to the hilt. Henceforth Irish members sat in the House of Commons at Westminster, and Irish peers in the House of Lords. But still, as in England, no Roman Catholic and no Protestant dissenter might sit. But in England Roman Catholics were few ; in Ireland they were four-fifths of the population, and half the Ulster Protestants were dissenters. The Union left untouched one of the primary grievances of the Irish people. Had Pitt been able to do as he wished, many subsequent rebellions and riots might have been averted.

LESSON 21

The Peninsular War and Its Social Aftermath

(See plates 10-12.)

WHEN the treaty of Amiens was made, both Napoleon and the British Government wanted peace, but the latter, suspecting from the beginning that Napoleon intended to turn the peace to account for aggressive purposes, delayed carrying out its promises to evacuate Malta, Egypt and the French stations in India, which the British had occupied. Perpetual recriminations ensued ; and in May, 1803, France and Britain were again at war.

Napoleon proceeded forthwith to concentrate a grand army of invasion at Boulogne, but found it impossible to carry it to England so long as the British fleet commanded the Channel. In 1805 he matured a scheme whereby the main British fleet under Nelson should be decoyed into distant waters while the Boulogne army was hurled upon England. At first the scheme prospered, for Villeneuve with his fleet managed to evade Nelson, slipped out from Toulon and vanished into the blue. Nelson, having sensed their destination, went in pursuit to the West

Indies. Villeneuve eluded him, recrossed the Atlantic at full speed to raise the blockade of the Brest fleet, found a British squadron waiting to intercept him, abandoned the attempt, and made his escape to Vigo and thence to Cadiz (July). By now Nelson was on his way back to the Mediterranean, and Napoleon realized that his plan for clearing the Channel was dead. Three months later, on Oct. 17, it was buried at Trafalgar, when Villeneuve, taunted by Napoleon into sailing out of Cadiz with the Franco-Spanish fleet, was caught in the open by Nelson. The Franco-Spanish fleet was destroyed, though Nelson fell in the hour of his greatest triumph. Thenceforth the seas were an open highway for the British but practically closed to Napoleon and his allies.

Berlin Decree. When Villeneuve failed to reach Brest, Napoleon abandoned the invasion scheme and flung his armies against the Coalition forces of Russia, Prussia and Austria—a coalition that Pitt, who had returned to office in 1804, had engineered. In a few weeks Napoleon smashed the continental powers, and it was from Berlin that in 1806 he launched the bolt—the Berlin Decree, creating what he called the " Continental System " —which was intended to bring Britain to her knees. Henceforth no British goods were to be admitted to any European port ; her trade would be ruined, her wealth would collapse, and she would be rendered powerless. Britain retaliated by Orders in Council in 1807, whereby all the continental ports under the control of France were declared to be in a state of blockade, and all ships bound for them liable to capture unless they had first touched at a British port. In the same year Russia joined the French bloc, and in December, by Napoleon's Milan Decree, all neutral vessels that attempted to touch at a British port before landing their cargoes on the Continent were made liable to seizure by the French. Inasmuch, however, as Britain held command of the seas, the " Continental System " led rather to a vast extension of smuggling than to the suppression of British trade with the continental countries.

Copenhagen and Corunna. Pitt died in January, 1806, but the war was continued under the " Ministry of all the Talents " of Grenville and Fox, and its successors under Portland and Perceval. The first act of the Portland ministry was to seize the neutral Danish fleet at Copenhagen lest it should pass to the French—an act which was widely condemned even in England

(1807). In 1808 Britain carried the war into a new field by dispatching troops to deliver Portugal from the French army of occupation and to support the Spanish insurgents. A small force compelled the French to evacuate Portugal, and when Napoleon in person swept irresistibly over Spain, Sir John Moore fell on the French communications. Napoleon, wholly misjudging the Spanish and British power of resistance, withdrew to work out his policy in Europe, leaving his marshals to complete the subjugation of Spain and drive the British into the sea. Moore, who had effected his immediate object, was killed at Corunna in January, 1809; but three months later Arthur Wellesley (Wellington) took up the command, drove Soult over the Portuguese border, and in July routed Marshal Victor at Talavera. In the same year a British diversion against Antwerp, well conceived but shockingly mismanaged—the Walcheren expedition —ended in complete disaster.

For the next four years Wellington, with much help from the Spanish guerrillas but very little help from the Spanish regulars, was fighting the Peninsular War against a succession of French marshals—Soult, Massena, Marmont, Jourdan—and so compelling Napoleon to keep three field armies in the Pensinsula, each of them larger than Wellington's, who never had a force sufficient to do more than deliver one or two smashing blows and then retire behind the impregnable Lines of Torres Vedras covering Lisbon. But in the fourth year (1813) Napoleon, after his disastrous Russian expedition (*see* Modern History, Lesson 22, Volume 4, page 500), withdrew troops from Spain; and Wellington, after the decisive battle of Vittoria, was able to drive the French armies, in spite of Soult's masterly conduct of the retreat, through the Pyrenees on to French soil. In April, 1814, he fought a last indecisive battle with Soult at Toulouse, in ignorance of the fact that Napoleon, overwhelmed by the armies of the rest of Europe, had already abdicated at Paris.

Battle of Waterloo. There ensued the Congress of Vienna, at which Britain was represented by Wellington, now a duke. In March of the next year, however, the far from peaceful deliberations of the delegates were rudely interrupted by the return of Napoleon from Elba and his triumphant entry into Paris. Wellington was put in command of a mixed force of British, Dutch, Belgians and Hanoverians, with headquarters at Brussels. At Quatre Bras, on June 16, 1815, he checked Ney, enabling

Blücher to retreat ; two days later the decisive battle was fought at Waterloo. From noon till late afternoon the British and their allies held the ridge ; the French gained some ground but failed, despite the furious charges of their cavalry, to break the British squares. Then about four in the afternoon Blücher and the approaching Prussians made their presence felt on the French right. Napoleon forthwith hurled the Old Guard at the British right centre, but it was mowed down by front and flank fire, and at last the British swept forward, just as the Prussians began to roll up the French right. The French were soon in headlong flight, with the Prussians in hot pursuit. Napoleon escaped from the field, but four weeks later surrendered himself on board a British frigate, and was sent for life to St. Helena.

As we have seen in our own day, war has a terrible aftermath, and the years following the close of the Napoleonic conflict were years of social unrest and misery. Peace and plenty had been expected, but instead there was unemployment on a large scale—so many ex-soldiers were seeking work—harvests were poor and bread was exceedingly dear. Moreover, foreign nations now began to produce their own manufactures in place of those which, despite the embargo, British manufacturers had managed during the war to sell to their customers on the Continent ; and the workmen discharged as a result of the slump were maddened by the sight of the new machines which were now coming into great favour amongst employers in the textile trade.

The " Peterloo Massacre." In 1816 there was much agitation against the political and economic conditions, and riots became frequent in many parts of the country. In the next year the Tory government were so alarmed at the disturbed state of the country that they suspended the Habeas Corpus Act for a year. In 1818 there was a brief spurt of industrial activity, but distress was again rampant the following year. On August 16, 1819, a great meeting of " Radicals "—persons desirous of radical alterations in the organization of the State—held in St. Peter's Field, Manchester, was broken up by the military. Shortly afterwards the Government, still putting their trust in repression instead of reform, passed the " Six Acts " of 1819, prohibiting any meeting of more than 50 persons " for the consideration of grievances in Church and State " save by the approval of the magistrates, forbidding the use of arms and instruction in military drill, increasing the punishments for seditious libel and imposing stamp duties on the popular press.

Peel's Penal Reforms. George III died in 1820, and was succeeded by his eldest son as George IV. The Tory ministry of Lord Liverpool, who had succeeded to the premiership in 1812 on the assassination of Spencer Perceval by a madman in the lobby of the House of Commons, continued in office with Lord Castlereagh and, after his suicide in 1822, George Canning, as Foreign Secretary. In that year Sir Robert Peel became Home Secretary, and at once set to work to reform the brutal penal code of the time. The next year Parliament none too readily concurred in his proposal that the death penalty should be abolished in respect of about a hundred crimes, and in 1829 Peel established the London police force, a fact which is responsible for the popular name of " Bobbies " still borne by London's constables. Canning succeeded Liverpool in 1827, but died within a few months. His place was taken by Lord Goderich, who in 1828 was supplanted by the duke of Wellington.

Catholic Emancipation. By now, reform was in the air, as it were. The cause of progress had been retarded by the " Cato Street Conspiracy " of 1820, which aimed at the murder of the whole cabinet ; but in 1824 and 1825, thanks mainly to Joseph Hume and Francis Place, the laws against workmen's combinations had been modified so that trade unions became possible ; and in 1828, as the result of a strenuous agitation led by Daniel O'Connell, known as " the Liberator," the Test and Corporation Acts—relics of the anti-Catholic bigotry of the 17th century—were swept from the statute book. In 1829 O'Connell scored a yet greater triumph—the emancipation of his fellow-religionists from the penal disabilities which they had endured for so long. When George IV died in 1830 the reformers were preparing for a yet further advance—the reform of Parliament itself. The general election of 1830 returned a Tory majority, but in November the Opposition, supported by some disgruntled Tories, defeated the Government in the Commons. Wellington at once resigned and the king (William IV) entrusted the formation of a ministry to Lord Grey, the leader of the Whig party, which, save for a brief interval, had not held office since the days of the American War.

LESSON 22

British Politics in the 19th Century

(See plates 12—14)

THE world which confronted the Whigs when they took office in 1832 after so long a banishment from office was very different from that which Lord Grey, their leader, had known when he first entered Parliament nearly fifty years before, or even when he held office under Fox in 1806. For a generation and more, dread of revolution and revolutionary propaganda had made repression of even established popular liberties seem an urgent necessity. The movement towards large-scale farming and the development of machinery had combined so as almost to eliminate the old yeomanry of the countryside and to effect a huge displacement of labour ; while a short-sighted sentimentalism had encouraged the improvident multiplication of families living habitually on the margin of destitution, even while the need for being self-supporting during war-time brought under cultivation a quantity of land which could only be worked when the price of its product was intolerably high. The new machinery meant that until there was a compensating expansion of the market the supply of labour must greatly exceed the demand for it ; unemployment meant destitution, while wages were barely at subsistence level. Of these grievances was begotten class hostility, involving demand on one side for political power and on the other for its repression. The constitutional problem of the past—the relations between Crown and Parliament—was no longer seriously in question ; it had become that of the constitution of Parliament itself, a body under the domination—in both Houses—of the land-owning class.

Repression—the " reaction " against the gospel of Rousseau—had been dominant when the Napoleonic war ended in 1815, but as the years passed the Jacobin bogey gradually lost its terrors, the severities of repression grew more repugnant to the public conscience, and the commercial and manufacturing classes became ever more resentful of their own exclusion from political power, and reverted to the pre-war Whig demands for parliamentary and social reform.

Grey's Reform Ministry. The Whigs came into office under Lord Grey in 1830, and the first Reform Bill was introduced the following year. It was defeated, but a general election returned a great Whig majority. A new Reform Bill was brought in, carried in the Commons, and rejected by the Lords (1831). Grey, instead of again appealing to the country, brought in a third Reform Bill, obtaining from the king a promise to create enough peers to ensure the passage of the bill should the Lords prove recalcitrant. Rather than destroy the character of the House, the Duke of Wellington persuaded 100 of its members, who detested the Bill as he did himself, to abstain from voting ; and thus it was passed. It abolished a crowd of decayed or " rotten " boroughs and the " pocket " boroughs which were practically in the gift of landed magnates ; erected the greater towns, which had hitherto been virtually disfranchised, into boroughs ; extended the franchise, making it uniform in boroughs (where it had hitherto been diverse), though on a different basis from the counties ; and, in effect, transferred the dominant influence among the electorate and in the House of Commons from the landed gentry to the manufacturing and trading community. But it still gave no political power to artisans and employees generally. In 1837 William IV died, and was succeeded by his niece, Victoria.

Chartist Demonstrations. Apart from foreign affairs, industrial and economic reconstruction became the main preoccupation of government. The unrest of the manual labour class was allayed but not removed, and was mostly openly expressed in the Chartist movement for further immediate democratic reforms, which in 1848, the " year of revolutions " on the Continent, created something like a panic till it collapsed of itself rather ignominiously. Parliament, with much hesitation, began to regulate relations between employers and employees by abolishing or limiting the labour of children, adolescents and women, and enforcing sanitary rules in mines and factories, while still rigidly forbidding combinations—whether of masters, who had no need of them, or of men, who were powerless for bargaining without them—for raising or lowering wages. The Corn Law, created in 1815 to save inferior land from falling out of cultivation, made the price of bread and the cost of living intolerably high for the poor ; still, expanding markets were diminishing unemployment. Rigid protection of other industries than agriculture was being slowly displaced by the theory of reciprocity, the half-way house between it and commercial Free Trade, and the manufacturers, far better equipped than their foreign competitors, were finding that they gained more than they lost by the lowering of tariffs. When the names Whig and Tory were giving place to Liberal and Conservative, the Anti Corn Law League in the manufacturing interest was urging the doctrines of Free Trade, but both political parties were still only half converted.

Repeal of the Corn Law. A Conservative government led by Sir Robert Peel lowered several tariffs, but his party began to rebel when he went farther. A potato famine in Ireland, where potatoes were the staple food of the peasantry, convinced Peel that cheap bread was the primary necessity, and in 1846 he carried the repeal of the Corn Law with the support of the Liberals, in the teeth of half the Conservative party, from whom the Peelites were permanently severed. Peel himself was driven from office ; the Peelites presently, though not immediately, coalesced with the Liberals, and in the budgets framed by Gladstone (1809–98), formerly a Conservative but now chancellor of exchequer in the Liberal government, all duties disappeared except those which applied equally to home products and imports. Great Britain held such a lead over all competitors in productive power that for the rest of the nineteenth century the bare idea of reviving tariffs was uncompromisingly scoffed at by both political parties. The main economic question became that of readjusting bargaining powers as between employers and employed, "capital" and "labour," through the legalized activity of trade unions of manual workers.

Reform Acts. With the disappearance of Chartism, the feeling grew that the admission of the "intelligent artisan" to the parliamentary franchise could not long be withheld. Though Liberal governments were almost continuously in office, this movement towards democracy was suspended for twenty years in deference to the Liberal chief, Lord Palmerston (1784–1865). It was a brief Conservative ministry formed after his death under the premiership of Lord Derby and with Benjamin Disraeli (1804–81) as chancellor of the exchequer and leader of the Commons that passed, in 1867, the second Reform Act, in conjunction with the Liberals, who practically gave it its final shape. Still, however, the agricultural labourer and all such as were not in constant employment were excluded from the franchise ; and it was only in 1884 that a Gladstone ministry, after a sharp tussle with the Lords as to procedure, passed the third Reform Act, which made the electorate virtually democratic (so far, at least, as men were concerned) and rearranged the constituencies—again with the rather reluctant cooperation of the Opposition.

The last thirty years of the century were a period of very active legislation, the protagonists being Gladstone almost throughout, Disraeli (who became Lord Beaconsfield in 1876), followed by Lord Salisbury (1830–1903) from 1881, and C. S. Parnell (1846–91), the leader of the agitation for Irish Home Rule—the question which developed in prominence till it broke up the Liberal party. Foreign relations apart, the other matters on which parties divided were chiefly industrial problems and the demands of Nonconformity for the disappearance of Church control over education.

The Irish Question. Gladstone attempted to allay Irish grievances by disestablishing the Anglican Church in Ireland (1869) and reconstructing the whole system of land-tenure there, while what might be called a constant underground civil war of outrages and assassinations was carried on by agitators whose supporters were for the most part among the Irish population of the United States. Successive governments dealt with the Irish question by repressive emergency Acts alternating with concessions, till the elections of 1885 definitely converted Gladstone to Home Rule ; half his party followed him, while the rest formed for a time a separate group, but finally coalesced with the Conservatives as the Unionist party.

In 1886 Gladstone's first Home Rule bill was defeated, whereupon Lord Salisbury came into power, supported by the Liberal Unionists. In 1892 Gladstone was again returned to office but not to power, since he was dependent on the support of a disunited Irish party in the Commons, while the Lords, refusing to recognize the government as representative of the electorate, rejected his measures wholesale, including a new Home Rule bill. Failing health and old age forced the " Grand Old Man " into retirement in 1894. Liberals were again in disagreement on questions of imperial policy ; and after a brief tenure of office by Lord Rosebery a general election gave the Unionists a sweeping majority, which soon found itself faced in South Africa with the problem of Boer v. Briton.

LESSON 23

The Expansion of Britain

(See plates 14—16)

FROM the study of home affairs in Great Britain during what is called the Victorian era we turn in this Lesson to the imperial developments overseas. New South Wales was the name given to the territory where the first Australian (convict) settlement was made at Sydney Cove, near Botany Bay, in January, 1788, under a military governor. Land was allotted to convicts when their term of punishment ended, and to the soldiers in charge when their term of service was over. For many years emigration from Britain was slow. To prevent occupation elsewhere by the French, who had sent out a prospecting expedition, British posts were established along the coast of New South Wales and on the island of Van Diemen's Land, which was afterwards called Tasmania and made a separate governorship.

More and more territory was occupied, settlement expanded into the interior, and in 1829 at Perth, on the other side of the continent, the colony of Western Australia was founded. In 1836 the province of South Australia (with its capital Adelaide) was separated from New South Wales ; in 1851, Victoria (Melbourne), and in 1859 Queensland (Brisbane). Both Western and South Australia were formed by private companies with little encouragement from the British government, and struggled hard for existence, helped by the natural fertility of the coastal belt and the excellent climate. Colonists were attracted in greater numbers when transportation was dropped in 1840 (except in Tasmania, where it was stopped in 1853) ; and a tremendous impulse was given to emigration from Great Britain after the discovery of gold in Victoria in 1851, hosts of miners seeking their fortunes at Ballarat and Bendigo. Thus industry was added to the agricultural interests of sheep-farming and corn-growing.

In 1842 representative government was partially introduced into New South Wales, which had begun with a purely military government ; and in 1850 this and the other colonies, with the exception of Western Australia, were granted virtually autonomous government on the same basis as Canada. Responsible government was extended to Western Australia in 1890. Final union as the Commonwealth of Australia was proclaimed in 1901.

Colonization of New Zealand. The two islands of New Zealand were colonized many years after the foundation of New South Wales. Settlement was impeded by the resistance of the vigorous native Maori race, a cultured and interesting people. Annexed in 1839, the first settlement of New Zealand was made at Wellington, founded in 1840, in which year the treaty of Waitangi was made with the Maori population. Although infringement and native revolt followed, in 1845 Sir George Grey did much towards restoring peace, unfortunately to be again broken by two bitter wars before harmonious development successfully continued.

South Africa. The Dutch Cape Colony in South Africa had also been definitely added to the empire in 1814—by no means to the satisfaction of the long-established Dutch settlers. The position there was complicated by the presence within the colony (which lay south of the Orange River) of Hottentots, and beyond that river of warlike tribes of negro Kaffirs ; the Dutchmen were mainly farmers (Boers), who were largely dependent on slave labour. In 1833 Parliament in England abolished slavery throughout the empire, paying to the slave-owners compensation which in their view was inadequate. Thereupon an immense number of the Boers, deprived of a substantial part of their property and of their available supply of agricultural labour, trekked across the Orange (1837) to be out of reach of the British government control from Cape Town. Over the colonial frontier they came in collision with Kaffir chiefs, but effected settlements ; while some of them, crossing the Vaal and piercing the Drakensberg range, fought with success against the Zulus, but retired when the Cape Town government took possession of the territory, which became the colony of Natal. In 1852, however, autonomy was conceded to the Transvaal or South African Republic, and in 1854 was almost forced on the Orange Free State between the Orange River and the Vaal.

Government of Canada. By Pitt's Canada Act (1791) the colony north of the St. Lawrence was divided in two : Upper, peopled mainly by emigrants from the new American Republic or from Britain ; Lower, with a population mainly French. In both, however, administrative posts became a practical monopoly of certain families of British descent. The French-Canadians, however, found a leader in Louis Joseph Papineau, who steadily opposed the union of Upper and Lower Canada ; he formulated the grievances of his party, and worked from 1815 to 1837 against the imperial government. In 1837 French dissatisfaction led to revolt in Lower Canada, followed by a rising in the Upper Province. Though not actively concerned in fighting, Papineau was " wanted " for high treason, but eventually escaped to Paris whence he returned, pardoned, in 1847.

The disaffection, being very limited, was promptly suppressed ; public opinion in Britain was stirred, however, and Lord Durham was sent out to Canada in 1839 to investigate grievances. His report urged the reunion of the two provinces, with responsible government. The first recommendation was effected by the Act of Reunion in 1840 ; " home rule " was granted in 1847, and was soon extended to the trans-St. Lawrence colonies. In the same decade the Maine and Oregon boundary disputes with the United States were settled by the British government in a manner far from satisfactory to colonial sentiment ; and it was not until after 1867, when the British North America Act created the Dominion of Canada as a confederation of provinces, that Canada began to progress as a self-governing nation.

In every case the autonomy bestowed on British colonies included, in marked contrast to the old colonial theory, the complete control of tariffs ; while on the victory of free trade doctrines in Great Britain the preferences hitherto given to colonial products were abolished. It was assumed that free trade would be also imposed in the colonies. They, however, needed protection to enable their growing industries to thrive ; Canada, in particular, needed protection against the competition of the United States. In 1858, therefore, the Canadian Assembly set up a small tariff wall against imports from both Britain and the United States, which was increased in 1859.

Dalhousie's Rule in India. The expansion and consolidation of the British dominions or *Raj* in India were almost continuous from the close of the 18th century onwards, though only two viceroys, Wellesley (sent as governor-general to India in 1798) and Dalhousie (in 1848) set out with the deliberate policy of increasing the territory under direct British administration. One after another, however, was forced into war by the action of some Indian potentate, who could only believe that he had been beaten if he was deprived of territory. The wars against the Marathas (1803-5 and 1817-19), Nepal (1814-15), Sindh (1843), where the British were clearly the aggressors, and the Punjab (1845-9) are notable examples. Oudh, on the other hand, was annexed in 1856 on account of the incorrigible misrule of its Wazirs ; while Wellesley had at the beginning of the century acquired much territory by his system of " subsidiary alliances," whereby princes were provided with forces by the British Government maintained from the revenue of districts ceded to it.

The eight strenuous years of Dalhousie's viceroyalty were a turning-point. In certain respects they crowned the process of development that had been in progress all through the century, while they brought to completion the expansion of the area under British administration—the rest being under the rule of hereditary Indian dynasties—by the application of the legal doctrine of escheat (lapse), whereby thrones to which there was no legal heir lapsed to the supreme government. This had been evaded by allowing the adoption of an heir by princes who had no son. By refusing sanction to several adoptions, Dalhousie added large territories, which alarmed the princes. It was on quite other grounds, and in answer to direct challenge, that he annexed the Punjab and Pegu by force of arms. The viceroy was firmly convinced that the British Raj was immensely beneficial, and that annexation, wherever legitimately possible, was desirable ; this view was fiercely resented by the Mahomedans, who had formerly been the masters of India, and by Hindus such as the Marathas, who had hoped to win a supremacy themselves.

Indian Mutiny. The two were irreconcilable, but in 1857, when Dalhousie had left India, they joined to get rid of the common adversary. Their propaganda spread disaffection in the sepoy army, resulting in the Great Mutiny, which broke out in the Ganges basin and extended over a period packed with tragedies, anxieties and heroisms. It was due to the foresight of Sir Henry Lawrence that preparations were made for the defence of the Residency at Lucknow, during the siege of which he himself fell. Another hero was John Nicholson, a famous frontier officer, who arrested the revolt in his own district, and later led the storming party at Delhi, September 14, 1857, where he was killed.

The mutiny was in no sense a national rebellion. It was a revolt of the native soldiers, and nearly all the princes stood loyal ; the issue was decided in six months. The outcome was the transfer of responsibility for India from the Company to the Crown,

consummated in 1876, with wholesome effect on oriental sentiment, by the proclamation of Queen Victoria as Empress of India
at the Delhi Durbar held in January, 1877.

The princes were guaranteed against the dreaded use of the
doctrine of lapse. No more Indian territory was absorbed into
British India, though the whole of Burma, portions of which
had come into British hands in 1826 and 1852, was annexed
in 1887, and independent Pathan tribes on the north-west
frontier were brought to some extent under British control,
following upon the (second) Afghan war of 1879–80. The Indian
administration was reorganized, but without departure from the
system which reserved all responsible posts to Europeans. A
new mouthpiece of criticism representing a certain class of native
opinion appeared—the National Congress—in 1887.

Ideas, as yet vague, of drawing closer the voluntary bounds
of imperial unity began to displace the earlier notion of inevitable
separation of the colonies, and were strengthened by the imperial
pageantry of Queen Victoria's jubilee in 1887. But the events
which crystallized this new spirit of imperialism took place in
South Africa.

Trouble in the Transvaal. The Transvaal, as we saw, was made
an independent republic in 1852. In 1877 it appeared to be on
the verge of war with a Kaffir chief which would certainly bring
upon it the powerful military body of the Zulus, with every
prospect of being wiped out and opening the floodgates of a hideous
war between negroes and whites. To prevent the disaster,
and under the mistaken impression that the Boers themselves
desired it, the British commissioner in South Africa annexed
the Transvaal. The aggressive attitude of the Zulus, however,
forced a war in 1879, which, after initial disasters, ended in the
overthrow and annexation of the Zulu state. Delivered from that
menace, the Boers repudiated the annexation in arms, and defeated
the British troops sent against them at Majuba Hill (1881).
Nevertheless, the home government stopped the war, and restored
the Republic by the Conventions of Pretoria (1881).

The discovery of gold along the reef at Johannesburg in
1884–5 resulted as in Australia, in the influx of a horde of miners
and adventurers from Europe. To that conservative Boer
Paul Kruger (1825–1904), who had become president of the
Transvaal in 1883, the invasion was most distasteful. The
Uitlanders (foreigners) were refused citizenship, or the franchise

within a reasonable period. They were taxpayers and objected to this ruling moreover, they were mostly English subjects and expected that British suzerainty would protect their interests. The details of the consequent quarrel with the British government are too complicated to be given here, but the outcome was that the South African or Boer War (1899-1902) was primarily brought about by a terrible blunder committed by Cecil Rhodes, prime minister of Cape Colony, and by Kruger's obstinacy.

LESSON 24

Foreign Relations under Victoria

(See plates 16 and 17)

THE Napoleonic wars secured to Great Britain a naval supremacy which no other power attempted to challenge until the 20th century. The British conquests had been made from defensive and not offensive strategy—to counteract Napoleon's aggressive designs. The acquisition of Malta and the Ionian islands was due to the need of closing the Mediterranean as a thoroughfare for the French to Egypt and the East. These islands Britain retained (in 1864 the Ionian group was handed over to Greece). At the close of the wars Britain alone of the great powers restored certain valuable conquests of territory to Holland and France, retaining Ceylon—a dangerous hostile base because nearest to India—and the Cape of Good Hope—the first link in the sea chain to India—paying a large indemnity to the Dutch for the retention of Cape Colony. From France, Britain retained only Mauritius, Tobago and Santa Lucia in the West Indian area, where British acquisitions had been partly due to the need for defending adjacent British colonies and partly to protect British traders from the French. The loss of the old American colonies was being counterbalanced by the birth of the various Australian colonies and by dominion in India, where British interests had now no serious European competition.

Rivalry with Russia. In relation to the other European powers, Britain had pursued, under the direction, first, of Castlereagh and, after his death, of George Canning, the policy of non-intervention in the internal affairs of sovereign states, modified by Canning's insistence that armed intervention by other powers would warrant it on Britain's part—thus to some extent limiting the repressive energies of the Holy Alliance of the three autocrats of Russia, Austria and Prussia, and helping the liberation of Spanish America from the rule of the Spanish monarchy. The Greeks were encouraged by British sympathy in their revolt against the Turk, but Russia was left to appropriate the credit of securing Greek independence and a predominant influence at the Porte.

From this may be dated the beginning of the political duel which throughout the century was the mainspring of British foreign policy with regard to Russia, the reason for which was the expansion of Russian power in central Asia, where the Russian borders were drawing gradually nearer and nearer to India. Russia was the only European power which could expand in that direction by land. The conviction that India had now become Russia's objective was irresistible in England ; and as the domination and, much more, the possession of Constantinople, with the Black Sea as a naval base, would be invaluable to the Czar for these purposes, British statesmanship was unswervingly directed to the preservation of the " integrity of the Turkish empire " and of a dominant British influence at Constantinople—and, more spasmodically, in Afghanistan.

Career of Palmerston. From the constitutional revolution of 1832 to his death Lord Palmerston (1784–1865), popularly known as " Pam," enjoyed a free hand at the Foreign Office in practically every Liberal ministry. He sympathized with Liberal movements abroad, and his motivating principle was to make British influence actively felt in Europe and to assert British interests in all circumstances and at all costs. A man of resolute character, he carried the Canningite " hands off " policy to its extreme limits. It was mainly his doing that Belgium acquired independence, and that England, instead of Russia, checked Mehemet Ali and thus recovered prestige at Constantinople in 1840

Palmerston's methods were high-handed and his language in diplomacy was aggressive and sometimes infuriating to foreign powers in its British self-confidence and complacency, while he treated foreign policy as his own private preserve, irrespective of his colleagues in the Cabinet and even of the Queen herself—in consequence of which he held only a subordinate position in the ministry which involved itself in the Crimean War (1854–6). But in the course of the war the ministry fell—Englishmen at home viewed the misery of the Crimean army with increasing dissatisfaction, sure that the government were to blame—and Palmerston, whose views and uncompromising character inspired public confidence, became prime minister for the first time at the age of seventy, and directed the war to its successful conclusion. From the British point of view, this, the only European war in which Britain took part between 1815 and 1914, was fought in defence of Turkey and to close the Black Sea to Russian war-ships in order to safeguard India—objects which for the time being were achieved—though the war originated in rival claims asserted by Napoleon III and Nicholas I of Russia on behalf of the Latin and Greek (or Orthodox) Churches, the opposing claims of which they respectively supported.

Wars with China. Some time earlier, in 1840–2, China had been brought into conflict with Britain over a trade dispute. That war had issued in the treaty of Nanking, the cession of Hong Kong to Britain, and the opening of certain " treaty ports " to European commerce. There was another China War in 1857—the year in which the Indian Mutiny also began at Meerut, spreading to Lucknow and to Cawnpore, where the garrison and 500 British women and children were massacred, and culminating in the relief of Lucknow by Havelock and Outram and the final suppression of the mutineers by Sir Colin Campbell. The trouble in China arose on a doubtful issue with a local governor—the *Arrow* incident. The British authority on the spot acted with high-handedness ; the governor retorted by setting a price on the heads of Europeans generally. This brought in the French, and the war was not ended till Peking had been taken, and the demands of the Europeans, including the establishment of foreign legations in the Inner City, were conceded by the Chinese government.

In the various revolutionary and nationalist conflicts in Europe from 1848 onwards Britain maintained a strict neutrality in action, while openly showing sympathies, always with a strong suggestion that British non-intervention was conditional on the non-intervention of other powers and on the safeguarding of British interests. During the twenty years following the Crimean War, Queen Victoria and her government remained interested spectators of the European developments which finally established a unified Italian kingdom among the great powers, separated Austria from Germany, and culminated in the Franco-Prussian War of 1870–71—a war which begot the German

Empire and the third French Republic. During the same period the American Republic achieved unification through the great Civil War, which prevented it from splitting into two republics with antagonistic economic and political interests. In that conflict, too, the Queen and her government remained neutral, while North and South in America each found it monstrous that Britain should not take their own side. British sympathies were, in fact, curiously divided by the two questions which were at stake—the political question of the right of secession, maintained by the South, and the social or moral question of the abolition of slavery. The latter question had been solved in England with regard to the West Indies in 1833, when Stanley (afterwards Earl of Derby) introduced and carried a bill for complete abolition at a purchase-money cost to Great Britain of twenty million pounds, paid to the slave-owners.

Congress of Berlin. In 1876, however, the Eastern Question was again forced to the front by the persistence of Turkish misrule. Disraeli (Lord Beaconsfield) was at the head of the British government. The eloquence of his rival Gladstone roused a passionate popular sympathy for Turkey's oppressed subjects, but forcible intervention by the powers was not compatible with that " integrity of the Turkish empire " which was Beaconsfield's cardinal doctrine. The powers could not agree. Russia invaded Turkey ; in January, 1878, Russian armies were at the gates of Constantinople, and the Czar imposed on Turkey the treaty of San Stefano, the terms of which were intolerable to England and also to Austria. Both demanded that the territorial conditions should be settled by a congress of the " Treaty Powers." Beaconsfield made it clear that England was prepared to fight ; for some weeks war and peace were in the balance ; Russia gave way ; the San Stefano treaty was revised at the Congress of Berlin, and Beaconsfield, who had there been the dominant personality—and had also, while the Congress was in session, concluded a separate agreement with Turkey, by which Britain was allowed to occupy Cyprus as a naval station of considerable value in return for a guarantee of Turkey's Asiatic dominions other than those ceded to Russia by the treaty—returned to England in triumph. But the Anglo-Russian antagonisms and suspicions become more marked than ever, and only began to be allayed when a joint Russian, British and Afghan commission delimited the Asiatic frontiers in 1887.

Affairs in Egypt. Egypt, however, proved a source of friction with France. Indebtedness to Britain, France and Russia had caused Egyptian administration to be brought largely into the hands of a joint board of control. The imminence of a revolution forced armed British intervention, France standing aside. Having suppressed the revolution in the general interest, the business of restoring order devolved upon the British, who, to France's annoyance, assumed a temporary protectorate. In the Sudan, however, in the region of the upper Nile—nominally, but never effectively, under Egyptian sovereignty—the fanatical barbarian power of the Mahdi had arisen. In the attempt either to reconquer or evacuate the Sudan, General Gordon found himself shut up in Khartum by the Mahdist hordes, and when at last a long-delayed relief expeditionary force arrived it was only to find that the place had been stormed two days previously and Gordon had fallen in the defence (1885). The Sudan was abandoned until its conquest thirteen years later by Kitchener.

After the fall of the Gladstone administration in 1886, foreign affairs were directed either by Lord Salisbury or Lord Rosebery, without serious variations of principle, on the general line of readiness to make unimportant concessions for the sake of agreement on fundamentals, the partition of Africa into " spheres of influence " among the European powers being the outstanding question ; while in relation to the eastern Mediterranean the overwhelming strength of the British fleet made it into something like an international police force, imposing order without challenging aggressive hostility.

LESSON 25

The Years Preceding the Great War

(See plates 18 and 19)

THE Unionists, led by Lord Salisbury, were in power and could rely on the support of half the Liberal party when the Boer republics, led in effect by President Kruger of the Transvaal, threw down their final challenge in October, 1899, on the issue whether South Africa should remain within the British Empire or become an independent Afrikander Dominion. The Boers immediately invaded Natal, and in a few weeks British garrisons were surrounded at Ladysmith, Kimberley and Mafeking. In attempting to relieve the former, General Sir Redvers Buller was defeated with great loss at Colenso and Spion Kop; Lord Methuen suffered severe reverses on the banks of the Modder and at Magersfontein; and Gatacre was defeated at Stormberg. At long last the empire awoke to the fact that the Boer communities had provided it with a very tough task, contingents of volunteers poured in from the self-governing colonies, and a large army under Lord Roberts and Kitchener took the field. At length the beleaguered towns were relieved, the Boers were defeated at Paardeberg and their capitals were occupied before midsummer, 1900. The Boer field armies were broken up, and the annexation of the republics was proclaimed. Nevertheless, the stubborn Boer farmers maintained a brilliant guerrilla struggle for another eighteen months before even they were convinced that to win was impossible against the tremendous odds, and accepted the peace of Vereeniging in May, 1902, on terms of which the generosity could not be disputed or misinterpreted as in 1881. Four years later full responsible government was restored to them.

Death of Queen Victoria. While the war was still in progress, a general election, with the war itself as the main if not the sole issue, had been held; and as on that issue the Liberal party was divided, the Unionists were returned to power with a barely reduced majority in 1900. Shortly after its close in 1902 Lord Salisbury retired, Mr. Balfour succeeding him as Prime Minister. Already, on January 22, 1901, before the victory was completed, in the sixty-fourth year of her reign, the longest in British history, the great queen had died. Her influence had always been directed towards constitutional harmony. Her reign covered a period of great democratic development, yet no decision of importance was made without her knowledge and approval. She did all in her power to popularize the monarchy, and left her son, Edward VII, far wider imperial dominions than she had inherited and a firmly established imperial throne.

Development of the Colonial Empire. The war, though it had revealed much defective army organization, had proved the military value of the colonies, remarkably emphasizing the inherent loyalty of the empire and its unity. The fact that it was no mere collection of unrelated territories, but an association of States bound together by close ties of common interests was significantly marked by the federation of the Australian colonies in the Commonwealth of Australia, on January 1, 1901, followed by the Union of South Africa in 1910. Thus following the example set by Canada in 1867, the other great British colonies became grouped as Dominions with an individually national sense.

The end of the war meant immediate resumption of pre-war party politics, though the rupture between the two wings—popularly labelled pro-Boer and Imperialist—of the Liberals was not easily bridged ; and for a time it was doubtful whether the leaders of the two sections would be able again to work in anything like harmony. The Irish question—the Nationalists, too, being divided—was at least in abeyance. Some success attended the Irish Land Purchase Act (1903), but its very success caused a difficulty, as the State could not find money immediately to satisfy the claims for advances to tenants to enable them to purchase land from owners willing to sell. Then, in 1903, Joseph Chamberlain, Colonial Secretary in Balfour's ministry, dropped a bomb as startlingly disruptive as Gladstone's conversion to Home Rule in 1886, or the repeal of the Corn Laws forty years earlier.

Chamberlain's Tariff Crusade. The immense development of national wealth which followed the financial reforms of Peel and Gladstone had convinced the country that Free Trade, in the sense of the total suppression of protective tariffs, was the only sane course for the country to follow.

Chamberlain, however, had become convinced that the empire would be bound far more closely together by a system of preferential tariffs—in effect, the protection of dominion or colonial products—and by a retaliation against hostile tariffs, in defiance of the doctrine universally accepted and taught in England for half a century. His personal crusade, aided by the new imperialist sentiment, won able converts, while it antagonized a large proportion of the Unionist party whose faith in Free Trade remained unshaken. The result was that, when a general election could no longer be deferred, the Liberals were returned to power (Jan., 1906) with a huge majority over the rest. Sir H. Campbell-Bannerman became Prime Minister. For the first time there was an organized, though small, Labour party of fifty members ; and of the four parties in the House, the Labour and the Nationalist groups were likely in the Commons to vote for the government as against the Unionists, whereas in the

Lords the Opposition leaders could count on the support of a sweeping Tory majority. The Liberals secured the support of Unionist free-traders by a pledge to suspend the Irish question during the present Parliament.

In India, reforms were introduced with the support of the viceroy, appointed before the fall of the Unionist government, which gave to Indians a greatly increased share in the responsibilities of government, condemned in many quarters as more than rash (1909) ; while seditious activities and propaganda—there were assassinations in London and in India, and bombs were thrown at the Viceroy in 1908—were repressed with a firmness no less shocking to the extremists on the other side.

Issues between Commons and Lords. Meanwhile, at home the Liberal government, now under the leadership of Mr. Asquith, Sir H. Campbell-Bannerman having resigned from ill-health in 1908, and with Mr. Lloyd George as Chancellor of the Exchequer, pushed forward a programme of democratic legislation which the Lords persistently rejected, and carried through Haldane's scheme of army reforms calculated to provide an army of the highest efficiency—a second line being formed as a Territorial Force—but without applying the principle of compulsory service.

The crisis in the government came with the unprecedented rejection by the Peers of Lloyd George's budget in 1909, which forced a dissolution. There were two issues at stake : the financial, the choice between the budget's new methods of raising revenue and Tariff Reform, which many free-traders even counted the less dangerous ; and the curtailment of the powers of the House of Lords precipitated by the rejection of the finance bill, which, if it became a precedent, would lay any Liberal government at their mercy. The election in January, 1910, gave the Liberals a bare majority, but sure of Nationalist and Labour support, they remained in office. The budget was passed ; but the death (May, 1910) of Edward VII made it necessary to appeal to the country on a formulated Parliament Bill, before calling on King George V to override the Peers' constitutional power of rejecting it, by, if necessary, creating a sufficient number of new peers, as had been threatened in 1832. The election of December, 1910, made no change in the party balance. The Liberals went forward with their programme, from which in their view—fiercely denounced by the Opposition—a measure of Irish Home rule was no longer excluded.

No creation of Peers was needed. The new Parliament Act withdrew all finance measures from the Peers and made their veto on other bills suspensory only—that is, a bill passed in three successive sessions by the Commons would become law whether passed or not by the Peers—but it deferred changes in the constitution of the House of Lords itself. The government established a scheme of National Insurance, and disestablished the Church in Wales. The great battle, however, arose over its bill for creating an Irish Parliament in Dublin. The Nationalists accepted it, but Ulster declared itself ready to fight it in arms. In 1914 the prospect of a civil war in Ireland was being freely canvassed.

Beginning of the World War. During the reign of Edward VII, and largely through the influence of his personality, diplomacy had all but obliterated the long persistent differences between Great Britain and France, and between Great Britain and Russia. These reconciliations were viewed with alarm in Germany, who was taught to believe that it veiled a conspiracy of the three powers aimed at her own destruction, as it added Great Britain to that conjunction of France and Russia which had always been Bismarck's bugbear. The assassination of the Austrian arch-duke at Serajevo enabled Germany with Austria to force war upon Russia and France, despite the utmost efforts of the British government to avert a collision. The question whether Britain should stand aside was decided by Germany's invasion of Belgium (Aug. 3) in defiance of the treaty which Bismarck had been careful to observe in 1870 ; and on August 4, 1914, war was declared, the Liberal government, under Mr. Asquith's premier-ship, being still in power and responsible for the declaration.

LESSON 26

Britain's Part in the Great War

(See plates 20—22)

WHEN Great Britain declared war on August 4, 1914, the government was supported by the country and, as was very soon apparent, by the empire. The British volunteer army was desperately small in comparison with the compulsorily recruited and trained armies of the continental powers ; but it was highly efficient. In the third week of the war, all of it except the necessary reserves had taken station beside the French and Belgians on the Belgian borders ; while the country was already dotted with the camps to which volunteers were pouring in for training. The Dominions were equally prompt in their response to the call to arms. The British fleet was actually posted at the moment when war was declared, so that no enemy squadron was able at any time to slip through it.

Britain had begun by discharging a sea-power's first function in all wars, the securing of naval supremacy. The only German squadron still on the high seas did indeed succeed in engaging and sinking a weaker British squadron at Coronel, in the Pacific, on November 1 ; but only to be itself trapped and sunk by a larger squadron at the Falkland Islands six weeks later. The remaining stray cruisers that were still at sea were soon hunted down, while the German grand fleet was bottled up in ports sheltered by mine-fields, whence only an occasional squadron could issue to make a hasty raid on the English coast and race back to its cover to escape annihilation. It was not till May, 1916, that it sallied out in force, came into touch with a detachment of the British fleet, commanded by Admiral Beatty, in the North sea, maintained a heavy running fight with it till the approach of the main British Fleet under Admiral Jellicoe, and continued to fight a very skilful rearguard action till it escaped to the cover of its own mine-fields. In the whole action the British suffered the more heavily, but the Germans enough not to repeat the venture ; they did not again challenge a fleet engagement. After this Battle of Jutland (1916) they confined themselves to an intensified submarine warfare on non-combatant ships, till in April, 1918, a British squadron, by a heroic exploit under Vice-Admiral R. Keyes, succeeded in sealing up their submarine bases at Zeebrugge and Ostend.

In the first stage of the war the British expeditionary force of 80,000 men under Sir John French, the " contemptible little army," was posted on the French left, and enabled the allied line, hinging on Longwy and Verdun, to swing back before the German onrush, always covering Paris, without being broken or outflanked. The retreat from Mons before very much stronger forces forms one of the most notable episodes in our military history. The British force performed its part no less honourably when the Germans were falling back and the two lines were establishing trench warfare in what may be called the permanent Western front from Switzerland to the sea, notably in securing and holding the famous Ypres Salient against massed attacks.

Campaigns in Gallipoli and Mesopotamia. In February, 1915, the British undertook the campaign of the Dardanelles, which, if it could have been brought to a successful issue, might have brought the war itself to a speedy conclusion. No troops could be spared from the Western front; the navy at first attempted to carry the straits by itself, though no similar attempt had ever succeeded. It failed because the straits were impassably sown with floating mines. But in April a military effort was added to the naval. The Australasian troops, the " Anzacs," on their way to Europe, were deflected to be landed on the unfortified Gallipoli peninsula, where they remained perpetually exposed to devastating bombardment till August, when an attempt was made to take the Turkish forts in flank by a landing at Suvla Bay. From want of water it missed success. That sealed the fate of the whole attempt, though it was not till December that by a brilliant operation the troops were withdrawn gradually without the knowledge of the Turks from the Gallipoli death-trap—Allied contingents, British included, had a little earlier occupied Salonica.

In the same year the British were repelling Turkish attacks on the frontier of Egypt, which was proclaimed a British Protectorate —and were themselves invading Mesopotamia from India. The expedition advanced almost to Bagdad, but had to fall back to Kut-el-Amarna, which was turned into a trap by floods that cut off alike retreat and the arrival of supports, so that Townshend was forced to surrender in April, 1916, after a stubborn defence. The campaign, however, was only in abeyance ; before twelve months were past Kut was in British possession again, Bagdad was occupied, and from that time the progress, though slow, was continuous. In 1917 an advance on Palestine from Egypt was held up at Gaza ; but later in the year Allenby, by turning the flank of Gaza, was able to occupy Jerusalem before Christmas, at the moment when the great crisis of the war was immediately impending.

In France and Flanders. We turn back, then, to the Western front, where for four years the British were fighting side by side with the French and in concert with them though not under a single command, until unity was at length established in March, 1918, under Marshal Foch, with the loyal cooperation of Field-Marshal Sir Douglas Haig, the British commander-in-chief. In

1915 the Allies and the Germans were fighting each other all along the line, with only occasional special concentration on particular points, as by the British at Neuve Chapelle in March and at Loos seven months later—both attempts at a break-through which were foiled—and the German onslaught at Ypres in April, where a gap was actually created by the first use of poison gas, but was reoccupied by the Canadians before the Germans could make good the advantage they had won.

After the failure of the great German thrust at Verdun in the first half of 1916 the Allies began the concerted push all along the line—a break-through being no longer regarded as practicable—intended to force the enemy back by sheer pressure, which, as concerns the British part in it, is known as the Battle of the Somme, beginning on July 1, 1916. Ground was gained, but only a strip and only by ceaseless and desperate fighting. After the long preliminary bombardment, it was here that the creeping barrage was first employed on a big scale, the infantry advancing behind a progressing screen of shells. It was on September 15, 1916, that British tanks appeared. Weather conditions made real progress impossible during the winter, but in the spring (1917) the struggle was renewed. Its most notable events were the capture of the Vimy ridge in April and of the Messines ridge, half of which was blown up, in June—after which weather conditions again made the farther advance through the Flanders mud to Passchendael disastrously costly. In April, 1917, changes in the war situation were the entry of America on the side of the Allies, and the Russian revolution.

In March, 1918, the Germans launched against the British right the attack which was to smash through the Allied line and ensure their own victory before the American armies were ready to take the field in full strength. This offensive sent the line back, often so broken that if the impetus of the thrust could have been maintained it must have been pierced ; but the impetus was never quite sufficient. In front of Amiens it was brought to a halt. This was followed by an attack on the British left, which was also in turn held up, though the line was driven in, in a deep curve. Reinforcements were now pouring in, and the next German concentration was directed against the French, not the British.

At mid-July that attack, too, was shattered. Before the end of the month Foch opened his great offensive, and the German retirement began. It was a renovated British army that took up its allotted share in the decisive campaign when its right advanced on August 9, in conformity with the preceding movement on the French left, the successive sections of the line coming into action at the planned intervals, battering the enemy back over the old battlefields—the advance never pausing—into their old strongholds. through them into their reserve trenches, till in mid-September the Canadians carried the Hindenburg line itself.

While the state of affairs on the western front was being so dramatically reversed, General Allenby achieved, by a surprise attack, a brilliant victory at Megiddo (September 19) and cleared the Turks out of Palestine ; on October 1 he was in Damascus. During the next month the Turkish army on the Tigris surrendered and an armistice was signed on October 30, giving the Allies possession of the Dardanelles and the Bosporus.

On the Italian front, Italians and British opened an attack on October 23 ; on October 27 the Austrians were in flight. On November 3 they signed an armistice. The Germans were standing alone and on the brink of crashing. Early in November there were revolutionary outbreaks and the Kaiser fled. On November 11 the Republican delegates signed their country's surrender.

LESSON 27

Britain Since the Great War

(See plate 22)

THE close of the Great War saw Britain enjoying a measure of power and prestige such as had not been hers since Waterloo. Under the dynamic leadership of Lloyd George she had brought victory out of defeat and now looked confidently to the building of a new Britain in a world freed from the menace of militarism—a land, as the premier phrased it, made fit for heroes.

Seeking a free hand in the making of the peace and in the transition from the war economy, the premier " went to the country " in December, 1918, at the head of a great array of candidates, Conservative and Liberal, who had accepted the Coalition " coupon." Against them were the Independent Liberals under Asquith, and the Labour party, led then by Arthur Henderson. The result of the election was a foregone conclusion

Asquith and most of the Liberal and Labour critics of the War period, including Snowden and Ramsay Macdonald, lost their seats, and in the new parliament 502 Coalition members were faced by but 63 Labourites, 28 " Wee Free " Liberals, led by Sir Donald Maclean, until Asquith's return to the House as M.P. for Paisley in 1919, 23 anti-Lloyd George Conservatives, and 91 Irish and Independents.

Treaty of Versailles. Backed by so tremendous a majority, Lloyd George set about the task of peace-making and reconstruction. With Clemenceau and President Wilson he formed one of the Allied triumvirate under whose aegis was at length produced the Treaty of Versailles, signed on June 28, 1919. Under the Treaty Britain acquired no territory in the strict sense, but in due course was rewarded by having entrusted to her by that new creation, the League of Nations, huge and valuable " mandated " territories, i.e., territories held in trust, as it were, for the League and for whose good government she could be called responsible at Geneva. In this way Palestine, Iraq or Mesopotamia, Togoland, Cameroon and Tanganyika became attached to the Empire, though not formally incorporated within it ; and at the same time and in similar fashion the Union of South Africa received German South-West Africa ; Australia certain Pacific islands ; and New Zealand, Samoa.

Industrial Unrest. While the peace-makers were scheming in Paris, at home the work of demobilization rapidly proceeded, and during 1919 millions of men returned to civil life and were either absorbed in industry or received the unemployment " dole." There was a strike on the railways, and serious unrest in the coalfields prompted the setting up of the famous Sankey Commission ; but on the whole the change-over to peacetime conditions was made with little friction. Trade was booming ; and a beginning had already been made with reconstruction in the shape of a new Education Act and a Representation of the People Act, which enfranchised women over thirty (1918).

The next year, however, there was a national strike of coal-miners for higher wages, and by Christmas there were nearly 750,000 men on the books of the Labour exchanges as unemployed. The end of the post-war boom came definitely in 1921. There was a three months' coal stoppage, unemployment increased, wages fell rapidly, and there was a widespread demand for economy in public administration and a reduction in taxation and government expenditure. In the political sphere the Coalition was rapidly losing its popularity, and the sudden *volte face* whereby, after years of the fiercest resistance to Irish claims, the Government opened up negotiations with the Sinn Fein leaders and speedily conceded to Arthur Griffith and Michael Collins more than Parnell or Redmond had ever dared to ask, did little to rehabilitate it in public opinion. The threat of a war with renascent Turkey proved the last straw ; most of the Conservative members of the Coalition revolted under Bonar Law and Baldwin, and in October, 1922, Lloyd George tendered his resignation. Bonar Law was his successor, and in the ensuing general election the Conservatives won 344 seats, the Labour party 142, and the Liberals 117.

First Labour Government. In the spring of the next year Bonar Law resigned and was succeeded by Baldwin, who in December asked the electorate to endorse his proposals for Imperial Preference. But the townsfolk were still fearful of a dear loaf, and the general election resulted in the return of only 258 Conservatives, as against 191 Socialists or Labourites and 156 Liberals. In January, 1924, a vote of confidence being denied him, Baldwin promptly resigned and a Labour government —the first in our history—took office under Ramsay MacDonald with Liberal support. After some conspicuous successes in European diplomacy, it fell after eight months, and the general election of 1924 resulted in the return of an overwhelmingly Conservative House of Commons—402 Conservatives, 151 Labour, and 50 Liberals and Independents. Baldwin became prime minister for the second time.

Baldwin's Second Ministry. His ministry was marked by four events of the greatest importance. The first was the return to the gold standard on April 29, 1925—pleasing to the " City " but with disastrous effects on British overseas trade, owing to the over-valuation of the pound in terms of the dollar and franc. The second was the Pact of Locarno (1925) between Britain, France, Germany, Belgium and Italy, mutually guaranteeing the frontiers of Western Europe. The third was the granting of the franchise to women on the same terms as men, thus making Britain completely democratic, so far as parliamentary representation is concerned. The fourth was the " general strike " (May 4–12, 1926) of workers on the railways and road transport, in iron and steel, printing and building, in support of the miners who had been " locked out " on their refusal to accept a reduction in their wage rates. The Government met the situation with energy, and after little more than a week the " general strike," which had never assumed a revolutionary aspect; was " called off " by the Council of the Trades Union Congress, although the miners remained " out " until the following December.

The strike had disastrous effects on British industry and commerce, but business was once again on the up-grade when in 1929 the economic blizzard reached our shores. A Labour Government had just taken office under Ramsay MacDonald (the general election figures were Labour 287, Conservatives 260, Liberal 59, Independent 9), but the fall in British exports and the reduction of income from overseas investments and shipping and financial services, combined with the cost of maintaining the vast and ever-growing number of unemployed, affected the finances to such an extent that it was found impossible to embark on any policy of industrial reorganization. In the summer of 1931 people at home, and more particularly abroad, began to be alarmed at Britain's mounting adverse trade balance and her unbalanced budget. There was a " run on the pound "; in a last effort to keep on the gold standard the Government borrowed gold from Paris and New York, but in August it was obvious that the situation was going from bad to worse.

National Government. On August 23 the Labour Government broke up, owing to a majority of the Cabinet refusing to agree to the drastic economies in allowances to the unemployed, wages of civil servants, etc., that were put forward by MacDonald and Snowden, the Chancellor of the Exchequer, as being necessary to balance the budget. MacDonald, the next day, was asked to form a National Government, and though the bulk of the Labour members refused to join the new coalition, he at once formed a cabinet composed of 4 Labour, 2 Liberal, and 4 Conservative ministers. The new Government immediately proceeded to balance the budget by drastic economies and increased taxation. These being insufficient to meet the situation, the gold standard was suspended on September 21. Then in October Parliament was dissolved and MacDonald asked the electors to give him a " doctor's mandate " to restore national prosperity by any and every means in the Government's power. The result of the appeal was an emphatic vote of confidence—556 supporters of the National Government were returned as opposed to 52 Socialists

LORD PALMERSTON. Henry John Temple, 3rd Viscount Palmerston (1784–1865), entered the House of Commons in 1809, and held many offices in Tory and Liberal governments. He was Liberal premier 1855–8, and again from 1859 until his death. BRITISH HISTORY 22

National Portrait Gallery

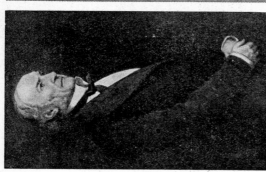

GLADSTONE v. DISRAELI. During a large part of the Victorian era, British politics was regarded as a struggle between Gladstone and Disraeli. William Ewart Gladstone (1809–98) became chancellor of the exchequer in Aberdeen's coalition government of 1852, and was Liberal prime minister 1868–74, 1880–85, 1886 and 1892–94. Benjamin Disraeli (1804–81) published several novels before entering Parliament in 1837. During the anti-Corn Law agitation he became the recognized leader of the Tory Protectionists, and was premier in 1868 and again from 1874–1880. He was created earl of Beaconsfield in 1876. BRITISH HISTORY 22

Left, after Millais. National Gallery

LORD SALISBURY. Robert A. T. G. Cecil, 3rd Marquess of Salisbury, (1830–1903), entered Parliament in 1853 and in 1881 became leader of the Conservative party. He was premier in 1885 and again 1886–92 and 1895–1902.
BRITISH HISTORY 22

After Richmond

VICTORIA, EMPRESS OF INDIA. Full imperial sovereignty over India was assumed during Lord Lytton's viceroyalty in 1877, when at a splendid Durbar held at Delhi Queen Victoria was proclaimed Empress of India. This study of the Queen Empress in her imperial robes is by Angeli.
BRITISH HISTORY 23

LORD DALHOUSIE (1812–60). Succeeding his father as earl of Dalhousie in 1838, he was appointed governor-general of India in 1847 and created a marquis two years later. He returned to England in 1856, after a highly successful period of Empire-building.
BRITISH HISTORY 23

National Portrait Gallery

Plate 14

Volume VI

CAPITALS OF THE SOUTHERN HEMISPHERE. Top, a Dutch engraving of 1777 showing Cape Town as it was when it was a Dutch port of call on the route between the homeland and the Indies. The Cape was ceded to Britain in 1814, and the first British settlers arrived there in 1820. Below is a view of Collins Street, one of Melbourne's principal thoroughfares, in 1857, when the city's expansion as a result of the gold discoveries was proceeding apace. The site of Melbourne was first occupied by whites in 1835, and two years later the settlement was named after the then British Prime Minister, Lord Melbourne. When Victoria was carved out of New South Wales in 1851 Melbourne was made its capital. BRITISH HISTORY 23

WINTER IN THE CRIMEA. During the winter of 1854–5 the troops in the Crimea suffered great hardships as a result of the severe cold and lack of proper stores and accommodation. This drawing is an " Illustrated London News " artist's impression of conditions at the front during the siege of Sebastopol. BRITISH HISTORY 24

BESIEGED LUCKNOW. From July 2 until September 25, 1857, the European inhabitants of Lucknow, with a garrison of 300 British and a few hundred loyal Sepoys, were besieged in the Residency or Government compound by the mutineers. This picture shows the " Cawnpore battery " as mounted during the siege. BRITISH HISTORY 23

Plate 16

Volume VI

and 7 Independents. After some ministerial reconstruction, the Government at once proceeded to deal with the position arising out of the adverse trade balance. Anti-dumping duties were placed on a long list of foreign goods; in February, 1932, a ten per cent tariff was imposed on nearly all goods imported from foreign countries; and in succeeding months further duties were imposed or duties already in existence increased.

Then in the summer an Imperial Economic Conference was held at Ottawa, with a view to the better development of the Empire. At the final session on August 20 agreements were signed on behalf of the Mother Country and the great Dominions whereby, in return for certain preferences granted by the latter to British goods, Britain for her part agreed to impose duties on foreign wheat and other foodstuffs, with preferences for Dominion produce, and to institute a quota system for bacon, beef, and mutton. Faced with so complete an abandonment of Free Trade principles, the Liberal ministers, Lord Snowden, Sir Herbert Samuel and Sir A. Sinclair, resigned from the Cabinet.

Economic matters continued to hold the centre of the stage, and in the next year a World Economic Conference was held in London under the presidency of the Prime Minister. In his opening speech on June 12, 1933, Mr. MacDonald declared that the policy of economic nationalism pursued of recent years, while impoverishing other nations, impoverished, too, those who pursued it, and he urged, therefore, that the nearer the world approached to economic unity, the better it would be for all. Progress towards this end was hampered, however, by the refusal of America to co-operate in any scheme of stabilization of the exchanges, and the Conference ended in disappointing fashion.

The Disarmament Conference, which had opened at Geneva in February 1932, was similarly ineffective. After discussing the limitation of capital ships, the abolition of submarines, gas and chemical warfare, bombing aircraft, and guns over a certain calibre, the Conference encountered heavy weather in the shape of Germany's insistence on an equality of status as regards armament as well as disarmament and Britain's insistence upon the retention of air bombing for police purposes on the fringes of the Empire. While the statesmen were deliberating, Japan was busily engaged in the subjugation of Manchuria, and Germany's withdrawal from the League of Nations and her open rearmament led to the virtual collapse of the Conference and all it stood for.

Early in 1935 a radical change in British armament policy was announced, in that the attempt to set an example to the world in reducing armaments was given up on the ground that its only result had been the reduction of the nation's armed strength below what was adequate for imperial defence and the satisfaction of Britain's commitments as a member of the League of Nations. Hence it was resolved to embark upon a policy of rearmament.

Towards the end of the year the Abyssinian question came to the fore, and Britain's part in the cause of " collective security " resulted in exacerbation of her relations with Italy, now embarked on a career of imperial aggrandizement. It was now that, as a whole-hearted supporter of the League of Nations policy of " sanctions " against Italy, and with considerable achievements in the home sphere in the shape of houses built, slums cleared, and unemployment reduced, the Government (since June headed again by Mr. Baldwin, who had changed places with Mr. Mac-Donald as Lord President of the Council) appealed to the country for a further vote of confidence. At the General Election held on November 4, 1935, 428 Government supporters were returned; Opposition parties numbered 184, of whom 154 were Socialists.

Hardly was the election campaign over when the Government was charged with abandonment of the League policy over Abyssinia ; and because of his part in the Hoare-Laval proposals for the partition of the Negus' realm, Sir Samuel Hoare, Foreign Secretary, had to resign, Mr. Anthony Eden taking his place.

On January 20, 1936, King George V passed away, and was succeeded by his eldest son as Edward VIII. As Prince of Wales the new king had won wide popularity, but he had not been long on the throne before his relationship with an American lady, Mrs. Simpson, led to adverse comment and ultimately to his abdication (December 10, 1936). On December 12 his brother, the Duke of York, was proclaimed king as George VI, and on May 12 of the following year he and his consort, Queen Elizabeth, were crowned with the customary pomp in Westminster Abbey.

Meanwhile, the international situation was going from bad to worse. Mr. Neville Chamberlain, who had become premier on Mr. Baldwin's elevation to the House of Lords in May 1937, became identified with a policy of " appeasement," the first-fruits of which were the dropping of Mr. Eden from the Foreign Office, and the signature of an Anglo-Italian Pact. An effort was made to localize the Spanish civil war, but the world was brought to the brink of war in 1938 by Germany's incorporation of Austria and her threat to the independence of Czechoslovakia. At the height of the crisis, Mr. Chamberlain three times went to Germany by air to meet Herr Hitler, and from Munich he returned on October 1, with an Anglo-German no-more-war declaration. The hope of a new era of peace and good-will was soon dissipated, however, and in 1939, when Czechoslovakia had also been absorbed by Germany, British rearmament was pushed ahead regardless of expense and effort. A new Peace Front was established, and Britain guaranteed Poland, Rumania and Greece against foreign aggression. Swiftly the situation deteriorated, and on September 3, following Germany's attack on Poland, Britain declared war on the Reich.

Changes in the Empire. In conclusion, a few words are necessary on Imperial relationships, in which there have been vast changes since the War. Egypt was conceded independence in 1922 ; Southern Ireland was granted dominion status in 1922 ; Iraq was declared free from mandatory control in 1932 ; Palestine has been a hotbed of disturbance owing to Jew and Arab rivalry.

A statutory commission to report on the possibility of instituting responsible government in India was appointed in 1927, under the chairmanship of Sir John Simon, and its report, issued in 1930, formed a basis for discussion. After Round Table Conferences in London in 1930 and 1931, a draft constitution was drawn up, and this was accepted by Parliament in 1935, and came into force on April 1, 1937. It provided for the federation of the British provinces and the native states, and in the former responsible government was set up, based on a popular suffrage.

Then mention must be made of the epoch-making resolution passed by the Imperial Conference of 1926, which defined the relationships existing between the individual states comprising the British Commonwealth. Great Britain and her self-governing Dominions are, it was stated, " autonomous communities within the British Empire, equal in status, in no way subordinate one to another in any aspect of their domestic or external affairs, though united by a common allegiance to the Crown, and freely associated as members of the British Commonwealth of Nations." This declaration was confirmed by the Statute of Westminster in 1931. Its effect was apparent when, during the abdication crisis of 1936, the consent of each Dominion was separately required for the change of monarch.

This Lesson concludes our Course in British History

E6*

LESSON 44

Some Products of Fatty Acids

Two classes of compounds derived from the fatty acids are of considerable importance ; the first of these is the acid chlorides, of which acetyl chloride—$CH_3 \cdot CO \cdot Cl$—is the best example. This compound, a colourless pungent liquid which boils at 55° C., is formed when phosphorus pentachloride is added to anhydrous acetic acid, the OH group being replaced by chlorine. Acetyl chloride reacts vigorously with water and, in fact, with any compounds which contain the OH group ; for example, with alcohol the univalent acetyl group CH_3CO- displaces the hydrogen of the hydroxyl group and ethyl acetate is formed, according to the equation :

$$C_2H_5OH + CH_3COCl \rightarrow CH_3COOC_2H_5 + HCl$$

For this reason acetyl chloride is used to detect the presence of a hydroxyl group in an organic compound. Acetyl chloride also reacts with anhydrous ammonia to give a compound called acetamide, thus :

$$CH_3 \cdot CO \cdot Cl + 2NH_3 \rightarrow CH_3 \cdot CO \cdot NH_2 + NH_4Cl.$$

Acetamide may be regarded as a derivative of ammonia in which one hydrogen atom has been replaced by the acetyl group ; it is a colourless, crystalline solid which, owing to the presence of impurities, usually has a strong smell of mice.

All the members of the fatty acid series give amides of this type ; their chemical properties are similar and are largely determined by the presence in the molecule of the univalent amide grouping, — $CO \cdot NH_2$.

When acetic acid is heated with chlorine in the presence of strong sunlight, which acts as a catalyst or of iodine, which acts as a chlorine carrier, each of the three hydrogen atoms in the CH_3 group may be replaced by a chlorine atom. These chloroacetic acids are analogous to the chlorine substitution products of methane and have the formulae :

$$CH_2 \cdot Cl \cdot COOH \qquad \text{chloroacetic acid.}$$
$$CH \cdot Cl_2 \cdot COOH \qquad \text{dichloroacetic acid.}$$
$$CCl_3 \cdot COOH \qquad \text{trichloroacetic acid.}$$

As might be expected, since they all contain the carboxylic group, these acids resemble the mono-carboxylic acids in chemical properties and, like acetic acid, form salts, acid chlorides, etc. They are of considerable importance in synthetic chemistry, as it is possible by replacing the chlorine atoms by other radicals or groups to build up complicated organic compounds.

The Esters. It has been mentioned that in some respects the alcohols behave like weak metallic hydroxides, reacting with concentrated acids to form esters which are analogous to inorganic salts. For example :

$$CH_3OH + HCl \rightleftharpoons CH_3Cl + H_2O$$
$$C_2H_5OH + H_2SO_4 \rightleftharpoons C_2H_5HSO_4 + H_2O$$

It is important to notice that these reactions are reversible and that in the presence of water the esters are hydrolysed with the production of alcohol and acid. The reaction is therefore usually carried out in the presence of a substance such as sulphuric acid or zinc chloride (Groves' Process), which removes the water as it is formed and causes the equilibrium to be displaced towards the right in the above equation.

As has been mentioned, the chlorine esters of the alcohols may also be prepared by the direct action of chlorine on the paraffin under the catalytic influence of sunlight, but as this method of preparation usually gives a mixture of a number of products, special methods of preparation are used when pure substances are required.

Chloroform or trichloromethane, $CHCl_3$, which is best prepared by distilling dilute aqueous alcohol or acetone with bleaching powder, is a most important halogen ester of methyl alcohol. The chloroform collects as a heavy oil, and may be separated from the impurities, alcohol, acetone, water, etc., with the aid of a separating funnel and purified by redistillation. Chloroform is a colourless, mobile, refractive liquid which is extensively used in surgery as an anaesthetic. On prolonged exposure to light and air it tends to decompose, and yields among other substances chlorine and hydrochloric acid. Since impurities of this kind are physiologically dangerous, it is important that chloroform for inhalation purposes should be protected from air and light. Pure chloroform gives no opalescence with silver nitrate solution, and this reaction is used as a test of its purity.

Bromine and iodine also form esters of this type ; bromoform, $CHBr_3$, is too dangerous to be used as a drug, but iodoform, CHI_3, a yellow crystalline solid, is widely used in medicine, surgery and as an antiseptic.

Carbon tetrachloride, CCl_4, a heavy colourless liquid with a sweet smell, is prepared in large amounts by chlorinating carbon disulphide in the presence of iodine or iron filings, which act as a chlorine carrier. Because of its non-inflammable nature, it is largely used as a fire-extinguisher ; the liquid is kept in small cylinders and a stream, pumped out under pressure, is directed at the seat of the flame. The vapour from the liquid forms a blanket over the flame which prevents combustion.

The halogen mono-substitution products of ethane are usually prepared by the action of the phosphorus penta-halide on ethyl alcohol. The reaction in the case of ethyl chloride is written :

$$C_2H_5OH + PCl_5 \rightarrow C_2H_5Cl + POCl_3 + HCl.$$

These three compounds, ethyl chloride, bromide and iodide, are colourless, volatile, pleasant-smelling liquids, which hydrolyse when heated with caustic potash, yielding ethyl alcohol and hydrochloric acid. When boiled with alcoholic potash, on the other hand, they are converted into olefines, thus :

$$C_2H_5I + KOH \rightarrow KI + C_2H_4 + H_2O$$

Like methyl chloride (boiling point $-23 \cdot 7°$ C.), ethyl chloride has a low boiling point ($12 \cdot 2°$ C.), and because of the freezing effect caused by the rapid evaporation when it is used as a spray, it is employed as a local anaesthetic.

Esters of Nitrous Acid. These esters are of considerable importance, since it has been proved that two distinct types of chemical compound exist, both of which have a composition corresponding to the formula $R \cdot NO_2$, where R may be any alkyl group. For example, when ethyl alcohol is distilled with nitrous acid—or a mixture of sodium nitrite and sulphuric acid—a colourless liquid, with a pleasant, fruity smell and a boiling point of $17°$ C., is formed. It is called ethyl nitrite, is insoluble in water, and is readily hydrolysed by dilute alkalis, yielding ethyl alcohol. If, on the other hand, ethyl iodide is warmed with silver nitrite and the liquid product fractionated, two substances are obtained, one of which boils at 17° C. and is identical with ethyl nitrite, while the other—which is called nitroethane—boils at 114° C. and has quite different properties. For example, it dissolves in, but is not decomposed by, caustic alkali, and while the nitrite, when reduced with hydrogen usually yields ammonia and alcohol, nitroethane is converted into a compound called an amine—in this case ethylamine. From a consideration of these and other chemical properties it was possible to decide on the arrangements of the atoms in the molecule in each case; the substances are represented constitutionally thus:

$$\text{ethyl nitrite} \qquad C_2H_5 \cdot O-N=O$$

$$\text{nitroethane} \qquad C_2H_5-N \underset{\diagdown O}{\overset{\diagup O}{}}$$

It has been shown that nitrous acid (HNO_2) is a mixture of the two forms $HO-N=O$ and $H-N \underset{\diagdown O}{\overset{\diagup O}{}}$, and the compounds above are obtained by replacing the hydrogen atom with an ethyl group.

Substances like these which have the same chemical composition but different chemical and physical properties are called *isomers*. There exists a complete series of compounds which are similar to nitroethane and which can be prepared from the halogen esters and silver nitrite in a similar way; they are called the *nitroparaffins*, and their chemical reactions are characteristic of the reactions of the univalent nitro group, $-N \underset{\diagdown O}{\overset{\diagup O}{}}$. Nitromethane is one of the most important; it is a colourless, pleasant-smelling liquid of boiling point about 101° C. and it has some use as a solvent of organic substances.

The alcohols also react under suitable conditions with nitric acid to give nitrates, with sulphuric acid to give hydrogen sulphates and sulphates, both of which are analogous to the corresponding inorganic compounds, and also with organic acids such as acetic acid to give esters. These organic esters are hydrolysed by aqueous mineral acids and alkalis and give amides with concentrated ammonia. Many occur in the fruit and flowers of plants, and it is to their presence that the sweet scents are due ; amyl acetate, $CH_3 \cdot CO \cdot OC_5H_{11}$, the acetyl ester of amyl alcohol, can be readily prepared in the laboratory and is widely used for flavouring sweets and cakes.

The Amines. The alcohols and ethers may be regarded as derivatives of water formed by the substitution of one or two alkyl radicals for the hydrogen atoms. In a similar manner the hydrogen atoms of the ammonia molecule may be replaced by alkyl groups or other organic radicals giving an important group of strongly basic substances known as amines ; these may be of three types according as one (primary amine), two (secondary) or three (tertiary) hydrogen atoms have been displaced :

$C_2H_5 \cdot NH_2$	$(C_2H_5)_2 \cdot NH$	$(C_2H_5)_3 \cdot N$
ethylamine	diethylamine	triethylamine
(primary)	(secondary)	(tertiary)

All of these compounds may be prepared by heating alcoholic ammonia with the alkyl iodide, and it is sometimes possible to separate the resulting mixture of amines chemically. A better method of preparing primary amines is to reduce the corresponding nitro compounds.

Like ammonia, these three amines are strongly basic, in the presence of hydrochloric acid, for example, they form a series of additive salts, which have the following composition :

$$C_2H_5NH_2 . HCl \qquad\qquad (C_2H_5)_2NH \cdot HCl$$
$$(C_2H_5)_3N \cdot HCl.$$

and are known as ethylamine hydrochloride, di- and tri-ethylamine hydrochloride. Also, as might be expected by analogy with ammonium $[NH_4]$ salts, the fourth hydrogen atom of the triamine salt is replaceable by an alkyl group giving a quaternary ammonium salt, such as $(C_2H_5)_4N \cdot Cl$, known as tetraethyl ammonium chloride.

The three types of amines may be distinguished by their reactions with nitrous acid. Primary compounds yield the corresponding alcohol, nitrogen and water, thus :

$$C_2H_5 \cdot N \boxed{H_2 + O} N \cdot OH \rightarrow C_2H_5 \cdot OH + N_2 + H_2O$$

secondary amines give yellow oils known as nitrosamines,

$$(C_2H_5)_2 N \boxed{H + HO} NO \rightarrow (C_2H_5)_2 N \cdot NO + H_2O,$$

tertiary amines do not react with nitrous acid.

LESSON 45

More about the Alcohols

THE series to which ordinary alcohol belongs are more properly called the primary alcohols. There are also secondary and tertiary alcohols, according as two or three instead of one hydrogen atom of methyl alcohol (CH_3OH) are replaced by alkyl groups, and we have seen that while the first oxidation products of the primary alcohols are aldehydes, those of the secondary alcohols, such as iso-propyl alcohol, are ketones. All of these alcohols, primary, secondary or tertiary, contain only one hydroxyl radical; they therefore belong to a particular class called the *monohydric alcohols*.

Since all the hydrogen atoms in a paraffin, such as ethane, for example, bear the same relation to the carbon atoms, it might be expected that more than one could be replaced by a hydroxyl radical in this way. This is indeed the case, the resulting compounds being called polyhydric alcohols; of these the dihydric and trihydric alcohols are the most important; they form well-defined series of compounds, which show a close relationship to those of the monohydric alcohols described above.

Dihydric Alcohols. The dihydroxy derivatives of the paraffins, discovered by Würtz in 1856, usually known as the glycols, form a homologous series of the general formula $C_nH_{2n}(OH)_2$. Of these, ethylene glycol, $C_2H_4(OH)_2$, is the simplest; it is formed when ethylene is cautiously oxidized with alkaline potassium permanganate solution, and is prepared in quantities by heating ethylene dibromide with dilute aqueous alkalis or alkaline carbonates. Its structural relationship to ethane is shown in its method of formation.

$$\begin{matrix} CH_3 & CH_2 & Br & K & OH & CH_2 \cdot OH \\ | & \longrightarrow & | & + & & \longrightarrow & | & +2KBr \\ CH_3 & CH_2 & Br & K & OH & CH_2 \cdot OH \end{matrix}$$

Ethylene glycol (Greek : *glykus*=sweet) is a thick, colourless liquid with a sweetish taste. It mixes with water and alcohol in all proportions, but is only sparingly soluble in ether ; it boils at about 197° C., so that the introduction of the second hydroxyl radical into the ethyl alcohol molecule considerably raises the boiling point. Chemically, it behaves like a di-primary alcohol, reacting with sodium metal to form a mono- and a di-sodium derivative and with acids to form mono- and di- esters. For example, when hydrogen chloride is passed into glycol heated to 100° C., ethylene chlorohydrin, $CH_2Cl \cdot CH_2OH$, is formed, while at higher temperatures the second hydroxyl is displaced, giving ethylene dichloride. The di-esters are also formed with acetyl chloride and with phosphorus pentahalide.

The oxidation products of glycol are interesting ; each of the —CH_2OH groups may be oxidized first to an aldehyde group, —CHO, and finally to a carboxylic group, —COOH, giving a variety of products thus :

$$\begin{matrix} CH_2OH & CH_2OH & CHO & CHO & COOH \\ | & | & | & | & | \\ CHO & COOH & CHO & COOH & COOH \\ \text{glycollic} & \text{glycollic} & \text{glyoxal} & \text{glyoxylic} & \text{oxalic} \\ \text{aldehyde} & \text{acid} & & \text{acid} & \text{acid} \end{matrix}$$

Of these the first, which is a hydroxy aldehyde, is obtained by gentle oxidation of glycol with hydrogen peroxide in the presence of a ferrous salt ; the other products are formed by oxidation with nitric acid under varying conditions.

Hydroxy-Carboxylic Acids. Glycollic acid is acetic acid in which one hydrogen atom has been replaced by a hydroxyl group ; it is therefore hydroxy-acetic acid, $CH_2(OH) \cdot COOH$. It is prepared by boiling the potassium salt of chloroacetic acid with water, a reaction similar in nature to the formation of ethyl alcohol from ethyl chloride. Since it contains both a carboxylic group and a hydroxyl group, glycollic acid behaves as a mono-basic acid and also as a primary alcohol. Thus, like the fatty acids, it forms salts with the metallic hydroxides and esters with the · alcohols, while, on the other hand, like the alcohols, it contains one hydrogen atom (that of the OH group) which may be replaced by a metal or an acetyl group. Glycollic acid is the first member of a homologous series of acids of this type, each of which may be regarded as an oxidation product of the corresponding glycol, or derivatives of the corresponding fatty acid. Carbonic acid or hydroxy-formic acid, $HO \cdot COOH$, is really the lowest member, but exists only in dilute aqueous solution.

The third member is hydroxy-propionic acid, and since in propionic acid, $CH_3 \cdot CH_2 \cdot COOH$, there are two alternative carbon atoms to which the OH group may be attached, two isomeric forms of this acid are known. These are distinguished by the Greek letters alpha and beta, according as the OH group is attached to the carbon atom nearer to the carboxyl group or to the one farther away. β-hydroxy-propionic acid, usually called hydracrylic acid, $CH_2OH \cdot CH_2 \cdot COOH$, is relatively unimportant; it can be obtained by boiling β-chloro-propionic acid, $CH_2Cl \cdot CH_2 \cdot COOH$, with water ; when oxidized by chromic acid, the $-CH_2 OH$ group is converted into $-COOH$, yielding malonic acid, $COOH \cdot CH_2 \cdot COOH$.

Lactic Acid. $_\alpha$-hydroxy-propionic acid or lactic acid, $CH_3 \cdot CHOH \cdot COOH$, is a substance of great interest. It derived its name because of its production during the lactic fermentation of the sugars and starches in milk (*see* Lesson 43, Vol. 5, p. 177). The chemistry of the souring of milk may be represented empirically by the equation

$$C_{12}H_{22}O_{11} + H_2O \rightarrow 4C_3H_6O_3$$
lactose or milk sugar $\qquad$ lactic acid

and that of the butyric fermentation, studied by Pasteur, thus

$$2C_3H_6O_3 \rightarrow C_4H_8O_2 + 2CO_2 + 2H_2$$

Lactic acid may also be obtained by heating ·-chloro-propionic acid with water or dilute aqueous alkalis (cf. glycollic acid). Like the other carboxylic acids, lactic acid behaves as a mono-basic acid, forming metallic salts called lactates, e.g. Ca $(C_3H_5O_2)_2 \cdot 5H_2O$. It differs from hydracrylic acid in containing the $>CHOH$ group, and consequently shows many of the reactions of a secondary alcohol.

The chief interest in lactic acid lies in the fact that it exists in three forms, all of which possess the same structural formula and are almost identical in chemical and physical properties. They can, however, be distinguished by the use of plane polarized light. Thus when a ray of polarized light is passed through a layer of lactic acid obtained from sour milk, it emerges without any appreciable alteration. This form of the acid is therefore said to be *optically inactive*. If, however, we take muscular tissue, such as that contained in meat extract, and treat it suitably, we can obtain another form of lactic acid which differs from the sour milk acid in possessing the curious power of twisting or rotating the plane of polarized light towards the right. It is therefore said to be *optically active*, and since it rotates the plane of the light to the right, is called dextro-rotatory. It is known as sarco-lactic acid (Gk. *sarx* = flesh) or d-(dextro) lactic acid. Careful examination of optically inactive lactic acid revealed the fact that it consists of a mixture of dextro-rotatory acid and another form, identical chemically, but which causes polarized light to be deviated in the opposite direction, that is, to the left hand. This form is therefore known as laevo-rotatory or simply l-lactic acid. The optical rotations of d- and l- lactic acids are the same but they take place in opposite senses. These three forms of lactic acid provide one of the simplest examples of what is known as *optical isomerism*. This subject is dealt with in the next Lesson in this Course.

Oxalic Acid. Glycollic acid is produced when one of the $-CH_2OH$ groups of ethylene glycol is oxidized to $-COOH$; if both $-CH_2OH$ groups are oxidized to COOH, the resulting product is oxalic acid, formula $(COOH)_2$. Oxalic acid is the first member of a homologous series of dibasic acids, called the di-carboxylic acids; it occurs in rhubarb and other plants such as the dock and sorrel, usually in the form of the potassium or calcium salts. It is prepared by oxidizing glycol, cane sugar or sawdust with nitric acid or atmospheric oxygen. Oxalic acid is a white, crystalline solid, which dissolves readily in alcohol and fairly readily in water. When heated alone or with concentrated sulphuric acid it decomposes into CO, CO_2 and water. It is a dibasic acid and reacts with bases to form both acid and normal salts, which, with the exception of those of the alkali metals, are only sparingly soluble or insoluble in water, e.g. $CaC_2O_4 \cdot H_2O$.

Malonic acid, the next member of the di-carboxylic acids, formula $CH_2 \begin{cases} COOH \\ COOH \end{cases}$, has already been mentioned as an oxidation product of hydracrylic acid. The third member is succinic acid, $\begin{vmatrix} CH_2 \cdot COOH \\ CH_2 \cdot COOH \end{vmatrix}$, which occurs in amber and also in many plants and in certain animal secretions. It is also formed during the alcoholic fermentation of sugar and in the oxidation of fats with nitric acid.

Tartaric and Citric Acids. Just as it is possible to form hydroxy-monocarboxylic acids, so by replacing the hydrogen atoms of the CH_2 groups with hydroxyls it is possible to obtain hydroxy-dicarboxylic acids. The most important of these acids is tartaric acid or dihydroxy-succinic acid $\begin{vmatrix} CH(OH) \cdot COOH \\ CH(OH) \cdot COOH \end{vmatrix}$ which occurs in many vegetable and fruit juices, in particular the juice of grapes and the berries of the mountain ash. It is obtained from argol or tartar, which is deposited in wine vats during the later stages of the fermentation of the grapes. Tartaric acid may be prepared in the laboratory from dichloro-succinic acid; it is a white, crystalline solid, which melts at 167° C. and, like other dicarboxylic acids, forms both normal and hydrogen salts. Of these the potassium hydrogen salt, $\begin{vmatrix} CH(OH) \cdot COOH \\ CH(OH) \cdot COOK \end{vmatrix}$ also called cream of tartar, is interesting as it is one of the few insoluble potassium salts, and is used as a means of detecting potassium in qualitative analysis (*see* Lesson 38, Volume 5, page 153). When potassium hydrogen tartrate is heated with antimonous acid and water, potassium antimonyl tartrate is formed.

Tartaric acid provides a classical instance of optical isomerism, four distinct modifications of this substance being known.

Citric acid is closely allied to tartaric acid. It has the formula $C_6H_8O_7$ and, like tartaric acid, occurs in the free state in many fruit juices, especially those of the citrous fruits such as lemon, orange and also in gooseberry and raspberry. It is a hydroxy-tricarboxylic acid and, like phosphoric acid, forms three classes of salts. Both tartaric and citric acids are used in preparing effervescent salts.

LESSON 46

Atom Grouping in Organic Molecules

THE use of graphic or structural formulae as a means of indicating the relationships which exist between the atoms in the molecule has already been emphasized. In such formulae each individual valency is represented by a single line or a point, which signifies that the particular atoms connected in this way are directly attached to one another. This method of representing the structure of organic molecules graphically was first employed by the French chemist Kekulé ; it embodied the two assumptions that the carbon atom in organic molecules is always tetravalent and that it readily links up with other carbon atoms to form a chain, the links of which may be a single valency bond (C—C), a double bond (C=C) or a triple bond (C≡C). Applying these principles to the paraffin or open-chain hydrocarbons, we see that in the case of each of the first three members, CH_4, C_2H_6 and C_3H_8, there is only one possible way of writing the formula of the molecule ; Kekulé's theory, therefore, agrees with the experimental fact that only one form of each of these three substances is known. When, however, we come to butane, we find two distinct isomeric compounds having the constitution C_4H_{10}, which agrees with Kekulé's theory that there are two possible ways of arranging the atoms in the molecule graphically, thus

normal butane
(b.pt. 0.5° C)

iso-butane
(b.pt. – 10.5° C).

With pentane three formulae are possible and three isomers are known ; as the number of carbon atoms in the molecule increases, the number of isomers also becomes larger, as many as 802 being theoretically possible in the case of $C_{13}H_{28}$. This form of isomerism is known as *structural isomerism*, since it is concerned with substances which have the same molecular formula but different structural formulae. In general we may say that any of the higher members of a homologous series of open-chain carbon compounds may exhibit this character of structural isomerism.

Molecules in Space. It has been mentioned that two distinct isomeric forms of lactic acid are known, which are almost identical chemically and differ only in their optical activity. Since both of these acids have the same structural formula :

$$\begin{array}{c} H \\ | \\ CH_3-C-COOH, \\ | \\ OH \end{array}$$

the existence of isomerism could not be accounted for by means of the Kekulé theory. It was instances of this kind which suggested that the two-dimensional formulae of Kekulé did not give a true picture of the configuration of molecules, and led to the development of the theory of *stereo*, or *spatial, isomerism* ; stereo-isomers are defined as substances which have the same molecular formula but differ in their molecular configurations in a manner which can best be explained to the student by examples.

The best example of this type is furnished by tartaric acid ; in fact, it was to the classical investigations of the brilliant French chemist, Louis Pasteur, into the nature of this acid that the discovery of stereo-isomerism was largely due. Four distinct forms of tartaric acid, each having the constitutional formula $C_4H_6O_6$, are known. The acid obtained from grape-juice is optically active ; it rotates the plane of polarized light towards the right—in other words, is *dextro-rotatory*. When the mother-liquor left over after the extraction of this acid is crystallized, a second acid is obtained which has the same chemical properties and therefore the same structural formula as tartaric acid; it differs however, in some physical properties, and in particular it is *optically inactive*—it is known as *racemic acid*. Sodium ammonium salts of these two acids can be readily prepared in the laboratory, and when dissolved in water they show similar differences in optical properties to those of the acids themselves.

It was while examining these properties that Pasteur discovered in 1848 that the two salts also differed in crystalline form. Thus while all perfect crystals of the salt obtained from d-tartaric acid, when examined under the microscope, had a configuration like that of d, in Fig. 1, the crystals of the salt from racemic acid were of two kinds, one of which was identical with the d form, and the other had the form shown as l in the figure; the two

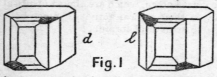

Fig. 1

forms were, in fact, related to each other as mirror images, just as the right hand is the mirror image of the left. So distinct were the crystal forms that Pasteur was able to separate them merely by picking out the different shapes, and from these salts he prepared two tartaric acids, one of which was identical with d-tartaric acid, and the other was the same in all respects except that it was laevo-rotatory to the same extent as the d-acid was dextro-rotatory. It was therefore called *laevo-rotatory* or *l-tartaric acid*.

Pasteur followed up these brilliant researches by discovering a fourth isomeric acid, obtained by heating the cinchonine salt of tartaric acid. This form, called *meso-tartaric acid*, resembled racemic acid in being optically inactive but unlike the latter, when converted into the sodium ammonium salt, it gave crystals of one form only.

Molecules and Light. The explanation of these phenomena was advanced simultaneously in 1874 by the French chemist Le Bel and the great Dutch chemist, van't Hoff. They pointed out that while the molecules of optically inactive substances, such as ethyl alcohol, acetic acid and so on, possessed a plane of symmetry, substances which showed optical activity had no such symmetry within the molecule; that is, their molecules are asymmetric. For example, in the case of tartaric acid, represented in the Kekulé fashion thus:

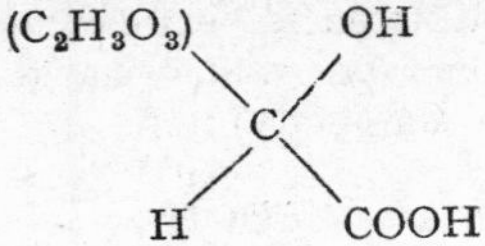

$$(C_2H_3O_3) \quad OH$$
$$C$$
$$H \qquad COOH$$

the carbon atom in the centre, to which four different groups are attached, has no plane of symmetry ; such a carbon atom is therefore termed an *asymmetric carbon atom*, and it is now known that all optically active molecules possess an asymmetric carbon atom. If the asymmetry of the molecule is destroyed, it loses its optical activity ; for example, when optically active sarco-lactic acid is reduced with hydrogen iodide it forms optically inactive propionic acid, as might be expected from a consideration of the formulae of these two compounds, viz.,

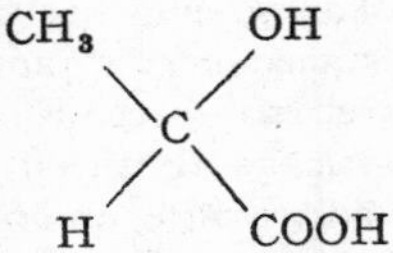

$$CH_3 \quad OH \qquad\qquad CH_3 \quad H$$
$$C \qquad\qquad\qquad C$$
$$H \qquad COOH \qquad\quad H \qquad COOH$$
sarco-lactic acid. 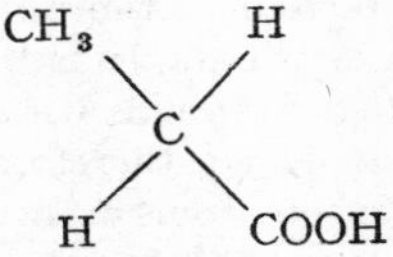 propionic acid.

As a result of Pasteur's work and the discovery of optical isomers, it became obvious that organic molecules could not be truly represented in one plane as Kekulé had suggested, but that they were spatially distributed in three dimensions. This led Le Bel and van't Hoff to put forward their theory of the *tetrahedral carbon atom*, that is, that the carbon atom is, as it were, situated at the centre of a tetrahedron and that the four valencies are directed towards the corners. When the

Fig. 2

four solid angles of the tetrahedron are occupied by different atoms, as, for example, in lactic acid, we have the asymmetrical carbon atom, and two distinct forms are then possible. One of these corresponds, let us say, to the right hand and rotates the plane of polarized light to the right, and the other is the

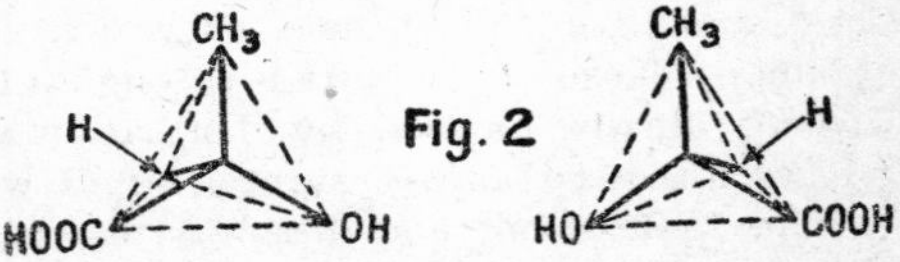

mirror image, or left hand, and rotates the plane to an equal
extent to the left. The differences between the four tartaric acids
can be readily explained on this basis, thus (Kekulé's plane
formulae are used for simplicity) :

$$
\begin{array}{ccc}
\text{COOH} & \text{COOH} & \text{COOH} \\
| & | & | \\
\text{H—C—OH} & \text{HO—C—H} & \text{H—C—OH} \\
| & | & | \\
\text{HO—C—H} & \text{H—C—OH} & \text{H—C—OH} \\
| & | & | \\
\text{COOH} & \text{COOH} & \text{COOH} \\
\text{d-tartaric acid.} & \text{l-tartaric acid.} & \text{meso-tartaric acid.}
\end{array}
$$

Racemic acid consists of a mixture of equal amounts of the
d- and l- acids, and is therefore inactive ; meso-tartaric acid is
inactive for a different reason. It will be seen from the formulae
that the upper half of the molecule of meso-acid has the same
configuration as the upper half of the molecule of d- acid, while
the lower half corresponds with the lower half of the l- molecule.
As might be expected, therefore, the optical activities of the two
asymmetric carbon atoms in the meso-acid are equal and opposite ;
the molecule is said to be internally compensated.

Tri-hydric Alcohols. Just as paraffins containing two or more
carbon atoms can be converted into di-hydric alcohols, so those
containing three or more carbon atoms may be converted into
alcohols having three hydroxyl groups. Of these trihydric
alcohols, glycerol, sometimes called glycerin, $CH_2(OH)CH$
$(OH)CH_2(OH)$, is the simplest and the most important. Its
preparation from fats and oils as a by-product in the manufacture of soap was mentioned in Lesson 43 (Volume 5, page 177) ;
the " spent lye " from the soap is filtered and evaporated, the
product cleansed by filtration through animal charcoal, and the
glycerol finally purified by distillation in superheated steam.
Glycerol is a colourless, syrupy liquid with a sweet taste ; it
is very hydroscopic and dissolves readily in water and alcohol.
Since it contains three hydroxyl groups, it forms three kinds of
esters, called mono-, di-, and tri-glycerides. The triglycerides
of the higher fatty and some related unsaturated acids, such as
oleic acid, form the main constitutents of animal fats and vegetable oils. When added to a well-cooled mixture of concentrated

nitric and sulphuric acids glycerol is converted into glyceryl trinitrate, $C_3H_5(ONO_2)_3$, known technically as " nitro-glycerin." The formation of this compound is merely a process of esterification, the water being removed as it is formed by the sulphuric acid. Nitro-glycerin is a colourless, oil-like liquid with a sweet, burning taste ; it has a peculiar physiological action, causing dilation of the blood-vessels, and in the form of a 1 per cent alcoholic solution is used medicinally. It is extremely dangerous and when subjected to detonation of any kind it explodes with terrific force. When mixed with *kieselguhr*, a kind of diatomaceous earth, it is absorbed in large quantities, and was used in this form by Nobel (1863) to manufacture the well-known explosive dynamite.

Glycerol is fairly readily oxidized and, like glycol, gives rise to a great number of products, according to the manner in which it is treated. Of these the most important is glyceric acid, $CH_2(OH)CH(OH)COOH$, which resembles glycollic acid and is obtained when glycerol is carefully oxidised with dilute nitric acid.

LESSON 47

The Carbohydrates and Artificial Silk

THIS large group of substances, having the general molecular formula $C_x(H_2O)_y$, is one of the most important in organic chemistry. Besides being the principal components of all plant and animal foods, carbohydrates are of extreme economic and industrial value, furnishing the raw material for the manufacture of alcohol, paper and vegetable textiles, such as artificial silk. Carbohydrates may be divided into two large classes—the sugars, which are crystalline, sweet to the taste and soluble in water ; and the non-sugars, which are without crystalline form or amorphous, tasteless, and in general insoluble. In the latter class are included the starches and the celluloses.

The sugars fall into two groups—the monosaccharoses, having six carbon atoms and the general formula $C_6H_{12}O_6$—sometimes called the hexoses—and the di-saccharoses or double sugars, which contain 12 carbon atoms and have the general formula $C_{12}H_{22}O_{11}$. The former are not affected by dilute acids, but the latter undergo hydrolysis, one molecule of di-saccharose absorbing one molecule of water and yielding two molecules of the same or different mono-saccharoses.

The Mono-saccharoses. The chemical properties of these substances indicate that they contain five hydroyxl groups ; moreover, an analysis of their oxidation products leads to the conclusion that some contain an aldehyde group and are therefore aldehydo-alcohols, sometimes called aldehydic sugars or aldoses ; while others contain a ketonic group, $>C=O$, and are keto-alcohols or ketoses. Structurally, they may be represented thus :

Aldoses, including glucose, galactose and mannose.

$$H-\underset{OH}{\overset{H}{C}} - \underset{OH}{\overset{H}{C}} - \underset{OH}{\overset{H}{C}} - \underset{OH}{\overset{H}{C}} - \underset{OH}{\overset{H}{C}} - \underset{O}{\overset{H}{C}}$$

Ketoses, including fructose and sorbose.

$$H-\underset{OH}{\overset{H}{C}} - \underset{OH}{\overset{H}{C}} - \underset{OH}{\overset{H}{C}} - \underset{OH}{\overset{H}{C}} - \underset{O}{\overset{}{C}} - \underset{OH}{\overset{H}{C}} - H$$

Natural sugars are always optically active and, with one or two exceptions, are dextro-rotatory. The existence of a number of optical isomers in each case might be anticipated, as an examination of the formulae given above shows that the molecules contain several asymmetric carbon atoms. In fact, the large diversity of the sugars is partly due to this property of stereoisomerism.

Glucose and Fructose. The very important sugar, glucose, occurs in many fruits, particularly in the grape, from which it derives its name of grape-sugar. It is also produced in the blood in large quantities in the disease known as diabetes, and in these cases is formed from various carbohydrates of the diet and sometimes from proteins. Glucose is prepared—together with another hexose called fructose—when cane-sugar (sucrose) is decomposed under the action of a dilute acid or certain enzymes. It has been mentioned that glucose is dextro-rotatory—hence the name " dextrose " ; in fact, the concentration of a solution can be estimated by measuring the angle of rotation produced by a column of known length. The apparatus used for this purpose is called a polarimeter, or in this particular case a saccharimeter.

Being an aldehyde, glucose is a strong reducing agent, and when added to alkaline solutions of cupric salts causes a red deposit of cuprous oxide—Cu_2O—to form. The reagent generally used is known as "Fehling's solution," and is made up by mixing sodium or potassium hydroxide with copper sulphate solution.

Isomeric with glucose are mannose and galactose, the latter of which is formed, together with glucose, by the hydrolysis of lactose or milk-sugar. Both of these sugars are dextro-rotatory and, like glucose, readily ferment with yeast, producing ethyl alcohol and carbon dioxide (*see* Lesson 42, Volume 5, page 172).

Fructose, also called laevulose, occurs with glucose in sweet fruits and honey. It is readily prepared by the hydrolysis, or inversion, of cane-sugar and the addition of lime, which forms a sparingly soluble compound with fructose, while that formed with glucose dissolves readily. Fructose is laevo-rotatory—hence the name laevulose—and ferments with yeast, though less readily than glucose. It also reduces Fehling's solution to an equal extent, though even more rapidly than glucose.

Much brilliant work has recently been done on the synthesis of glucose and fructose by the great German chemist, Emil Fischer. Starting with formaldehyde CH_2O, which on treatment with milk of lime polymerizes to a sugar-like substance having the formula $C_6H_{12}O_6$ and known as formose, Fischer obtained another sugar, and by a series of rather complicated reactions he has succeeded in converting this into both glucose and fructose.

The Di-saccharoses. The three most important di-saccharoses are cane-sugar (sucrose), milk-sugar (lactose), and malt-sugar (maltose). Cane-sugar occurs in large quantities in the ripe sugar-cane and in beetroot, and in smaller amounts in sweet fruits. In the extraction of sugar, the canes are first crushed in a hydraulic press, the juice is then heated with milk of lime to remove the acids present, and the excess of lime precipitated by passing carbon dioxide into the liquid. The extract is filtered through animal charcoal, concentrated by evaporation in vacuo, and the crystals which form are separated from the syrupy mother-liquor (molasses) by means of centrifugal machines. In the extraction from beet the root is cut into slices and the sugar extracted with water at about 80° C. by a diffusion process; the extract is then treated as in the case of cane-sugar. The yellow or brown sugars made directly from cane or beet juice are known as raw sugar; further refinement is carried out by dissolving the raw sugar in water and filtering through animal charcoal, when most of the colour is removed.

Aqueous solutions of sucrose are dextro-rotatory, but when warmed with dilute acids or when subjected to the influence of the invertase ferment of yeast it hydrolyses, giving equal quantities of glucose and fructose. Since fructose is laevo-rotatory to a greater extent than glucose is dextro-rotatory the resulting solution is laevo-rotatory, and this process of hydrolysis is therefore usually referred to as the inversion of cane-sugar. Chemically, sucrose is a non-reducing sugar—that is, it does not reduce Fehling's solution, and its properties indicate that it contains eight hydroxyl groups.

It is of interest to notice that sucrose is of even greater import-ance as a food than starch, and that among the Western nations each person consumes annually an amount of sugar almost equal to his own weight. Like fats, carbohydrates are necessary sources of energy, but are consumed much more rapidly by the animal organism and give rise to considerably less heat.

Starch and Cellulose. The second class of carbohydrates are highly complex bodies, having the general formula $[C_6H_{10}O_5]_n$ where n represents a rather large number. Since these compounds appear to be formed by the combination of a number of molecules of mono or di-saccharoses with the loss of water, they are usually grouped together under the name *poly-saccharoses*.

Starch is one of the most abundant products of plant life ; it occurs in large quantities in all kinds of grain, as, for example, wheat, barley, maize, rice, and also in potatoes, arrowroot, sago and tapioca. It forms a very important plant food, and under the influence of enzymes is converted into the simpler soluble sugars or the more complex gums and celluloses. When viewed under the microscope it appears to be made up of striated granules, which have a definite size and shape depending on the source from which the starch is obtained. Some typical starch grains in the cells of an orchid plant are shown in the microphotograph in Volume 2, Plate 23. Starch is used commercially chiefly for stiffening linen and also as an adhesive and in the production of alcohol. It is obtained in quantities by digesting potatoes, maize, or rice with water and removing the suspended starch mechanically. It is insoluble in cold water, but in boiling water the granules burst, forming an opalescent solution which sets to starch paste on cooling.

Artificial Silk. Cellulose in the form of cotton or wood pulp forms the basis of artificial silk. The general method of production is to dissolve the cellulose in some suitable solvent or convert it into some soluble form, such as cellulose nitrate, xanthate or acetate, and then to force the solution through fine capillary orifices into some substance which reprecipitates the cellulose or cellulose derivative. The silk is thus obtained in the form of very fine filaments, which compose the thread woven into fabrics. It is important to notice that artificial silk, or rayon, as it is more properly styled, is not silk at all, being entirely different from natural silk, which is a protein material containing nitrogen.

For fuller details of the character and chemical properties of the carbohydrates the student is advised to read the chapter on this subject in " Organic Chemistry," by J. Read.

LESSON 48

Benzene and Its Derivatives

ORGANIC compounds may be classed into two large divisions, which are distinguished by fundamental structural differences. The first of these, which includes the paraffins, the olefins, the acetylenes and their derivatives, and is referred to as the aliphatic (Gk. *aleiphar*, fat) or fatty group, we have already considered at some length. The second division includes benzene and its derivatives, and is known as the aromatic group on account of the peculiar odour which most of these substances possess. As we have seen, aliphatic compounds are characterized by having an open chain-like structure ; aromatic compounds, on the other hand, contain what is called a closed chain or benzene nucleus. It is of interest to notice that the aliphatic group which includes the fats, carbohydrates and proteins, is of much greater biochemical significance than the aromatic group. The latter came into prominence as a result of the discovery of the first coal-tar dye by the great English chemist W. H. Perkin, in 1856, and the importance of coal-tar products is mainly scientific and industrial, as in the manufacture of dyes, perfumes, explosives, antiseptics and illuminants.

Coal-Tar Products. Benzene derivatives are constituents of many essential oils and of some petroleums, but by far the most important source of these substances is the tar obtained during the production of coal gas by the destructive distillation of coal. In the manufacture of gas, coal is heated to a temperature of about 1,000º C. in an air-tight iron or clay retort. The more volatile products are driven off and first passed through air condensers, where a considerable quantity of coal-tar and also a strong-smelling yellow liquid, which is known as gas-liquor, separate out.

The uncondensed gases pass through water scrubbers and purifiers, which remove the last traces of ammonia and also such impurities as carbon dioxide, sulphuretted hydrogen, and so on ; the purified gas, which consists mainly of hydrogen and methane with small amounts of carbon monoxide and unsaturated hydro-carbons such as acetylene and ethylene, is led into the gas holder for use as a source of heat and light. The products in the condensing tanks separate into two layers, the lower of which is the thick, black, oily liquid known as *tar*, and the upper the gas-liquor, from which most of the ammonia and ammonium salts of commerce are obtained. The solid residue left behind in the retorts is known as *coke*, and amounts to about 70 per cent of the coal.

Coal-tar is said to contain about 300 substances. The constituents of the tar are first separated by means of fractional distillation, the vapours being condensed over comparatively short ranges of temperature in long iron or lead worms immersed in water. The distillate is collected in fractions, the composition of which is given in the table below. The light oil is further

FRACTIONAL DISTILLATION OF COAL-TAR

Fraction	Temperature	Constituents
1. Light oil or crude naphtha	up to 170° C.	B e n z e n e, toluene, xylenes.
2. M i d d l e o i l or carbolic oil	,, ,, 230° C.	Phenols, naphthalene and cresols.
3. H e a v y o i l o r creosote oil	,, ,, 270° C.	Cresols, etc.
4. Anthracene oil or green oil	,, ,, 400° C.	Anthracene.
5. Pitch	residue	

purified and then separated into its constituent substances by refractionation. This yields pure and commercial benzene (b.pt. 80° C.), toluene (b.pt. 110° C.), xylene (b.pt. 138°-142° C.) and also some crude higher boiling compounds known commercially as solvent naphtha. The middle oil is centrifuged to remove the crystalline naphthalene which separates out, and the mother-liquor, after suitable treatment, .yields pure phenols and also cresols. The heavy creosote oils are used without further treatment as fuels and as a preservative for timber. The anthracene oil is allowed to crystallize, and the crystals of anthracene are removed, warmed and pressed.

The more or less elementary substances given in col. 3 of the table are called " primaries " ; they are the source of hundreds of secondary products, known as " intermediates," which are obtained by various chemical processes such as nitration, sulphonation, oxidation, reduction, and so on. Thus, to mention a few typical products, benzene yields nitro-benzene, from which aniline and many azo dyes are made ; toluene yields nitrotoluenes, benzaldehyde, benzoic acid, etc. ; phenol yields nitrophenol ; naphthalene yields naphthols, and anthracene yields anthraquinone, parent substance of many dye-stuffs.

Benzene and Derivatives. This substance, which has the constitutional formula C_6H_6, is the first member of a homologous series of which the next two members are toluene and xylene. Almost the whole of the benzene of commerce—known as " benzol "—is obtained from coal-tar, though small amounts are also present in some petroleums and in the tar obtained from the destructive distillation of wood. Coal-tar benzene, even after careful purification, contains traces of a sulphur compound called thiophene, C_6H_4S, which resembles benzene so closely in physical and chemical properties that it is a matter of some difficulty to separate these two substances. Thiophene, however, reacts with concentrated sulphuric acid and can be removed by shaking the benzene with this reagent. Benzene has been synthesized by the polymerization of acetylene in red-hot tubes ($3C_2H_2 \rightarrow C_6H_6$), and is prepared in the pure state by heating sodium, or calcium benzoate with soda-lime (compare the production of methane from sodium acetate). Benzene is a colourless, mobile liquid with a characteristic sweetish smell ; it burns with a luminous smoky flame, boils at 80.4° C., does not mix with water, but mixes readily with organic liquids, and as it dissolves fats, resins, rubber, etc., it is widely used as a solvent and also for cleansing purposes.

Chemically, benzene is a very stable compound; it is not affected by boiling with concentrated alkalis, and is decomposed only very slowly by such strong oxidizing agents as potassium permanganate or chromic acid (contrast acetylene). Under certain conditions, however, it reacts with nitric acid to form nitro-benzene, with sulphuric acid to form benzene sulphonic acid, and, in the absence of light, with the halogens, a reaction greatly accelerated by the presence of iodine or iron. In each of these cases the resulting compound is a *substitution product*, not an addition product, which at first sight is curious in view of the apparently unsaturated nature of the benzene molecule, viz. C_6H_6. It was this peculiar stability of benzene, as well as some other reactions—such as its formation from acetylene by a sort of molecular condensation—and also the fact that, when vigorously oxidized, it is decomposed into carbon dioxide and water and yields no intermediate compounds, that led the French chemist Kekulé to put forward the celebrated theory of the benzene ring. According to Kekulé, the six carbon atoms are united to one another in the form of a closed ring, on the outside of which, so to speak, are attached the six hydrogen atoms, one to each carbon atom. Since the carbon atoms are distributed symmetrically, they form a hexagon-like structure as shown in the diagrams (Figs. 1, 2, 3 and 4) above.

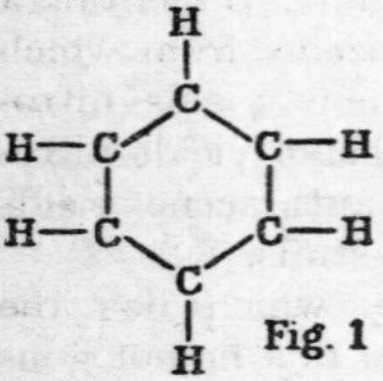

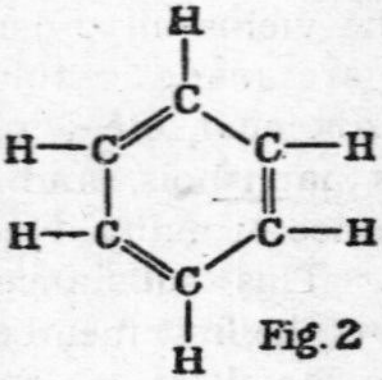

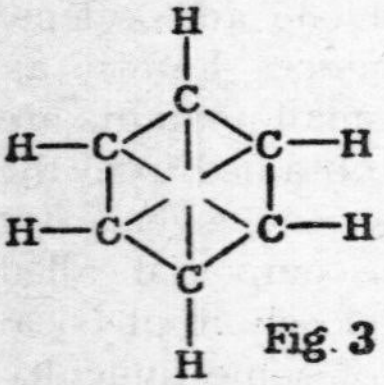

It will be noticed, however, that in Fig. 1 the carbon atoms are only trivalent, and as carbon is assumed to be tetravalent in all its organic compounds, Kekulé introduced alternate double bonds into the ring as shown in Fig. 2. Because of the great stability of the benzene nucleus as compared with unsaturated double-bonded hydrocarbons, objections were later raised to this formula and the " centric formula," Fig. 3, in which the spare carbon valencies are directed towards the centre of the ring, was suggested as an alternative. This point is, however, of minor importance, the benzene ring being briefly designated by a hexagon as shown in Fig. 4.

Nomenclature of Benzene Compounds. In the abbreviated formula the hydrogen atoms are omitted, and the presence of an atom or group at one of the corners of the hexagon indicates that the hydrogen atom at this particular point has been replaced by the atom or group shown. Each of the six hydrogen atoms may be replaced in this way by a substituting atom or group— sometimes called a " substituent "—as, for example, in compounds like di-nitrobenzene, $C_6H_4(NO_2)_2$, tetrachlor-benzene, $C_6H_2Cl_4$, hexa-carboxy-benzene, $C_6(COOH)_6$, and so on. When one substituent group has been introduced, the resulting compound obviously exists in one form only, since the benzene ring is symmetrical. The introduction of a second substituent, however—either the same as the first or different—can take place in three different positions in the molecule. There are, therefore, three isomeric di-substituted compounds. To facilitate matters of nomenclature the carbon atoms in the ring are numbered in a clockwise direction as shown in Fig. 4 ; the three isomeric di-nitrobenzenes are then written graphically as follows :

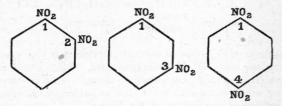

they are also distinguished by the prefixes ortho-, meta- and para- (more shortly o-, m- and p-), according as the substituents are in the 1 : 2, the 1 : 3 or the 1 : 4 positions, as seen above. Substitution in the para- position leads to a symmetrical molecule.

Similarly, there are three isomeric tri-substituted benzenes, three tetra-substituted benzenes, and so on. It is interesting to note that the existence of the large number of known isomeric benzene compounds was of considerable importance in confirming the theory of the benzene ring propounded by Kekulé.

LESSON 49

More Derivatives of Benzene

BENZENE forms a homologous series of compounds having the general formula C_nH_{2n-6}, the higher members of which are obtained when the hydrogen atoms of benzene are replaced by alkyl groups. The second member, methyl-benzene or toluene, $C_6H_5 \cdot CH_3$, exists in one form only; but the next, having the molecular formula C_8H_{10}, occurs in four isomeric forms—ethylbenzene, $C_6H_5 \cdot C_2H_5$, and the three dimethylbenzenes usually known as the xylenes, having the formula $C_6H_4(CH_3)_2$. It is obvious that the number of possible isomers increases rapidly with the number of carbon atoms.

Two general methods are used for the preparation of these compounds and are of considerable importance. In the first, known as *Friedel and Crafts' reaction*, benzene or one of its homologues is treated with an alkyl halide in the presence of anhydrous aluminium chloride; the reaction in the case of the preparation of toluene may be written:

$$C_6H_5 \cdot H + Cl \cdot CH_3 \rightarrow C_6H_5 \cdot CH_3 + HCl$$

benzene   methyl   toluene
         chloride

By using a large excess of methyl chloride it is also possible to prepare the di- and tri-methylbenzenes. The second method, discovered by Fittig and known as *Fittig's reaction*, consists in heating a halogen derivative of the aromatic hydrocarbon with an alkyl halide and sodium metal, thus:

$$C_6H_5 \cdot Br + 2Na + I \cdot CH_3 \rightarrow NaI + NaBr + C_6H_5 \cdot CH_3$$

Like benzene itself, these homologues are all comparatively stable, but yield nitro and sulphonic derivatives; on treatment with strong oxidizing agents the attached alkyl groups—known as side chains—are oxidized, being ultimately converted into carboxyl groups.

The nomenclature of benzene derivatives has been systematized by the adoption of the names " phenyl " for the benzene radical, C_6H_5-, sometimes written Ph ; " phenylene " for the $C_6H_4<$ radical ; " benzyl " for the toluene radical, $C_6H_5CH_2-$, and so on.

Nitro Compounds of Benzene and the Production of Aniline.
When an aromatic hydrocarbon is treated with a mixture of concentrated nitric acid (12 parts) and sulphuric acid (16 parts) at ordinary temperatures, a process called nitration takes place, one hydrogen atom being replaced by a nitro (NO_2) group giving a mono-nitro compound. Thus benzene yields nitrobenzene according to the equation :

$$C_6H_6 + HNO_3 \rightarrow C_6H_5 \cdot NO_2 + H_2O.$$

If the acid mixture is present in large excess and the liquid heated, di- and tri-nitro compounds are formed ; in the case of benzene, the principal product is meta-dinitrobenzene. These aromatic nitro compounds are generally relatively insoluble in water, but dissolve readily in organic solvents such as benzene, ether, etc. Like the nitro-paraffins they are fairly stable, being unaffected by boiling caustic potash.

Nitrobenzene is perhaps the most important of this class of compounds, since on reduction it yields aniline, the source from which the aniline dyes are prepared. Nitrobenzene is a pale yellow oil, slightly heavier than water, and having an odour which resembles that of bitter almonds. Although the vapour is a fairly active poison, it is sometimes used under the name of " oil of mirbane " as a cheap perfume and as a flavouring essence. When treated with a reducing agent in acid solution, as, for example, hydrogen produced by the action of hydrochloric acid on tin, zinc or iron or—which is more usual—a solution of stannous chloride in hydrochloric acid, the nitro group is reduced to the amino group (NH_2), giving amino-benzene, a substance usually known as " aniline " (from *an-nil* the Arabic word for indigo). In practice the aniline is obtained combined with the acid in the form of a complex salt ; it is liberated by the addition of lime or caustic soda, and is separated by distillation in a current of steam or extraction with ether. This method of reducing aromatic nitro compounds to the corresponding amino compounds can be applied to practically all types ; in the case of di-nitro compounds it is possible, by stopping the reaction at the prescribed point, to reduce only one nitro group, the resulting product being called a nitraniline, e.g. $C_6H_4 {\textstyle {<}} {NO_2 \atop NH_2}$.

Aniline is a colourless oil of peculiar odour, which, together with analogous substances, yields the dyes of the rosaniline group, including magenta, fuchsine, and many others. Structurally, it is a primary amine and may be regarded as an ammonia molecule, in which one hydrogen atom has been replaced by the phenyl group. As might be expected, therefore, it retains some of the basic properties of ammonia; and although neutral to litmus, it reacts fairly readily with acids to form salts such as aniline hydrochloride $C_6H_5 \cdot NH_2 \cdot HCl$, and with acetylchloride to form a substance known as acetanilide, $C_6H_5 \cdot NH \cdot CO \cdot CH_3$. This compound is a flaky white, crystalline solid used medicinally under the name of antifebrin to reduce temperature in fever.

Other members of the benzene series also form primary amines, which are analogous to aniline and have similar chemical properties. The toluene compounds, or toluidines, of which there are three having the constitutional formula $CH_3 \cdot C_6H_5 \cdot NH_2$, are widely used in the production of dyes.

The Diazonium Reaction and the Azo Dyes. This reaction, discovered in 1858 by P. Griess, is probably the most important of the reactions of the aromatic amino compounds. It takes place whenever a primary amine, such as aniline or toluidine, having the NH_2 group attached directly to the nucleus, is treated with well-cooled nitrous acid; a mixture of sodium nitrite and sulphuric acid is generally used. In the case of aniline, the following reaction takes place:

$$C_6H_5 \cdot NH_2 + O \cdot NOH + HCl \rightarrow C_6H_5 \cdot N_2 \cdot Cl + 2H_2O$$
$$\text{phenyl diazonium chloride.}$$

Phenyl diazonium chloride is a typical diazo salt; these compounds are colourless, crystalline solids readily soluble in water. In the dry state they are explosively reactive and are therefore not isolated from their aqueous solutions. When heated, these solutions yield phenols, as, for example, C_6H_5OH; with concentrated halogen acids they give halogen derivatives such as C_6H_5I; while on treatment with a solution of a cuprous salt, such as cuprous chloride, in the presence of hydrochloric acid or cuprous cyanide in potassium cyanide solution, the diazonium group may be replaced by Cl, (CN), Br, I, and indirectly by COOH and other groups. This latter reaction is known as *Sandmeyer's reaction*, and is a valuable means of preparing derivatives of the aromatic hydrocarbons.

But perhaps the most important reaction of diazo salts is the so-called coupling reaction which is the basis of the production of the intensely coloured orange or red azo dyes. This reaction takes place with the separation of hydrochloric acid when a diazonium compound is added to a solution of a phenol in dilute caustic alkali or to tertiary aromatic amines (see below) dissolved in dilute acid :

$$\langle \rangle - N_2 \,\, \boxed{Cl + H} - \langle \rangle \,\, ONa \rightarrow$$

diazobenzene   phenol in
chloride   NaOH

$$\langle \rangle - N{=}N - \langle \rangle \,\, ONa + HCl$$

sodium p-hydroxyazobenzene.

In general, the coupling takes place in the para position (*see* Lesson 48, page 149), and the bright colours of the resulting azo compounds are attributed to the grouping $-N = N-$, which is known as the *azo chromophore*. Chromophore is the name given to the group of atoms in the molecule to which the colour is considered to be due.

Compounds Related to Aniline. Aniline is a primary amine, it is also possible to have secondary amines, which are formed when a second hydrogen atom of ammonia is replaced by another hydrocarbon group, as in methyl aniline $CH_3 \cdot NH \cdot C_6H_5$, and tertiary amines, in which all three hydrogen atoms have been displaced, as in dimethylaniline $C_6H_5 \cdot N \cdot (CH_3)_2$. These more complicated amines also form the source of many dyes; dimethylaniline, for example, is used in the production of methyl orange, which is used as an indicator in the titrations involving acids and alkalis (*see* Lesson 39, Volume 5, page 158).

Some Other Derivatives of Benzene. When benzene is heated with concentrated sulphuric acid, it dissolves slowly, forming benzene-sulphonic acid, according to equation :

$$C_6H_5 \,\, \boxed{H + HO} \,\, SO_3H \rightarrow C_6H_5 \cdot SO_3 \cdot H + H_2O$$

This reaction illustrates an important difference between aromatic and aliphatic hydrocarbons. The sulphonic acids are comparatively stable, crystalline compounds which possess many of the properties of strong acids. Under the right conditions they can be fairly readily converted into other compounds, and so are of some importance in synthetic chemistry. For example, when fused with caustic potash, they yield phenols ; when heated with potassium cyanide, they are converted into cyanides ; with phosphorus pentachloride they give acid chlorides ; and with concentrated ammonia, amides, e.g. benzene sulphonamide, $C_6H_5 \cdot SO_2 \cdot NH_2$.

The Phenols and Related Compounds. The hydroxy compounds of the aromatic hydrocarbons, which correspond to the aliphatic alcohols, may be divided into two classes : the phenols, in which the hydroxyl groups have displaced hydrogen atoms of the benzene nucleus, and the aromatic alcohols, in which the hydroxyl group is attached to a side chain. As an example of the first class we may take phenol itself, also called hydroxy-benzene, C_6H_5OH, and of the second, benzyl alcohol, $C_6H_5 \cdot CH_2OH$. Like the aliphatic alcohols, the phenols may be divided into monohydric, dihydric, trihydric, and so on, according as they have one, two, three or more hydroxyls combined directly with the carbon of the nucleus. In general, the phenols have weakly acidic properties reacting with sodium hydroxide to form phenates; like the alcohols, they react with phosphorus pentahalides and also give rise to esters and ethers.

LESSON 50

Carbolic Acid and Its Derivatives

In the preceding Lesson it was mentioned that the hydroxy compounds of the aromatic hydrocarbons are of two types, the phenols and the aromatic alcohols. The simplest member of the first class is ordinary phenol, also called carbolic acid, C_6H_5OH ; it is obtained in quantities from the middle oil extracted from coal-tar, but also by the hydrolysis of salts of diazo-benzene or by fusing benzene-sulphonic acid or its salts with caustic potash. When pure, phenol is a colourless crystalline solid which absorbs water readily and turns pink on exposure to the air. It acts as a protoplasmic poison, and is widely used as a disinfectant, germicide and as an antiseptic. When treated with dilute nitric acid, it yields a mixture of ortho (o-) and p-nitrophenol, but with a hot nitrating mixture (concentrated nitric and sulphuric acids) three nitro groups are introduced into the molecule, the product being $2 : 4 : 6$ trinitrophenol, or picric acid. This has the formula

and is a very important compound. It is a bright yellow. crystalline solid and was the first artificial dye used; it is also used as an explosive, known as lyddite. With an aqueous solution of ferric chloride, phenol produces a deep violet colour, a reaction which is used as a test for this substance. It also forms the basis of a number of valuable medicinal compounds such as salicylic acid, aspirin and phenacetin, also of many important dyes, as, for example, phenolphthalein.

The next homologue of phenol is hydroxy-toluene, which exists in three isomeric forms (o- m- and p-) usually called the cresols. These substances occur in coal-tar and can be prepared by the methods available for phenol. The cresols are less toxic than phenol and better antiseptics; they are used for this purpose under the name of lysol. Of the higher monohydric phenols, *thymol* is perhaps the most interesting; it has the odour of oil of thyme, in which it occurs, and is also used as an antiseptic; it has the constitution

Of the three (o- m- and p-) dihydric phenols, having the formula $C_6H_4(OH)_2$, *quinol* or *hydroxy-quinone* is the most important. It has the structure HO⟨ ⟩OH, is a strong reducing agent and is used as a photographic developer.

Three trihydric phenols are known, of which *pyrogallol* is the most interesting; like quinol, it is a strong reducing agent, and under the names "pyrogallic acid" or "pyro" is used as a developer in photography. It has the structure

$$
\begin{array}{c}
\text{OH} \\
\bigcirc \!\! \begin{array}{l} \text{OH} \\ \text{OH} \end{array}
\end{array}
$$

Aromatic Alcohols and Aldehydes. The aromatic alcohols in which the hydroxyl radical is introduced into a side chain, differ from the phenols in showing many properties which are identical with those of the aliphatic alcohols. For example, they form esters, ethers, aldehydes and ketones, usually by reactions similar to those by which the corresponding aliphatic compounds are prepared. They resemble the phenols, however, in reacting with nitric acid to form nitro-compounds, and with sulphuric acid to form sulphonic acids, reactions which are both due to the presence in the molecule of the benzene ring.

Benzyl alcohol, the first member of this series, $C_6H_5 \cdot CH_2OH$, is prepared by the hydrolysis of benzyl chloride ($C_6H_5 \cdot CH_2Cl$) with boiling aqueous sodium carbonate solution or by treating benzaldehyde with cold caustic potash. Like alcohol, it reacts with metallic sodium to form a sodium alcoholate, and with strong hydrochloric acid or phosphorus pentoxide to form benzyl chloride. On treatment with concentrated nitric acid it is oxidised to benzaldehyde, $C_6H_5 \cdot CHO$.

Salicylic alcohol, or saligenin, is another important aromatic alcohol; it has the formula $HO \cdot C_6H_4 \cdot CH_2OH$, and is therefore both a phenol and an alcohol. It is produced, together with glucose, by the hydrolysis, under the influence of enzymes, of a substance known as salicin, a glucoside occurring in the bark of the willow (*Salix*).

The oxidation of an aromatic alcohol such as benzyl alcohol results in the formation of an aldehyde which may be of two types, according as the alcohol (sometimes called carbinol) group, —CH_2OH, is attached to a side chain or to the nucleus itself. Compounds of the former type resemble the aliphatic aldehydes very closely and are relatively unimportant, but the second class differ in several respects. It is also prepared on a large scale directly from benzene by what is known as Gatterman's Reaction. The mixture of carbon monoxide and hydrogen chloride is passed

GENERAL GORDON
Charles George Gordon
(1833–85), after serving in
the Crimea, spent some
years in China and Egypt.
Returning to the Sudan in
1884, he was besieged in
Khartum, and killed by the
followers of the Mahdi.
BRITISH HISTORY 24

HONG KONG IN ITS EARLY DAYS. Before 1839 the island of Hong Kong was
merely a resort of Chinese fishermen, but in that year refugee English traders
from Canton established themselves on its shores, and two years later the island
was formally ceded to Britain by the Chinese Government. Kowloon, on the mainland opposite, was ceded in 1860, and further territory was leased in 1899. This
picture shows the port about the time of its cession. BRITISH HISTORY 24

BRITAIN'S SOVEREIGNS IN THE 20th CENTURY. Left, Edward VII (1841–1910). Eldest son of Queen Victoria and Albert Prince Consort, he was created Prince of Wales almost at birth, married Princess Alexandra of Denmark in 1863, and ascended the throne on the death of his mother in 1901. Dying in 1910, he was succeeded by his second son, George V (1865–1936), his eldest son, the Duke of Clarence, having died in 1892. King George, when Duke of York, married Princess Victoria Mary, daughter of the Duke and Duchess of Teck, in 1893.

BRITISH HISTORY 25

Photos, Stuart, Russell

QUEEN VICTORIA. This photograph shows the great queen as she appeared in the last years of her reign and was visualized by millions of affectionate subjects. She died in 1901. BRITISH HISTORY 25

Plate 18

Volume VI

PRESIDENT KRUGER (1825-1904). Born in Cape Colony, he trekked into the Transvaal as a boy and was president of the Transvaal republic 1883-1900. During the Boer War he fled to Holland and died in Switzerland.
BRITISH HISTORY 25

DAVID LLOYD GEORGE. Born 1863, he entered parliament in 1890 as Liberal member for Carnarvon. From 1908-15 he held office as Chancellor of the Exchequer and was Premier 1916-22.
BRITISH HISTORY 25

LEADERS IN THE TARIFF CONTROVERSY. Joseph Chamberlain (left ; 1836-1914) was M.P. for a Birmingham division from 1876 until his death—first as a Radical, then as a Unionist. Colonial Secretary in 1895, in 1903 he resigned to champion the cause of " Tariff Reform." On the opposite (Liberal Free Trade) side, one of the chief figures was H. H. Asquith (right ; 1852-1928), Chancellor of the Exchequer 1905-8, Premier 1908-16, and created earl of Oxford and Asquith in 1925.
BRITISH HISTORY 25

'GASSED.' Here in this famous picture by J. S. Sargent we see British soldiers, blinded by mustard gas, being led by a hospital orderly down to the dressing-station. BRITISH HISTORY 26

Photo, Imperial War Museum

BRITAIN'S FIGHTING CHIEFS. Left to right: Admiral Sir David Beatty (1871–1936). He won distinction at Jutland and in November, 1916, was appointed to the command of the Grand Fleet. In 1919 he was made an earl. Admiral Sir John Jellicoe (1859–1935) commanded the Grand Fleet 1914–16. In 1925 he was made an earl. Field-Marshal Sir John French (1852–1925) led the British Army in France from August, 1914, to December, 1915. He was created Earl of Ypres in 1921. Sir Douglas Haig (1861–1928) succeeded French as C.-in-C. He was created Earl Haig in 1919.

BRITISH HISTORY 26

Plate 20

Volume VI

with the hydrocarbon in the presence of anhydrous cuprous chloride and aluminium chloride.

Benzaldehyde is a colourless, refractive liquid with a pleasant smell like that of bitter almonds. It is used as a flavouring essence and in the manufacture of various dyes, and is obtained by the hydrolysis of amygdalin, a glucoside present in bitter almonds. Like the aliphatic aldehydes, it may also be prepared by the oxidation of benzyl alcohol or by heating a mixture of calcium benzoate and calcium formate. Benzaldehyde, and, in fact, aromatic aldehydes in general, resemble the fatty aldehydes in readily undergoing oxidation to form the corresponding acid and reduction to the corresponding alcohol. They differ from the fatty compounds in that they do not reduce Fehlings solution and, when shaken with caustic potash, they produce a mixture of the corresponding alcohol and acid, thus :

$$2C_6H_5 \cdot CHO + KOH \rightarrow$$
$$C_6H_5 \cdot CH_2OH + C_6H_5 \cdot COOK$$
$$\text{potassium benzoate}$$

Aromatic Ketones, Quinones and Acids. Like the aliphatic ketones, the aromatic ketones have the general formula $R \cdot CO \cdot R^1$, where R and R^1 may be the same or different radicals, one of which is aromatic. *Acetophenone*, $C_6H_5 \cdot CO \cdot CH_3$, is a typical ketone and is formed when calcium benzoate is heated with calcium acetate. It is a crystalline solid and is used as a hypnotic in medicine under the name of hypnone. When calcium benzoate is heated alone, *benzophenone* is formed ; it has the formula $C_6H_5 \cdot CO \cdot C_6H_5$ and resembles acetophenone very closely.

Aromatic hydrocarbons also yield another class of ketone-like compounds, in which the carbon atom of the ketone ($> C=O$) group is part of the benzene ring. These substances are generally di-ketones and are known as *quinones* ; the commonest quinones have the two carbonyl groups in the para or symmetrical position. *Quinone* itself, sometimes called p-benzoquinone, is formed by the oxidation of quinol or when aniline is oxidised with a mixture of sulphuric acid and potassium dichromate. On reduction with sulphurous acid, quinone is converted into quinol ; its molecule is written graphically as diagram on right.

All of these quinones crystallize in brightly coloured plates, which are generally yellow ; the colour is attributed to the presence in the molecule of the quinonoid-chromophore,

$$O = \langle\!\!\!=\!\!\!=\!\!\!\rangle = O$$

which is the basis of a large number of very important dye-producing compounds.

Two types of aromatic acid also exist, those which contain the carboxyl group (—COOH) attached to the benzene nucleus and those in which it is attached to a side chain. These two types are similar in chemical properties, both forming salts, esters, amides and so on in a manner exactly analogous to the fatty acids. In addition to the simple mono-carboxylic acids, di- and poly-carboxylic acids are known, and in most cases one or more hydrogen atoms of the nucleus may be replaced by other atoms or groups, such as—OH, —NO$_2$, —Cl, alkyl groups, and so on.

The simplest monocarboxylic acid is *benzoic acid*, $C_6H_5 \cdot COOH$, which occurs m the free state in gum benzoin, a naturally occurring resin, from which it may be obtained by sublimation. It is also prepared by oxidizing toluene or benzyl alcohol. Benzoic acid is a white crystalline solid, which dissolves in water and forms well-defined salts, called benzoates, and also esters. With phosphorus penta-chloride, it forms benzoyl chloride, $C_6H_5 \cdot CO \cdot Cl$, which reacts with ammonia to form benzamide, $C_6H_5 \cdot CO \cdot NH_2$ (compare acetamide). Benzoic acid is a powerful antiseptic and is used as a food preservative for coffee extracts, fruit juices and cordials.

The most important di-carboxylic acids are the three (ortho, meta, and para) *phthalic acids*, which have the formula $C_6H_4(COOH)_2$. They are prepared by oxidizing the corresponding xylenes, the ortho-compound being also obtained commercially by the oxidation of naphthalene with fuming sulphuric acid in the presence of a little mercury, which acts as a catalyst. The ortho acid, generally known simply as phthalic acid, is of great industrial importance, as it is the parent substance used in the production of indigotin (which furnishes artificial indigo), fluorescin, eosin, and many other dyes. For this purpose it is usually converted into phthalic anhydride, an "inner" anhydride formed when the acid is distilled, thus :

$$\text{C}_6\text{H}_4 \begin{array}{c} \text{COOH} \\ \text{COOH} \end{array} \rightarrow \text{C}_6\text{H}_4 \begin{array}{c} -\text{CO} \\ -\text{CO} \end{array} \text{O} + \text{H}_2\text{O}$$

Some aromatic amino and hydroxy-acids are of importance. *Anthranilic acid*, or o-amino-benzoic acid, $NH_2 \cdot C_6H_4 \cdot COOH$, is obtained from phthalic anhydride and is an intermediate product in the preparation of indigotin. *Salicylic acid*, or o-hydroxybenzoic acid, $C_6H_4(OH) \cdot COOH$, occurs in considerable quantities in the form of the methyl ester in oil of wintergreen ; it is obtained by the oxidation of salicylic alcohol. Owing to its phenolic character, salicylic acid is a powerful antiseptic and, as it has no appreciable smell, it is frequently used as a disinfectant in place of phenol ; it is also used medicinally, mainly as an anti-rheumatic. Gallic acid is a trihydroxybenzoic acid (3 : 4 : 5, that is, the hydroxyl groups are attached to the three adjacent carbon atoms in the ring, one place removed from the carbon atom to which the carboxyl group is attached ; *see* Lesson 48, page 149). It occurs in the free state and also as a glucoside in nut galls, tea, and other vegetable products, and is prepared by hydrolysing tannin with hot dilute acids. Like pyrogallol, gallic acid is a strong reducing agent, because of the ready oxidizability of the hydroxyl groups. With ferric salts, it gives a blue-black precipitate which forms the basis of the manufacture of inks. Ink consists essentially of a solution of gallic acid and a ferrous salt, together with a little sulphuric acid and a blue dye to give the solution a certain amount of permanent colour. On exposure to the oxygen of the air, the ferrous salt is immediately converted into ferric salt, which reacts at once with the gallic acid.

LESSON 51

Dyes and Dyeing Processes

NAPHTHALENE and anthracene both occur in fairly large quantities in coal-tar, and as they give rise to a number of intermediates which are extensively used in the dye industry, they are of considerable importance. Naphthalene, crystallizing in large lustrous flakes, which melt at 79° C. and have the characteristic odour of moth-balls, is the most abundant of the coal-tar hydrocarbons. It burns with a smoky, luminous flame, and before the days of electric light was often used to increase the luminosity of coal-gas. Naphthalene has the formula $C_{10}H_8$ and is therefore not a homologue of benzene; however, it shows many of the chemical properties characteristic of the aromatic hydrocarbons, as, for example, a tendency to form nitro compounds with nitric acid and sulphonic acids with sulphuric acid. Also, when mixed with an alcoholic solution of picric acid, it forms yellow, crystalline naphthalene picrate. Like benzene, it is a very stable compound, but when boiled with dilute nitric, chromic or sulphuric acid it is oxidized fairly rapidly, especially in the presence of mercury, the products being ortho-phthalic acid, carbon dioxide and water. This indicates that the molecule of naphthalene contains at least one ortho-di-substituted

benzene ring (*see* above), and as a result of other reactions, it was shown to consist of two closed chains of six carbon atoms "condensed" together in the ortho position, as shown in Fig. 1.

As in the case of benzene, the above structural formula was confirmed by a study of the isomerism of the various substitution products. It will be seen that there are two possible mono-substitution products (contrast benzene, which gives rise to only one in each case), and in order to simplify matters of nomenclature, the carbon atoms in the molecule are either numbered or lettered with the Greek letters alpha and beta, as shown in Fig. 2.

DYES AND DYEING PROCESSES

The most important derivatives of naphthalene are the naphthylamines, the sulphonic acids and the two naphthols. α-naphthylamine is prepared in a similar manner to aniline by the reduction of the nitro compound, which is formed when concentrated nitric acid acts on naphthalene. It has the formula $C_{10}H_7 \cdot NH_2$. When treated with concentrated sulphuric acid, naphthalene is converted into the mono-substituted acids, naphthalene α-*sulphonic acid* at 80° C. and β-*sulphonic acid* at between 160° and 200° C. Several other complex isomeric sulphonic acids may be obtained by the action of sulphuric acid on other

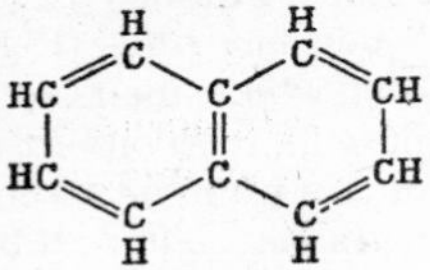

Fig. 1

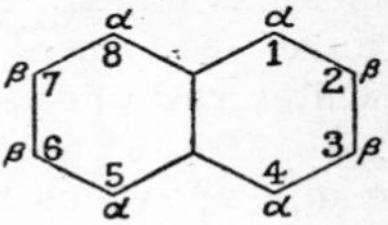

Fig. 2

Fig. 3

Fig. 4

Fig. 5

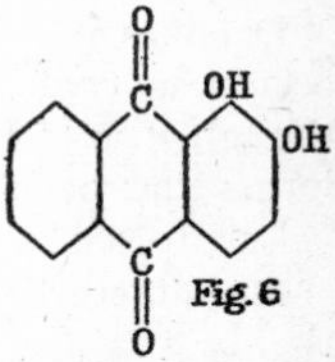

Fig. 6

naphthalene compounds, such as the naphthylamines ; of these probably the most important is the product formed from α-naphthylamine, known as *naphthionic acid* and having the formula $C_{10}H_6 \cdot (NH_2) \cdot SO_3H$. This substance, which may be diazotized in the ordinary way and also coupled with diazo salts (*see* Lesson 49, p. 154), is widely used in the production of Congo red and other dyes.

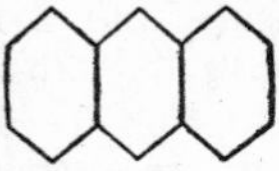

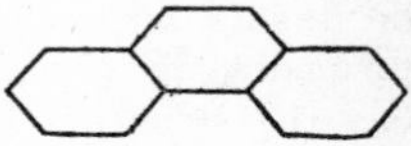

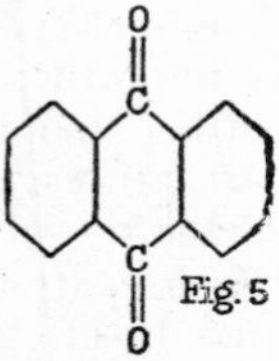

When these sulphonic acids are fused with caustic soda, they are converted into the naphthols (α- or β-). This reaction is similar to those by which the phenols are produced ; it is written thus :

$$C_{10}H_2 \cdot SO_3Na + NaOH \rightarrow Na_2SO_3 + C_{10}H_7 \cdot OH \text{ (a or β naphthol)}.$$

The naphthols resemble the phenols and since they also couple with diazo salts, they are of considerable importance in the dye industry.

Besides these substances, naphthalene is also the main source of *phthalic acid*, a compound which is extensively used in a manner described in the preceding Lesson in making synthetic indigotin, the main constituent of natural indigo dye.

Anthracene has the constitution $C_{14}H_{10}$, and has been shown by methods similar to those applied to naphthalene to consist of three " condensed " benzene rings (Fig. 3) ; it is a fairly stable, white crystalline solid which melts at 213° C. When oxidized with nitric or chromic acid, it is converted into a yellow, crystalline compound which has the quinone structure shown in Fig. 5, and is known as *anthraquinone*. This substance, when heated with concentrated sulphuric acid, forms a mono-sulphonic acid, which on fusing with caustic soda and a little potassium chlorate furnishes the very important dye known as *alizarin*. Alizarin has the structure shown in Fig. 6 ; it forms the basis of the Turkey red dye, which until recently was obtained exclusively from the madder plant.

Phenanthrene, $C_{14}H_{10}$, is isomeric with anthracene and also occurs in coal-tar. It has the structure shown in Fig. 4, and though it is of theoretical rather than commercial importance, it forms the basis of some substances, such as morphine, which belong to the class of compounds known as the vegetable alkaloids.

Manufacture of Dyes. As recently as eighty years ago, all the dyes in use were obtained directly from some natural source, and it was considered impossible for the chemist to manufacture in the laboratory the bright colours which are formed under the influence of life forces in Nature. This belief was rudely shaken in 1856 when W. H. Perkin, a young London student, while engaged in an abortive attempt to prepare quinine from aniline oil made from coal-tar products, prepared a synthetic purple dye, known as " mauveine " or Perkin's mauve. This was the first synthetic aniline dye.

At the present time many thousands of different dyes are made synthetically. Only a very few of these correspond to natural dyes, with which they are then chemically identical ; the great majority do not exist in Nature at all.

Chemical Composition of Dyes. Substances which are called dyes, in addition to being coloured, must also be able to " fix " themselves or be fixed to the fabric to be dyed in such a way that they remain reasonably fast to soap and water and also sunlight. Azobenzene, for example, is intensely coloured, but it is not a dye since it is readily removed by washing. Similarly when calico or cotton is treated with picric acid the cloth is coloured yellow but the colour dissolves in water, although picric acid is firmly fixed by wool or silk, and may be used to dye these fabrics.

The colour of dyestuffs is attributed to the presence in the molecule of certain groups of atoms called chromophores. Of these the most important are the nitro group ($N \lessgtr \begin{smallmatrix} O \\ O \end{smallmatrix}$), as in picric acid, and Martius' or naphthol yellow, the azo-chromophore ($-N=N-$) which gives rise to scarlet, brown or yellow dyes such as methyl orange, para-red, crocein scarlet and Bismarck brown, and the para- and orthoquinone rings, known as the quinonoid-chromophore, which is present in malachite green, the rosaniline or magenta dyes, fluorescin and eosin. The parent substance of any group of coloured compounds which contains the chromophore is usually known as the *chromogene*; it may or may not be a dye, and if not, is converted into a dye by the addition to the molecule of certain groups such as $-OH$, $-SO_3H$, $-NH_2$, $-NMe_2$, and so on, which are called *auxochromes*. It will be noticed that these groups are either acidic or basic, and different methods of applying the dye to the fabric must be adopted in each case.

LESSON 52

Chemistry of Drugs and Vitamins

I T is impossible to give here anything like a full account of the chemistry of medicines, but a short description is given of a group of complex nitrogenous compounds, known as the vegetable alkaloids, which constitute the active principles of most drugs, and are therefore of extreme importance. Most alkaloids contain carbon, hydrogen, nitrogen, and sometimes oxygen; they are usually crystalline solids—exceptions are coniine and nicotine, both volatile liquids—and are insoluble in water but readily soluble in such organic solvents as alcohol, ether, chloroform, and so on. Generally speaking, they may be considered to be derivatives of pyridine C_5H_5N—a nitrogenous ring compound having a similar structure to benzene, as shown on right, and quinoline, which has the formula C_9H_7N and the structure:

Chemically, they are tertiary aromatic bases (*see* Lesson 44, p. 130, on amines) and react with acids to form salts which are crystalline and usually soluble in water.

Alkaloids are very widely distributed in Nature, the most important occurring in such plants as the hemlock, poppy, deadly nightshade, tobacco plants, the cinchona tree and the nux vomica. They occur usually in the combined state with lactic, citric or tannic acids or some other acid peculiar to the particular plant in which they are found, and are extracted by treating the macerated plant with dilute acid, neutralizing the filtered solution with dilute alkali and recovering the precipitated alkaloid by filtration and extraction with ether or chloroform. Owing to the fact that many alkaloids often occur together, the final purification is usually a matter of some difficulty, but can be carried out by fractional crystallization and chemical treatment of various kinds. Most alkaloids give insoluble precipitates with tannic, picric and phosphomolybdic acids, and also, with a solution of mercuric iodide in potassium iodide, and these reactions are used as tests for the presence of these substances.

Coniine and Nicotine. The alkaloid of the spotted hemlock (*Conium maculatum*) has the relatively simple formula $C_8H_{17}N$. It is an oily, volatile liquid, having an unpleasant mouselike odour and a taste suggestive of tobacco. It is strongly basic and both the base and its salts are extremely poisonous, causing paralysis of the muscles of respiration.

The tobacco plant belongs to the same natural order as the deadly nightshade and henbane—the Solanaceae or Atropaceae—and it yields a very poisonous alkaloid, known as nicotine. This substance, which has the formula $C_{10}H_{14}N_2$, occurs combined with citric and malic acids, and can be obtained by boiling the leaves with a solution of milk of lime and extracting the alkaloid from the distillate with ether. Like coniine, it contains no oxygen and is a colourless oil with a pungent odour.

Smokers often describe as nicotine the oily mess which is apt to accumulate in a pipe. If this, or 1 per cent of it, were pure nicotine, a few drops only would suffice to end the smoker's career. Actually, nicotine is fairly readily oxidized, and practically all the nicotine in that portion of the tobacco undergoing combustion at any moment is oxidized away. A certain small amount, however, is volatilized by the warmth from the burning tobacco and is taken in by the smoker together with the smoke. This amount, though exceedingly small, is sufficient, in cases of excessive smoking, to cause very definite physiological effects known as nicotine poisoning, which gives rise also to the feeling of sickness and vertigo that sometimes accompanies the first attempts at smoking strong tobacco. With continual smoking, in moderation, the nervous system becomes inured to the small doses of alkaloid constantly being administered.

Atropine, Cocaine and Hyoscine. Atropine, hyoscyamine and hyoscine occur in the deadly nightshade (*Atropa belladonna*), henbane (*Hyoscyamus niger*) and other plants of the Solanaceae family. They can be extracted by pressing the leaves or the roots of the plants, mixing the juice with potash and extracting the alkaloid with chloroform. Atropine and hyoscyamine are isomeric, crystalline compounds having the formula $C_{17}H_{23}NO_3$, but they differ in melting point, optical properties and in their action on the body. As their names suggest, atropine is the principal alkaloid of the deadly nightshade and hyoscyamine of henbane ; the former possesses the remarkable property of causing the pupil of the eye to dilate and has an important use in ophthalmic surgery. Hyoscyamine can be converted into atropine by treatment with bases.

Hyoscine, which also occurs in henbane, has the formula $C_{17}H_{21}NO$, and in spite of the trivial change in constitution from the associated alkaloids, atropine and hyoscyamine, it possesses quite different physiological properties. One grain injected under the skin will arrest consciousness and cause sleep within sixty seconds, a potency exceeding that of morphine or hydrocyanic acid.

Cocaine has the same chemical formula as hyoscine and a close structural relationship to atropine. It is a colourless, crystalline compound from coca leaves, and is used in minor surgical operations as a local anaesthetic.

The Opium Alkaloids. The juice which exudes from the ripe capsules of a certain kind of poppy—*Papaver somniferum*—when dried, is known as opium. This extract contains at least

25 alkaloids as well as some peculiar acids, salts and some neutral principles such as albumen, glucose and fats. A dilute solution of opium in alcohol—about 1 grain in 15 minims—is known as laudanum. Morphine, which occurs to the extent of about 10 per cent in opium and has the formula $C_{17}H_{19}NO_3$, is the most important of this group ; it is obtained by extracting opium with boiling water, adding milk of lime, which precipitates all the other alkaloids, and filtering. The filtrate is then treated with ammonium chloride, boiled until ammonia ceases to be evolved, and the morphine, which crystallizes out on standing, is purified by recrystallization from alcohol. Morphine has a bitter taste and is extremely poisonous, one drop being a fatal dose. In small amounts, however, it has a pronounced narcotic and pain-soothing action, and is a very valuable drug.

Strychnine and Quinine. Strychnine, which is perhaps the most poisonous of all alkaloids, occurs in the seeds of the nux vomica ; it crystallizes in beautiful rhombic prisms, which melt at about 284° C., are practically insoluble in water and only sparingly soluble in organic solvents with the exception of chloroform. The structure of the strychnine molecule, which has the composition $C_{21}H_{22}N_2O_2$, is not definitely known, though it appears to contain a seven-atom ring. In minute doses, strychnine is used as a heart and respiratory stimulant ; half a grain (0·03 of a gram) has caused death in half an hour.

With the possible exception of morphine, quinine is the most important of the alkaloids. It is contained, together with four other closely allied substances, in the bark of the red cinchona tree, which is indigenous to South America and is now being cultivated on a large scale in India. It is obtained in the form of the sulphate by extracting the powdered bark with dilute sulphuric acid and purifying the resulting mixture of alkaloid sulphates by fractional crystallization. Quinine crystallizes in the form of colourless needles, which are only sparingly soluble in water and rotate the plane of polarized light to the left. Both the sulphate and the hydrochloride are soluble in water and are universally used to lower the body temperature in cases of fever and also as a specific remedy for malaria. "Ammoniated tincture of quinine" is made by dissolving the sulphate in aqueous alcohol containing ammonia.

Caffeine or Theine. Closely analogous to the vegetable alkaloids and interesting because it is the essential ingredient of both tea leaves (2–4 per cent) and coffee beans (1 per cent) is the substance known as caffeine or theine. This compound, which crystallizes in silky needles and is only sparingly soluble in water, is a derivative of xanthine, an intermediate product in the series of chemical changes by which the body substances known as nucleo-proteins break down into uric acid. Caffeine has the formula $C_8H_{10}N_4O_2$, and is really 1 : 3 : 7 trimethylxanthine. Unlike morphine and alcohol, caffeine is a true stimulant ; it possesses the remarkable property of preventing sleep purely by its immediate action on the brain, and its stimulation is even and balanced and has no subsequent reaction.

For more detailed information about the extraction and chemical properties of the alkaloids and the associated compounds, the student is referred to " Organic Chemistry " by J. Read, or " Plant Alkaloids " by Henry.

The Vitamins. Perhaps the most interesting and important discovery in connexion with the chemistry of vital processes is that of the vitamins. These substances, many of which have now been synthesized, are essential constituents in very small, sometimes infinitesimal, amounts of all food materials. Six different vitamins have been more or less identified ; they are usually known by letters of the alphabet. Vitamin A ($C_{20}H_{30}O$) is found in animal fats, being present in milk, butter, cheese and fish oil, especially cod-liver oil, and appears to be essential to growth. It is fairly readily oxidized when heated in air, as, for example, when milk is boiled in an open pan ; but it is not destroyed by the pasteurizing process, in which the milk is kept at a fairly high temperature in a closed vessel. Vitamin B is present in the germ of rice and other cereals, in green vegetables and fruit juices ; it was the absence of this vitamin which led to the neuritic disease, known as beri-beri, prevalent among Eastern Asiatics who lived mainly on fish and polished rice. Vitamin C ($C_6H_8O_6$) is generally known as ascorbic acid, since its absence from the diet leads to the dread disease known as scurvy ; this vitamin is present in fresh green vegetables and the juices of such fruits as the lemon and the orange, and the comparative rareness of scurvy in the British Navy nowadays is attributed to the compulsory issue of a daily ration of lime juice, introduced in 1804. Vitamin C is soluble in water and is often removed from vegetables in cooking. Vitamin D is invariably associated with Vitamin A in animal fats, especially in cod-liver oil ; its absence from the diet leads to the infantile disease known as rickets, once very common in over-crowded districts in industrial towns. In addition to the natural sources, Vitamin D can be produced artificially by the action of ultra-violet light, obtained either from a mercury lamp or from sunlight, on a complex substance known as ergosterol, which is present in the skin in small quantities. It is now called calciferol and has the formula $C_{28}H_{44}O$.

The discovery of the vitamins marks an important stage of progress in the elucidation of the chemistry of vital processes. Much information has already been obtained about the composition of foods, the requirements and functions of the human body, the causes and prevention of diseases, and it is perhaps not too fantastic to imagine that within the next few years chemistry may find an " open sesame " to the problem of prolonging the normal expectation of life, a problem which has so far resisted even the most penetrating inquiries.

Books Recommended for Further Study. " Catalysis in Theory and Practice," Rideal and Taylor (Macmillan) ; " Chemistry in Daily Life," Glasstone (Methuen) ; "Romance of Modern Chemical Discoveries," Prescott (Sampson Low) ; " Chemistry in the Service of Man," Findlay (Longmans).

This Lesson concludes our Course in Chemistry.

LESSON 19

The World's Timber Supplies

ENGLISH folk, accustomed to dells and dingles, coppices and spinneys, tree-clad slopes flanking lush meadows, are continually reminded of the circumstance that once England was forest-clad. The English arable is comprised of forest clearings and is marginal transitional land, excellent neither for trees, because it lacks water, nor for grain, because rainfall is excessive.

Man has cleared the primary forests of the northern hemisphere, except possibly in the timber stands of Siberia situated far from railway or the sea. Some of the cleared land is arable in Britain, Germany, Sweden ; much of it is secondary forest, straggling tree growth where Nature scantily fills the gaps left by the lumber-jack ; some of it is afforested land, timber factories where seedling trees, outplanted from nurseries, mature in majestic slowness—for a century is required to replace what has been removed within a day.

The great natural resources are minerals, timber and fish. The fish supply is thinned but slowly, and Nature almost seems to balance the fisher's destruction. Man digs for the coal, the iron ore, the bauxite, and Nature makes no renewal. In seeming compensation for the absence of increase is the durability of the product ; yet he is faced with a threatened shortage of the least durable mineral, coal.

Between these two lies timber, along with its accessory forest products. Neither renewed like the fish, nor utterly destroyed like the coal, the utility we extract from the trees has a more fluctuating value than either of the others. Like the coal, timber is steadily more difficult in the winning. Across the north of the world, on the colder, wetter, polar side of the great grasslands, are the temperate forests of deciduous and coniferous trees, which yield the soft woods, the easily workable timber— relatively cheap, because there are extensive natural supplies ; becoming dearer, since the suitable trees are now farther afield.

On the grand scale, from the slopes of the Rockies in British Columbia and Oregon, across the continent, to the somewhat exhausted lumbering areas of Quebec, Newfoundland and New England, beyond the sea in Scandinavia, Finland and Russia and beyond into Siberia, the temperate forest belt makes a brave show on the map; but Man has, from the point of view of a natural resource, made a travesty of the map. Instead of showing that in these areas timber trees exist and await the lumberer, the map-colours merely indicate the fact that trees of a sort do grow after a skimpy fashion.

The forest indications in part of the southern hemisphere—in southern Chile, in South Island, N.Z., in Australia—are not on the grand continuous scale of the north, and the timber is of negligible value. It is true that in New Zealand afforestation proceeds under such favourable conditions that timber threatens

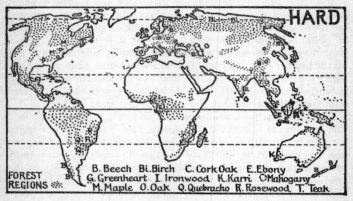

FOREST REGIONS

B. Beech Bi. Birch C. Cork Oak E. Ebony
G. Greenheart I. Ironwood K. Karri O. Mahogany
M. Maple O. Oak Q. Quebracho R. Rosewood T. Teak

to be more valuable to New Zealand than any other product, but the possible scale is so small that the total yield will have little more than a local value and the home-grown wood will but supplant imported timber.

Within the tropics occurs that other area where rainfall is adequate; here are the hard wood forests, which yield teak and mahogany, ebony and log-wood; expensive timbers from the cost of their winning and their transport, they are, therefore, comparatively little used. They are timbers which are prized for specific qualities, such as those which justify the use of teak in battleships or those in which our forefathers gloried when they dined round the mahogany.

Timber is scarce. We veneer the cabinet woods, and turn the soft woods into three-ply. We make buildings of steel and reinforced concrete, and in the older countries, a modern house made almost wholly of wood is a rarity. Despite the import of window frames completely fashioned, we tend to the use of metal frames. The old oak house beams of our ancient cottages are sufficiently valuable to be transported long distances and used again. We cut the immature trees for their cellulose content and turn them into paper and artificial silk, and it is worth while to collect the dust in the saw-mills to augment the yield.

Timber is impermanent. The soft woods tend to be destroyed in use as coal is , the hard woods last longer, as do metals. From the tree to the saw-mill plank, on to the packing-case maker,

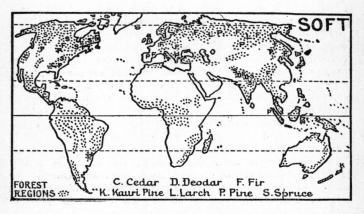

SOFT

FOREST REGIONS

C. Cedar   D. Deodar   F. Fir
K. Kauri Pine   L. Larch   P. Pine   S. Spruce

thence to the chopper of firewood and the domestic hearth, is but one of the many avenues of destruction. From the forest to the pulp-mill, on to the printing press, thence to the dustbin and the incinerator is another.

This lack of permanence has an important consequence, for it has given rise to a vast business in varnishes and polishes, all designed to delay the destroying hand of decay, and much of it planned to make usable such timbers as our forefathers would have scorned. This business is based on forest products, resins and gums, and has produced its own mechanical devices, whether they be cellulose sprayers or weighted floor polishers.

LESSON 20

Vegetable Oils, Gums and Pigments

THE oils, gums and pigments of vegetable origin are chiefly used as preservatives. Soaps preserve surfaces from the accumulations of layers of dirt; lubricants preserve rotating surfaces from heating and thus from binding together with resultant fracture or damage; gums and varnishes yield preservative coats against the deterioration due to damp; pigments have a primary preservative function in addition to their decorative purpose. Waxes are used as preservative seals; oils are used in cooking designed to delay the period when food decays; illuminating oils serve to extend the period of light.

The oils are either fixed, when they decompose at high temperatures, or essential (volatile), when they can be distilled and concentrated. The vegetable oils are palm, olive, linseed, castor, cotton-seed, colza or rape, ground-nut and sesamum. Allied to the oils are the similar but more viscous butters, such as those obtained from the cocoa bean or from copra, the dried kernel of the coconut.

Vegetable Oils in Commerce. Palm oil is limited to the Guinea Coast of West Africa, chiefly to Nigeria. The oil is obtained from the fleshy part of the fruit and is expressed from the kernel. The former is used locally; the latter is a factory product subsequent to transportation overseas. One of its prime uses is as a preservative to prevent oxidation in the basic iron sheets before they are coated with tin to make tin-plate.

Coconut oil and butter are expressed from the kernel (copra) of the coconut, the fruit of one of the varieties of palm. Copra comes from south India, Ceylon, the East Indian Islands, the Philippines, and Malaya.

Olive oil is characteristic of the Mediterranean region, chiefly of Italy and Spain and the intervening French coastland, where it enters into the dietary of the populace. The tree thrives in other winter-rain regions, but there the production of oil is insignificant, except in California and South Australia. Cotton-seed oil is one of the commonly used adulterants of olive oil. The production of seed is a valuable portion of the yield of the U.S.A. cotton belt, and no other oil seeds are so extensively produced. Linseed oil, or flax-seed oil, is obtained in India, Russia and the Argentine. It is used in mixing paints and varnishes, and is essential for oil-cloth and linoleum. These seed oils are by-products of the fibre-production for textiles; in both, the seeds are utilized for

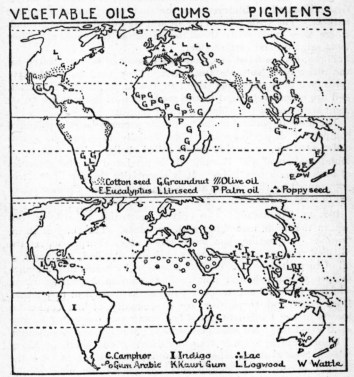

VEGETABLE OILS   GUMS   PIGMENTS

::::Cotton seed G.Groundnut ///Olive oil
E.Eucalyptus L.Linseed P Palm oil ..Poppy seed

C.Camphor I Indigo ..Lac
oGum Arabic K Kauri Gum L.Logwood W Wattle

the production of synthetic cattle fodder after the oil has been expressed.

Rape (colza) and sesamum oils mainly come from India. Colza is obtained from varieties of cabbage plants. In northern Europe colza oil was produced as an illuminant; it has also lubricating properties. Its cake is of inferior quality. Sesamum is a herb grown for its oil yield ; its seeds yield gingelly oil, which may be used in cooking, lighting and lubricating.

Castor oil is pressed from the seeds of a small tree which is indigenous to India but is grown in Mediterranean lands ; it is best when cold-drawn, and is used medicinally as a mild purgative. Ground-nut oil is obtained from the seeds of a plant of extensive habitat. The seeds form in the air and are forced into the ground, where they ripen some three inches below the surface. They yield salad oil and cattle fodder.

These oils are fixed oils, and hence one can be substituted for the other after suitable treatment. They tend to yield fatty substance of a vegetable origin of the same general character, and are extensively used in the production of soaps, after treatment with one of the alkalis, soda or potash.

The most important of the vegetable waxes is lac, the principal component of sealing-wax. Commercially it occurs as grains called seed-lac, or in thin flakes called shellac. The best lac is found in Bengal and Burma. It is produced by the activities of insects upon tree twigs. It is essentially the sap of the tree transmuted by the insects, and is a kind of resin. Chinese insect white wax is of similar origin.

Oils by Distillation. The volatile, essential, or ethereal oils are, in the main, associated with perfumes. The chief of them, however, turpentine, has more sober uses. Turpentine is the distilled resin of coniferous trees. Highly distilled, it is spirit or oil of turpentine. It is used as a solvent for resins in the manufacture of varnish and paint. The commonest resin is rosin, which is the solid substance left in the distillation of turpentine. Both rosin and turpentine are a speciality of the coniferous forests of the United States. The coniferous forests of Europe yield wood-tar, from which creosote is obtained, and wood-pitch.

Kauri gum is a fossil resin localized in the north of North Island, New Zealand, where it is sought by fossickers after the fashion of primitive gold-diggers. It yields the finest of all varnishes. Copal, or gum copal, is a similar resin from trees which thrive in the shorelands of the Indian Ocean. Otto of roses is an essential oil distilled from rose leaves at Kazanlik in Eastern Rumelia and in India. Friar's balsam is a compound tincture due to gum benzoin, chiefly produced from a tree which grows in Siam, Indo-China and Sumatra. Bergamot is the essential oil from a citrous tree cultivated in Italy and Sicily.

Camphor is a solid essential oil obtained by treating with steam chips of a tree which is grown in the Far East. The chief supply comes from Formosa. Dragon's blood is a red resin from an East Indian palm; it is used for varnish, stains and dentifrice. Oil of eucalyptus comes from Australia; apart from its medicinal use, the oil serves different purposes in the manufacture of soap, varnish and perfumes. Frankincense is a resinous gum exported from Aden. Gamboge is a gum resin used for water-colours and in medicine. Gum arabic comes from Kordofan and Senegal. Gum tragacanth is used in the cotton trade and is supplied by Izmir (Smyrna).

Mastic is a gum resin from the Mediterranean which yields an almost colourless varnish. Peppermint is an essential oil which yields menthol as a residue of distillation. Myrrh is a gum resin chiefly supplied from Bombay.

Dyes and stains and tanning materials are largely of vegetable origin, although the chemist has been extraordinarily successful in the manufacture of synthetic colouring materials, such as the aniline dyes, a by-product of coal.

The chief tree dye is logwood from Central America; the extract is dark red and is used for blues, browns and black. Fustic comes also from Central America, Nicaragua; it is a basis for the yellows. Reds are obtained from red Brazil wood, and from West African cam-wood; they are also obtained from madder, a plant which used to be grown extensively in Europe. Indigo is obtained from a shrub cultivated in India.

The astringent tanning materials are quebracho from the Argentine; myrobalans, a fruit from India; sumach, twigs and leaves from Italy; valonia, the acorn cups of an oak supplied by Izmir; and wattle, a bark of the Australian acacias.

LESSON 21

The World's Coal

EVERY British housewife knows that coal varies in appearance, brightness, combustibility, heating power, and so on, and yet she has had experience of only a few of the kinds of black stuff which goes by the label coal. Had British house coal not been of superior quality, Britons would never have become devotees of the open house grate, one of the least economical methods of warming houses. Had British coal not been easy of access and comparatively superabundant, the Industrial Revolution would have run a different course, and the British Navy and Mercantile Marine would have had a different history.

"Coal" is a term used for an average of the best anthracite and the worst lignite or brown coal; it is not possible to particularize about the dozens of qualities of coal between these extremes of the best and the worst. For economic geography "coal" is no more than a combustible mineral, which is used by different human beings in different parts of the world in different ways. To the users coal has vastly different values. It therefore happens that the statements which follow are only

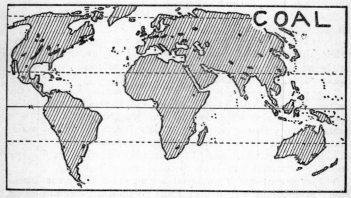

true in a very broad sense and are indicative of tendencies rather than of hard facts. Coal is, moreover, one of the utilities which is destroyed in consumption, and is not replaceable; hence the gaining of coal is bound to follow the law of diminishing returns; either it will be more difficult or more expensive to mine, or it will peter out and the seam become exhausted.

There are three main facts concerning coal. First, the visible extractable coal is almost limited to the northern hemisphere and to the shorelands of the North Atlantic Basin; there may be huge reserves of coal elsewhere, but they do not at present count. Secondly, coal is used almost entirely by the white man; it is the main element in the background of the white man's civilization. The accompanying map shows the distribution of the coalfields ; only those east of the Rockies and west of the Urals matter. The coal of Europe is important only along the line which starts in the neighbourhood of Glasgow, and proceeds somewhat sinuously through Bristol to north-east France, Westphalia, and Silesia. This fact is immediately obvious from the table given below, in which the unit of calculation is the estimated quantity of coal mined in the world in the year 1880 ; this is taken as 100.

The " world " column shows the tremendous slackening in the rate of increase in the quantities mined and used ; in the first decade the jump was 60 per cent ; it fell away through 50 per cent to 33 per cent and finally to 5 per cent. The " rest of the

THE WORLD'S USAGE OF COAL DEPOSITS.

Date	World	Britain	United States	Germany	France	Rest of World
1880	100	45	20	19	6	10
1890	160	58	45	29	8	20
1900	240	73	80	44	10	33
1910	360	83	140	68	11	58
1920	410	73	185	74	12	66
1930	436	77	157	91	21	90

world " column shows the gradual expansion in the areas from which the mineral has been obtained ; the quantity mined in the rest of the world is now ninefold what it was fifty years ago. The " rest of the world " in 1930 embraced Russia, Poland, Czechoslovakia, Belgium, Japan, China, Holland, Spain, Hungary, and Yugoslavia ; of which countries the first six mined each as much coal as was mined in France fifty years ago. It must be emphasized that coal means combustible mineral which may be anthracite or lignite barely distinguishable from peat.

The third main fact about coal is that most of it is consumed in the country of origin. The United States has exported a little coal, chiefly to Canada, but the quantity never exceeded the quantity mined in France. Germany has sold coal during this century but never in any relatively large quantity, never exceeding 5 per cent of production. Britain has been the chief dealer in coal ; the values—in figures which fit the values in the above table—were respectively at the years specified : 6, 10, 19, 29, 12, 11 ; the trade has declined. Except in 1920–1930 the total has always exceeded the total product of France. The coal mine in the Saar coalfield has been included in the produce of France for the relevant years, and accounts in part for the relatively high figure, 21, for France, in 1930. Despite this addition, France has always been a buyer of coal ; the proportional values of French purchases have been at the years specified : 3, 3, 5, 6, 7, 9. Roughly, a third of the coal used in France has been of foreign origin.

Other steady buyers on a smaller scale have been Italy, Sweden, and India, in addition to Canada, as previously mentioned. New Zealand mines roughly one-thousandth of the world's coal and buys from abroad. Chile mines about as much coal as New Zealand. Elsewhere in the Southern Hemisphere, of which the total production does not equal 3 per cent of the world's supplies, South Africa and Australia each mine as much coal as is mined in Holland, rather more than is mined in Spain, and about as much as is mined in Canada. The quantity of coal mined in India and China is in each country about 9 per cent of the coal mined in Britain, and almost double the quantity for Australia or South Africa.

Britain mines about a sixth of the world's coal ; the rest of the British Empire mines less than a quarter of Britain's total, which brings the total for the Empire to about 20 per cent. of the world's supplies. Britain's consumption of coal is about seven-eighths of the total mined.

All these facts may be summarized in the statement that the coal trade is one of the most important of the home trades of each country. Since British coal exports are important when they supply bulky cargoes for outgoing merchant vessels, the decline in coal exports achieves an added secondary significance. This fact is notable in connexion with the modern development of world, instead of country, prices for commodities ; whereas the price of wheat is of the type which is labelled a world price, the price of coal tends to remain a local or country price, and the wages of the miner, entering as they do so largely into the cost of the coal, will be determined by local conditions, while the wages of the farmer of East Anglia will depend in part upon wheat prices in Chicago. Primarily coal is a local product, locally consumed.

LESSON 22

Petrol in the Petrol-pump Age

R AW petrol is a mineral product, like coal, which is consumed in use and is not renewed by natural means thereafter, nor is it renewable. The total world production is in the neighbourhood of 250 million tons annually. In the seventies of the last century it was less than one million. The rate of progress in production has been phenomenal. In 1890, ten million; in 1900, twenty million; in 1910, forty-five million; in 1920, a hundred million tons were garnered—roughly, a doubled yield per decade.

The United States have continuously dominated the production; in general, two-thirds of the world's total has been obtained within that country. In the early days the States were the sole source. Then Russian supplies became available, and by 1890 the States' proportion was down below two-thirds, Russia was responsible for nearly 40 per cent, and small amounts, each less than 1 per cent, were gained in Canada, Rumania and Galicia. By 1895 Russia produced as much as the States, and by 1900 Russia had reached her peak period, during which for a year or two Russian supplies were about half the grand total. The decade 1890–1900 was a unique period, for not only did the supplies from the States decline relatively with great rapidity down to 40 per cent for a year or two, but new sources of small magnitude were tapped in British India, Japan and the Dutch East Indies, while Galicia and Rumania had increased outputs.

By 1910 the States were back in the former dominant position, which has been steadily maintained since that date. Russia had begun a decline, both absolute and relative, which persisted until quite recent years; the lowest ebb occurred in 1920, when Russian supplies, instead of being 50 per cent, were but 5 per cent of the world's total. In 1910 Galicia, Rumania and the Dutch East Indies each produced just under 5 per cent of the world's total for that year, and Mexico and Peru had been in production in small quantities for a year or so. Galicia had reached its peak period; unlike Russia, Galicia has not reattained an output equivalent to the most productive years, for the output now is less than 1 per cent of the world's grand total, and but a third of the peak yield for Galicia.

Mexican supplies had become relatively important by 1920; from 1 per cent in 1910 they had advanced to as much as 25 per cent of the world total in ten years. The Mexican peak period followed immediately, and the supplies are now down to 1½ per cent of the total. By 1920, also, supplies from Iran were marketed; they amounted to about 2 per cent of the total, a relatively small proportion which has been since maintained with but a slight increase. Small supplies were available from Trinidad, Venezuela, Argentina and Sarawak. In 1938 the position was: U.S.A. 63 per cent, Russia 11 per cent, Venezuela

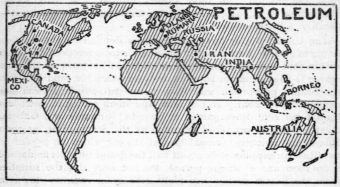

CHIEF SOURCES OF PETROLEUM

10 per cent, 3 per cent Iran, 2½ per cent Dutch East Indies and Rumania, 1½ per cent Mexico and Iraq, with about 1 per cent from Colombia, Trinidad, Argentina and Peru.

The margin of variation in reference to the production of raw petrol is less complicated than the margin of variation in regard to consumption, for the data of consumption may include refined petrol, benzine, and other heavier oils, the products of the refineries. This range, however, is not of great importance, for, as in production so in the case of consumption, the United States dominates the situation: in that country roughly four times as much petrol is consumed as in all the rest of the world. Even if this estimate be too high, it is obvious that the States use a relatively higher proportion of the world's supplies than the two-thirds which they produce. The next greatest consumers are Britain and Russia, neither of which uses a tenth of the amount consumed in the States.

In the States consumption has kept pace in its growth with production, so that in the world market the States have achieved steadily greater importance and have required and used not only home supplies, but supplies from the minor foreign sources. Consumption in Russia has followed the vicissitudes of production ; consumption in Britain has, on the whole, steadily doubled in quantity per decade. After Britain comes France, where consumption has been steadily about 30 per cent of that of Britain. In Germany, before the War, consumption was at the British rate ; since the war it has been smaller than that of France. Italy has increased her small consumption relatively rapidly in recent years ; other important consumers in Europe each use less than 5 per cent of the British amount.

In its larger aspects the situation is quite simple. The United States produce, buy, sell, and use more petrol not only in the gross, but also per head of the population ; the American is petrol (or gasoline) minded. Britain, without home supplies, except such as may be obtained by the chemist from coal distillation, or hydrogenation, is definitely a buyer of what the United States chooses to count as a surplus. The price of petrol is controlled by the States.

The by-products of the petrol industry are of some interest. The derricks and other apparatus of the wells, the distillation plants, are largely local to the mines ; the lengthy pipe lines for economical transport from the wells to the sea coast of Baku, in Iran, and in Iraq, and the special variety of ship—the tanker. —are curious phenomena to the natives of the outlying lands of production and are an excuse for the white man's interest and intervention in semi-barbaric areas.

The special docking arrangements at British ports provide a new source of employment in Britain. The petrol can and the roadside pump are part of our national life, and the distribution of petrol to the pumps has even had its influence on the distribution of British milk supplies. The post- and pre-war contrast has, probably, in no other respect so definite an object lesson. The sequence—cheap, plentiful petrol ; internal combustion (petrol) engines, motor cars ; aeroplanes—is passing before our eyes, and the end is not yet.

LESSON 23

Electric Power in the Modern World

ELECTRIC power has three supreme advantages. The first, probably, is the extensive range of its application from the minute to the monstrous, from the gigantic machines of a great power station to the driving of a toy train equipped with lit signal lamps. The second is its automatic character, the facility with which it may be controlled. The third is its ease of transmission, an ease which tends rapidly to increase. There is a supreme fascination in the engineer's story of the million and one uses to which electrical power is put, of the steady improvements in wireless apparatus—in, for example, the ability to transmit photographs over hundreds of miles almost instantaneously. The competition between gas and electricity for domestic purposes attracts the attention of the housewife ; central heating by electrically-heated water has its advantages.

Electricity is a secondary source of power It is not primary, like running water ; it depends largely on the provision of spinning, i.e. whirling, shafts and wheels. Its extensive use—despite its manifold advantages—depends on primary costs, on the cost of the provision and upkeep of the rotating wheel or shaft. Hence the geographer is interested in " white coal," for this term has been applied to running water harnessed to the driving of turbines as a source of rotatory power. White coal is actual when a waterfall like Niagara is the force used in many power stations situated adjacent to the water ; it is potential in every waterfall or cascade. It is actual when the farmer of Scandinavia, or New Zealand, or elsewhere utilizes the rapid streams of his farmland to supply rotation for an electric plant, which will furnish current for his house and farm-buildings, for his machines, and for somewhat unusual drying fans which help to make his hay. White coal is actual in Switzerland and similar mountainous areas, where torrential streams occur ; it is actual within a radius of many miles from the power station. This radius, once small, is now being effectively increased ; and it is possible that London's electric power might come from the taming of torrents in the Highlands.

ELECTRIC POWER

Black coal, as lumps or dust, or indirectly by the oil distilled from it, is a primary heating source from which steam and electricity may arise as secondaries. Black and white coal compete. Effective transmission of current will send the power stations to the coalfields and save transport. This is but one of the reasons why the expensive and toilsome transport of coal tends to decrease ; this is one of the reasons also why there tends to be less and less manual labour to be done in the white man's world.

Electrical machinery requires minerals and metals, of which copper is one of the chief ; it calls into being new applications of metallurgy. Most of this machinery tends to be permanent and is very slowly destroyed in use ; it is the medium whereby Man almost captures one of the world's natural resources which is everlasting. Coal, petrol and gas are destroyed in use ; running water continues. The rain, the snow and the sunshine combine with the slope of the ground to supply continuous power at no cost ; electricity makes it possible to harness this power. It would seem obvious that in the long run electric power must be the cheapest driving force in the world. In the long run electric power will tend to spread the workers over the land and obviate the necessity for folk agglomerations in the areas least suited for happy human lives.

Petrol has an advantage, for the moment, that it can be stored on a moving power-machine more successfully than electricity, which is handicapped by the dead weight of the lead in the accumulators ; yet this advantage will vanish when the inventor has solved the problem of electric storage.

The foregoing remarks suffer geographically, since the subject matter under consideration is elusive. Developments occur with great rapidity ; power stations arise whenever the demand for power justifies their equipment ; there is little or no regularity to be observed. Statistics are therefore lacking, or confusing, and are subject to great variation. For industrial purposes the United States, where natural gas occurs, are the chief users of gas for power. But the power obtained from water is twice as great ; the power obtained from steam is ten times as great ; and the horse power obtained from electrical plant in the U.S.A. is now more than half the horse power obtained from steam engines. In the production of this power two-thirds of the primary force is procured from steam and most of the remainder from water. Electric power obtained primarily from water is largely used in the factories of Canada, Italy and Japan. In none of these countries is coal easily available in the factory districts, while water power is at hand ; yet the total horse power of the electrical output of these three countries is comparatively small in relation to the output of the U.S.A.

In all these countries the advance in the quantity of horse power used during the post-war period has been very definite, not only electrically but also in connexion with coal and water supplies ; and this fact emphasizes the suggestion that there is much less manual work to be performed by the white worker, and tends to account for the present state of surplus production of commodities.

Man is not yet far from the beginnings of the use of electrical power. Light falling upon a photo-cell small enough to be held in the hand produces electric impulses which can be turned to useful purposes. After a summer noteworthy for the strength and continuity of its sunshine, solar radiant energy of immense potential usefulness goes astray. The energy is there for the capture ; we await the invention of a receiving and storing apparatus capable of large-scale use. When that day dawns, manual labour will almost cease to be productively necessary. The present over-production, which forces attention to salesmanship in order that people may be cajoled into the purchase of things which they do not really need, so that employment may be maintained at a 45-hour week, is the writing on the wall. Electricity harnessed to our service will make a ten-hour week seem unnecessarily long.

Suggestions for Further Reading. " Handbook of Commercial Geography " (25s.) and " A Smaller Commercial Geography " (5s.), both by G. G. Chisholm (Longman) ; " A Geography of the World," by B. C. Wallis (4s. Macmillan) ; the last mentioned is economic in the second half. Also W. P. Rutter's " Commercial Atlas of the World " (Pitman).

This Lesson concludes our Course in Economic Geography.

ECONOMICS

LESSON 45

Why Unemployment is Always with us

No economic problem has provoked such a conflict of opinion as that of unemployment. The most popular view is that our modern problem of unemployment is essentially the product of industrial progress. According to this view, the application of science to industry has resulted in so great an increase of Man's power to produce, that production continually outstripping consumption. The social credit policy of Major C. H. Douglas for instance, which aims at increasing the purchasing power of consumers in order that consumption may keep pace with production, is based on this view. Another popular explanation is that the root of the trouble is the unequal distribution of wealth. Thus Mr. J. A. Hobson believes that if we could attain a greater measure of economic equality, so that a smaller proportion of the national income would be saved and a greater proportion would be devoted to consumption, the periodic depressions which characterize modern industry would be eliminated. Both these popular explanations, however, are frowned on by most of the academic economists. In their opinion, trade depressions, with their resultant unemployment, are to be regarded as a problem in the technique of credit control.

In this connexion it is important to remember that unemployment is not entirely the product of trade slumps. Even in times of good trade there is a not inconsiderable percentage of unemployment. In fact, unemployment is a complex problem : it is the product of many contributory factors. In normal times, such as the years immediately preceding the War, we may distinguish four such factors, viz., seasonal influences, changes in the tastes of consumers, changes in the technique of production, and the trade cycle.

First, as regards seasonal influences. It is a well-known fact that activity in certain industries fluctuates according to the season of the year. The building trade is an eminent example of such an industry, being comparatively slack in the winter and busy in the summer. This is due to the fact that building operations are impeded by rain and frost. In countries like Germany, where the frosts are severe, the seasonal fluctuations in building are very considerable. The tourist traffic is also highly seasonal, and, like building, is at its peak in summer.

Changes in the tastes of consumers constitute the second factor in the unemployment problem. An example is the depression in the woollen textile industries since 1925, which is partly due to changes in women's fashions since the War, and the fact that new materials such as artificial silk have come to the fore.

Changes in industrial technique form a much more important factor. The introduction of new methods into an industry often has the immediate effect of displacing workers by enabling it to satisfy its market with a smaller labour force. As we have seen in Lesson 11 (Volume 2, page 175), these displaced workers tend to be absorbed in the course of time by the general expansion of industry consequent upon the cheapening of production.

But the transfer of workers from one industry to another not only involves the problem of re-training, but also in many cases the shifting of workers from one part of the country to another, since our basic industries are largely localized. What alternative employment is there for a coal miner in South Wales, or an iron and steel worker in Barrow or Middlesbrough? The surplus workers in these districts must, it is obvious, be moved to another part of the country. But, as Adam Smith long ago pointed out, of all kinds of luggage the human being is the most difficult to transport. Housing, for example, presents a formidable obstacle. The worker cannot take his house with him nor can he always find accommodation in the district to which he wants to go. Then there is the problem of family employment. The sons and daughters, and, in many cases, the wife of the displaced worker may be in employment. The introduction, therefore, of labour-saving devices, even though it may not permanently displace labour, is an important factor in the unemployment problem.

The coal industry provides an extreme example of the transfer problem created by technical progress. In the first place, post-war machines are more economical in the use of the fuel from which they derive their power. It has been estimated that modern machines use on the average about one-third of the fuel required in pre-war days to provide the same amount of power. Secondly, the development of the internal combustion engine has to a large

extent substituted oil for coal as a source of power. This substitution is exemplified mainly in the enormous expansion of
road transport—a development which has taken place largely
at the expense of the railways which use coal—and in the rise of
the motor ship. Thirdly, coal has to meet another competitor
in the form of electricity. In those cases in which electricity is
generated from coal the displacement of the latter has only taken
place to the extent that electricity is a more economical method of
generating power. The development of electricity, however, has
been largely due to the harnessing of water power. How great
have been the economies in fuel consumption and the growth of
alternative sources of power, is shown by the fact that the
United States' coal consumption, which was 479 million tons in
1913, had increased by 1925 only to 499 million tons, though
the industrial activity of the U.S.A. had risen by more than 50
per cent.

Thus the depression and unemployment in the coal industry
which prevailed in the years of comparative good trade prior to
the slump of 1930 were mainly due to the march of technical
progress ; they were—to use a new term—a manifestation of
technological unemployment. But why, it may be asked, have
not the superfluous miners been absorbed in other branches of
industry ? Mainly because of the difficulty of re-training miners
for other occupations and of transferring them to other areas.
A further factor, according to many eminent authorities, has been
the restrictive regulations of the trade unions, which have
hindered the expansion of employment in the new industries
that have been springing up since the War.

LESSON 46

Conflicting Views on Unemployment

THE course of modern industry does not exhibit that continuous progress which we should expect from the steady
advance in the technique of production. It is characterized
by alternate periods of good and bad trade. In good years trade
activity rises steadily, culminating in a boom ; in bad years trade
activity declines, at first rapidly, remains for a year or two at a
low level, and then begins to rise again.

The phenomena of the trade cycle seem to run counter to the main implications of economic theory. The core of economic theory is the price mechanism. Now, the function of the price mechanism is to maintain equilibrium in the economic organization : it maintains, that is to say, between the specialized parts of the economic organization the harmony which is necessary if it is to function effectively. Thus, any change either in demand or in the technique of supply is reflected in the price mechanism, thereby providing the stimulus to the necessary adaptation of price. An increase, for example, in the demand for tea and coffee at the expense of beer and whisky will, generally speaking, cause the prices of the former commodities to rise and of the latter to fall. As a result, capital and labour will tend to shift from the latter industries to the former. Such adaptations, as we have seen, do not always take place smoothly ; but the dislocation caused by the frictions cannot account for the general depression of industry seen in a trade slump.

One of the best-known explanations of the periodic depressions to which industry is subject is the theory put forward by Major C. H. Douglas. According to him the root cause of the trouble is the present system of credit. Under this system manufacturers have to pay back to the banks as repayment of the loans advanced to them a considerable proportion of the costs of the goods which they produce. As a consequence the incomes of the members of the community fall short of the aggregate costs of the manufacturers, thereby creating a situation in which there is insufficient purchasing power to buy all the goods that are produced. This insufficiency of purchasing power, in Major Douglas's opinion, is greatly accentuated by the advance in modern times of Man's capacity to produce. At the root of his theory is the conviction that the banks use their monopolistic position to restrict the supply of credit, thereby creating an insufficiency of purchasing power. But, it may be asked, what evidence is there that the banks act in this manner ? The fact that the producers have to repay their loans to the banks surely does not mean that purchasing power is withdrawn from circulation, for the banks promptly re-lend the money thus received. Nor, assert the orthodox economists, does the increase in Man's capacity to produce create a situation in which there is insufficient purchasing power to buy all the goods that are produced, for new inventions and new processes mean that manufacturers can produce more cheaply,

BRITAIN'S SEA AND AIR POWER. The lower photo shows Jellicoe's battleships steaming through the North Sea to engage in the Battle of Jutland. The photo above is of a squadron of "Bristol fighters" returning to their aerodrome in France after a bombing raid across the German lines. BRITISH HISTORY 26

Fawcett & Hooper's "The Fighting at Jutland" (Macmillan); Imperial War Museum

'OVER THE TOP.' This impression by John Nash of the Artists' Rifles advancing to the assault at Marcoing in December, 1917, conveys something of the conditions under which men had to fight—and die. BRITISH HISTORY 26

Crown copyright; photo, Imperial War Museum

BRITAIN'S POST-WAR PREMIERS. Andrew Bonar Law (centre; 1858–1923) was born in New Brunswick. After a successful career in business, he entered Parliament as a Unionist in 1900, and in 1911 became the leader of his party. After holding high office in the Coalition governments, he became Conservative prime minister in October 1922, but resigned in May, 1923, through ill-health. He was succeeded by Stanley Baldwin (right; b. 1867), Unionist M.P. for Bewdley since 1908 and Chancellor of the Exchequer in the Bonar Law ministry. After the Conservative reverse in the General Election of 1923 James Ramsay MacDonald (left; 1866–1937), leader of the Socialists for many years, formed the first Labour government. This fell in the autumn of 1924 and Baldwin became premier for the second time. In 1929 MacDonald formed his second ministry. Two years later, in the National government, he retained the premiership, and Baldwin became Lord President of the Council. BRITISH HISTORY 27

Plate 22   *Volume VI*

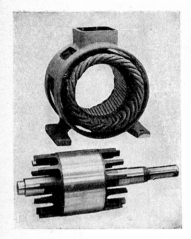

A.C. MOTORS. Fig. 1 (left). The stator and rotor of a small squirrel-cage motor. Three-phase current, supplied to the stator windings, generates a rotating magnetic field which causes the rotor to revolve. The rotor shown is an aluminium alloy casting, and requires no electrical connexion with the power supply. **Fig. 2** (above). A typical slip-ring rotor. ENGINEERING 34

Courtesy of the General Electric Co., Ltd.

INDUCTION MOTOR. Fig. 3. A large motor suitable for 3-phase current at 2,200 volts, developing 500 h.p. at 326 r.p.m. The slip-rings are enclosed in a flame-proof cover. ENGINEERING 34

Courtesy of the General Electric Co., Ltd.

TRANSFORMER CONSTRUCTION. Fig. 2. Showing a 66,000/22,200 volt three-phase transformer, under construction. **Fig. 3** (top left). Transformer tank with gilled tubes. ENGINEERING 35

Courtesy of the General Electric Co., Ltd.

Plate 24

Volume VI

and, therefore, can sell at lower prices. This fall in prices enables consumers to buy the increased supply of commodities—unless prices have fallen so low as to make the production of the goods in question quite unremunerative to the manufacturer, or the purchasing power of the public is so low, so depleted, as to forbid their purchase of the goods even at the lowest prices at which they are put on the market.

Another popular view attributes the periodic gluts which characterize modern industry to the unequal distribution of wealth. The cruder form of this view suggests that, as the workers do not receive in wages as much as they produce, general over-production must inevitably take place. No economist would suggest that the present distribution of wealth is anything but unsatisfactory from the point of view of human welfare, but neither would he endorse the view that it gives rise to over-production in this sense. That part of the value of the product of industry which does not go to the worker does not disappear ; it forms the income of the capitalist and the landowner. And the capitalist and landowner spend their incomes as do the workers. But, it may be argued, the wealthy classes, unlike the workers, save a large part of their incomes. True ; but saving, too, creates employment—at least, in normal times. When a man saves, he puts the money in a bank or instructs his broker to buy shares ; in either case the money will be used to create employment. The banks use the savings of the community which are entrusted to them in accommodating business men with the circulating capital necessary for their business. The money with which shares are purchased filters through to the company promoter or to some enterprise which is extending its plant. Thus, the part of savings which is invested in the purchase of shares creates employment in the building industry, in the coal, iron, steel industries, and in all the other industries connected with the building of factories and the production of machines, while the savings in the banks are used to provide the circulating capital necessary to cooperate with this equipment.

A second form of the view that periodical gluts are due to the unequal distribution of wealth is Mr. J. A. Hobson's under-consumption theory. Mr. Hobson, while rejecting the theory that there is not sufficient purchasing power to buy the increasing flow of commodities, believes that, as the result of the unequal distribution of wealth, too great a proportion of the national income is saved, and too small a proportion devoted to consumption.

The unequal distribution of wealth, Mr. Hobson argues, results in a higher proportion of the product of industry being saved than would be the case if a more equalitarian distribution prevailed. This is due to the fact that, as a general rule, the larger a man's income, the larger is the proportion of it which he saves. It is not uncommon for a wealthy man to save half his income, whereas one-tenth would be a high proportion for a man with £200 or £300 a year. Now, there is at any time an economically right proportion between spending and saving. If the saving of a community exceeds this proportion, then over-production, in the sense of more goods being produced than the community is *willing* to purchase, will ensue, for an undue proportion of the money available for the purchase of the increased supply of goods made possible by the savings of the community will be in the hands of the rich—in the hands, that is to say, of those who wish to save, and not to consume. While, therefore, there is sufficient money to purchase all the goods that are produced, markets are nevertheless glutted because the wealthier classes have no desire to increase their consumption *pari passu* with the increase of production.

With the aid of this analysis Mr. Hobson claims that he can explain the course of the trade cycle. Briefly, his explanation is as follows. During a trade depression production falls off rapidly, as employers, finding that they cannot sell their products at remunerative prices, curtail production by discharging a number of their workers. As a result of the decline in production, the glut in the markets of the world is gradually worked off, and a

point is reached when consumption overtakes production. Once demand exceeds supply, however, prices begin to rise and industry once more moves on the upward path of the trade cycle. For, once prices have begun to rise, employers will find it profitable to expand production, and the rise in prices and the expansion of production will for a time be cumulative. The expansion of credit by the banks, in response to the demand of manufacturers for larger loans to meet their rising commitments, accentuates both the rise in prices and the rise in production. This process is illustrated diagrammatically in the preceding page.

The initial stimulus may come at any point in the circle. If, for example, the decline in production which takes place in a depression causes prices to rise, then profits will rise also. The rise in profits stimulates enterprise. Business men, that is to say, will expand the production of existing undertakings and launch out on new ones. The expansion of enterprise, in its turn, leads to an expansion of credit, for business men require more loans from the banks to meet their expanding commitments. The expansion of credit, by putting more money into circulation and thereby increasing the capacity and willingness of buyers to buy, drives prices up. But higher prices mean higher profits, which in turn lead to greater enterprise, and so on. Thus, once trade has started on the upward phase of the trade cycle, the process tends to be cumulative.

LESSON 47

Underconsumption and Unemployment

ACCORDING to Mr. J. A. Hobson, the rise in prices, by effecting a redistribution of the national income in favour of the capitalist class, sows the seeds of the ensuing slump. The redistribution of the national income is due to the fact that in a period of rising business activity prices always rise faster than wages. Profits, therefore, which are determined by the margin between prices and costs (which consist largely of wages), rise faster than prices. Thus the capitalists, whose incomes are mainly determined by the rate of profit, tend for a time to receive a larger share of the product of industry. This change in distribution is effected at the expense of the working class, for rising prices reduce the real wages of the workers, as each pound of their wages now buys less than before. But, it will be pointed out, is it not a well-known fact that in a trade boom the aggregate income of the working class is increased ? True ; but this fact is quite compatible with their receiving a smaller proportion of the national income, since in a boom the industrial machine provides a larger product for distribution.

Now, according to Mr. Hobson, this change in distribution in favour of the rich, which takes place progressively in the upward phase of the trade cycle is responsible for the ensuing slump ; for it results in an excessive proportion of the national income being saved, inasmuch as the great bulk of saving is done by the rich. The proportion, therefore, of the national income which is saved increases *pari passu* with the activity of trade. Now saving, in the social sense of the word, resolves itself, as we have seen, into the buying of capital goods, plant, machines, ships, etc., instead of the buying of consumable goods. While the increased quantities of capital goods are being produced in response to the increase in saving, the boom proceeds merrily enough. The trouble begins, according to Mr. Hobson, when the new factories and new machines have been completed and begin to operate. More consumable goods will now be forthcoming, but the workers who buy the great bulk of these goods now have a smaller proportion of the national income with which to purchase them. They have not, therefore, sufficient purchasing power to buy all the goods that are now being produced. It is not that the purchasing power does not exist, but that it is in the wrong hands—in those of the rich, who do not desire to increase their spending in proportion to the increase in production.

Such, in brief outline, is the over-saving or under-consumption theory of Mr. Hobson. It is a theory which has gained widespread support, particularly in the Labour movement. In academic circles, however, it has been almost unanimously rejected. Mr. Hobson, it is said, has not proved his basic assumption that at any time there exists an economically right proportion between spending and saving, in the sense that any attempt to exceed that proportion would lead to over-production. There is no reason to believe that the community could not double or treble the amount it saves without over-production taking place, the field for profitable investment being infinitely wider than Mr. Hobson seems to think. Moreover, say his critics, Mr. Hobson overlooks the fact that an increase in saving not only leads to an increase in production but also to a fall in prices, for the fall in the rate of interest consequent upon the increase in the supply of savings enables producers to adopt more efficient methods of production (see Lesson 37, Volume 5, page 217). In other words, the increase in the supply of savings enables the various industries to augment their material equipment, thereby lowering their costs of production ; goods can now be produced more cheaply than before. It is not necessary, therefore, that the capitalists should increase the proportion of their incomes which they devote to consumption in order that the increased supply of goods should be sold, since the lower prices will enable the workers to buy the greater quantity of goods which is now forthcoming without any increase in their money wages.

In recent years an increasing number of experts have adopted the view that the trade cycle is a monetary phenomenon. The monetary theory which would seem to fit most of the facts, and which obtains most support from eminent economists, is that put forward by Professor von Hayek, the Austrian economist. According to this theory, the ultimate cause of the trade cycle is the recurring disharmony between investment and saving produced by inappropriate fluctuations in the volume of credit.

Before we proceed to a brief description of this theory, it is necessary that we should clearly understand the two principal conceptions which it employs. By investment is meant the application of resources to the creation of capital. A business man invests money in his business when he devotes part of his resources to extending the plant or the premises of his concern. Thus the volume of investment in any year consists in the amount of money spent in extending the material equipment of the community, i.e. factories, machinery, ships, and the raw material required to cooperate with these things. Saving, on the other hand, does not consist in any positive action, but in abstention from spending. If a man spends only half of his salary and allows the balance to accumulate in the bank, he is performing the function of saving. Thus the volume of saving in any year amounts to the total money income of individuals minus the amount spent by them on current consumption.

Now, so long as a man invests his own savings in his own business, there is no question of disharmony arising between the volume of investment and the volume of saving. But how is this harmony to be maintained when, as is usually the case, the people who save and the people who invest are different people ? As we saw in the Lessons on the financial organization, the banks and other financial institutions act as middlemen between these two sets of people, the savers and the investors. Now it is quite clear that in the long run the banks cannot lend more than is being deposited with them. If they continued to do so their cash reserves would eventually be drained away, since the greater the volume of loans which the banks create, the greater the volume of cash withdrawals from them for the payment of wages and other items of expenditure. In the long run, therefore, the banks are compelled to limit their lending to the extent allowed by the amount of money deposited with them by the public. The banks achieve this objective by raising or lowering the price of credit. If credit is particularly abundant, the banker—who is compelled to lend to the maximum of his capacity by the necessity of covering the expenses of his business and the interest he has to pay to his depositors before he can begin to make a profit for himself and his shareholders—will lower the price of credit, in order to induce his customers to borrow more. On the other hand, if credit is particularly scarce, he will raise the price of credit in order to discourage his customers from borrowing so much. Thus the banks maintain equilibrium between the volume of investment and the volume of saving by appropriate changes in the bank rate.

LESSON 48

Inflation and Its Effects

THE capacity of the banks to grant loans depends, in the long run, on the amount of money deposited with them by the public. In the short run, however, it is a well-known fact that the banks not only can but often do lend more than is deposited with them. This excessive lending by the banks is known as inflation. The power of the banks to inflate is due to the fact that the granting of additional loans results in withdrawals of cash only after a considerable period of time.

At the beginning of a boom the manufacturers, to whom the banks grant additional loans, use their overdrafts mainly for the purpose of buying the raw materials for their business, or for buying new plant and machinery. In either case they use their overdrafts for making large payments to other manufacturers or merchants, and these large payments are made by cheque. The banks, therefore, in the early stages of a boom do not experience any considerable drain on their cash reserves. Only in the advanced stages of the boom, when the volume of employment has greatly increased and when the level of wages has substantially risen, do the banks begin to experience a serious drain of cash. For the manufacturers, in order to meet their higher wages bills, will have to draw increasingly larger amounts of cash every week. It is this cash drain which, increasing cumulatively in the advanced stages of a boom, compels the banks in the long run to restrict the volume of credit to the volume of deposits.

What are the effects of an inflation of credit by the banks? The main effect is to inflict " forced saving " on the community. For the additional purchasing power placed by the banks in the hands of the producers enters into competition with the purchasing power already in the hands of the consuming public. There is increased competition, therefore, for the available supply of goods and services, which drives up their prices. It is this rise in prices which inflicts the " forced saving " on the public, for consumers will find that at the higher level of prices their incomes do not go so far. They are, therefore, compelled to consume less (i.e. are forced to " save "), because their incomes are not worth so much as formerly in terms of goods and services.

The effects of inflation on consumption and production may be illustrated by what took place in the Great War. During this period one of the main problems which confronted the Government was the necessity of obtaining the necessary resources for increasing as rapidly as possible the production of war equipment. Three methods were open, all of which the Government, in fact, adopted. It could increase taxation ; it could raise loans ; it could inflate. All these methods achieved the same result of restricting the consumption of the general public, thereby liberating resources for the production of war equipment. The increase in taxation restricted consumption by compelling the public to hand over a larger part of their incomes to the Government. The raising of loans induced the public voluntarily to restrict consumption by handing over part of their incomes in return for war bonds. This method was the same as that used by company promoters when they float a new company. In the case of war loans, however, the resources liberated from the production of consumers' goods were used, not to augment the ordinary industrial equipment of the community, but to increase the output of war material.

The third method—that of inflation—while achieving the same result, was more complicated. It was effected by the Government paying for a considerable part of the war material it purchased not out of the proceeds of loans or out of revenue, but by borrowing from the Bank of England. If, for example, the Government owed £100,000 to a war contractor, it arranged an overdraft with the bank so that it could draw a cheque for this amount. The manufacturer, on receiving the cheque, paid it into his account at one of the joint stock banks, so that the latter would find its account at the Bank of England increased by £100,000. As a bank regards its balance at the Bank of England as cash, the bank in question found itself in a position to lend more to its customers ; and its customers, many of whom were war contractors, were clamouring for more credit. Thus the purchasing power of the community was greatly inflated. In time, of course, this inflation led to increased withdrawals of cash from the banks and, in order to meet this situation, the Government had to increase the supply of Treasury notes.

The immediate effect of this inflation was to raise the prices of all those goods required for the furthering of the war, for the additional purchasing power which the Government obtained by borrowing from the Bank of England—an addition which was not offset by a contraction of purchasing power elsewhere, as is the case with normal borrowing—enabled it to increase its demand for these goods. Thus the industries concerned in the production of war equipment became exceptionally profitable. In response to this increase in demand, capital and labour were attracted on an enormous scale into the industries concerned with the production of war equipment. But at whose expense did this expansion of the war industries in response to inflation take place ? Clearly, it was at the expense of the general public, for the expansion of the war industries necessarily entailed a corresponding contraction in the industries producing consumers' goods, thereby raising the cost of living. The war-time inflation, therefore, resulted in " forced saving," as each pound spent commanded a smaller quantity of goods.

The effects of an inflation of credit by the banks in a trade boom are analogous to that of the war-time inflation. In this case, however, the new money goes into the hands, not of war contractors, but of business men who have been induced by the fall in the rate of interest to start new enterprises or to extend the equipment of old ones. But why, it will be asked, does this stimulus to business activity created by inflation necessarily bring the reaction of the slump ? The answer is to be found in the fact that, as we have seen, the expansion of credit ultimately leads to a drain of cash from the banks, as rates of wages rise and the volume of employment expands. This cash drain is a warning to the banks that they are lending in excess of the savings of the public. To maintain their stability, therefore, they are compelled to restrict credit by raising the rate of interest.

Now it is this rise in the bank rate which is the proximate cause of the collapse of the boom. All those new enterprises and extensions of existing enterprises which had arisen in response to the inflation of credit by the banks now become unprofitable at the higher rate of interest. Nor is the depression confined to these enterprises. All those industries, such as iron, steel and coal, which supply the raw materials for the construction of material equipment will experience a sharp decline in demand. Finally the depression spreads to the industries producing consumers' goods, as unemployment in the industries producing capital goods curtails the purchasing power of the public.

On one point, then, the experts are in pretty general agreement. They agree that if the trade cycle is to be eliminated, credit must be controlled so that investment and saving keep in step. But how this policy is to be carried out is a matter of dispute.

LESSON 49

Theory of the Trade Cycle

THE average level of unemployment in a normal period, such as the two decades preceding the War, has been estimated by the Government actuary as from $4\frac{1}{2}\%$ to 5%. In good years unemployment fell to $2\frac{1}{2}\%$; in bad years it rose to $7\frac{1}{2}\%$. With a fair approximation to accuracy, therefore, we may consider $2\frac{1}{2}\%$ as being the minimum level of unemployment due to those factors which are continuously operative, viz. seasonal fluctuation, changes in consumers' demand, and changes in the technical processes of production. The remaining 2% or $2\frac{1}{2}\%$, in the opinion of the academic economists, was due to the trade cycle.

Since the War, however, the level of unemployment has been consistently far higher than the pre-war level. In the years from 1920 to 1928 inclusive, the average percentage of unemployment was 12.1%, compared with the 5% of pre-war days. Even in years of comparatively good trade, such as 1928 and 1929, the level of unemployment was higher than in the years of bad trade before the War.

At the outset it is as well to remove a popular misconception. Unemployment is often associated with the population problem. This country, it is thought, is over-populated and the unemployed are evidence of a surplus population. According to this view the only real cure of unemployment is emigration and birth control. We cannot enter here into a discussion whether Great Britain is or is not suffering from over-population, but one illustration will show that there is no necessary connexion between unemployment and over-population. It is generally agreed that India is considerably over-populated, yet India suffers but little from unemployment. The United States, on the other hand, are, or were until recently, an under-populated country ; a continuous influx of labour has been necessary for the adequate exploitation of their vast resources. Yet the United States, even before the great world slump, had a considerable percentage of unemployment. The explanation is, of course, that the more highly developed a country is, the more difficult is the task of co-ordinating the various specialized parts of its economic organization. Clearly, the problem of maintaining the harmonious development of the highly specialized industries of the U.S.A. is of a quite different order from that of maintaining equilibrium in India where the principal occupation is agriculture.

Post-War Unemployment. Three main factors, all brought into being by the War, have been responsible, in whole or in part, for the higher post-war level of unemployment in Britain.

First, there is the lop-sided development of industry during the War. The colossal demands which the needs of war-time set up for coal, iron and steel, munitions, ships and so on, naturally resulted in an expansion of these industries far beyond peace-time requirements. The problem of adapting British industry from war- to peace-time needs would have been difficult even if the lop-sided development had been confined to this country. But the similarly lop-sided development which took place during the War in all the industrialized countries of the world greatly intensified the problem. Moreover, the War gave a powerful stimulus to technical progress in the basic industries, thereby intensifying the peace-time problem of surplus capacity in these industries.

Secondly, we have the severing during the War of the export industries from their normal contacts. One of the most characteristic features of an advanced industrial organization is its ability to adapt itself continuously to changing conditions. The conditions of industry in the modern world are never static. On the productive side new processes, new forms of organization, new designs, new competitors are constantly arising. On the side of demand new fashions, changing tastes, new markets necessitate almost daily adaptation. Through contact with its markets and its foreign competitors an industry is able to ascertain these changes and adapt itself piecemeal to the ever-changing conditions. Now, from 1914 to 1920 these essential piecemeal adjustments in our export industries were suspended. For during the War the contacts of Lancashire, the West Riding, South Wales and the north-east coast with their export markets were almost severed. For the bracing atmosphere of foreign competition was substituted the hot-house atmosphere of war demands. The basic industries had scarcely time to consider costs, so important was it to increase the output of munitions, ships and uniforms. Immediately after the War came the peace-time boom. Civilian demand which had been banked up during the War now forced prices to an unprecedented height. It was not until the crash in the autumn of 1920 that industry emerged into the bleak atmosphere of abnormal competition.

Thus in 1921 British industry found it necessary to effect in a day changes which should have been effected by piecemeal adjustment over six years. Certain industries, of which engineering is an eminent example, resolutely faced the situation, by adapting their productive capacities and their type of product to the needs of the market. Other industries, especially cotton and coal, believed the depression to be temporary, and carried on in the hope of a return in the course of a few years to pre-war conditions. In the unsettled situation created by fluctuating currencies, tariffs, and the dislocations and impoverishment of Europe it was difficult for the export industries to be certain of their true position. Delay has only served greatly to intensify the problem of adjustment.

The Gold Standard and Unemployment

THE third and final factor making for a high level of un-employment is the fluctuation in the foreign exchanges and our return to the gold standard at the pre-war parity. During the Great War all the belligerent countries, except the U.S.A., were driven off the gold standard. At the end of the war, therefore, the various currencies, not being tied to any standard, were subject to severe fluctuations owing to the serious budgetary difficulties with which most countries were beset. But it was not merely the fluctuations of foreign curren-cies which intensified the difficulties of our export industries. In 1925 the British Government decided to return to the gold standard at the pre-war parity. As the £ then stood at 10 per cent below the pre-war parity, it was necessary to raise the value of the £ to this extent by deflating the currency.

Financially speaking, there was much to be said for this policy. It enhanced the prestige of the £, thereby helping to restore London's pre-war position as the financial centre of the world. It raised the value of British foreign investments to their pre-war value. But, as Mr. Keynes pointed out at the time, the return to the pre-war parity was open to grave objections. In the first place, it necessitated a downward revision of wages and other costs, to correspond to the rise in the value of the £, a policy which would inevitably create much social friction even if it were successful.

On the whole, the employers were unsuccessful in reducing costs to the level required by the higher value of the £. Fixed interest charges remained substantially unchanged, as also did the level of wages. Thus the return to gold had the effect of raising " real wages," not to mention other costs, such as interest charges, rates and taxes, with the result that the competitive power of British industry was seriously impaired, resulting in a loss of markets and rise in unemployment.

As regards the long term aspect of the unemployment problem, we can only suggest here that its cure is mainly a question of promoting the adaptability of industry to the changes taking place in the modern world and of pursuing a credit policy which will maintain harmony between investment and saving. By eliminating or at least mitigating the trade cycle and removing the rigidities of post-war industry the backbone of the unemployment problem would be broken.

Meanwhile, is it possible to create employment ? There are two main proposals by means of which, it is claimed, employment can be created : namely, tariffs and public work schemes. Let us, first, deal with the argument for Protection in its simplest aspect. On the one hand, it is pointed out, a considerable proportion of our capital and labour, even in the best of times, stands idle. On the other hand, we import from abroad large quantities of goods which we could quite well produce for ourselves. Do we not every year import manufactured goods to the value of from £200/300,000,000 ? What could be more obvious than to set our idle capital and labour to work by imposing a tariff high enough to keep out a sufficient proportion of these foreign goods ?

But, as we have seen in the Lessons on international Trade, imports are paid for by exports. If, therefore, the volume of imports is cut down by the imposition of tariffs, there will be a corresponding decline in the volume of exports. The effect of a tariff is not to increase employment, but to change the character of employment ; the protected industries tend to expand, while the export industries suffer a corresponding contraction.

Moreover, the Free Trader maintains that Protection is not merely futile, but by stimulating the less efficient industries at the expense of the more efficient it is positively harmful—for an industry which not only maintains its position in the home market but also competes successfully in foreign markets must be regarded as a relatively efficient industry. Now a policy of Protection tends to injure the export industries in two ways. In the first place, it diminishes the demand of foreigners for our goods, since the extent to which we are successful in keeping out foreign goods is also the extent to which we restrict the capacity of foreigners to buy from us. Secondly, a policy of Protection tends to raise the costs of production in the export industries, thereby impairing their power to compete abroad.

A tariff which is at all comprehensive raises costs in two ways. It raises the cost of at least part of the commodities used by the export industries as raw material, namely, that part which is derived from abroad and subject to the tariff. Nor could the tariff be restricted to manufactured articles, since what is a manufactured or finished article to one industry is often the raw material of another.

But a tariff not only raises costs directly by taxing the raw materials of industry. It also raises costs indirectly by taxing articles of popular consumption, thereby raising the cost of living. Such a rise will be especially marked if agriculture is placed among the " protected " industries. Now this rise in the cost of living will naturally stimulate the trade unions to agitate for a rise in wages, and in so far as they are successful, manufacturers will be faced with a rise in their costs. In so far as they are unsuccessful, the workers will be subjected to a fall in their standard of living—the very thing Protection is designed to obviate.

Thus a policy of Protection seriously handicaps the export industries, which, in virtue of their capacity to compete in foreign markets, must be ranked among the relatively efficient industries of the country : and in recompense for this disadvantage it provides a stimulus to the less efficient industries, the industries, that is, which cannot hold their own even in the home market.

LESSON 51

Some Arguments for Protection

WE now proceed to a discussion of the case for Protection —that policy which aims at encouraging or assisting the industries of a country either by the imposition of customs duties upon foreign goods entering the country or by the application of subsidies or bounties to home producers.

From the time of Edward III until a little less than a hundred years ago, England was a Protectionist country. The adoption of a Protectionist system in 1932 was therefore a return to the principles that have guided national policy for a great part of our history. Thanks to the inventiveness of her engineers, the existence of a guaranteed market in her newly won overseas possessions, and of a great store of available capital, Britain had a long start in the Industrial Revolution, and the distance between her and her competitors was increased by the Napoleonic Wars, which put back European progress for a generation. Hence by the 'forties of the last century Britain was the workshop and the market of the world. Her capitalists, anxious to " get rich quick," objected equally to restrictions on labour and on the course of trade ; and though they were denied a free hand in the way they managed their factories, they were at length successful in obtaining the complete abolition of all the governmental restrictions on commerce.

For a generation or two the new policy seemed to justify itself beyond cavil or doubt, and men spoke of the inevitable coming of a universal system of Free Trade, when all nations would seek their own interests by specialization, just as did individuals. But in the 'seventies there came a change. The new nations that had come into being, Germany in particular, chafed at their position of economic subordination and determined to do all in their power to make themselves as nearly as possible self-supporting, both in agriculture and in industry. Hence tariff walls arose which served to keep out, to some extent at least, British goods, and behind which the home manufacturers were able to establish the industries which, according to the doctrinaire Free Traders should never have been born. The alliance of Protection and nationalism was intensified by the Great War, which ended with the creation of a number of new sovereign states, each of which was determined to stand on it own feet—to be independent in the sphere of industry as in that of politics.

The Protectionist sees in this series of events the justification of his theory. He admits that universal Free Trade might, or even probably would, result in the greatest possible development of the economic resources of the world, but in the circumstances of today, when the trend is everywhere towards national self-sufficiency, he maintains that any country which remains on a Free Trade basis in a Protectionist world invites ruin.

Now let us consider some of the particular arguments advanced by Protectionists. One of the most popular is that without tariffs it is impossible for this country to maintain its relatively high standard of living. If by this is implied that a high-wage country can *never* compete successfully with a low-wage country, then the contrary was demonstrated throughout the 19th century by Britain, for during that period Britain maintained a far higher standard of living than any of her competitors, owing to the fact that she possessed practically a manufacturing monopoly in virtue of her power to produce cheaply. In the 20th century, too, the fact that a high standard of living does not incapacitate a country for successful competition has been illustrated by the United States, where the highest standard of living in the world prevailed and still prevails so far as the employed population is concerned.

The main assumption underlying this argument is that a high standard of life in a country causes the cost of production there to be high. This, however, is not necessarily so. An employer, in estimating the cost of his labour, does not merely take into account his wages bill ; an equally important consideration is the efficiency of his labour. This brings us to the question, what determines the standard of living in any country ? Why, for example, is the general level of wages higher in this country than in France ? Why is it lower in this country than in the United States ? The answer, as we saw in Lesson 39 (Volume 5, page 222), is that everything depends on the productivity of labour. The productivity of labour, in its turn, is determined by two factors, the efficiency of the worker and the efficiency of the economic organization of the country in which he works. Hence, if we desire to raise the standard of living in Britain, it can best be done by promoting measures which raise the efficiency of the worker or of the economic organization. Protection, declares the Free Trader, can do neither of these things ; on the contrary, by causing labour to shift from the more efficient to the less efficient industries (i.e. the industries which require Protection) it must tend to lower the standard of life.

Another argument, one much favoured by business magnates, is that Protection promotes mass production. Lord Nuffield has argued that the larger the scale on which he is enabled to produce his motor-cars the smaller is the proportion of overhead charges which he must allocate to each car produced—hence Protection for the motor industry means cheaper cars. The Free Trader would deny this, on the ground that there is a confusion between *scale* of production and *volume* of production. If, he argues, the motor industry experiences an increased demand for its product, then an increased output can take place as a result of an increase in the size of the firms in the industry (i.e. production will be on a larger scale), or it may be the result of the establishment of new motor-manufacturing firms, involving no increase in the scale of production. If the Protectionist is to prove his point, he must show that the first alternative is the one that results.

Another Protectionist argument is that Protection may help to mitigate the severity of unemployment by acting as a kind of insulator against the vagaries of the outside business world. Manufacturers in a protected home market are sure of selling at least a proportion of their product, and hence are able to plan for the future with a greater degree of certainty than they would if they were fully exposed to "dumping" and the competition of producers working with comparatively insignificant labour costs and untrammelled by the provision of a labour code. To this the Free Trader rejoins that Protection cannot be considered as a preventive against unemployment, inasmuch as Germany and the U.S.A.—two heavily Protectionist countries—have experienced unemployment on a colossal scale. Whatever, then, the merits of a policy of Protection in particular circumstances of time and place—and it must be remembered that political considerations, e.g. the desire to be as self-sufficient as possible, may outweigh the economic—it seems that we cannot look to it as a cure for the burden of unemployment.

LESSON 52

Relief Works and Unemployment

WE now turn to the second proposal for creating employment namely the promotion of public work schemes. The advocates of this proposal must be prepared to answer affirmatively two questions. First, do public work schemes provide a net addition to employment? Second, is there work available which is socially profitable and at the same time of such a nature that it can be carried through in a period of emergency?

In the first place, then, we have to ask whether public work schemes can create a net addition to employment. Now, in several quarters it is denied that the State can create employment by such schemes. The Treasury, for example, which is the most influential department of the Civil Service, holds this view.

What is the basis of this belief that, if the State promotes, say, the construction of roads, it would not thereby create additional employment? In order to employ extra men on road construction, it is pointed out, the State would have to raise the necessary money in one of two ways. It must either borrow the money or raise it by taxation. In either case, it is asserted, there would be no net increase in employment; the only change would be that a certain amount of money which was formerly spent or invested by private individuals would now be spent by the State.

Mr. Harold Cox, prominent exponent of economics from the Free Trade angle, held this view. Writing in 1931 on the subject of "The Futility of Relief Works," he asked:

"Where is the money for State grants to come from? It can only come from the pocket of the tax payer . . . . There is no increase in the demand for labour, if the tax payer's money is taken from him to be spent by the State instead of by himself; there is merely a transference of employment. And such a transference may prove to be an injury instead of a benefit to the community. For the man who loses a job because the tax payer has to cut down personal expenditure, was previously producing something which, at any rate, had the merit of commanding a sale; but there is no guarantee that anybody will want the things produced when the State pays for work merely for the purpose of providing employment . . . ."

Effect of Relief Works. Thus Mr. Cox not only denied the possibility of creating additional employment, but also that there is profitable relief work for public authorities to undertake. Let us concentrate on the first point and ask what would happen if the State put in hand road construction schemes involving the expenditure of £100,000,000.

In the first place, the road contractors who undertake the work and the industries which supply them with materials will take on more men—men who were previously unemployed. Now this will mean a reduction in the £200,000,000 or so a year which is spent on the dole. Clearly, this reduction in unemployment pay is a net gain to the State and would contribute towards the cost of the new roads without entailing any transfer of expenditure. This would be our first source of finance for creating additional employment.

Our second source is the idle savings of the community. In a time of depression, as we have seen, business men lack the confidence to launch out on new enterprises. As a consequence, a not inconsiderable proportion of the savings of the community remains idle in the banks. Thus the banks have more to lend than business men are willing to borrow.

Now the road contractors will require more credit in order to pay their increased wages bill and to obtain the necessary materials. When they go to the banks for additional credit they will be received with open arms. For the banks, in a period of depression, are only too anxious to find a safe and profitable outlet for their idle funds. Nor will the additional credit which the road contractors receive decrease the supply for other purposes as would be the case in normal times ; it would merely mean that, the idle savings of the community, which otherwise would run to waste, were being utilized. The idle savings of the community, then, are the second source of finance for creating employment.

Our third and final source is the wealth which the work schemes would create. As Professor Clay puts it, expansion itself provides the resources out of which expansion is possible. In many cases the new values created by the development work contribute substantially towards the expenditure involved.

There are, then, three sources of finance from which a net addition to employment can be created, namely, the saving on the dole, the savings which now run to waste by lying idle in the banks, and the values created by the work schemes themselves.

The next point we have to consider is whether there is work which is both available and suitable for public work schemes. The suggestions usually put forward are road construction, land drainage and reclamation, electricity development, bridges, improvement of harbours, telephones, and housing. Of these items housing is by far the most important. On no social problem is there such unanimity of opinion as on that of housing. The Church, all three political parties, and the local authorities are agreed that the slum areas are a disgrace to our civilization and ought to be cleared as soon as is possible.

By far the greatest experiment in public works so far embarked upon is the " New Deal " sponsored by President Roosevelt in the U.S.A. since 1933. The Industrial Recovery Act (I.R.A.) provided for the expenditure of nearly £800 millions on public works, and in one year more than two million workless were put back into employment. Despite much criticism from those who deplored the increase in taxation and in the burden of the national debt, the public works programme became, in the President's words, " a permanent feature of our modernized industrial structure." Such schemes as that for the development of electric power and industries based thereon in the Tennessee Valley, and the reafforestation and other land improvement work of the Civilian Conservation Corps, may be said to be of much more than American application. Nevertheless, it must be admitted that the vast expenditure of wealth and labour did not result in the complete absorption of the unemployed ; indeed, years after the launching of I.R.A. America's workless were still in excess of ten million.

The " New Deal," taken in conjunction with the many economic innovations in such states as Germany and Italy where a policy of " autarky " or national self-sufficiency is in vogue, serves to remind us that economics is, as Professor Sir W. J. Ashley, leading member in England of the historical school of economists, wrote in 1888, " not a body of absolutely true doctrines, revealed to the world at the end of the last and the beginning of this century, but a number of more or less valuable theories and genaralizations".

" As modern economists have taken for their assumptions conditions which only in modern times have begun to exist," he went on, " so earlier economic theories were based, consciously or unconsciously, on conditions then present. Hence the theories of the past must be judged in relation to the facts of the past, and not in relation to those of the present. History seems to be proving that no great institution has been without its use for a time, and its relative justification. Similarly, it is beginning to appear that no great conception, no great body of doctrines which really influenced society for a long period, was without a certain truth and value, having regard to contemporary circumstances. . . . Modern economic theories, therefore, are not universally true ; they are true neither for the past, when the conditions they postulate did not exist, nor for the future, when, unless society becomes stationary, the conditions will have changed."

Books Recommended for Further Reading. H. Clay's " Economics for the General Reader," Macmillan ; E. Cannan's " Wealth," King ; Sir W. Layton's " Study of Prices," Macmillan ; H. D. Henderson's " Supply and Demand," D. H. Robertson's " Money," in Cambridge Economic Handbook Series ; G. Bernard Shaw's " Intelligent Woman's Guide to Socialism, Capitalism, etc.," Penguin Books.

This Lesson concludes our Course in Economics.

ENGINEERING

Some Alternating Current Motors
(See plate 23)

I T has been shown in Lesson 32 (Volume 5, page 258) that, with direct current, the action of a motor is just the reverse of the dynamo, and that a direct current machine will operate either as a generator or as a motor, according as to whether it is supplied with energy in the mechanical or the electrical form. The same is true, in principle at any rate, of alternating current, but there are certain peculiar properties about alternating current which lead to variations in the machines connected with its use.

In the generation of alternating current (Lesson 33, Volume 5, page 261), the field magnets are supplied with direct current in order to produce a steady magnetic field, and the movement of the conductors relative to the field generates an electric current in the conductors. If such a machine is to be used as a motor, the conductors must be supplied with alternating current, while the field magnets are supplied with direct current. Though it is easy to obtain the direct current for the field-coils of the generator, by mounting a small direct current dynamo on an extension of the alternator shaft, it would be very inconvenient to have to provide direct current for the magnetic field in the case of all the small motors supplied from one large generator. Such an arrangement would involve having separate supplies of alternating current and direct current, and would, for obvious economical reasons, be unsuitable except in certain exceptional cases. The one special feature of a motor of this type is that it operates in step with the generator, on account of the alternations in the supply current, and it gives, therefore, a definite constant speed. For most industrial purposes, however, it is not suitable, for the reasons given above, and a motor is used in which only an alternating current is required.

Induction Motors. One of the special advantages of using three-phase alternating current is in its application to the driving of motors, due to the possibility of producing a rotating field by this means. A three-phase generator supplies alternating current to three separate conductors, which may, however, be insulated from each other and enclosed in a single cable for transmission purposes. The currents in the three conductors increase and decrease and reverse in direction in exactly the same manner, but not at exactly the same time; in other words, they are out of phase with one another. If now the three conductors be connected to three field-coils arranged around a circle, each coil will generate a magnetic field which increases and decreases in intensity, and changes in direction, in phase with its supply current. Just as the currents in the three conductors attain their maximum values one after the other, in a definite rotation, so the magnetic fields set up by their currents attain their maximum values one after the other, in the same rotation. The resultant effect is that of a magnetic field moving around from one field magnet to the next. A conductor placed in this field will have a current induced in it by the action of the rotating field, and it will be acted upon by a force tending to carry it around with the rotating field. In this way the rotor may be caused to rotate owing to the variations in the magnetic field, and without being connected to any supply of electricity.

Squirrel-cage Motors. What is perhaps the very simplest type of alternating current motor is the squirrel-cage motor, which operates on the principle outlined above. A revolving magnetic field is produced by the supply of three-phase current to the poles of the field magnets. The number of poles must, for three-phase current, be three or a multiple of three. The rotor consists of a drum in the surface of which conductors are embedded. These conductors are simply connected together at the ends, and give the rotor the appearance of a cage, from which it derives its name. In some small motors the conductors are eliminated altogether, the currents induced in the body of the rotor giving the necessary driving torque. The stator and rotor of a small motor of this type are shown in Fig. 1 (Plate 23). The ends of the stator windings providing the rotating magnetic field are clearly seen. The rotor in this case is an aluminium alloy casting, and is provided with vanes projecting at the ends for cooling.

The squirrel-cage motor, with its simple rotor, and lack of electrical connexions to the rotor, is relatively cheap to manufacture, and is used wherever possible. The elimination of sliding electrical contacts for the supply of current to the rotor is a great advantage in cases where sparking, at the commutator of a direct current machine or at the slip-rings of an alternating current machine, may have disastrous results.

ALTERNATING CURRENT MOTORS

The disadvantage of this simple motor is that it has a very low starting torque, that is, it develops very little power until it has got up to speed. It is therefore unsuitable for purposes where the motor is required to start under load, and is only applicable when the motor may first be run up to normal speed, and the load then thrown on. The starting torque may be increased by supplying current to the conductors of the rotor, through slip-rings on the shaft. For three-phase current, three slip-rings are required, and the construction of the rotor is much more expensive than for the squirrel-cage type. The supply current to the rotor is only required at starting, to increase the torque which the conductors would normally supply themselves, and as the speed rises the rotor current is gradually cut out. A rotor for a motor of this type is illustrated in Fig. 2 (Plate 23). This shows the arrangement of the conductors along the surface of the rotor, the three slip-rings at the farther end of the shaft, and the ventilating fan at the near end.

A large motor of the slip-ring type is shown in Fig. 3. The slip-rings are enclosed in a flame-proof casing on the left-hand end of the shaft, in order to prevent the emission of sparks to the surrounding atmosphere. This motor is suitable for three-phase current at 2,200 volts, and develops 500 horse-power at a speed of 326 revolutions per minute.

Single-phase Motors. In a motor supplied with single-phase current, the magnetic field is a pulsating one, and not a rotating field. When the rotor is at rest, currents are induced in the conductors by the action of this pulsating field, but they exert equal forces on the rotor in opposite directions, and there is no tendency for the rotor to revolve. When the rotor is revolving, however, the induced currents do produce a twisting moment on the shaft. It is therefore necessary to provide some means of bringing the motor up to its normal speed before the single phase is switched on. One method of doing this is to supply a separate winding for starting, and this winding is supplied with current through a choking coil, which alters the phase of the current passing through it. The other part of the winding is supplied with the normal current. The effect is the same as if two-phase current were supplied, and a rotating magnetic field is produced. When the rotor attains its normal speed the special starting supply is cut out, and the motor runs on the single-phase current.

Construction of A.C. Transformers

(See plate 24)

I N large electrical distribution systems, where electrical energy is conveyed over long distances, high voltages are invariably used. For a given power to be transmitted, the current flowing in the conductor is inversely proportional to the voltage, and, as the size of the conductor must be proportional to the strength of the current, it follows that the higher the voltage the smaller the conductor. If the power is conveyed by underground cable, the conductor must be insulated from the surrounding earth, and there is an economic limit to the extent to which the voltage may be raised. The higher the voltage the more difficult and expensive it becomes to provide the necessary insulation, and a point is reached where the increase in the cost of the insulation more than offsets the decrease in the cost of the conductor itself.

If, however, aerial conductors are used, the conductor wire is left bare, and requires only to be insulated from the poles or towers from which it is supported. The limiting factor here is the mechanical strength of the conductor ; it must be strong enough to withstand the pull exerted by the supports without too much sag in the middle. From the point of view of economy, so long as the wire is strong enough, the smaller it is the better ; hence very high voltages are employed. In the vast scheme for the distribution of electricity throughout Great Britain by means of the " grid," the main lines of the system are arranged to transmit energy at as high a pressure as 132,000 volts.

This high voltage is, in general, only useful for the *transmission* of electricity. When the energy is to be converted to some other form, to light in the lamp, to heat in the radiator, or to mechanical energy in the motor, it is usually desirable to work with much lower voltages than that given above. The problem of insulation limits the voltage which can be used economically with domestic as well as industrial appliances. The same problem limits the voltage at which the electricity can be generated. When the electricity is generated its voltage may be raised (stepped up) for transmission purposes, and when it reaches its destination its voltage may be reduced (stepped down) to a value suitable for use by the consumer. This is known as transforming the voltage, and is carried out in a transformer.

The above remarks apply equally well to both alternating current and direct current, but transformers for the two types of current are essentially different both in construction and in operation. For alternating current it is possible to use a piece of stationary apparatus to give any desired transformation, but for direct current moving machinery is required. Apart from the expense, the difficulty of insulating the moving conductors sets a limit to the extent to which the direct current voltage may be raised. This has led to the general adoption of alternating current for extensive systems of supply.

Electro-Magnetic Induction. A simple arrangement by which the principle of the transformer may be illustrated is shown in Fig. 1. Two conductors are lying close to each other; one is

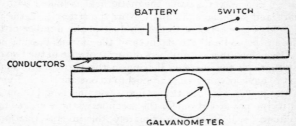

ELECTRO-MAGNETIC INDUCTION, **Fig. 1.** Diagram illustrating the principle of the transformer. For details see text.

connected to a storage battery through a switch, so that a current may be started or stopped in this conductor by closing or opening the switch. The ends of the other conductor are connected to a galvanometer, an instrument used to indicate the passage of an electric current in a circuit. When the switch is closed and current flows in the first conductor, the needle of the galvanometer makes a momentary movement, and returns to its zero position. While the current is flowing at a steady rate in the first circuit, the galvanometer in the second remains at its zero position, showing that no current is flowing in that circuit; but when the switch is opened, and the current in the first conductor falls to zero, the galvanometer again indicates a current in the second conductor, but this time in the opposite direction to that obtained by switching on. It may thus be shown that a current is induced in the second circuit when the current in the first is changed, and the induced current flows only during the time the first current is changing in strength. Also, the direction of the induced current depends upon whether the first current is increasing or decreasing. This induced current is caused by the changing density of the magnetic field in which the conductor is lying, and the strength of the induced current depends upon the strength of the magnetic field and upon the rate at which it changes in strength. If the first circuit be supplied with alternating current, the intensity of the magnetic field surrounding this conductor will be continually changing, and a similarly changing current will be induced in the other conductor.

In practice, in order that the second conductor may have the full benefit of the magnetic field due to the first, the two conductors are formed in coils, and a continuous iron core passes through both coils. In this way the same magnetic field is linked with both primary and secondary circuits. Now the strength of the magnetic field is proportional to the product of the number of turns of wire in the coil and the strength of the current flowing in the coil. By using different numbers of turns of wire in the two coils, the strength of the currents flowing in the two circuits may be caused to have any desired relationship to one another. Further, since the power put into the primary winding is approximately equal to the power got out of the secondary, the voltages in the two circuits will have approximately the inverse relationship to that of the currents. For example, if a transformer be required to reduce the voltage from 3,000 to 300, the voltage on the primary coil is ten times that on the secondary, therefore the current in the primary side is one-tenth of that in the secondary, and hence the number of turns in the primary coil must be ten times the number in the secondary coil. The high voltage winding consists of a large number of turns of comparatively fine wire, while the low voltage coil is made up of a smaller number of turns of thicker wire.

Actually, all the energy put into the primary side of a transformer does not appear in the secondary ; there are losses of energy in transformation. These losses may be divided into two separate parts : copper loss, that is, the loss due to the resistance of the copper conductors ; and iron loss, due to the resistance of the iron to the lines of magnetism. The copper loss may be reduced by using conductors of large cross-section, and the iron loss may be reduced by using a core of large cross-section, but in both cases the size and cost of the transformer are increased. The energy lost in both directions is converted to heat, and the total loss must be kept within definite limits to prevent overheating of the transformer and the breakdown of the insulation.

Transformer Construction. A large three-phase transformer in course of construction is shown in Fig. 2 (Plate 24). There are three cores, connected at top and bottom ; the illustration shows only the bottom connexion in position. The three phases are shown at different stages of construction ; first, the iron core alone ; second, the low voltage winding surrounding the core ; third, the high voltage winding which is placed over and around the low voltage winding. It will be noticed that the outer windings are separated by distance pieces ; the object of this is to facilitate the easy flow of the cooling medium around and over the windings.

In small transformers the quantity of heat generated is usually so small that it is easily disposed of by radiation to the atmosphere. For the large sizes shown in Fig. 2, however, it is necessary to provide some positive method of cooling. A blast of cooling air is sometimes blown over the windings, but more often the transformer is immersed in oil, which circulates around the winding and then passes through some cooling device. A typical tank is shown in Fig. 3. The transformer is immersed in oil inside the tank, and the heat given up to the oil is radiated from the external tubes through which the oil circulates. These tubes are often of plain round section, but in the case shown they are made with projecting fins or gills, in order to increase their capacity for transferring the heat from the oil to the atmosphere.

LESSON 36
Rotary and Motor Converters
(See plate 25)

IF electricity is required for lighting or heating, alternating current and direct current are equally suitable ; but if required for driving a motor, then the nature of the work the motor has to do must be taken into account. It may happen, therefore, that the transmission and the application of the electricity may conflict as regards the suitability of alternating current or direct current. Fortunately, however, there is no need to forgo the advantages of either type, because the current may be converted from alternating to direct, or from direct to alternating. As alternating current is generally used for transmission, the conversion is usually from alternating to direct current. The machines used are known as converters.

Rotary Converter. The conversion from one type of current to another may be carried out with two machines coupled together. For converting alternating to direct current, an alternating current motor may be supplied with power from the transmission line and arranged to drive a direct current generator. In this case two complete machines would be required, each having its own armature and field windings. The arrangement may be simplified, and the cost reduced, by combining the two machines into one, with only one field system and one armature winding.

In the Lessons dealing with the generation of direct current and alternating current, it was pointed out that the underlying principle is the same in both cases. A revolving conductor has alternating current generated in it as it passes alternating north and south poles of the field magnet. If the conductors be connected to slip rings on the shaft, the alternating current may be taken off for use in the external circuit; if the slip rings be replaced by a commutator, a continuous current will flow in the external circuit. In the rotary converter the armature conductors are connected to slip rings at one end of the shaft and to a commutator at the other end, and the alternating current supplied to the slip rings is passed to the commutator, where it is changed to direct current.

In general appearance the rotary converter resembles a direct current generator. The armature winding, the field coils, and the commutator are the same as in the direct current generator. Instead of an engine supplying mechanical power, however, the converter has slip rings for the application of electrical power. The converter is, of course, reversible in its action; that is, if direct current be supplied to the commutator end of the machine, alternating current will be generated at the slip rings. A typical armature for a rotary converter is shown in Fig. 1 (Plate 25), the commutator may be seen on the left hand end of the shaft, and the slip rings on the right.

Motor Converter. The motor converter consists of an alternating current induction motor, direct coupled to a direct current generator. In addition to the mechanical connexion between the two machines, there is electrical connexion between the rotor of the induction motor and the armature of the direct current generator. Part of the energy supplied to the induction motor is converted to mechanical energy and is used to drive the direct current machine as a generator. The remainder passes directly from the rotor of the induction motor to the armature of the other machine, and is converted to direct current at the commutator. In respect of this latter part of the energy the set acts as a rotary converter.

The construction of the motor converter is illustrated in Figs. 2 and 3. Fig. 2 shows the stationary part of the combined machine, the stator of the alternating current motor at the near end and the field magnets of the direct current generator behind. The combined rotor and armature is shown in Fig. 3; the direct current armature and the commutator are on the left, and the alternating current rotor and the slip rings on the right. The cooling fan is placed in the centre.

In general, the rotary converter and the motor converter are similar in their operation. The rotary converter is simpler in construction and is generally more efficient than the motor converter. The latter has advantages for some purposes, however, as it is less sensitive to sudden fluctuations in load, and will give a better performance where such fluctuations are of frequent occurrence.

Mercury-Arc Rectifier. This rectifier is a stationary piece of apparatus which converts alternating current to direct current. It consists of a closed vessel from which the air has been evacuated by a suction pump. At the bottom of the vessel is a small reservoir containing mercury, and projecting into the upper part of the vessel are a number of iron electrodes to which are attached the conductors carrying the supply of alternating current. The direct current given out by the rectifier is taken away by a conductor which penetrates into the mercury reservoir.

If a direct current were supplied to the iron electrode, and the space inside the vessel filled with mercury vapour, a continuous arc discharge would take place from the iron to the mercury in the reservoir. If the connexions were reversed, however, the electrical discharge would not take place in the opposite direction. The current must flow from the iron to the mercury—not from the mercury to the iron. The iron is the positive electrode, or anode, and the mercury is the negative, or cathode. If now an alternating current be substituted for the direct supply, only that part of the current flowing in the positive direction will be transmitted through the mercury vapour to the cathode. When the supply current changes in direction no discharge takes place. Thus the current arriving at the cathode is always in the same direction, and direct current will flow in the circuit leading from this cathode.

If only one anode were used, the output from the cathode would be discontinuous, flowing only during half of each cycle. Further, the voltage during this half cycle would vary in the same manner as the supply voltage, that is, it would increase from zero to its maximum value, and then fall to zero again. A current of this nature would, of course, be unsuitable for most purposes for which direct current is required, one of the most important requirements being a steady continuous voltage. In practice, however, it is usual to supply the rectifier with three-phase current ; and by making the connexions in a special way, six anodes may be used, giving six discharges in each cycle. These discharges overlap to such an extent that the individual variations are almost wiped out, and the current flowing from the cathode is continuous and at an approximately constant voltage.

Most of the energy supplied to the anodes is transmitted through the mercury vapour to the cathode, and the only loss is that due to the heat generated during the discharge from one electrode to the other. This heat vaporizes some of the mercury at the bottom of the rectifier, maintaining an adequate supply of vapour to continue the arc. Vapour in excess of that required is cooled and condensed in another part of the rectifier and trickles back to the reservoir. The energy lost in rectification by this method is less than that lost in the converting machinery described earlier in this Lesson, and on account of this higher efficiency the mercury-arc rectifier is being used to an increasing extent in electrical engineering.

LESSON 37

Britain's Electric 'Grid' System

BEFORE one can appreciate the advantages of a system of inter-connected electricity generating stations it is necessary to consider the conditions of operation of an isolated station. In any district served by such a station the demand for electricity varies from hour to hour, and fluctuates between wide limits. The maximum demand may well be of the order of twice the average load taken over the whole day. The maximum daily load will itself fluctuate from day to day, and may be much greater at one season of the year than at another. The actual nature and extent of this fluctuation in the demand on a station depends upon the nature of the load, whether for industrial or domestic purposes, but in all cases the station must be designed to meet the maximum load. This means that for comparatively long periods a large proportion of the available plant in the station is not working to its full capacity, and, therefore, at less than its maximum efficiency. Also, in an isolated station a considerable quantity of spare machinery must be installed in case of a breakdown of the main plant. Finally, it has been proved conclusively that even when working under its best conditions a small station cannot operate as efficiently as a large station, as large units are both more economical and more efficient.

The advantages of an inter-connected system of generation and distribution may be given under four heads. (1) A comparatively small number of very large central stations may be employed, with consequent economy in first cost. (2) It is not necessary to provide such a large proportion of stand-by machinery as in an isolated station, because in the event of a breakdown of the generating plant a supply can be obtained from the station to which it is connected. A bigger proportion of the capital invested in the plant is thus used productively. (3) In many districts, owing to the varying demands of the industries, the times at which the peak loads occur will be different. In such cases it is not necessary for each station to be able to meet its peak load, as a supply will be available from other stations, which have a surplus of energy at that particular time. Thus a smaller total quantity of plant is required, it is operated nearer its maximum capacity, and, therefore, nearer its maximum efficiency. (4) The sites for new stations can be chosen with reference to the available supplies of fuel and water, and are not so much dependent upon local boundaries. Also, the country's natural resources of water power may be utilized to their maximum capacity by supplying power to the transmission network.

The importance of the points outlined above was recognized by those responsible for the co-ordination of our supplies of power, and it was realized that there would be a great advantage in having a national system covering the whole country with a network of inter-communications between important stations. Accordingly, as a result of the Electricity (Supply) Act of 1926, a Central Electricity Board was set up, its object being to undertake the erection of the " grid," and to superintend the operation of the selected stations. The function of the Board is to cooperate with the electricity supply industry in reducing the costs of production, at the same time increasing the area over which the supply is available.

The design and construction of this " grid " scheme of inter-connexion have now been completed, and the results of its operation have so far been satisfactory. For the purpose of the application of the scheme the country was divided up into a number of large areas, called regions, and for each region a scheme was prepared, giving details of the proposed generating stations and transmission lines, together with an estimate of the probable cost of putting the scheme into operation. Although these schemes for the different regions were drawn up separately, and the construction was carried out at different times, everything was done with a view to a properly co-ordinated scheme for the whole country. This final scheme is described and illustrated in the Fifth Annual Report of the Central Electricity Board (published by Whitehead Morris, price 5s.).

Another advantage of a system of supply such as the " grid " is the standardization of equipment thus rendered possible. Previously, the various supply companies used altogether different systems, some direct current, some alternating current, at varying voltages ; and those supplying alternating current used different frequencies. The " grid " has been designed for three-phase alternating current, at a frequency of 50 cycles per second. The

ELECTRICAL CONVERTERS. Fig. 1 (top). Armature of tap-started rotary converter. **Fig. 2** (centre) Stator of motor converter. **Fig. 3** (bottom). Armature and rotor of motor converter (to different scale). ENGINEERING 36

Courtesy of the General Electric Co., Ltd.

BATTERSEA POWER STATION. These photographs of the generating station of the London Power Company, on the south bank of the Thames at Battersea, show (**Fig. 2,** bottom) jetty and coal handling plant and (**Fig. 3,** top) the foundations of the north chimney tower. ENGINEERING 38

Courtesy of the London Power Co., Ltd.

Plate 26   *Volume VI*

BATTERSEA POWER STATION. Fig. 4 (above). View of the interior of the combustion chamber of one of the boilers. **Fig. 5** (below). General view of the turbine room with two of the main units in position. ENGINEERING 38
Courtesy of the London Power Company, Ltd.

TURBO-ALTERNATORS. **Fig. 6.** High-pressure and intermediate pressure cylinders on the test bed ; upper halves removed to show the rotors in position. **Fig. 7** (below). Stator before fixing for 80,000 K.V.A. alternator.
ENGINEERING 38

Courtesy of the London Power Company, Ltd.

Plate 28

Volume VI

main transmission lines work at a pressure of 132,000 volts, and most of the secondary distribution lines at 33,000 volts. In order to obtain the maximum possible span between supports for the conductors, it was decided to use steel-cored aluminium conductors supported from steel towers.

In any inter-connected system such as the " grid," efficient operation of the whole can only be obtained with some form of central control, and for each region a single control station has been established. This station is so equipped and connected with the various generating stations that the control engineer can see at a glance the operation of the whole system in that region. He has continuous information as to the plant in operation and available for operation at each station, the energy being taken from or supplied to the general system by each station, and the power in each feeder circuit, as well as the operation of the various transformers and circuit-breakers.

LESSON 38

Battersea's Monster Power Station

(See plates 26-28)

ONE of the most interesting power stations erected in connexion with the grid scheme of inter-communication and electrical distribution is that put into operation at Battersea. The site for the station was chosen only after prolonged discussion and investigation of several available alternatives, and Battersea was decided upon because it offered definite advantages from the overall economic point of view.

The station has been designed for an ultimate capacity of 400,000 kilowatts, but for the present only a portion of this is being developed. In Fig. 1 (page 227), which is a plan of the station, it will be seen that the site is bounded on the north by the river Thames and on the west by railway sidings. The coal is brought up the river in 2,000-ton colliers, but arrangements have also been made for transport by rail as an alternative if necessary. Only half of the final building has so far been erected, giving accommodation for nine steam-raising units and three generating sets. Of these only six boilers and two generating sets were installed. The spaces to be devoted to the remainder of the equipment are clearly indicated on the plan.

The coal is unloaded from the colliers by the two cranes shown on the coaling jetty, and dropped into hoppers which feed it on to the coal conveyor. This conveyor consists of two belts, 1A and 1B in Fig. 1, which raise the coal as it passes to the eastern end of the jetty. It then falls through chutes on to the second pair of conveyor belts, 2A and 2B, which raise the coal to the top of the distributing tower A. It is so arranged that the coal may be taken from this tower to the storage ground or direct to the boilers, as may be required, or it may be discharged into railway wagons for transportation to other stations to which the colliers have no direct access. These cranes and conveyors are shown in Fig. 2 (Plate 26), the tower A being in the background. On the right of this photograph are seen the rollers for the conveyor belt by which the coal is brought from tower A to the storage ground, or back from the storage ground to the tower when required for use in the boilers. This belt is No. 3 in Fig. 1, on which the coal store is also shown. This storage ground, which will accommodate 75,000 tons of coal, is served by a travelling bridge on which there are two conveyor belts, Nos. 4 and 5. When coal is being delivered to storage it is dropped from belt No. 3 to No. 4, and tipped off belt No. 4 in any required position. When coal is being taken from storage it is lifted by the two cranes shown on the travelling bridge and dropped on the upper conveyor belt. No. 5. This in turn deposits the coal on the main belt No. 3, which takes it to the distributing tower A. From the distributing tower the coal is delivered to the boiler house by means of double conveyor belts 6A and 6B, 7A and 7B, and 9A and 9B. A single belt, No. 8, on the right-hand side of Fig. 1, may be used to deal with coal delivered to the station in railway wagons.

Below the coaling jetty is the intake for the condenser circulating water, provided with a screening chamber for the removal of solid matter which might cause obstructions in either the pumps or the condensers. The circulating water outlet is at the western end of the jetty, and when the second section of the station is built a second outlet will be provided at the eastern end. The power station building itself is of steel-framed construction, encased in brickwork of a brownish colour. The two chimneys for the present boiler house are situated one at each end, and are supported on reinforced concrete platforms, one of which is shown in course of construction in Fig. 3. On this platform a rectangular

BATTERSEA POWER STATION

brickwork tower has been built up to a height of 200 feet, to accommodate part of the special gas-washing plant necessary to remove the sulphur fumes. The chimney proper rises from the top of this tower to a height of 337 feet above ground level.

The boiler house is 500 feet long, and can accommodate nine boilers, of which only six were installed at first.

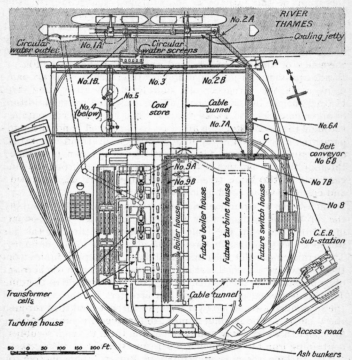

FIG. 1. PLAN OF BATTERSEA POWER STATION
Courtesy of London Power Co.

Each boiler is capable of a maximum output of 330,000 lb. of steam per hour. The steam is generated at a pressure of 650 lb. per sq. inch. and is superheated to a final temperature of 875 to 900 deg. Fahrenheit. The boilers are of the water-tube type, with mechanical stokers. Fig. 4 (Plate 27) is an internal

(227)

view of the combustion chamber of one of the boilers, showing the furnace bed and the pit into which the ashes are discharged as the burning fuel is pushed forward and downward. The coal is fed into the furnace at the left-hand side of the illustration, and is gradually pushed forward by the new supply entering behind it. The rate at which the burning coal is moved towards the front of the furnace is so controlled that combustion is complete before the ash is pushed over into the pit.

Each boiler has a steam drum 47 feet long, 48 inches internal diameter, and weighing about 36 tons. Besides the ordinary boiler tubes above the furnace, additional tubes are fitted around the sides of the furnace, behind the blocks shown in Fig. 4. Besides providing a greater useful heating surface, this arrangement cools the furnace walls and lengthens their life. The heating surface of the boiler is further increased by the addition of an economizer and an air heater. The feed water is pumped through the economizer on its way to the boiler, and the temperature raised to a value approaching the saturation temperature of the steam. The air for combustion of the fuel is pumped through the air heaters, extracting further heat from the flue gas, and at the same time increasing the furnace temperature and ensuring rapid combustion.

Each boiler is equipped with eight fans ; four of these supply the air to the furnace while the other four draw the products of combustion from the boiler and pass them through the gas washers and scrubbers before discharging them to the chimney. The arrangements for the removal of dust and sulphur fumes from the flue gas are a special feature of this power station, on account of its proximity to the residential area of the West End of London. The gas is passed first through grit arresters for the removal of the suspended ash carried over from the furnace, and then through the washers. The sulphur fumes are removed by subjecting the flue gas to a water spray and then passing them through scrubbers containing iron filings which are kept moistened.

The turbine room is illustrated in Fig. 5. The photograph shows two of the main units after installation. The turbines are at the ends nearest the camera in each case. In the set in the foreground the three separate steam cylinders may be distinguished , the high-pressure turbine comes first, then the intermediate-pressure turbine, both with circular polished covers. On the other side of the intermediate-pressure cylinder may be seen two large pipes supplying the steam to the middle of the low-pressure turbine. The steam flows from the middle towards both ends, and is then discharged into two condensers mounted just below the turbine.

The high-pressure and intermediate-pressure cylinders are made of cast steel, while the low-pressure cylinder is of cast iron. The turbine blades throughout are of machined stainless steel. Fig. 6 (Plate 28) shows the high-pressure and intermediate-pressure cylinders, with the upper halves removed to show the rotors in position. The high-pressure cylinder is at the farther end, as is evident by the difference in the diameters of the two rotors. The condensers attached to each turbine set have a total cooling surface of 60,000 square feet, and require nearly three million gallons of water an hour. The condensed steam is extracted from the condensers by centrifugal pumps and delivered into the boiler feed system, whence it is returned to the boilers by the feed pumps.

As regards the construction of the alternating current generator, it is perhaps sufficient to refer to Fig. 7, which is a view of the stator during construction, in order to obtain some idea of the size of the machine. Each alternator generates three-phase current at a pressure of 11,000 volts and a frequency of 50 cycles per second, and has a capacity of 80,000 K.V.A. The stator weighs 130 tons, while the rotor weighs 64 tons. On an extension of the main generating set are the service set, generating power for use in the station, and the exciters for both main and service generators. The overall length of the turbo-generator is 102 ft.

It has been possible in this brief Course in Engineering to deal only with the broad outline of the subject ; the following books are recommended for additional reading : " Structural Engineering," Husband and Harby (Longmans) ; " Reinforced Concrete Simply Explained," Faber (Oxford University Press) ; " Elementary Hydraulics," F. C. Lea (Arnold) ; " Heat Engines," Low (Longmans) ; " Applied Mechanics," Goodman (Longmans) ; Electrical Manufacture Series (Pitman) and Electrical Transmission and Distribution Series (Pitman).

This Lesson concludes our Course in Engineering.

LESSON 44

Scott's Successors in the Field of Fiction

(See plates 29 and 30)

ONE of Scott's contemporaries and followers in fiction was John Galt (1779–1839), who wrote a long series of Scottish tales and was the real progenitor of the so-called " Kailyard School," revived with so much clatter in the 'nineties. "Annals of the Parish," "The Entail," "The Provost," and "Sir Andrew Wylie" are among the best of Galt's novels.

In "The Adventures of Hajji Baba," by James Justinian Morier (c. 1780–1849) intimate knowledge of Persian life is displayed, and there is some of the real stuff of romance in "Salathiel," by George Croly (1780–1860).

Thomas Love Peacock (1785–1866) poured no little wit and knowledge of character—chiefly of his own character, with its hedonism, worldly virtues and venial sins—into the seven novels which stand to his name : "Headlong Hall," "Melincourt," "Nightmare Abbey," "Maid Marian," "The Misfortunes of Elphin," "Crotchet Castle" and "Gryll Grange." These works remain, like those of Landor, caviare to the general reader, but because of their erudite satire should not be neglected by the student. Lightened by whimsical humour, they are enhanced by the songs and lyrics scattered through them.

Frances Trollope (1780–1863), the mother of Anthony Trollope, was an industrious writer, of whose many novels "The Vicar of Wrexhill " and "The Widow Barnaby " are best remembered. Her books throw much illumination on the manners of one of the most interesting periods of modern English history.

Susan Edmonstone Ferrier (1782–1854) was a caustic but kindly-hearted delineator of old maids, pretty inanities, gauche doctors, and mock heroes. Like Maria Edgeworth and Fanny Burney, Miss Ferrier, in "Marriage," "The Inheritance," and "Destiny," laid bare the "humours " of her time. A gifted satirist of her sex, she found a wealth of material in the society amidst which she moved in Edinburgh.

Mary Russell Mitford (1787–1855) wrote "Our Village," a series of delightful sketches which enshrine the life of the little hamlet of Three Mile Cross, near Reading, with a fancy, brightness and pleasant humour all her own.

Mary Wollstonecraft Shelley (1797–1851), the second wife of the poet, and daughter of William Godwin and Mary Wollstonecraft, wrote in " Frankenstein " a novel which, despite its horrible theme—the creation by a student of a semi-human monster—possesses sufficient of the elements of human interest and of imaginative vitality to preserve it from oblivion.

With William Nugent Glascock (1787–1847) began the novel of the sea, which developed in the hands of Michael Scott (1789–1835), author of " Tom Cringle's Log " and " The Cruise of the Midge," two of the breeziest sea stories ever written, though discursive and lacking literary grace, and in the hands of other writers, until Captain Frederick Marryat (1792–1848) made the fiction of the sea a real asset of our national literature. Marryat's " Peter Simple," " Jacob Faithful," and " Mr. Midshipman Easy " are perhaps the best and most popular of his many works.

Irish novelists of the period include William Carleton (1794–1869), a peasant writer, who received his education in a " hedge school," and wrote, from what in his day was an unaccustomed angle, some very notable accounts of Irish peasant life ; he is perhaps best represented by the collection of sketches entitled " Traits and Stories of the Irish Peasantry," but his novel " Fardorougha the Miser " is a powerful tale ; Samuel Lover (1797–1868), writer of songs, dramas, and high-spirited, rollicking stories of conventionally acceptable Irish humour, achieved great popularity with " Rory O'More," later to be eclipsed by his " Handy Andy " ; and Charles James Lever (1800–72), author of " Charles O'Malley " and some three dozen other stories. Lever's brilliant caricatures, however, must not be taken as forming a real picture of Irish life.

The historical novels of George Payne Rainsford James (1799–1860) possess little interest today, and with those of the more popular William Harrison Ainsworth (1805–82) show the sharp decline of romance from the heights of the Waverley Novels, though Ainsworth may be considered as the father of the novel which depends upon a succession of exciting incidents for its popularity. There is undeniably some exhilaration to be derived from his " Old Saint Paul's," and " The Tower of London."

A much more important and attractive figure is George Henry Borrow (1803–81). There is a sort of cult of Borrow which glorifies the gipsy life, the foaming tankard and the swagger of vagabond scholarship. One may have little sympathy with this and yet owe many happy hours to " Lavengro " and " The Romany Rye," as well as to his inimitable travel books, such as the " Bible in Spain." Borrow is only a novelist in the picaresque sense, his fictional works lacking form and being mainly rambling records of imaginary experiences.

We encounter a novelist in a large way of business, as distinguished from one who might be described as an inspired amateur, when we turn from George Borrow to Edward George Earle Lytton Bulwer-Lytton (1803–73). One of the most prominent and, during his lifetime, one of the most popular of the Victorian novelists, he played a part in fiction similar to that played by Byron in poetry. He posed as the man of the world in " Pelham," as the man of feeling in " Ernest Maltravers," and as the man of mystery in " Zanoni." The novel of horrors has in " A Strange Story " a supreme example ; than " The Haunted and the Haunters," no better ghost story has been written. Lytton, with high success, too, essayed the historical romance in " The Last Days of Pompeii," " The Last of the Barons," " Rienzi," and " Harold " ; the criminal novel, in " Paul Clifford " and " Eugene Aram " ; and the novel of domestic life and ambition, in " The Caxtons," " My Novel," and " What Will He Do With It ? " A writer who, with Ainsworth and Lytton, came under the lash of Thackeray's satire, but who was a much greater man than either, was Benjamin Disraeli (1804–81). Disraeli won greater distinction as a statesman than as a novelist, and his works are valuable chiefly as so many keys to the secret of his extraordinary progress from obscurity to power and place. " Coningsby," " Sybil," " Tancred," " Lothair," and " Endymion " possess permanent interest for the student of politics and social conditions.

A novelist of very different type from these romantic authors, a novelist who wrote of nothing she did not understand and yet with purposeful artistry, was Elizabeth Cleghorn Gaskell (1810–65). Her fictional writings form a real link between the work of Jane Austen and that of Charlotte Brontë, whose biographer she was. " Mary Barton " is a passionate tale of the sorrows of the Manchester poor, and a book of live power. But Mrs. Gaskell's supreme achievement and perpetual memorial is " Cranford," a work of pathos, grace, eloquence and humour.

LESSON 45

Dickens and Thackeray

(See plate 31)

WITHIN a few months of each other, in the beginning of the second decade of the nineteenth century, were born two great men of English letters, masters in the art of fiction, who commanded a warmth of personal interest accorded to no other English writer before or since, and who still retain a secure place in the admiration and affection of a vast number of readers. To a certain extent complementary, Dickens and Thackeray confirm each other's views of a particular era in the history of England, though depicting phases of life widely apart.

William Makepeace Thackeray was born at Calcutta, July 18, 1811, son of an Indian Civil Servant, and was sent to England when he was six years old From private schools he passed on to Charterhouse and thence to Trinity College, Cambridge. In 1831 he entered the Middle Temple, but abandoned law for journalism, becoming a principal contributor to " Fraser's Magazine," a leading member of the " Punch " staff, and, in 1860, the first editor of " The Cornhill Magazine." He died on Christmas Eve, 1863. A confirmed clubman, Thackeray mingled freely in the best society of his time, and found the right subjects for his art in the world of rank and fashion and wealth, and the brighter side of life in England. Versatile and cultured, he wrote some delightful light verse, some of the best parodies in the language, some charming whimsicalities—notably " The Rose and the Ring "—and some first-rate criticism in " The English Humourists of the 18th Century " and in " The Four Georges," delivered as lectures in England and the United States. " The Book of Snobs " and the humorous " Yellowplush " memoirs of life below stairs were contributed to " Punch."

But it is on his imaginative and romantic novels that his fame securely rests. Chief among these are " Vanity Fair " (1848), " Pendennis " (1850), " Esmond " (1852), " The Newcomes " (1855), and " The Virginians " (1859). He was writing " Denis Duval " when he died. He was a student of 18th century England, and his books fall into two groups—those dealing with contemporary life and manners, of which " Vanity Fair " is the supreme example, and to which " The Newcomes " and " Pendennis " also belong, and those dealing with the 18th century of which " Esmond," that perfect picture of life in the reign of Queen Anne, with its sequel " The Virginians," is the predominant romance.

The final test of a great novel is that it teaches certain truths of human life and conduct, that it adds to the reader's store of knowledge and wisdom. This test can be applied to Thackeray's fiction. Of " Vanity Fair " it may be said that it admirably exemplifies Thackeray's creed, which is that goodness, however scorned, is its own sufficient reward ; at the same time no one can read this splendid novel without sympathy for and understanding of that attractive adventuress, Becky Sharp.

Thackeray has been lightly called a cynic. The word, applied to him, is misused. At the same time there is force in the contention that while Thackeray saw, loved, felt and makes us love the higher, brighter, purer side of life, he had a surer hand when depicting what was base and artificial. For explanation of this we must look to the political and social circumstances of the time in which he lived and wrote, and to his peculiar sensitiveness to all around him. Thackeray was no cynic, but he is the greatest of English satirists, a man who gibbeted snobbery for all time.

Dickens. Very different from those of Thackeray were the early environment and experiences of Charles Dickens, who on February 17, 1812, first opened his eyes upon the world which his genius was to do so much to make happier and better. No summary of his career is needed here ; the whole story is told in the Life of Dickens by his friend and confidant, John Forster— itself a classic, ample in its information, intimate in its knowledge, and wonderfully stimulating to read.

It is beyond all computation how many have been helped to smile through their tears and to take their courage in both hands under the influence of the inimitable, imperishable humour of Charles Dickens. Dickens saw the soul of goodness in ordinary things ; his was the saving grace of humour enriching those novels, too familiar by name to require setting forth here. He has enshrined in his wonderful portrait gallery not only the tragic and comic annals of the poor of a period, happily now no more, but he has shown us the possibilities of goodness and of happiness even in the most unlikely circumstances and characters. What

Dickens stood for in a social sense has been largely attained ; and the pose that affects to find his writings crude or antiquated is an unworthy affectation to be pitied, perhaps, as much as condemned. Dickens was " self-educated " ; he had obvious limitations, but his absolute genius is even more pronounced than that of Thackeray, of whose pictures of high life Dickens's transcripts from humble life may be said to form a necessary counterpart. Mawkish and sentimental sometimes, melodramatic and unreal on occasion, failing to inspire certain characters in fashionable society with life, Dickens's gallery contains portraits such as Micawber, Pickwick, Pecksniff, Sam Weller, the Marchioness, Mrs. Gamp, Betsy Trotwood, Uriah Heep, Squeers, the Wilfers, the Boffins, and the rest—too many to count—sure of immortality while the English language lasts.

LESSON 46

More Victorian Novelists

(See plates 32 and 33)

A NOVELIST who, like Charles Dickens, " wrote with a purpose," but who, unlike Dickens, was a scholar of no mean attainments rather than a genius, was Charles Reade (1814-84). He attacked prison scandals in " It is Never Too Late to Mend," private lunatic asylums in " Hard Cash," and " coffin ships " in " Foul Play." He has left us a vivid picture of industrial life in " Put Yourself in His Place," but his greatest book is indubitably " The Cloister and the Hearth," a medieval romance based on the " Colloquies " of Erasmus. He also wrote a number of plays, which brought him little renown.

Joseph Sheridan Le Fanu (1814-73) was an Irish novelist with a strong bent towards the " uncanny." He wrote some sixteen books in all, of which " Uncle Silas " is perhaps the best.

Anthony Trollope (1815-82) should be approached first of all in his " Autobiography." His series of Barchester novels—" The Warden," " Barchester Towers," " Dr. Thorne," " Framley Parsonage," " The Small House at Allington," and " The Last Chronicle of Barset "—represent very faithfully English clerical life in the 'fifties and 'sixties. The same people recur in the various books, including that masterpiece of comedy characterization, the redoubtable Mrs. Proudie. Trollope's studies of life in a cathedral town (Barchester is a thinly disguised Winchester) and diocese are invaluable to the student of the Victorian era, and will almost certainly enjoy in the future far greater popularity than they have had since Trollope passed away.

Charlotte Brontë (1816-55) struck in " Jane Eyre," " Shirley," and " Villette " the first clear bell-note of English womanhood in fiction, describing love for the first time from an average woman's point of view. Her work is part of her own pathetic life-story, her combined passionate energy and glow of expression breaking through the enforced self-suppression of her shadowed life. Emily Jane Brontë (1818-48) also displayed exceptional if morbid power in " Wuthering Heights " ; and Charlotte's youngest sister, Anne Brontë (1820-49), wrote two novels, " Agnes Grey " and " The Tenant of Wildfell Hall," which, while they gain in interest from their personal associations, vividly picturing moor-land scenery and the life of a governess, possess none of the power of her sisters' work. Before taking up the books of the three sisters, the student should read Mrs. Gaskell's classic " Life " of Charlotte Brontë and Clement Shorter's valuable appreciation, " Charlotte Brontë and Her Sisters." " Jane Eyre " is essentially melodramatic in detail, but there is artistry in the faithful observa-tion and sympathetic portrayal of character in " Villette," which is largely autobiographical. On the whole, though it is the custom to credit Charlotte with the honours of this remarkable trio of sisters, Emily, in both her prose and her poetry, " so terribly strong, so exquisitely subtle," was the most gifted of them. But there is probably no more humanly moving story in the annals of literature than that of these three shy, quiet and intensely courageous women, away there in the bleak and dismal sur-roundings of Haworth, transferring to paper their emotional and unconventional spiritual experiences, and making, eventually, the whole English-speaking world listen to them.

Charles Kingsley (1819-75) was a follower of Frederick Denison Maurice and Thomas Carlyle, and a manly exponent of " mus-cular Christianity," or " Christian Socialism." His books possess the prime quality of stimulus, " Alton Locke " and " Yeast " in particular. " Westward Ho ! " and " Hereward the Wake," fine historial romances, will always have a warm place in the hero-loving, adventure-seeking heart of youth. At one time rather overrated, he has now fallen into neglect. His brother, Henry Kingsley (1830-76), was in some respects a better novelist.

" Ravenshoe " is a finer piece of romantic fiction than " West-ward Ho ! " which would be named by most critics as the fine flower of Charles Kingsley's story-telling powers.

In George Eliot (Marian Evans) (1819—80) we have a great Eng-lish novelist. Like Charlotte Brontë, George Eliot put herself and her actual experiences into what she wrote. Her books are, for the most part, real, sincere, vigorous. Her genius flowered late ; some of her writings have the effect of finished buildings from which all the scaffolding has not been taken down. With her the writing of fiction was the art of thinking aloud, the novel was a form of philosophy ; but in the forefront of her philosophy —which, like Carlyle's, was devotion to duty—her characters stand out with life-like fidelity. She was influenced by her foreign, and especially German, studies.

A remarkable thing about George Eliot was that her undoubted scholastic attainments in no way fettered her power of objective imagination. The " Scenes of Clerical Life," " Adam Bede," " The Mill on the Floss," " Silas Marner," and, perhaps her greatest work, " Middlemarch," display her genius at its best. " Romola," a story of the Italian Renaissance, will always have its admirers. It betrays scholarship of no ordinary kind, but it was brilliant taskwork, and its author said afterwards that she was a young woman when she began the book and an old one when she finished it. " Daniel Deronda," another piece of task-work, should be studied with Disraeli's " Tancred " by those interested in the mysteries of the Hebrew character. But it is on her studies of the English lower middle class town and country life of her day, pictured with such humour and vivacity, such understanding and such solidity, that her fame securely rests.

The novel had now become a definite art form in the hands of numerous brilliant exponents, among whom were many women. The names of Mrs. Henry Wood, T. A. Browne (" Rolf Boldrewood "), Mrs. Lynn Linton, Charlotte M. Yonge, Dinah Maria Mulock (Mrs. Craik), Mrs. Oliphant, Ada Ellen Bayly (" Edna Lyall "), G. J. Whyte-Melville, Thomas Hughes, Wilkie Collins, George Macdonald and James Payn—each stands for one or two novels which after more than sixty years are still finding admiring readers.

None of them wrote such a classic of romance as " Lorna Doone," by Richard Doddridge Blackmore (1825–1900). It is on record that its original success in 1869 was due to a confusion in the public mind between the Lorna of the tale and the Lorne which became Princess Louise's name on marrying the Marquis of Lorne. The fictional Lady Lorna is the heiress of the Earl of Lorne, and on this most adventitious interest a masterpiece of romantic fiction, which was else sinking into oblivion, enjoyed a blaze of popularity. Although he has depicted heroines equal in charm to Lorna in " Cradock Nowell," " Alice Lorraine," and " The Maid of Sker," his construction in these stories is weak.

No novelist has been made the object of more frequent or less availing efforts to " log-roll " him into fame than William Hale White (1831–1913). There are critics who acclaim him one of the greatest writers of English, and put him, in respect of style, even before George Meredith. His best-known books, " The Autobiography of Mark Rutherford," " Mark Rutherford's Deliverance," and " The Revolution in Tanner's Lane," have never won any great measure of popularity, for, despite all the truth of " Mark Rutherford's " observation and wisdom of reflection, there is in his style a coolness, an intellectual detachment, that does not make for warmth of appreciation in the ordinary reader of novels. He lacks neither humour nor pathos, but is too continuously, and always somewhat sadly, concerned about immortality and the sectarian creeds that seek to confine it to their own narrow borders, to awaken the real glow of affection in his readers. He substitutes problems for romance.

Theodore Watts-Dunton (1832–1914) was the author of only one romance, " Aylwin," which he did not allow to leave his fastidious pen until he was sixty-six, but that beautiful story of the Romany life ranks quite easily among our modern classics.

If we except the prolific hack-work of Percy Fitzgerald, probably no author of his time wrote so much as Sabine Baring-Gould (1834–1924) ; " John Herring " and " Mehalah " were his best novels. Perhaps his most interesting book is " The Vicar of Morwenstow," a romantic semi-biography of the solitary and eccentric Cornish parson Robert S. Hawker, the author of " Cornish Ballads and other Poems," lover of birds, beasts, the soil, his chapel and glebe in the wild and lovely country near Tintagel. John Henry Shorthouse (1834–1903) did nothing else to compare with his " John Inglesant," a tale of indefinable charm of style in the historical manner, written in exquisite English, which achieved instant success on its publication in 1881.

LESSON 47

Meredith, Hardy and Stevenson

(See plates 34 and 35)

GEORGE MEREDITH (1828–1909) had the good fortune to become the most eminent figure of his later days in the English world of letters, sharing with Hardy the sunset glories of the " last of the great Victorians." Though his first book, a volume of poems, was published in 1851, Meredith did not begin to be appreciated by the public until quite thirty years later. To the student of contemporary English fiction Meredith, though he has not the depth or the breadth of wisdom possessed by Thackeray, or the humanity of Dickens, is something greater than a popular writer. He is, and has been for two generations, a great influence.

There are various reasons for the power he exerted over contemporaries. The chief is that he chose to look at life with his own eyes, and to depict it in his own words. He described his people as " actual, yet uncommon." But his characters all talk Meredith—even his fools are epigrammatic. His novels are analytical, not perceptive. He delights in analysing traits of character, in presenting a study of temperament rather than in building up concrete human beings. Meredith is thought-compelling. He gives exercise to the mind.

None of Meredith's novels can be fully appreciated at a first reading. Knowledge, as well as industry, is essential. His style is admittedly difficult ; it is like a river with many tortuous windings, but with noble reaches. But his English, at its best, is the best English of the time. He is to be studied, not imitated ; and the study should result in a disregard for the iteration of toil-worn phrases.

The best of Meredith's novels to begin with is " The Ordeal of Richard Feverel." If we ask " What is education ? " we have here an answer equivalent to many debates in Parliament and many speeches on political platforms. We have education not merely described, but seen in action. If we ask " What are love and passion ? " we have but to take up " Richard Feverel " to see these dominating attributes of our common human nature set forth with a freshness, a vigour, a reverence, a sympathy, a feeling for external nature—with a temperamental knowledge, in short—unrivalled by any other writer of contemporary fiction. If we seek the analysis of motive, of a particular trait of character, we cannot do better than study the dissection of Sir Willoughby Patterne in " The Egoist." " Beauchamp's Career," " Diana of the Crossways " and " Harry Richmond " are the best of Meredith's other novels ; " The Shaving of Shagpat " is the most imaginative.

Samuel Butler. As " reader " for Chapman and Hall, Meredith turned down " Erewhon," the first book written by Samuel Butler (1835–1902). With regard to its rejection by these publishers the author writes in his preface to the revised edition : " I believe their reader advised them quite wisely. They told me he reported that it was a philosophical work, little likely to be popular with a large circle of readers." There was certainly little to link the philosophy of " the first of the moderns " with that of the last but one of the great Victorian novelists.

Most thinkers of today owe something to Butler's ideas ; indeed, so penetrating have they been that it is difficult to realize—unless one is acquainted with " The Notebooks of Samuel Butler," in which his views are set forth in detail—how subversive they were in the writer's own period. " Erewhon " and its sequel, " Erewhon Revisited," stand in the highest rank of that class of fiction to which " Gulliver's Travels " belongs. The sequel, published thirty years after " Erewhon," is the finer work of art and contains the ripened Butlerian conclusions ; both books are attacks on the civilization of his day presented with irony, vivid flashes of humour and genuine satire. His great novel, " The Way of All Flesh," was published posthumously in 1902.

Sir Walter Besant (1838–1901) was a good, but not a great novelist. He wrote to some purpose, however, as his " All Sorts and Conditions of Men " gave a real impetus to social work in the East End of London. Besant was not an inspiring figure of romance—he was too eminently respectable ; but he never did a really poor piece of work, and " Ready-Money Mortiboy " and " The Golden Butterfly," written in collaboration with James Rice (1843–82), are first-rate stories.

Thomas Hardy. The note of paganism sounds in the writings of Thomas Hardy (1840–1928) as in Meredith, and yet it cannot be said that the novels of Meredith and those of Hardy have any noteworthy qualities in common. Meredith's earth-worship makes him in some sort a chastened optimist, while Hardy's reading of earth, with all his merry humour and brave fronting to fate, leaves him rather an unquerulous pessimist, resigned, uncomplaining, thrilling with pity for his fellows. To a far greater degree than we find it in Meredith, Hardy has dramatic power. But his voice—it is his novels only that are now being considered—is that of the countryside, of the countryside that is far removed from town. To him the greenwood tree suggests not merriment, but destiny; a pair of blue eyes not heaven, but fate. Life is a tragedy with a few interludes. Yet the philosophy of this old Dorset seer is stern, not weeping. The words of religion are quoted freely in his novels, but in the spirit of the soothsayer and son of the soil.

The peasants he introduces to us belong to a part of England whose exclusiveness has now been broken into. Their ways and modes of thought are depicted with a realism that is pitiless, though the novelist lightens his narratives with many a flash of genuine humour. Hardy is a writer who must be approached with an understanding of his own environment, which is the environment of the characters of his novels. His art may be locally circumscribed, but it is great art, nevertheless. His characters are conceived grandly.

His best works appeared in the following order : " Under the Greenwood Tree " (1872), " A Pair of Blue Eyes " (1873), " Far From the Madding Crowd " (1874), " The Return of the Native " (1878), " The Mayor of Casterbridge " (1886), " The Wood-landers " (1886–7), " Tess of the D'Urbervilles "—his greatest novel—(1891), and " Jude the Obscure " (1894–5). The student would do well to take up his novels in this sequence ; but " Far From the Madding Crowd " may be mentioned as thoroughly representative of his art. The hostile reception of " Jude the Obscure " finished his career as a novelist, and he then turned to building up his second great reputation—that of a poet—as a preface to his crowning achievement " The Dynasts," 1904–8.

R. L. S. Robert Louis Stevenson (1850–94) as a predominant influence in nineteenth century prose has already been dealt with ; here it is his fiction, especially his novels, in which we are interested. There are many competent critics who avow a greater admiration for Stevenson the traveller, the essayist, the writer of short stories, than for Stevenson the novelist. **Yet it**

was as a novelist that Stevenson brought the greatest influence to bear upon contemporary literature, and it was as a novelist he was most read.

His best writing is to be found in his short stories, his travels and his essays, and his main service to contemporary letters was concerned with style. He brought to the novel a keener sense of form, and, the world being still young for him, he set about furthering the revival of the latent spirit of romance, which Blackmore a decade earlier had awakened in " Lorna Doone." " Treasure Island " and " Kidnapped " restored to literature a story material that had been long worked only by crude writers for young uncritical readers, and " Catriona " alone, written seven years later, as a continuation of " Kidnapped," ought to silence critics who talk of Stevenson's inability to draw feminine character, though, like most sequels, it suffers by comparison.

Stevenson was too good a critic of himself to attempt to fill the great canvases which the genius of Scott could so easily crowd with unforgettable figures of romance : his was a smaller and more fastidious talent. But he was as much above Scott in the difficult art of the short story as Scott excelled him in the long sustained imaginative narrative.

LESSON 48
Novelists of Recent Yesterdays
(See plate 36)

WILLIAM DE MORGAN (1839–1917) presents one of the curious phenomena of literature—a novelist who makes his first try at the art when he is sixty-five, and, moreover, in the brief remainder of his days produces another half-dozen novels of such unusual length that they would equal in volume a dozen of any modern novelist—and all are good ! " Joseph Vance," with which he made an immediate success, is typical, and is like nothing else written in the twentieth century. As a story it is formless and inert, but it is a veritable portrait gallery of Victorian character, charged with the most agreeable humour and a happy sort of philosophy, the lesson of which would seem to be that life, despite all its sadness and sorrows, is so spiced with interest that it is worth living. " Alice-for-Short," which followed in 1907, is a sort of female Joseph Vance, and is well-nigh the equal of the first book in every respect. De Morgan has nothing to tell the hasty reader ; you must take him at your ease and your reward in pleasure will be great.

Of English novelists born in the forties and early fifties of last century, who loomed rather large in the literary world of their day, very few call for more than nominal mention here. There was Robert Buchanan (1841–1901), for example, a restless soul who wielded the pen of poet, playwright, novelist and critic with varying success. " God and the Man " is his best novel. But of the twenty or so that he wrote few, if any, have any vitality today. Highly successful in his lifetime, again, but not greatly read today, was William Black (1841–98), author of " A Daughter of Heth " and many a pleasantly competent tale in which Scottish scenery, " complete with trout stream," formed the background. William Clark Russell (1844–1911) had the real sense of the sea and was no indifferent successor to Marryat, though he never just managed to achieve that last unmistakable touch which carried a good story into the category of the great. " The Wreck of the Grosvenor " established him as a novelist and remains his most memorable achievement. David Christie Murray (1847–1907) is another instance. He wrote numerous long novels, many of which were widely read, and while his best fall short of classic heights, " Despair's Last Journey," written near the end of his somewhat clouded and unhappy life, might be ranked with the finest fiction published in the last decade of the nineteenth century.

With these novelists, distinguished in their day, mention may also be made of Flora Annie Steel (1847–1929). In 1867 she married an officer in the Bengal Civil Service, and lived for many years in India, obtaining a profound knowledge of the country and people. Her novels include a really fine romance of the Indian Mutiny, " On the Face of the Waters," which was followed by another Indian story of great power, " The Hosts of the Lord."

Mrs. Humphrey Ward (1851–1920) concerned herself with the interpretation of social life. Her novel " Robert Elsmere," published in 1888, created a positive clamour at the time, but lies quite peacefully in its grave today. This is less the fault of the book than of the age ; its chief use in the future will be to illustrate a social phase that has passed. " Marcella," " History of David Grieve," " Helbeck of Bannisdale " and " Eleanor " are later novels ; these also are limited not only in subject but also by Mrs. Ward's didactic style.

Another woman writer who made popular contributions to English fiction was Lucas Malet (1852–1931), whose novels " The Wages of Sin " and " Sir Richard Calmady " have fine qualities and enjoyed a considerable measure of commercial success. Lucas Malet may have derived much of her literary talent from her father, Charles Kingsley.

A name which some people might expect to find included among those of great novelists is that of Sir Hall Caine (1853–1931). As a novelist he attracted notice first by " The Deemster," published in 1887, which was followed by " The Bondman " in '90, " The Scapegoat," 1891, and " The Manxman," '94, all books which throw light on Manx customs and superstitions. There were in these novels qualities which suggest that his work might have been not only popular, as it was in very large degree, but important from the literary point of view. That it is not important is due to the assiduous manner in which he sought with large subjects and grandiose effect to impress the multitude in such novels as " The Christian," " The Eternal City " and " The Prodigal Son." In all these flamboyant and highly-coloured romances the dramatic becomes overstrained and the melodramatic results.

Among novelists born in the 'forties and 'fifties who remain figures of importance in English literature are Henry James, George Moore and George Gissing. Although born in New York, Henry James (1843–1916) was an Englishman by adoption, and most of his work was done in England, where he had lived from early manhood. He was never " popular," but he became a cult, and to admire Henry James was a touchstone of literary percipience. Some of his short stories, such as " The Turn of the Screw," are likely to outlive all his long novels. He had great charm and some obscurity of style, and he was a sound critic, especially of French literature. Henry James must certainly be ranked among great novelists, a leader of the analytical school, and although the fastidiousness of his language, amounting often to mannerism, lends itself to parody, it undoubtedly exercises a wholesome influence upon literary style.

George Moore (1852–1933) occupies an eminent niche in the gallery of modern novelists. Like Henry James, a fastidious stylist, George Moore had an unshakable belief in his own immortality. As a novelist he began with " A Mummer's Wife " (1885), which, like " Esther Waters " (1894) and other of his novels, was a work of the realistic type, showing unmistakable traces of the influence of the French realists. He might be chosen as our outstanding representative of the realist school, but, being an Irishman of a various talent and an exponent of the Celtic revival, he is not so easily " placed." In his novel " The Lake " he first created the last and most beautiful of his three styles. His short stories of Irish character, under the title of " The Untilled Field," are among his finest writings.

Presumably, George Gissing (1857–1903) should be classed with the French-inspired realists, but that is rather from the Zolaesque nature of his subject matter than his manner. He is capable of wonderful graces of style, and the astonishing thing is to find so much pessimism and stark despair, such pictures of poverty and sordid distress, penned in such admirable prose. We need not turn to him if entertainment be our desire ; but if we would understand the lower, sombre side of social life in the latter years of the nineteenth century we could not read more impressive studies than his " New Grub Street " and " Odd Women." Of striking interest also—in a different vein—is his "Charles Dickens : a Critical Study." Gissing's thinly-veiled autobiography in fictional form, " The Private Papers of Henry Ryecroft," has all the importance of a human document.

LESSON 49

Seven Novelists of Enduring Fame
(See plates 37 and 38)

WITHIN the compass of the decade 1857 to 1867 were born those distinguished leading writers of fiction, Joseph Conrad, Maurice Hewlett, Eden Phillpotts, Rudyard Kipling, John Galsworthy, H. G. Wells and Arnold Bennett. Each in his own way has added to the prestige of the English novel ; their work retains significance today and will survive.

Joseph Conrad (1857–1924) wrote a rich and characteristic English, although he was a Pole and, so far as can be judged by his fiction, never quite grew into the English habit of mind. Perhaps in some subtle exoticism partly lies the secret of his charm ; also it lies in his philosophy of loyalty, in his recurrent themes of the universal brotherhood of the sea and the integrity of human relationship, in his appeal to the hearts of a seafaring nation by his powerful expression of the terror and fascination of the sea. At one time he seemed to suffer from the kindly-intentioned efforts of well-meaning friends, something like a Conrad cabal among the critics appearing to be bent on forcing this Polish writer of English stories, with his wide, unconventional outlook, upon a half-reluctant British public. But all who began to read him, in however hypercritical a mood, were soon so caught by his splendid powers of descriptive narrative and character-ization that they went on eagerly from story to story—all held by his strange mixture of the painful and beautiful, powerful and gloomy, squalid and graceful, romantic and realistic.

" The Nigger of the Narcissus," for all the abounding merits of his later books, is his most characteristic piece of work, his finest plotless novel—the story was always secondary to his artistic delight in the creation of people—just as " The Arrow of Gold," written a quarter of a century later, is his least successful. But what a choice of delightful reading he has left for the generations arriving !—" An Outcast of the Islands," " Lord Jim," " Typhoon," " Nostromo," " Chance," " Victory," and his volumes of short stories. Particularly Joseph Conrad excelled in his creation of atmosphere and emotional tension, in his psychological penetration and ironic power.

As novelist, essayist and poet Maurice Hewlett (1861–1923) was a literary artist of rare distinction. He made his reputation in 1898 with " The Forest Lovers," a romance of the kind of nebulous medievalism which was initiated by William Morris, and he followed this initial success—with which he himself was none too elated—with " Richard Yea and Nay," " New Canter-bury Tales," " The Queen's Quair," " The Fool Errant," " Brazen-head the Great," " A Lover's Tale," and " Mainwaring." In these he gave modern English fiction a high place in the realm of romance, winning wide popularity as a teller of stories without departing from the very high standard required by his own fastidious taste. It may be added that some of Maurice Hewlett's most lovely work is embodied in his essays, collected into four volumes, " In a Green Shade," " Wiltshire Essays," " Extem-porary Essays," and " Last Essays." He also wrote some beautiful verse, including " Pan and the Young Shepherd," and " The Song of the Plow."

SEVEN NOVELISTS OF ENDURING FAME

Eden Phillpotts (b. 1862) has written many good novels, the majority of them—in which the best are included—being identified with Devonshire and, more particularly, with the Dartmoor country and people. " Sons of the Morning " and " Children of the Mist " were among the earliest of these intimate studies and vivid presentations of Devonshire life, and these were followed by a long sequence of West Country novels, notably by " The Secret Woman " and " The Mother," revealing a steady growth of dramatic power and fine technique. Eden Phillpotts is definitely in the line of the great English novelists. A man of great versatility, he also made some notable contributions to humorous literature and published not a little verse of considerable merit. Mention has already been made of his plays in Lesson 18 (Volume 2, page 279).

As a fiction writer, Rudyard Kipling (1865–1936) is not so great in the novel as in the short story form, in which not a few competent critics regarded him as supreme, but it would not be easy to name a better novel than " Kim," written within the early years of the present century. Excelling, however, as a teller of stories, it is in his Jungle Books, in his " Plain Tales from the Hills," " Under the Deodars," " Many Inventions," and other collections of short stories—mostly dealing with an Anglo-Indian day that is past—that Kipling achieved and retains success. While he continues to be widely read, reaction against his aggressive imperialism set in with disillusionment after the disintegrating experiences of the Great War. This reaction has sometimes caused literary criticism to be warped by an overwhelming prejudice from which the rising generation may happily be free.

In John Galsworthy (1867–1933), dealt with as a dramatist in Lesson 18, we have a writer of great importance to English letters. His rise to fame and authority was deliberate and steady—plays, novels and stories. No novelist of fame ever took his work more seriously than Galsworthy ; in the sense, that is, of feeling deep responsibility in the possible influence of his novels. He chronicled the fortunes of his Forsyte family with something of the care and minuteness of concern which Zola gave to his much more ambitious record of the Rougon-Macquart family. His seriousness of purpose was most happily reinforced by the highest literary gifts and the saving grace of humour, the absence of which might have produced merely boredom where we have sustained an approving interest. At times he was not above resort to melodrama, as in the death of Bosinney in " The Man of Property," which seems to be dictated by no purpose other than the needs of a dénouement ; it is arbitrary, not inevitable. And if he has a fault of attitude, it is that he assumes a virtue if the clothes be shabby and a vice if they are modish. But withal Galsworthy was a great novelist, and " The Man of Property " is a great novel. It is the first of a trilogy, the others being " In Chancery " and " To Let," which, with two " interludes," " Indian Summer of a Forsyte " and " Awakening," make up that noble volume " The Forsyte Saga."

Both H. G. Wells (b. 1866) and Arnold Bennett (1867–1931) have received consideration in Lesson 39 (Volume 5, page 301). Wells stands in the very foremost rank of contemporary English authors. More subjective than objective in style, his books are not to him ends in themselves. All his novels, stories, philosophic and miscellaneous writings are expressions of a mind profoundly curious about life and its meaning. " The Time Machine " was the forerunner of a memorable succession of scientific romances which includes " The Island of Dr. Moreau," " The Sleeper Awakes," " The First Men in the Moon," and " The Food of the Gods," while " Kipps " and " Tono-Bungay " are good examples of his skill in the novel of character, afterwards developed with even more intimacy of analysis in " Ann Veronica" and " The New Machiavelli," and, best of all, in his immortal " History of Mr. Polly." Largely as the result of his intellectual activities during the period of the Great War, Wells emerged as the most prominent figure in the post-war literary world, and his novel " Mr. Britling Sees It Through " seems destined to remain one of the works of fiction of really prime importance that owe their origin directly to the War.

Arnold Bennett possessed hardly any quality in common with Wells, although the two men's names were at one time commonly bracketed together. In the realm of fiction, Bennett's masterpiece is " The Old Wives' Tale," a really great novel, in which the genius of the author fuses into a living work of art the most ordinary and, indeed, unpromising material. That is his most worthy characteristic ; the ability to take the commonest appurtenances of life in a group of smoke-wreathed pottery towns and to present them to us with such a persuasive air that we find ourselves as interested in his narrative as if it had been woven out of the time-approved stuff of romance. Only a great novelist can do that, and Arnold Bennett, who wrote also quite ordinary novels, schooled himself to the doing of it, by the will to achieve great fiction rather than by any heaven-born gift of narrative power. " Clayhanger," " Hilda Lessways " and " These Twain " are a trilogy which show the novelist at his best ; and of his later work, when he had abandoned the Five Towns for a wider field, " Riceyman Steps " is as good as anything he ever did ; character, atmosphere, story, humour and sympathy are all exemplified in this moving tale of mean streets.

LESSON 50

Romance and Humour in Recent Fiction

(See plate 39)

CONTEMPORARY with the novelists dealt with in the preceding Lesson was a numerically large company of writers of fiction to whom the epithet " considerable " is justly applicable, although, when contrasting them with the great ones of the past, such as Scott or Dickens, one must say " oceans divide " them " and the waste of seas." First among these in point of time was Sir Rider Haggard (1856–1925). As a teller of tales he needed elbow room ; he could get effects only on large canvases and, if the metaphor will serve, with rather loud colours laid on with a big brush. He wrote a great many novels, and most of them bore a family resemblance to " She " or " King Solomon's Mines " in choice of theme and treatment. High-class melodrama would be descriptive of most of the popular novels that bear the name of Rider Haggard, for his talent was to invent and describe happenings, hairbreadth escapes, perils by land and sea ; not with deft unnoted touches to fashion living and memorable character, which is the essential power of all really great novelists.

Sir Arthur Conan Doyle (1859–1930) made his world-wide reputation as a writer of short stories. But the artistry of the interminable Sherlock Holmes series is not of a very exalted order, although there is undeniable creative power in the conception of the central character. Doyle is most likely to stand the test of time in such a purely romantic and beautiful story as " The White Company." " Micah Clarke " and " Rodney Stone " are also fine novels, and there are short stories in the collection, published under the title of " The Last Galley," that show a mastery of the story-teller's art.

Which, if any, of the novels of Sir Anthony Hope (1863–1933) is destined for permanence it would not be easy to determine. Nevertheless, the author of " The Prisoner of Zenda " has to his credit the imperishable distinction of having founded a school in fiction, the vogue of which has outlasted his generation, while the fact of his achievement remains independent of fashion. Ruritanian romance, in which the play of love and adventure has to be dressed in the costume of today and performed in imaginary realms that bear close resemblance to certain minor European states as they existed before the Great War, calls for a delicate fancy and a precise art if it is to avoid the impression of unreality. These were abundantly present in Hope's " Prisoner of Zenda," one of the most delightful romantic stories written in any time ; and in " Rupert of Hentzau " the novelist almost succeeded in producing a sequel that rivalled the first story.

The nearer one approaches the present day the more patent becomes the impossibility of dealing, however briefly, with the work of individual novelists, and the chronological method adopted hitherto must be discarded for one of classification. The three names already mentioned in this Lesson remind one that it was in the realm of romance that English fiction at the turn of the century was strongest, and the names of acceptable novelists most readily multiply in the mind. S. R. Crockett, with " The Raiders " ; Stanley Weyman, with " A Gentleman of France " ; Neil Munro, with " John Splendid " ; John Oliver Hobbes (Mrs. Craigie), with " Robert Orange " ; A. E. W. Mason, with " The Courtship of Morrice Buckler."—though later turning to modern life as in " The Four Feathers " ; Quiller-Couch, with " Troy Town " and " The Splendid Spur " ; John Buchan, with " John Burnet of Barns " and his " Greenmantle " stories ; Seton Merriman, with " The Sowers," " The Vultures " and other fine stories ; Raphael Sabatini, Warwick Deeping, George Preedy—these are some names that connote the pleasures of reading for any intelligent person in mood for the romance.

Some charming, if somewhat sentimental, studies of modern social life were added to English fiction by William John Locke (1863–1930), a fine and finished story-teller excelled by none of the favourites of his time in portrayal of romantic character. His cultured style, his restraint, his breadth of vision and sympathy, all went to the making of a novelist who was one of the leaders of his age in the art of fiction. "The Morals of Marcus Ordeyne," which appeared in 1905, is probably the best of his stories, and there is high entertainment in "The Beloved Vagabond," "Stella Maris," and "The Joyous Adventures of Aristide Pujol."

High place among the writers taking their themes from the social life of their time must be accorded to Leonard Merrick (b. 1864), author of "The Man Who Was Good," whose long series of really brilliant novels ought to have made him one of the most popular, as he is certainly one of the finest, writers of his time, but somehow did not ; and also to W. B. Maxwell (1876–1938), author of "The Guarded Flame" and other fine novels. Maxwell was a son of that able novelist, Miss M. E. Braddon, from whom he doubtless inherited his literary talent, as also, though in less degree, did his brother Gerald Maxwell.

R. S. Hichens (b. 1864) and E. F. Benson (b. 1867) are two other writers who have devoted much of their talent to the describing of life in the upper strata of society in their time. Both these men began their literary career by achieving wide notoriety with a daring "roman à clef," a novel, that is, in which real living personages are introduced thinly disguised as fictitious characters : Hichens with "The Green Carnation," a mordantly witty lampoon on Oscar Wilde, then at the zenith of his social success, and Benson with "Dodo," an impudently amusing caricature of one of the best known and most brilliant great ladies of the day. Both men then proceeded to produce much work of good quality, for the most part, but not entirely, dealing with modern social life.

Archibald Marshall (1866–1934) has written much fiction of a high order of merit and has been not inaptly dubbed the modern Trollope. And, to conclude this very brief list of some of the more notable contributors to this category of fiction, that brilliant novelist W. Somerset Maugham (b. 1874) must be named, whose "Liza of Lambeth," published so long ago as 1897, placed him very definitely with the realists. He is almost the only distinguished novelist who is also a distinguished playwright, and whose plays are not merely the dramatizing of his novels.

Masters of Humour. It is as writers of short stories—though they have all produced good novels—that we are most apt to think of those delightful humorists, W. W. Jacobs (b. 1863),

Pett Ridge (1860–1930), and Barry Pain (1864–1928). The last named was one of the group that cultivated what was called the "new humour" given to the world in the monthly magazine "The Idler," under the editorship of Jerome K. Jerome (1859-1927), himself the author of the perennially amusing "Three Men in a Boat," and author also of a really good novel, "Paul Kelver." Morley Roberts (b. 1857), another fine writer—his "Rachel Marr" is a great novel—reveals a rich vein of humour in some of his short stories, the form of fiction in which he is perhaps seen at his best. George Birmingham (Canon Hannay) (b. 1865), Stephen Leacock (b. 1869), and that incomparable jester P. G. Wodehouse (b. 1881) have done and are doing delightful and memorable work in the field of pure amusement. But of them all it is W. W. Jacobs to whom the palm must be awarded and whose supremacy as humorist and perfect literary craftsman must be acknowledged.

LESSON 51

Characteristics of Post War Fiction

(See plate 40)

ANY finality of opinion about war novels being impossible at present, all that can be done is to name a few of literary quality which were the outcome of the war-time experiences of their authors. H. G. Wells' "Mr. Britling Sees it Through" has already been mentioned as one of the works of fiction of really prime importance that originated directly from this source. Selection of others must be largely a matter of individual choice ; but high place among them must be given to H. M. Tomlinson (*see* Lesson 40, Volume 5, page 306) for his "All Our Yesterdays," to C. E. Montague (1867–1928) for "Rough Justice" and "Disenchantment," written with rare literary grace, and to R. H. Mottram (b. 1883), who established his reputation with "The Spanish Farm," a trilogy of which the second and third parts were entitled "Sixty-four—Ninety-four" and "The Crime at Vanderlynden's."

Psycho-analysis was a more or less familiar term before the war, but it was not until after hostilities had ceased that psycho-analytical methods of treatment attracted the attention of the commonalty and turned the thoughts of the more intellectual of them inward upon themselves. The consequence was an interest in psychological processes that frequently was quite disproportionate to the facts and conditions of normal life, resulting in the production of a mass of fiction dealing with neurotics and the mentally unfit, with complexes and repressions, to which the term " morbid " is hardly inapplicable. In the decade before the war were published several brilliantly conceived if somewhat bitterly delivered psychological novels, notably " The Fortunes of Richard Mahoney " and " Maurice Guest " by Henry Handel Richardson, " The Combined Maze " by May Sinclair, " A Room with a View " and " Howard's End " by E. M. Forster, all of which were intensely admired by the few and influenced the writing of subsequent novelists. Already, in 1913, D. H. Lawrence had experimented significantly in " Sons and Lovers "; his later books, while evincing his rare literary quality, are somewhat marred artistically by his obsessions with thwarted passion and dreary enmity of the sexes, by both a lack of clarity and a lack of reticence. He remains, however, an important figure, both as poet and novelist.

Other writers of fiction who refused to follow tradition include James Joyce (b. 1882), Dorothy Richardson and Virginia Woolf. All three have made experiments with conventions of action and time—or rather both the action and time factors almost cease to exist in their books. Mr. A. C. Ward has pointed out in " Twentieth Century Literature " that in novels by these experimenters plot, action, character and thought are drowned in the " stream of consciousness " without beginning and without end. The backward and forward swirl of impressions is dulled in effect when carried to the extreme of a full-length novel. As interesting experimenters, however, these authors must not be contemptuously dismissed. Mr. Ward observes :

" What is ignored by Dorothy Richardson, James Joyce, Virginia Woolf and others is that the time-factor is governed wholly by varying intensity of human experience. The nearly seven hundred pages of ' Ulysses ' (James Joyce ; now published in England) cover only one day in the lives of three people, whose sensations are flattened out, like a desert unbroken by any sand-hill or oasis. So also, Dorothy Richardson's books amble onward everlastingly as Miriam (Miriam Henderson is the heroine of many chronicles : ' Pointed Roofs,' ' Back-water,' ' Honeycomb,' ' The Tunnel,' ' Interim,' etc.) goes through a life which has few emotional contours. Virginia Woolf is not so tedious as the other two, though she is exasperatingly shapeless. ' Jacob's Room ' and ' Mrs. Dalloway ' are like snippets cut from a number of cinematograph films and indiscriminately joined up. Some fragments throw lively coloured ' views ' upon the screen ; more often, however, only the irritation of discontinuity is provided.''

Mention of Virginia Woolf recalls her admirable '' A Room of One's Own,'' and may serve to introduce a reference to the difference in the women novelists' outlook since the emancipation of woman. Up to even a few years before the war, women, with comparatively few exceptions—Elizabeth Robins was one with her powerful novels '' The Magnetic North '' and '' The Dark Lantern ''—were still writing what the publishers, that is, men, thought they ought to write. Post-war women novelists have refused to be shackled, and this freedom has left its mark on English fiction as a whole. Among the many interesting women writers of fiction may be singled out Sheila Kaye-Smith, with her strongly delineated pictures of Sussex scenes and characters in '' Sussex Gorse,'' '' Joanna Godden '' and '' Tamarisk Town '' ; Mary Webb (1881–1927), whose novels '' Gone to Earth,'' '' The House in Dormer Forest '' and '' Precious Bane '' are set in Shropshire and the Welsh Marches, and whose style is at its best impregnated with poetry and a magical harmony between Nature and Man ; and Rose Macaulay, who has devoted her wit, her clarity and her powers of imagination to the production of satirical novels such as '' Potterism,'' '' Dangerous Ages,'' '' Told by an Idiot,'' and '' Staying with Relations.''

Crime and mystery stories form a large part of the fiction written today. From the spate of pseudo-psychological sex novels many readers have sought refuge in '' detective '' fiction. A notable writer in this connexion was Edgar Wallace (1876-1932), not because he was a literary star of even third magnitude, but because he was a meteoric phenomenon that flashed round the entire orbit of the heavens and caught the attention of the people of all literate nations before plunging abruptly into the silent darkness. His books were translated into every European language, and sold in hundreds in every bookshop on the Continent. His plays—'' The Ringer,'' '' The Squeaker,'' '' The Green Pack,'' '' On the Spot,'' and others—filled every theatre in which they were performed.

POST WAR FICTION

The conclusion at which one must, however, arrive from a general survey of modern fiction is that the average good novel of today is as superior to the average novel of the mid-Victorian days as a modern express locomotive is superior to the old " Puffing Billy." This means that the literary art, as distinct from genius, which may be, but is not always, above and independent of convention, has vastly improved from the days of our grandfathers. We have only to examine any representative story by at least a score of novelists of the younger school to realize how admirably wrought and patterned is the texture of our contemporary fiction as compared with that of the mid-Victorian era. How distinguished, for instance, is the work of Aldous Huxley (b. 1894) in " Point Counterpoint " and in " Brave New World " ; of Osbert Sitwell in that bold satire " Miracle on Sinai " ; of Charles Morgan in " The Fountain " ; of A. P. Herbert (b. 1890) in " The Water Gipsies " ; of Louis Golding in " Magnolia Street " ; of John Cowper Powys in " A Glastonbury Romance " ; of Norah Hoult in " Time, Gentlemen, Time " and " Youth Can't Be Served " ; of Helen Simpson in " The Woman on the Beast " ; of Helen Waddell in " Peter Abelard."

At the same time, it should be noted that in this age of transition the novel cannot be regarded as having any set form. While writers in the traditional vein, such as J. B. Priestley (b. 1894), famous for " The Good Companions " ; A. J. Cronin (b. 1896), author of " Hatter's Castle " and " The Citadel " ; and Robert Graves (b. 1895), author of " I, Claudius " and " Claudius the God," continue to flourish, the influence of such experimenters in style and content as James Joyce and Virginia Woolf are still to be felt. Two main tendencies may be observed in the 'thirties ; first, a continued analysis of the thought and behaviour of particular sections of society along the methods of the Anglo-American writer, Henry James (1843–1916) ; secondly, a long neglected but growing intrusion of political and social themes into pure fiction. In the first group must come the names of Elizabeth Bowen, author of " The House in Paris " and " Death of a Heart " ; Ivy Compton-Burnett, author of " A House and its Head " and " Daughters and Sons " ; and Christopher Isherwood, distinguished for " The Memorial " and " Goodbye to Berlin." Writers in the second group include James Hanley (b. 1901), Edward Upward, and Storm Jameson.

This Lesson concludes our Course in English Literature.

LESSON 45

Peculiarities of Some Nouns

THE plural of certain compound nouns in French and the gender of others call for special attention. Some nouns have a different meaning according as they are of the masculine or feminine gender. Compound nouns written without a hyphen are considered single words, and form their plural according to the general rules: *un chèvrefeuille*, a honeysuckle plant; *des chèvrefeuilles*, honeysuckle plants; but the following plurals should be noted: *un bonhomme, des bonshommes*, old fellows; *un gentilhomme, des gentilshommes*, noblemen; *monseigneur, messeigneurs*, my lords; *monsieur, messieurs; madame, mesdames; mademoiselle, mesdemoiselles*.

When a compound noun consists of two nouns joined by a hyphen, both take the mark of the plural: *un chou-fleur, des choux-fleurs*, cauliflowers. But note: *timbre(s)-poste*, postage-stamp; *mandat(s)-poste*, post-office order.

When a compound noun consists of two nouns joined by a preposition, the first noun alone takes the sign of the plural; *un arc-en-ciel, des arcs-en-ciel*, rainbows; *un chef-d'œuvre, des chefs-d'œuvre*, masterpieces. Exceptions are: *un (des) pied-à-terre*, temporary quarters; *un (des) pot-au-feu*, broth; *un (des) tête-à-tête*, private interview.

When a compound consists of a noun and an adjective, both components take the sign of the plural: *un coffre-fort, des coffres-forts*, strong-boxes. But note that the noun alone takes the sign of the plural in all the feminine words consisting of *grand'* and a noun, as *grand'mère, grand'mères*, grandmothers.

In compound nouns made up of a verb, and of a noun, only the noun can take the sign of the plural: *un passe-port*, a passport; *des passe-ports*, passports. Exceptions are: *un porte-monnaie, des porte-monnaie*, purses; *un reveille-matin, des reveille-matin*, alarums; *un porte-clefs, des porte-clefs*, turnkeys; *un casse-noisettes, des casse-noisettes*, nutcrackers; *un porte-lettres, des porte-lettres*, letter racks; *un couvre-pieds, des couvre-pieds*, foot-coverlets.

EARLY 19th CENTURY WOMEN NOVELISTS. Left, Mary Russell Mitford (1787–1855), the daughter of a Hampshire physician whose extravagances kept her poor all her life, published her first poems in 1810, and subsequently maintained the family by writing sketches of country ways and scenes for the magazines. Centre, Mary Wollstonecraft Shelley (1797–1851), daughter of William Godwin and Mary Wollstonecraft, eloped with Shelley in 1814 and married him two years later. "Frankenstein," written at Byron's suggestion, was the first of her four novels, and she also wrote travel sketches and poetry. Right, Mrs. Gaskell (née Elizabeth Cleghorn Stephenson: 1810–65) spent her early years at Knutsford, Cheshire—the original of Cranford. She married in 1832 William Gaskell, a Unitarian minister in Manchester, and thus came in contact with the industrial society mirrored in her novels. ENGLISH LITERATURE 44

Left and centre, National Portrait Gallery; right, after Richmond

AINSWORTH AND BULWER-LYTTON. William Harrison Ainsworth (1805–82) studied for the bar but abandoned the law for the life of historical novelist and magazine editor. The above portrait is after Maclise. Edward George Earle Lytton Bulwer-Lytton (1803–73) wrote a number of " best sellers " and played some part in politics. He was created a baron in 1866

PEACOCK AND BORROW. Thomas Love Peacock (left ; 1785–1866) was a close friend of Shelley for some years, and from 1819 to 1856 an official of the East India Company. He wrote a number of poems, but is best remembered for his satiric novels, in which his cultured egoism and whimsical humour find expression. A lover of the classics and good living, he makes sharp contrast with the sincerely religious George Borrow (right ; 1803–81), who after a spell of hack-journalism in London wandered gipsy-fashion through England and Wales, and as a Bible Society colporteur in Spain, Russia and Morocco. Throughout his life he loved the " wind on the heath " in preference to the cultivated joys that meant so much to Peacock.

ENGLISH LITERATURE 44

Right, National Portrait Gallery

Plate 30   *Volume VI*

W. M. THACKERAY (1811–63.) Born at Calcutta, he won distinction as a journalist before "Vanity Fair" led to his recognition as one of the greatest writers of the age. He was a much-appreciated lecturer and admirable book-illustrator.

ENGLISH LITERATURE 45

After S. Lawrence

CHARLES DICKENS (1812–70). Born at Portsea, son of a clerk in the Navy Pay office, he spent his early years in unhappy poverty. In 1832 he became a House of Commons reporter, but three years later he abandoned reporting for literature. He married Catherine Hogarth in 1836. His later years were spent at Gad's Hill, near Rochester, Kent.

ENGLISH LITERATURE 45

After Maclise

CHARLES KINGSLEY (1819–75). Born at Holne, Devonshire, he was rector of Eversley, Hants, from 1844 until his death. In 1860 he was appointed professor of history at Cambridge, and in 1873 canon of Westminster. He was a leading figure among the Christian Socialists.

ENGLISH LITERATURE 46

THE BRONTE SISTERS. This portrait of the three daughters of the Rev. Patrick Bronte, incumbent of Haworth, Yorks.—Anne (1820–1849), Emily Jane (1818–1848), and Charlotte (1816–1855)—was painted in 1835 by their only brother, Patrick Branwell (1817–1848).

ENGLISH LITERATURE 45
National Portrait Gallery

Plate 32

Volume VI

PECULIARITIES OF SOME NOUNS

When *garde* is the first part of a compound word, it usually takes the sign of the plural if it denotes a person : *une garde-malade*, a sick-nurse ; *des gardes-malades*, sick-nurses. If it denotes an object, it commonly remains invariable : *une garde-robe*, a wardrobe ; *des garde-robes*, wardrobes.

When a compound noun is made up of invariable words, they remain unchanged : *un passe-partout*, a master-key ; *des passe-partout*, master-keys ; *des on dit*, gossip.

The following nouns have a different meaning in the masculine and feminine genders :

aide (m.), a helper
aide (f.), help, assistance
aune (m.), alder-tree
aune (f.), ell
cerise (m.), cherry-colour
cerise (f.), cherry
crêpe (m.), crape
crêpe (f.), pancake
critique (m.), critic
critique (f.), criticism
enseigne (m.), ensign, standard-bearer
enseigne (f.), standard, signboard
faux (m.), forgery
faux (f.), scythe
fourbe (m.), rogue
fourbe (f.), imposture
guide (m.), guide
guide (f.), guiding-rein
livre (m.), book
livre (f.), pound
manche (m.), handle
manche (f.), sleeve
Manche (f.), English Channel

manœuvre (m.), workman, mechanic
manœuvre (f.), manoeuvre [dom
martyre (m.), martyr-
martyre (f.), female martyr
mauve (m.), mauve colour
mauve (f.), marshmallow
mémoire (m.), memoir, bill
mémoire (f.), memory
mode (m.), mood, manner
mode (f.), fashion
mort (m.), dead man
mort (f.), death
moule (m.), mould, model
moule (f.), mussel
mousse (m.), cabin-boy, ship-boy
mousse (f.), moss
office (m.), office, service, functions
office (f.), pantry, servants' hall

orange (m.), orange colour
orange (f.), orange
page (m.), page (attendant)
page (f.), page (of a book)
paillasse (m.), clown
paillasse (f.) straw mattress
paille (m.), straw-colour
paille (f.), straw
pendule (m.), pendulum
pendule (f.), time-piece
physique (m.), the physique of a person
physique (f.), physics, natural philosophy
pique (m.), spade (a suit of cards)
pique (f.), pike
poêle (m.), stove, pall
poêle (f.), frying-pan
politique (m.), politician

politique (f.), politics, policy

poste (m.), post, situation, guard-house

poste (f.), letter-post, stage-post

rose (m.), rose-colour, pink

rose (f.), rose

somme (m.), nap, sleep

somme (f.), sum, total

tour (m.), turn, circuit, trick, lathe

tour (f.), tower

trompette (m.), trumpeter

trompette (f.), trumpet

vapeur (m.), steamer

vapeur (f.), vapour, steam

vase (m.), vase, vessel

vase (f.), ooze, mud

voile (m.), veil

voile (f.), sail

LESSON 46

A Lesson on Adjectives

THE adjective agrees in gender and number with the noun or pronoun to which it refers : *Les beaux arbres*, the beautiful trees ; *les belles fleurs*, the beautiful flowers. When it refers to more than one noun, it must be in the plural number : *Le roi et le berger sont égaux après la mort*, The king and the shepherd are equal after death. If the nouns are of different gender the adjective must be masculine and plural.

When an adjective comes after two nouns joined by *ainsi que, de même que, comme*, as ; *aussi bien que*, as well as ; *plutôt que*, rather than ; *non plus que*, no more than ; it agrees with the first only : *La panthère, comme le lion, est carnassière*, the panther, like the lion, is carnivorous.

When *avoir l'air* means " to have an air," the adjective agrees with air : *Cette dame a l'air fier et hautain, cependant elle est très affable et très prévenante*. That lady has a proud and haughty air, nevertheless, she is very affable and very obliging. But when the meaning of *avoir l'air* is " to seem," " to appear," the adjective agrees with the subject of the verb : *Cette dame a l'air bien malheureuse*, That lady seems very unhappy.

When *demi* (half) precedes a noun, and is joined to it by a hyphen, it is always invariable. If it follows a noun, it agrees with it in gender, but is always in the singular number : *Une demi-heure, une heure et demie*. Compound adjectives consisting of two adjectives or of an adjective and a past participle require both their components to agree with the qualified noun : *des pommes aigres-douces*, sourish apples.

Nouns used as adjectives of colour are usually invariable, but *rose* (pink), *cramoisi* (crimson), *pourpre* (purple), and *écarlate* (scarlet) are dealt with as adjectives : *des chapeaux roses*, pink hats. When colour is expressed by a combination of two adjectives, both of them remain invariable : *Elle a les cheveux châtain clair et les yeux bleu foncé*, she has light auburn hair and dark blue eyes.

Comparison of Adjectives. The comparative of equality, of superiority and of inferiority are respectively formed by means of *aussi . . . que*, *plus . . . que*, and *moins . . . que* : *Il est aussi modeste que vaillant*, he is as modest as he is brave ; *Les remèdes sont plus lents que les maux*, remedies are slower than diseases : *La Seine est moins large que le Rhin*, the Seine is less broad than the Rhine.

In negative sentences *aussi* may be replaced by *si* : *Le fils n'est pas si grand que le père*, the son is not so tall as the father.

When the second part of a comparison of superiority or of inferiority is followed by a verb in a finite tense, that verb takes *ne* before it unless it be preceded by a negative verb : *Les sciences et les arts sont plus cultivés aujourd'hui qu'ils ne l'ont jamais été*. The sciences and the arts are more cultivated now than they have ever been. " More and more " is expressed by *de plus en plus*, and " less and less " by *de moins en moins*. " All the more " is translated by *d'autant plus*.

Position of Adjectives. When one noun is qualified by two or more adjectives, each of them follows its own rule in regard to position : *Voilà une jolie petite maison*, There is a pretty little house ; *une petite maison blanche*, a little white house.

If the adjectives are joined by a conjunction and one of them regularly follows the noun, then both of them must be placed after it : *Une belle femme*, a beautiful woman , *une femme riche*, a rich woman ; *une femme belle et riche*, a woman beautiful and rich.

A certain number of adjectives have different meanings according as they precede or follow the qualified substantive. It will be seen from the following list of the most important of them that the double meaning is possible in connexion with special substantives only :

ANCIEN : *Un ancien élève*, a former pupil ; *l'histoire ancienne*, ancient history. BON : *Un bon homme* (frequently written *bonhomme*) a simple man, an old man , *un homme bon*, a kind, charitable man. BRAVE : *Un brave homme*, a worthy man ; *un homme brave*, a brave man. CERTAIN : *Une certaine chose*, a certain thing ; *une chose certaine*, something about which there is no doubt. CHER : *Mon cher ami*, my dear friend ; *des objets chers*, expensive articles. DERNIER : *Le dernier mois de l'année*, the last month of the year *la semaine dernière*, last week. DIGNE : *Une digne femme*, a worthy woman ; *une femme digne*, a dignified woman. DIVERS : *Diverses personnes*, (several) persons , *des opinions diverses*, conflicting opinions. FAMEUX : *Un fameux imbécile*, a precious fool ; *un auteur fameux*, a famous author. FAUX : *Une fausse clef*, a false key ; *une clef fausse*, a wrong key. GALANT : *Un galant homme*, a man of honour, a gentleman ; *un homme galant*, a courteous man, a ladies' man. GRAND : *Un grand homme*, a great man ; *un homme grand*, a tall man. HONNETE : *Un honnête homme*, an honest man ; *un homme honnête*, a civil man. MALHONNETE : *C'est un malhonnête homme*, He is a dishonest man , *un enfant malhonnête*, a rude, uncivil child. MAIGRE : *Un maigre dîner*, a meagre dinner ; *un repas maigre*, a lenten meal (without meat). MAUVAIS : *Il a mauvais air*, He has a disreputable appearance ; *Il a l'air mauvais*, He has an evil look. MECHANT : *Un méchant poète*, a wretched poet, a poetaster , *Il a la mine méchante*, He has an ill-natured, spiteful look. NOUVEAU : *Il porte un nouvel habit aujourd'hui*, He is wearing a new (different) coat today ; *Je n'aime pas les chapeaux nouveaux*, I don't like the new-fashioned hats. PAUVRE : *C'est un pauvre auteur*, He is an author of no great merit ; *C'est un auteur pauvre*, He is a needy author. PETIT : *Un petit homme*, a man of low stature ; *un homme petit*, a despicable man. PROPRE : *Il a écrit cette lettre de sa propre main*, He has written that letter with his own hand ; *Cet enfant n'a jamais les mains propres*, That child never has clean hands. SEUL : *Un seul homme*, a single man ; *un homme seul*, a solitary man. SIMPLE : *Un simple soldat*, a private ; *un homme simple*, an unpretending man. VRAI : *Un vrai coquin*, a thorough knave ; *C'est une histoire vraie que je vous raconte*, It is a true story I am telling you.

Complement of Adjectives. Adjectives are frequently followed by a complement to which they are joined by a preposition.

ON ADJECTIVES

The principal prepositions used for this purpose are *à, de, en, envers* and *pour*.

The proposition *à* is commonly used after adjectives denoting habit, fitness, resemblance, comparison, conformity, inclination, advantage, utility, necessity, and their opposites :

adroit à, clever at	*hardi à*, bold in
ardent à, keen for	*propre à*, fit for
assidu à, assiduous in	*impropre à*, unfit for
bon à, good, fit for	*nécessaire à*, necessary for
exact à, exact in	*semblable à*, similar to
fort à, clever at	

The preposition *de* is commonly used after adjectives denoting separation, cause, origin, supply, satisfaction, want, desire :

ami de, friendly to	*fou de*, doting on
atteint de, struck by, seized with	*furieux de*, furious at
	heureux de, delighted with
débarrassé de, free from, rid of	*inquiet de*, anxious about
désolé de, distressed at	*nourri de*, fed on
doué de, endowed with	*pourvu de*, provided with
empressé de, eager to	*ravi de*, delighted with
ennemi de, hostile to	*stupéfait de*, amazed at
fâché de, sorry for	*triste de*, sad at
	fort de, relying on, confident in

Adjectives denoting proficiency, abundance, are frequently followed by *en* ; *abondant*, abounding in ; *expert*, expert in.

Adjectives denoting feeling, behaviour, disposition towards, are followed either by *pour* or by *envers* :

(*a*) Followed by *envers* :

affable, affable towards	*généreux*, generous towards
amical, friendly to	*indulgent*, indulgent towards
bon, kind to	*ingrat*, ungrateful to
charitable, charitable to	*injuste*, unjust towards
dur, harsh towards	*juste*, just to (towards)

(*b*) Followed by *pour* :

affable, affable to	*indulgent*, indulgent for
bon, kind to	*injurieux*, insulting to
bienveillant, friendly towards	*nécessaire*, necessary for
commode, convenient for	*utile*, useful for

LESSON 47

More About Pronouns

PERSONAL pronouns can take the place of determinate nouns only—that is to say, of nouns preceded by an article, a possessive, or a demonstrative : *Il nous a fait parvenir sa réponse, et la voici*, he has forwarded us his answer, and here it is. The relation between pronoun and noun must always be expressed in such a way as to leave no room for ambiguity.

On, being an indefinite personal pronoun, may stand for either the first, the second, or the third person, singular or plural. When *on* occurs several times in the same sentence it must always relate to the same person. The verb of which *on* is the subject is always in the third person singular. Adjectives in agreement with it are usually masculine and singular.

When it is clear from the context that *on* refers to a feminine subject, the adjective is feminine : *On devient forte alors qu'on devient mère*, one (a woman) becomes strong when one (she) becomes a mother.

Lui is both masculine and feminine when it is the indirect object or dative of the conjunctive form of the personal pronoun ; otherwise it is exclusively masculine. *Lui* preceded by a preposition refers to persons. When the reference is to inanimate objects, *y* or *en* is used. Thus, in speaking of a tree, we say : *N'y montez pas*, do not climb on it. The same remarks apply to *elle* when it is in the disjunctive form. Thus, in speaking of a science or profession, we say : *Il s'y est adonné*, he has devoted himself to it. With the prepositions *après, avec, contre*, of which the meaning cannot be expressed by *y* or *en*, both *lui* and *elle* may be used with reference to inanimate objects.

The pronoun *le* is invariable when it stands for (*a*) an adjective, (*b*) a noun used adjectively, (*c*) an infinitive, or (*d*) a whole clause :

(*a*) *Cette femme est belle, mais elle ne le sera pas toujours*, that woman is good-looking, but she will not always be so ; (*b*) *Ceux qui sont amis de tout le monde ne le sont de personne*, those who are friends (friendly) with everybody are so with nobody ; (*c*) *Ces hommes font bien de se cacher ; ils doivent le faire*, these men do well to keep themselves retired (lit. to hide themselves) ; they

(262)

must do so. (*d*) *Si le public a eu quelque indulgence pour moi, je le dois à votre protection*, if the public has had some indulgence for me, I owe it to your protection.

Le, la, les, may be placed between the pronoun *ce* and the verb *être* if they refer to inanimate objects and are not followed by a relative clause : *Est-ce là votre grammaire ?* *Oui, ce l'est*, Is that your grammar ? Yes, it is ; *Sont-ce vos maisons ?* *Oui, ce les sont*, Are those your houses ? Yes, they are.

When the pronoun refers to persons, or is followed by a relative clause, it is better to use *lui, eux, elle, elles* . *Sont-ce vos amis ?* *Oui, ce sont eux*, Are those your friends ? Yes, they are ; *Est-ce là votre maison ?* *Oui c'est elle qu'on aperçoit parmi les arbres*. Is that your house ? Yes, that is it which you perceive among the trees.

Soi is both masculine and feminine, but always singular. When used of persons, it can only refer to an indefinite subject, such as *on, chacun, quiconque, personne, tout le monde, tout homme*. etc. : *Chacun pour soi*, each for himself. When *soi* is used of inanimate objects, it may refer to a definite subject ; *La vertu est aimable en soi*, virtue is lovable in itself.

When several verbs have the same pronoun as their object, that pronoun must be repeated if the verbs are in a simple tense : *Les morts et les vivants se succèdent et se remplacent continuellement*, the dead and the living continually succeed and replace each other.

If the verbs which have a pronoun for their common object are in a compound tense, that object does not require to be repeated. In that case, however, the auxiliary is also omitted : *Ils nous ont rencontrés et salués*, they met and bowed to us. If the pronoun which is the common object of two or more verbs is not governed in the same case by each of them, it must be repeated : *Ils nous ont rencontrés et nous ont parlé*, they met us and spoke to us.

Demonstrative Pronouns. What is known as the pleonastic use of *ce*—that is, the use of *ce* when the sense of the sentence does not require it, and when, indeed, it has no equivalent in the English sentence—is subject to the following rules :

(*a*) When the nouns which are respectively the subject and the attribute of some tense of the verb *être* can change places without materially affecting the sense of the sentence, the verb may take *ce* before it, and very generally does so : *La vraie noblesse*, *c'est la vertu*, true nobility is virtue. (*b*) When both the subject and the attribute of *être* are infinitives, the verb must be preceded by *ce : Travailler c'est prier*, to work is to pray. (*c*) If the verb is negative, the use of *ce* before it is not necessary : *Brailler n'est pas répondre*, bawling is not answering. (*d*) The negative verb may begin the sentence. In that case it must be preceded by *ce*, and the second infinitive takes either *que de*, or *que* alone before it : *Ce n'est pas répondre que de brailler*. (*e*) *Ce* is not used before *être* if its subject only is an infinitive : *Bien écouter est une des plus grandes qualités de la conversation*, to listen well is one of the greatest qualities of conversation. (*f*) When a sentence begins with *ce qui, ce que*, or *ce dont*, the verb *être* takes *ce* before it if it is followed by a noun or by an infinitive : *Ce qui m'indigne le plus, c'est l'injustice des hommes*, what makes me most indignant is the injustice of men. (*g*) When in a sentence beginning with *ce qui, ce que*, or *ce dont*, the verb *être* is followed by an adjective, it does not take *ce* before it : *Ce que vous nous dites là est absurde*, what you are telling us is absurd.

In English, the relative pronoun may have a whole clause for its antecedent ; in French the relative must be preceded by *ce : Il trouvait sa bonne ménagère qui lui souriait à travers les vapeurs du repas du soir, ce qui lui réjouissait le coeur*, he used to find his good housewife, who smiled at him through the fumes of the evening meal, which delighted his heart.

In English, " all " may immediately precede a relative pronoun. In French, *ce* must be placed between them : *Tout ce qu'il voyait lui semblait admirable*, all that he saw seemed to him (to be) admirable. If " all " refers to several persons or objects, *ceux* or *celles* are used between it and the relative : *Il est respecté de tous ceux qui le connaissent*, he is respected by all who know him.

When referring to persons or objects previously mentioned, *celui-là, celle-là, ceux-là, celles-là*, indicate the former, whilst *celui-ci, celle-ci, ceux-ci, celles-ci* indicate the latter. *Ceci* is used to indicate a statement that is going to be made, and *cela* a statement that has just been made : *Retenez bien ceci ; il faut être juste envers tout le monde*, bear this well in mind : you must be just to everybody. *Il faut aimer son prochain comme soi même ; n'oubliez jamais cela*, you must love your neighbour as yourself ; never forget that. Colloquially, *cela* is contracted into *ça*.

LESSON 48

Relative and Indefinite Pronouns

THOUGH frequently omitted in English, the relative pronoun must always be used in French, and it should be as near its antecedent as possible. The neglect of this rule produces ambiguity, and sometimes nonsense. The absurdity is obvious in : *J'apporte des joujoux pour mes enfants qui sont dans ma poche*. It mu⁺ be avoided by saying : *J'apporte pour mes enfants des joujoux qui sont dans ma poche*, I have brought for my children some toys that are in my pocket.

Sometimes it is not possible to avoid ambiguity by bringing the antecedent and the relative close together. In that case the ambiguity is removed by using *lequel, laquelle, duquel, de laquelle*, instead of *qui, que, dont : tous les voyageurs ont parlé de la fertilité de ce pays, laquelle est véritablement extraordinaire*, all travellers have spoken of that country's fertility, which is really extraordinary. Sometimes ambiguity is avoided by putting the conjunction *et* between the relative and a noun, and thus indicating that this particular noun is not intended to be the antecedent of the relative. *Nos soldats, acharnés à la poursuite des ennemis, et qui ne connaissaient pas la disposition du terrain, se trouvèrent bientôt séparés les uns des autres par les marais et les fondrières*, our soldiers (who were) doggedly intent on the pursuit of the enemy, and who did not know the lie of the land, soon found themselves separated from each other by the marshes and the quagmires.

If the antecedent of a relative pronoun is a noun, or a personal pronoun preceded by a preposition, that preposition must not be repeated before the relative. It is therefore incorrect to say : *c'est à lui à qui je parle*. The relative must be replaced by the conjunction *que : c'est à lui que je parle*, it is to him that I am speaking. It is permissible, however, to omit the preposition before the antecedent, and to place it before the relative : *c'est lui à qui je parle*, it is he to whom I am speaking ; *c'est mon père dont il parle*, it is my father he is talking about.

If the antecedent of the relative is a personal pronoun in the conjunctive form, that pronoun must be repeated in the disjunctive form before the relative : *il était inutile de lui parler, à lui qui ne comprenait pas le français,* it was useless speaking to him, who did not understand French.

Qui has neither gender, number, nor person of its own, but it communicates the number and person of its antecedent to the verb of which it is the subject, and the gender and number of that antecedent to adjectives or participles in agreement with it : *c'est moi qui suis chargé de vous conduire,* it is I who am commissioned to conduct you.

Qui with a finite tense is frequently used in French instead of the English present participle : *le voilà qui vient là-bas,* there he is coming yonder.

Qui preceded by a preposition refers to persons only. After a preposition, the relative referring to animals or inanimate objects must be *lequel, laquelle,* etc. : *il faut bien choisir les personnes à qui on donne sa confiance,* we should carefully choose the persons on whom we bestow our confidence ; *c'est une condition sans laquelle je ne consentirai à rien,* it is a condition without which I will not consent to anything.

Sometimes, when the antecedent is vague and indefinite, such as *ce, voilà, rien,* the relative *quoi* is used instead of *lequel,* etc., after a preposition : *il n'y a rien sur quoi on ait plus écrit,* there is nothing about which more has been written.

The expression *de quoi* is used to indicate means, cause, sufficiency : *il n'est pas riche, mais il a de quoi vivre,* he is not rich, but he has enough to live on.

Dont is used for both persons and things, masculine and feminine, singular and plural. *C'est un homme dont le mérite égale la naissance,* he is a man whose merit equals his birth.

Dont cannot be preceded by a preposition. When there is a preposition, the relative must be either *de qui,* or *duquel, de laquelle,* etc., for persons, and *duquel, de laquelle,* etc., alone, for things. *C'est un guide à l'expérience de qui vous pouvez toujours vous fier,* he is a guide to whose experience you can always trust.

In English, the noun following *whose* is never accompanied by the article. In French, the noun after *dont* always takes the article. *C'est un écrivain dont les œuvres sont connues de tout le monde,* he is a writer whose works are known by everybody.

In English, the noun following *whose* may be either the subject or the object of the relative clause. In French, only the subject of the relative clause can come immediately after the verb. *Je plains les cultivateurs dont les champs ont été dévastés par l'inondation*, I pity the farmers whose fields have been devastated by the flood ; *je plains les cultivateurs dont l'inondation a dévasté les champs*, I pity the farmers whose fields the flood has devastated.

Indefinite Pronouns. *Autrui* is never used as the subject of a verb, and very seldom without a preposition before it. It is more vague and general in its meaning than *autres*. *Attendez d'autrui ce que vous faites à autrui,* expect from others what you do to others.

Chacun may have either *son, sa, ses,* or *leur, leurs* for its corresponding possessive :

(*a*) When *chacun* is the subject of the verb, possession is expressed by *son, sa, ses ; chacun doit corriger le devoir de son voisin,* each one must correct his neighbour's exercise.

(*b*) *Chacun* is followed by *son, sa, ses,* when it comes after the object of the verb and is not necessary to complete the sense of the sentence : *ils ont donné leur avis, chacun selon ses vues,* they have given their advice, each according to his views.

(*c*) When *chacun* is placed before the direct object of the verb it takes *leur, leurs* as its possessive. *Ces deux généraux ont chacun leur mérite,* those two generals have each their merit ; *les abeilles bâtissent chacune leur cellule,* bees build each their own cell.

(*d*) When the verb is in the first or second person plural, the possessives corresponding with *chacun* are, respectively, *notre, nos,* and *votre, vos. Nous devons secourir les malheureux chacun selon nos moyens,* we should help the needy, each according to our means.

(*e*) The reflexive pronoun corresponding with *chacun* is *se, soi : chacun pour soi,* each one for himself.

Personne, meaning somebody, anybody, is always masculine. In connexion with *ne,* it means nobody ; *nous avons attendu deux heures, mais personne n'est venu,* we waited two hours, but nobody came.

Quelqu'un, meaning somebody, anybody, is always masculine. It is sometimes used in the plural with the meaning of some, a few : *quelques-uns croient tout le contraire,* some believe the very opposite.

Quelque chose, meaning something, anything, is masculine. *Si l'on vous offre quelque chose, ne le refusez pas,* if you are offered anything, do not refuse it. This is to be distinguished from *quelque chose que*, whatever, in which *chose* is a noun, and consequently feminine : *quelque chose qu'il ait faite, vous ne devez pas vous en étonner*, whatever he has done, you cannot be surprised at it.

Quiconque, whoever, is masculine, and has no plural : *quiconque n'observera pas cette loi sera puni*, whoever does not observe this law will be punished.

The indefinite personal pronoun *on* has already been dealt with as a personal pronoun.

LESSON 49

Syntax of the Verb

WHEN a verb has for its subject a collective noun, or noun of multitude, followed by another noun in the plural as its complement, that verb is in the singular or in the plural, according as the leading idea is expressed either by the collective or by its complement : *Une nuée de sauterelles obscurcit l'air*, a swarm of locusts obscured the air. *Une nuée de barbares désolèrent le pays*, a swarm of barbarians laid waste the country.

Every verb in a finite tense agrees with its subject in number and person : *Le cœur d'une mère est le chef-d'œuvre de la nature*, a mother's heart is Nature's masterpiece.

After *la plupart*, whether a plural complement is actually expressed or only understood, the verb is always in the plural : *Quand on en vint aux voix, la plupart se déclarèrent de mon avis*, when it came to voting, the greater number declared themselves of my opinion.

After the adverbs of quantity, *peu, beaucoup, moins, assez, trop*, followed by a plural, the verb is always in the plural : *Beaucoup de gens promettent ; peu savent tenir*, many people promise ; few know how to keep promises.

When *peu* is preceded by *le*, the verb is in the singular if *le peu* expresses want or deficiency : *Le peu de gens avec qui on peut communiquer des sciences abstraites m'en avait dégoûté*, the few (=the lack of) people with whom one can discuss the abstract sciences had put me out of conceit with them. When *le peu* expresses a small quantity, or a small number, the verb agrees with the noun following it : *Le peu d'amis que j'avais sont venus à mon secours*, the few friends I had have come to my help.

The verb of which *tout le monde* is the subject is in the singular : *Tout le monde est sujet à l'erreur*, everybody is liable to error.

When preceded by *ce*, the verb *être* is in the third person singular if it is followed by a plural pronoun of the first or of the second person, or by two or more nouns in the singular : *C'est nous qui avons le plus souffert de sa tyrannie*, it is we who have suffered most from his tyranny. Though preceded by *ce*, the verb *être* requires to be in the plural if it is followed by a plural noun or by a personal pronoun in the third person plural : *Ce furent les Phéniciens qui inventèrent l'écriture*, it was the Phoenicians who invented writing.

When the verb *être* preceded by *ce* is followed by two (or more) substantives of which one is singular and the other plural, it takes the number of the substantive nearest to it : *Ce sera le même théâtre et les mêmes décorations*, it will be the same theatre and the same decorations. When the verb *être* preceded by *ce* is equivalent to the impersonal verb *y avoir*, it may, if followed by a plural noun, be either in the singular or the plural : *C'était* (or *c'étaient*) *tous les jours de nouvelles plaintes*, there were new complaints every day.

The verb *être* preceded by *ce* remains in the singular if it is followed by a noun and a numeral adjective which, though plural in form, convey an idea of unity. *C'est quatre heures qui sonnent*, it is four o'clock that is striking.

When the subject of a verb consists of several nouns or pronouns in the singular, the verb itself is in the plural : *L'hirondelle et le rossignol annoncent le retour du printemps*, the swallow and the nightingale announce the return of spring. When the various part of the subject are not of the same person, the verb is in the plural and agrees with the person that has priority. In that case it is usual, but not essential, to introduce an additional plural pronoun representing that person : *Vous et moi (nous) sommes contents de notre sort*, you and I are content with our lot.

When two subjects are joined either by *ni* or by *ou*, the verb is usually in the plural, unless it is obvious that one subject excludes the other : *Ni l'or ni la grandeur ne nous rendent heureux*, neither gold nor greatness make us happy. *Ni Corneille ni Racine n'est l'auteur de ces vers*, neither Corneille nor Racine is the author of those verses.

A verb having *l'un et l'autre* for its subject must be in the plural : *L'un et l'autre rapportent les mêmes circonstances*, the one and the other (=both) record the same circumstances.

Complement of the Verb. The same noun may be the complement (or object) of two verbs, provided both verbs govern the same case : *Les enfants doivent aimer et respecter leurs parents*, children should love and respect their parents. Here, *parents* is the direct object (or accusative) of both *aimer* and *respecter*. It is incorrect to say : *Les enfants doivent obéir et respecter leurs parents*, because *obéir* requires an indirect object (or dative), whilst *respecter* governs a direct object (or accusative). The proper construction is : *Les enfants doivent obéir à leurs parents et les respecter*, children must obey their parents and respect them.

When a verb has several complements joined by *et*, *ou*, or *ni*, all these complements must be of the same kind—i.e. either all nouns or all infinitives, etc. ; but not one noun and one infinitive : *Il aime le chant et le dessin*, he likes singing and drawing ; *Il aime à chanter et à dessiner*, he likes to sing and to draw. It would be incorrect to say : *Il aime le chant et à dessiner*, he likes singing and to draw.

Use of Auxiliaries. All transitive verbs take *avoir* for their auxiliary : *j'ai donné*. Most intransitive verbs take *avoir* for their auxiliary : *il a succombé*. All reflexive verbs are conjugated with *être* in their compound tenses : *je me suis blessé*.

The passive voice consists throughout of the verb *être* with a past participle added to it : *il est aimé ; ils ont été battus*.

The following intransitive verbs are always conjugated with *être :* *aller*, to go ; *arriver*, to arrive ; *choir*, to fall ; *décéder*, to die ; *échoir*, to fall due ; *éclore*, to be hatched, to blossom ; *entrer*, to enter ; *mourir*, to die ; *naître*, to be born ; *repartir*, to set out again ; *ressortir*, to go out again ; *retourner*, to go back ; *venir*, to come ; and the derivatives, *rentrer*, to come back, to re-enter ; *revenir*, to come back ; *devenir*, to become ; *intervenir*, to intervene ; *parvenir*, to succeed, to attain to ; *provenir*, to proceed from ; *redevenir*, to become again.

A certain number of intransitive verbs, though almost always conjugated with *être*, are occasionally to be found conjugated with *avoir*. They are : *descendre*, to go down ; *monter*, to go up ; *partir*, to set out, to go off ; *retomber*, to fall again ; *tomber*, to fall ; *sortir*, to go out. Any intransitive verb used transitively requires *avoir* for its auxiliary : *Avez-vous descendu nos bagages ?* have you taken down our baggage ?

A certain number of verbs, of which the following are the chief, are conjugated with *avoir* or with *être*, according as they denote action or state resulting from action : *accourir*, to run up ; *cesser*, to cease ; *changer*, to change ; *croître*, to grow ; *déborder*, to overflow ; *dégénérer*, to degenerate ; *disparaître*, to disappear ; *échouer*, to run aground, to fail ; *embellir*, to beautify ; *grandir*, to grow up ; *grossir*, to increase in size ; *maigrir*, to become thinner ; *passer*, to pass ; *rajeunir*, to become young again ; *vieillir*, to grow old. *Cet enfant a bien grandi en peu de temps*, that child has grown a great deal in a short time. *Comme il est grandi !* how he has grown !

Some verbs have different meanings, according as they are conjugated with *avoir* or with *être*. Such are *convenir*, to suit, to agree : *Cette maison nous a convenu*, that house has suited (pleased) us. *Nous sommes convenus d'acheter cette maison*, we have agreed to buy that house. *Demeurer*, to dwell, to stop : *Il a demeuré longtemps à Paris*. he lived a long time in Paris ; *l'affaire en est demeurée là*, the matter stopped there. *Echapper*, to escape notice, to be forgotten, to slip from, to be said unwittingly : *Ce que je voulais vous dire m'a échappé*, what I wished to tell you has escaped me (i.e., my memory). *Il lui est échappé un mot qu'il ne voulait pas dire*, a word he did not wish to say escaped him.

LESSON 50

Use of the Subjunctive

THE verb of the subordinate clause must be in the subjunctive when the verb of the principal clause expresses surprise, admiration, wish, consent, prohibition, doubt, fear, command : *Je m'étonne qu'il ne voie pas le danger où il est*, I am astonished that he does not see the danger in which he is.

The verb of the subordinate clause must be in the subjunctive when the verb of the principal clause is either negative or interrogative : *Je n'ai employé aucune fiction qui ne soit une image sensible de la vérité*, I have used no fiction but what is a living image of truth. *Croyez-vous qu'il vienne ?* Do you think he will come ? *Exception :* When the interrogation is merely formal, and really

amounts to a direct statement, the subjunctive is not required :
Croyez-vous que les Parisiens sont des sots ? Do you think Parisians
are blockheads ?

The verb of the subordinate clause must be in the subjunctive
after impersonal verbs and phrases : *Il vaut mieux qu'il ne vienne
point*, it is better he should not come. *Exception :* (*a*) The
indicative is required after *il s'ensuit*, it follows ; *il résulte*, it
results ; *il arrive*, it happens : and after impersonal phrases in
which there occurs an adjective expressive of certainty, such as
évident, sûr, certain, vrai, except when these are either negative
or interrogative : *Il arrive souvent qu'on est trompé*, it often happens
that we are mistaken. (*b*) *sembler*, though used impersonally,
requires the indicative if it is preceded by one of the personal
pronouns *me, te, nous, vous. lui, leur ;* but, if used negatively or
interrogatively, it follows the rule : *Il me semble qu'il n'y a pas
de plus grande jouissance que celle de faire des heureux*, it seems to
me that there is no greater happiness than that of making people
happy. *Il ne me semble pas que l'on puisse penser différemment*,
it does not seem to me that anyone can think otherwise.

The verb must be in the subjunctive when it is preceded by a
relative pronoun having for its antecedent a noun qualified by a
superlative, or by some word equivalent to a superlative, such as :
le premier, the first ; *le dernier*, the last ; *le seul*, the only ; *Le
chien est le seul animal dont la fidélité soit à l'épreuve*, the dog is the
only animal whose fidelity can be relied on. When the superlative is followed by an indirect object the verb is in the indicative :
Le soleil est le plus grand des corps que l'on aperçoit dans le ciel, the
sun is the largest of the bodies that we perceive in the heavens.

After *quel que (quelle que, quels qu, quelles que)*, whatever ;
qui que, whosoever ; *quoi que*, whatsoever, the subjunctive is
required in the subordinate clause : *Quel que soit le mérite d'un
homme, il ne peut échapper à l'envie*, whatever a man's merit may
be, he cannot escape envy. *Quelque . . . que*, and *si . . . que*,
meaning whatever, however, require the verb following them to
be in the subjunctive : *Quelque effort que fassent les hommes, leur
néant paraît partout*, whatever effort men may make, their
nothingness is everywhere apparent.

The subjunctive is used (*a*) after conjunctions indicating time
before which, or time up to which, as *avant que, en attendant que,
jusqu'à ce que ;* (*b*) after conjunctions indicating purpose or result,
as *afin que, pour que, de crainte que, de peur que ;* (*c*) after con-

junctions implying a condition or supposition, as *en cas que, au cas que, à moins que . . . ne, pourvu que, supposé que ;* (*d*) after conjunctions implying a concession, as *quoique, bien que, encore que, soit que . . . soit que ; soit que . . . ou que ; pour peu que, si tant est que ;* and (*e*) after conjunctions involving a negation, as *non que, non pas que, loin que, sans que* .

(*a*) *Je lui ai payé cette somme avant qu'il partît,* I paid him that amount before he left. (*b*) *Ce livre est toujours sur le bureau, afin qu'on puisse le consulter,* that book is always on the desk, so that it may be consulted. (*c*) *Pourvu qu'on sache la passion dominante de quelqu'un, on est assuré de lui plaire,* providing we know the master-passion of any one, we are sure to please him. (*d*) *Quoi-qu'il soit pauvre, il est un honnête homme,* although he is poor, he is an honest man. (*e*) *Je dis cela, non que je veuille me plaindre, mais pour que vous sachiez ce qui s'est passé,* I say this, not that I wish to complain, but that you may know what has taken place.

The subjunctive occurs in elliptical sentences expressing a wish or a command , and, in such cases, the conjunction *que* is sometimes omitted : *Vive le Roi !* Long live the King !

The subjunctive is used idiomatically in the expression *je ne sache,* followed by a negation, and *que je sache,* preceded by one : *Je ne sache rien qui soit plus digne de notre amour que la vertu,* I know nothing that is more worthy of our love than virtue ; *Cette affaire ne le regarde nullement, que je sache,* this matter does not concern him in any way that I know of.

Sequence of Tenses. When the verb of the governing clause is in the present, whether indicative, subjunctive, or imperative, or in either of the future tenses of the indicative, the verb of the subordinate clause must be in the present subjunctive if it be intended to express an action or a state considered as either present or future in respect of the governing verb : *Il faut que je sorte maintenant,* I must go out now.

When the verb of the governing clause is in the present, whether indicative, subjunctive, or imperative, or in the future indicative, the verb of the subordinate clause must be in the perfect subjunctive if it be intended to express an action, or a state considered as past in respect of the governing verb : *Je ne crois pas que vous ayez fait tous vos efforts,* I do not think you have done your utmost.

When the verb of the governing clause is in any past tense of the indicative or subjunctive, or in either tense of the conditional, the verb of the subordinate clause must be in the imperfect subjunctive if it be intended to express an action or a state considered as either present or future in respect of the governing verb : *Je voulais qu'on retardât le départ,* I wished the departure to be delayed.

When the verb of the governing clause is in any past tense of the indicative or of the subjunctive, or in either tense of the conditional, the verb of the subordinate clause must be in the pluperfect subjunctive if it be intended to express an action or a state considered as past in respect of the governing verb : *Je ne savais pas que vous m'eussiez écrit,* I did not know that you had written to me.

When the verb of the governing clause is in the past indefinite, the verb of the subordinate clause is frequently put in the past subjunctive instead of the pluperfect subjunctive : *Il a fallu qu'il se soit donné bien des peines,* he must have given himself a great deal of trouble.

A past indefinite in the governing clause may be followed by a present subjunctive in the subordinate clause to express an action or a state which is still present : *Cet auteur n'a employé aucune fiction qui ne soit une image de la vérité,* that author has used no fiction that is not an image of truth.

LESSON 51

Use of the Past Participle

THE past participle, when not accompanying an auxiliary verb, is practically an adjective, and agrees in gender and number with the noun or pronoun to which it refers : *Voyez-vous là-bas ces collines couronnées de bois sombres ?* Do you see yonder those hills crowned with dark woods ? A certain number of past participles, however, really become prepositions when they precede a substantive, and are then invariable. The chief of them are : *attendu,* considering ; *vu,* seeing ; *excepté,* except ; *y compris,* including ; *ci-inclus,* enclosed ; *Excepté vous et moi,* except you and me. These participles agree in the ordinary way when they come after the noun or pronoun to which they refer : *Vous et moi exceptés,* you and I excepted.

USE OF THE PAST PARTICIPLE

When the past participle is accompanied by the verb *être*, to be, as is the case in all the tenses of passive verbs, and in the compound tenses of some neuter or intransitive verbs, it agrees in gender and number with the subject of the verb : *La vertu obscure est souvent méprisée*, obscure virtue is often despised.

When the past participle is used in connexion with *avoir*, to have, to form the compound tenses of an active verb, it agrees in gender and number with the direct object of the verb, providing that direct object precedes the verb : *J'ai reçu toutes les lettres que vous m'avez addressées*, I have received all the letters which you have addressed to me.

It follows that, as a neuter verb cannot have a direct object, its participle is always invariable : *La justice et la modération de nos ennemis nous ont plus nui que leur valeur*, the justice and moderation of our enemies have done us more harm than their valour.

Pronominal or reflexive verbs are conjugated in their compound tenses with the help of *être*, to be. This auxiliary, however, is equivalent to *avoir*, to have ; and the rule for the agreement of the past participle is the same as in the case of the past participle conjugated with *avoir* : *Ces hommes se sont repentis*, those men have repented. In this sentence *se* is the direct object of the pronominal verb *se repentir*, to repent ; and consequently the past participle agrees with it. *Elle s'est plu à me contredire*, she delighted in contradicting me. In this example, the pronominal verb *se plaire*, to delight in, is made from the intransitive verb *plaire*. The pronoun s' (=*se*) is governed by it in the dative.

The past participle of an impersonal verb, or of a verb used impersonally, can never have a direct object with which to agree : *Les chaleurs qu'il a fait pendant l'été*, the heat which was experienced during the summer. Here *il a fait* (=it has made) is used impersonally and idiomatically (=there has been).

The past participle *été* never changes : *La maison a été brûlée*, the house was burnt. *Nous sommes ce que nous avons toujours été*, we are what we always have been.

When the past participle conjugated with the auxiliary *avoir* and preceded by a direct object is followed by an infinitive, that past participle agrees with the object if it is the governing verb. It does not agree if the infinitive is the governing verb : *Les dames que nous avons entendues chanter*, the ladies whom we heard sing (singing). Here, the past participle agrees because it belongs to the verb governing *que*, whom. Here *chanter* may be translated by the English present participle *singing*. *Les airs que nous avons entendu chanter*, the melodies which we heard sung. Here the past participle does not agree because not it, but *chanter* is the verb governing *que*. It is to be noted that in this case the French infinitive is translated by the English past participle *sung*.

The past participle *fait* does not come under this rule. When immediately followed by an infinitive it always remains unchanged (*fait*) : *Une femme s'est présentée à la porte ; je l'ai fait passer*, a woman presented herself at the door ; I made her pass in.

It frequently happens that a governing infinitive is understood after the past participles of *devoir*, *vouloir* and *pouvoir*, i.e., *dû*, *voulu*, *pu*. In that case the past participle does not agree with the preceding object : *Je lui ai rendu tous les services que j'ai pu*, I have rendered all the services which I could (i.e. render him).

A past participle preceded by the relative pronoun *que*, and followed by the conjunction *que*, never agrees with the relative : *Les lettres que j'ai prévu que vous recevriez*, the letters which I foresaw you would receive.

The past participle does not agree with *en*, some, any : *Il a acheté plus de livres qu'il n'en a lu*, he has bought more books than he has read. Preceded by *en*, it may, however, agree with some other word also preceding it : *J'ai reconnu la maison d'après la description que vous m'en avez faite*, I recognized the house from the description you gave me of it.

After *le peu* the past participle remains unchanged if *le peu* is equivalent to " the want of " : *Le peu d'affection que vous lui avez témoigné l'a découragé*, the little affection you showed him discouraged him. If, on the contrary, *le peu* represents a positive quantity, a certain amount, the past participle agrees with the complement of *le peu*, i.e. the following noun : *Le peu d'affection que vous lui avez témoignée l'a encouragé*, the little affection you showed him encouraged him.

Negation. Negation is usually expressed by *ne* and *pas* or *point* (which is rather stronger than *pas*). *Ce n'est pas moi qui vous l'ai dit*, it is not I who told you. The second part of the negation is omitted, after *savoir*, used with the meaning of *pouvoir*, to be able : *Je ne saurais en venir à bout*, I cannot manage it. Here the present conditional of *savoir* is used instead of the present indicative of *pouvoir*. When *savoir* has its ordinary meaning of " to know " it requires *pas* when used negatively : *Il ne sait pas le français*, he does not know French.

When a verb used negatively is followed by a negative relative clause, that relative clause takes *ne* only : *Il n'y a personne qui ne le respecte*, there is no one but respects him.

When the negation is expressed by any word but " not," such as " never," " nobody," " nothing," etc., *ne* is used, but *pas* must be omitted : *Je ne dois rien*, I owe nothing.

In negations the order of the words is usually : first, *ne* ; second, verb ; third, second part of the negative expression. But when " nobody " or " nothing " is the subject of the sentence, *personne*, or *rien*, must precede *ne* : *Personne n'a voulu lui parler*, nobody would speak to him.

" Neither—nor " must be expressed by *ne—ni* : *Elle n'a ni frère ni sœur*, she had neither brother nor sister.

Several negative expressions may occur in the same sentence, in which case *ne* is used only once : *Personne ne m'a jamais rien dit*, nobody has ever said anything to me.

Ne is used alone and without any negative meaning : (*a*) After verbs and other expressions indicating fear : *Je crains que vous ne perdiez votre argent*, I fear you will lose your money. (*b*) After *que*, " than," in comparisons of superiority or inferiority having a verb for their second term : *Vous écrivez mieux que vous ne parlez*, you write better than you speak. (*c*) After *à moins que*, " unless " : *J'irai me promener, à moins qu'il ne fasse mauvais temps*, I shall go for a walk unless it is bad weather.

Remarks on Adverbs. *Auparavant* and *avant* both mean " before " (of time) ; but *auparavant*, being an adverb, has no complement, whilst *avant*, which is a preposition, requires one : *Nous lui avions déjà écrit quelques mois auparavant*, we had already written to him a few months before ; *Je le verrai avant vous*, I shall see him before you.

Davantage and *plus* both mean " more," but *davantage* must not be followed by *que* or by *de*. It therefore stands only at the end of a sentence : *Vous avez de l'argent, mais il en a davantage*, you have money, but he has more.

Dessus, " on, over " ; *dessous*, " under, underneath " ; *dedans*, " within, in " ; *dehors* " without, out," which are adverbs and take no complement, are to be carefully distinguished from the prepositions, *sur*, *sous*, *dans*, *hors*, which require complements.

Plus tôt and *plotôt* both mean " sooner," but *plus tôt* refers to priority of time, whilst *plutôt* indicates preference : *Il est revenu plus tôt que je ne croyais*, he has come back sooner than I thought ; *Donnez-nous la mort plutôt que l'esclavage*, give us death rather than slavery.

Au moins and *du moins* both mean " at least," but *au moins* indicates a minimum, whilst *du moins* corrects or limits a former statement : *Ce voyage vous coûtera au moins mille francs, du moins c'est ce qu'il m'a coûté l'année dernière*, that journey will cost you at least forty pounds—at least, that is what it cost me last year.

LESSON 52

Concluding Remarks on Prepositions and Conjunctions

PREPOSITIONS, with the single exception of *en*, require verbs that follow them to be in the infinitive. After *en* the verb must be in the present participle : *En voyant son père il se mit à pleurer*, on seeing his father he began weeping. The prepositions *à*, *de*, and *en* must be repeated before each complement : *Il dut la vie à la clémence et à la magnanimité du vainqueur*, he owed his life to the clemency and the magnanimity of the victor.

Other prepositions are usually repeated when the complements are opposed to each other in meaning : *Dans la ville et dans la campagne*, in town and country.

The prepositions *jusque*, as far as ; *attenant*, adjoining ; *par rapport*, with regard to ; *quant*, as to, require the preposition *à* after them : *Il nous a accompagnés jusqu' à Londres*, he accompanied us as far as London. But when *jusque* is construed with *où*, *ici*, *là*, *dans*, and *chez* it does not take *à* as well ; *Il nous a accompagnés jusque chez nous*, he accompanied us as far as our house.

The preposition *de* is required after *auprès*, near ; *autour*, around ; *loin*, far ; *près*, near ; and *proche*, close, and prepositional phrases including a noun, as *à force*, by dint ; *Ils demeurent près de l'église*, they live near the church ; *Je suis loin de chez moi*, I am far from home.

ON PREPOSITIONS AND CONJUNCTIONS

Avant (before) requires no preposition before a noun or pronoun, but takes *de* before a verb : *Viendrez-vous nous voir avant de partir ?* Will you come and see us before leaving ?

When helping to form compound words, the preposition *à* conveys the idea of fitness, agency, peculiarity : *Un bateau à vapeur*, a steamboat.

The preposition *de* is joined to a noun of material to form a qualifying phrase : *Un chapeau de paille*, a straw hat. *De* is used after *plus* and *moins* to express " than " before a numeral : *Vous avez plus de dix fautes*, you have more than ten mistakes. *De* is also used before *plus* and *moins*, " more " and " less," when those words follow a numeral with a noun expressed or understood : *Vous avez douze fautes ; il en a deux de moins*, you have twelve mistakes ; he has two less.

The preposition *de* is used for " by " in expressions indicating excess or difference : *Vous le dépassez de toute la tête*, you are taller than he (exceed him) by a whole head. *De* is used for " with " after verbs and adjectives expressing plenty, want, providing, depriving, etc. : *Il s'était rempli les poches de petits cailloux*, he had filled his pockets with little pebbles.

When the verb " to be " has an infinitive coming after it for its logical subject that infinitive takes *de* or *que de* before it ; *C'est mal de* (or *que de*) *parler comme cela*, it is wrong to speak so. An infinitive following " than " takes *de* before it : *Il mourrait plutôt que de trahir sa patrie*, he would die rather than betray his country.

When a noun or an adjective used substantivally serves as an epithet to qualify another noun, *de*, meaning " of a," is put before the qualified noun : *Un drôle d'individu*, a queer fellow.

The essential difference between *en* and *dans* is that *en* is only exceptionally used with the definite article, *le, la, les*, whilst *dans* always requires it. Consequently, nouns following *en* have usually an indeterminate meaning : *On l'a mené en prison*, he has been taken to prison ; *On lui a permis d'entrer dans la prison*, he was allowed to enter the prison. *En* frequently means " in the character of " " like " : *Vous parlez en soldat ; je dois agir en roi*, you speak as a soldier ; I must act as a king. In expressions of time there is a great difference between *en* and *dans*. *En* indicates " time, how long," whilst *dans* indicates " point of time when " ; *Je ferai cet ouvrage en deux jours*, I shall take two days to do that work ; *Je ferai ce travail dans deux jours*, I shall begin doing that work two days from now. *En* is used in connexion with all the seasons except spring, which takes *au ; Il fait moins chaud au printemps qu'en été*, It is less warm in spring than in summer.

A travers and *au travers* both mean " through," but *à travers* means " through " in the sense of " across "; whilst *au travers*, which is always followed by *de*, rather means " right through," and implies a greater effort : *Nous courûmes à travers les champs*, we ran through the fields ; *Il se fraya un passage au travers de la haie*, he forced his way through the hedge.

Vers and *envers* both mean " towards "; but *vers* refers to direction, whilst *envers* is used figuratively, in connexion with feeling, sentiment, etc. : *Le premier moment de la vie est le premier pas vers la mort*, the first moment of life is the first step towards death ; *Il s'est montré ingrat envers ses bienfaiteurs*, he showed himself ungrateful towards his benefactors.

Use of Conjunctions. The conjunction *ni*, " neither," may be either used or omitted before the first of several subjects : *Le soleil ni la mort ne se peuvent regarder fixement*, neither the sun nor death can be steadfastly gazed at : *Ni l'or ni la grandeur ne nous rendent heureux*, neither gold nor greatness makes us happy. The conjunction *ni* may be used to avoid the repetition of *sans*, " without "; *Sans crainte ni pudeur*, or *sans crainte et sans pudeur*, without fear or shame.

The English expressions " nor . . . either " " not . . . either," are to be translated by *ni . . . non plus, ne . . . pas non plus : Je ne le connais pas, ni elle non plus*, I do not know him nor her either ; *Je ne lui écris pas, et il ne m'écrit pas non plus*, I do not write to him, and he does not write to me either. The expression " either . . . or " may be expressed either by using *ou* before each term, or omitting it before the first. *Le bonheur ou la témérité ont pu faire des héros*, either good fortune or rashness may have produced heroes.

Soit and *soit que* both mean " whether," but *soit* precedes a noun, whilst *soit que* is followed by a verb. Both of them may be repeated before each term, or replaced by *ou* or *ou que* before the second : *La fortune, soit bonne ou mauvaise, soit passagère ou constante, ne peut rien sur l'âme du sage*, fortune, whether good or bad, whether fleeting or constant, has no power over the soul of the wise man.

ON PREPOSITIONS AND CONJUNCTIONS

The conjunction *que* may be used to prevent the repetition of either *comme*, as ; *quand*, when ; or *si*, if. When replacing the last of these, it requires the verb that follows it to be in the subjunctive : *Comme nous l'avons déjà dit et que nous le verrons plus clairement ailleurs*, as we have already said, and as we shall see more clearly elsewhere : *Quand on est jeune et qu'on se porte bien on devrait aimer les exercises du corps*, when we are young and are in good health we ought to like bodily exercise ; *Si vous le rencontrez et que vous lui parliez, faites-lui mes amitiés*, if you meet him and speak to him, give him my kind regards.

Que may be used instead of *afin que*, in order that ; *sans que*, but that ; *lorsque*, when ; *depuis que*, since ; *de peur que*, lest ; and *avant que*, until : *Approchez que je vous parle*, draw near, that I may speak to you. When, however, *que* takes the place of a conjunction which does not itself require the subjunctive (except the conjunction *si*), it is not followed by the subjunctive : *Je le ferai quand je serai revenu et que j'aurai le temps*, I shall do it when I have returned and have the time.

This Lesson concludes our Course in French.

GEOGRAPHY

Egypt and the Great Rift Valley

WITHIN five degrees, or less than 350 miles, from the equator in the north-east of the Black Continent. a long and relatively narrow lake—comparatively unknown to the world in general—lies for approximately 200 miles north and south among the lower heights which connect the peaks of equatorial Africa (Elgon, Kenya, Ruwenzori. etc.) with the tangled peaks of Abyssinia. Lake Rudolf is geographically noted as one of the largest rift valley lakes of the world ; politically, it is a knot—not a corner—where four states meet.

There Italian Ethiopia meets **three** sections of the British Empire, the Anglo-Egyptian Sudan, Uganda and Kenya. From this knot the southern boundary of Ethiopia, followed by the southern boundary of British Somaliland, leads to the coast on the shore of the Gulf of Aden. This sinuous line runs athwart the slopes from Ethiopia to the Indian Ocean and forms one edge of an irregular quadrilateral, almost a parallelogram ; the other corresponding edge is the shore of the Mediterranean Sea belonging to Egypt and Libya—a land edge opposed to a sea edge, both almost equally useless, since neither is frequented by many people.

From the knot, roughly to the north-west, a curving boundary is the western limit of the Anglo-Egyptian Sudan and Libya. At Dufile a long side of the parallelogram which crosses the Nile defile swings round along the western water-parting of the Bahr-el-Ghazal (Nile) catchment-basin. runs across the north-eastern slope of the Tibesti highlands and, keeping to the higher ground on the west of Fezzan, bounds Libya and Tripolitania, to reach the sea on the shore of the Gulf of Gabes. The corresponding long edge, 1,000 miles away to the east, is the Red Sea, a water edge except where a land boundary lies east of Sinai. Again a land edge lies opposed to a sea edge, and again both are almost equally useless.

Political Divisions. This rough parallelogram is north-east Africa. It includes six states : Egypt, a nominally independent area ; the Anglo-Egyptian Sudan and British Somaliland, a

British pair; an Italian pair, Libya and Italian East Africa (including Eritrea and Ethiopia); and the tiny French Somaliland.

The land edges matter little. The sea edges matter as much as the walls of a subterranean corridor joining a Paddington station on the Great Western with a Euston or a Victoria; here and there the walls are broken and a few folk may be seen about

SKETCH MAP OF NORTH-EAST AFRICA

their purely local temporary affairs. The corridor itself is negatively important. It is a nuisance aggravated by its length; the cost of its transit is an economic waste, apparently inevitable under present conditions.

Opposed to the corner at Lake Rudolf—one of the vacant places of the world—is the Suez canal—one of the world's expensive traffic corners. On the sea margin Tripoli, Alexandria, Port Said, Suez, Port Sudan, Massawa and Jibuti have the character of booths on the subterranean corridor dependent on the passers-by.

Within the area, the delta and trench of the Lower Nile provide the only productive areas that really matter. This is the Egyptian section of the Nile, and this is Egypt. Here are a half of the 30 million or so inhabitants of the area, concentrated as densely as the populace of south-east Lancashire in a tiny fraction of the total land space. Only 3 per cent of the total area of Egypt is tilled. As much land is used for wheat and as much wheat is produced as is used in Great Britain similarly—and Britain's wheat is a declining industry ; the barley produced in Egypt is about as much as was obtained in impoverished Austria ; as much maize is grown as in Mexico ; the quantity of rice grown exceeds slightly that of Spain. In the production of cotton alone does Egypt achieve agricultural importance. For 50 years the amount of cotton grown in Egypt has been steadily about 10 per cent of the quantity grown in the United States ; Egypt vies with China as the world's fourth producer of cotton, following the United States, India and Russia. The Egyptian total exceeds three times as much as the total for the whole of the rest of Africa. Except for phosphates and some sugar cane, Egypt has no other productions of note.

The present century has seen definite attempts to grow cotton successfully in the Anglo-Egyptian Sudan ; these attempts have resulted in the sinking of British capital in the Sudan, e.g. in the damming of the rivers to produce irrigation water, as at Sennar on the Blue Nile. From the world's point of view these attempts are futile. At its best the yield from the Anglo-Egyptian Sudan is half that of Mexico, a tenth that of Egypt, and a hundredth of that of the United States, and not more than 5 per cent of the amount by which American yield may fluctuate between successive years. The quantity is insufficient to matter ; its effect on the world's price level of raw cotton must be negligible ; the industry could be swamped out of effective competition by rigging the prices in the great cotton markets. Were the yield multiplied by 25 it would then suffice for the Lancashire mills—and nothing like so great an increase is possible.

Outside Egypt, there are no large towns in north-east Africa. Port Said, with its 126,000 inhabitants, is but a convenient shopping place set in the wall of the sea corridor—a port and coaling station with an unsavoury reputation. Alexandria, with over 680,000 people, is the port of entry for the Nile valley, and is the most populous port of the Levant. Cairo, twice as well peopled as Alexandria, is by far the largest city in Africa. Like the neighbourhood which it serves, it is a museum and gains by the hosts of visitors of antiquarian tastes or caprice who frequent it annually.

North-east Africa is on the whole an area of negatives—no rain, no natural vegetation, no relief from oppressive sunshine, few cultivated crops of other than local importance, few whites, few resources. The single exception is the heavy summer rains on the Ethiopian mountains ; these provide the flood waters for the Nile, on which Egypt depends and without which the whole area would be as unimportant as Greenland.

LESSON 34

Africa's Western Projection

NORTH-WEST Africa includes practically the whole of the western projection of the continent. Its eastern boundary is approximately 10° E., so that its east-west extent is roughly 30° i.e. some 2,000 miles, and its width between the Gulf of Guinea and the Mediterranean Sea is 30°, i.e. some 2,000 miles. Including Nigeria in the south-east corner, as well as a section of the Sahara between 10° E. and the Tibesti highlands, the area is squarish with a curved sea-coast. Between the Gulf of Gabes and Tibesti the eastern boundary separates first Tunisia and then Algeria from Libya. Algeria adjoins Morocco in the north-west and in the extreme west Rio de Oro. In the Atlantic off the coast of Rio de Oro are the Spanish Canary Islands and farther north the Portuguese island of Madeira. South of Algeria is the French Sudan, which meets the northern extension of French Equatorial Africa in the east. French territory reaches the coast of the Atlantic in Senegal and French Guinea, and the coast of the Gulf of Guinea at the Ivory Coast and in Dahomey · it surrounds Nigeria, the British Gold Coast, Sierra Leone and Gambia, the Portuguese Guinea, and the independent Liberia adjoining Sierra Leone.

These last islands within French Africa depend on the coast and sea traffic, and their northern boundaries, such as the edge of the northern territories of the Gold Coast, represent the limit of the white man's influence among the blacks as it worked inland from the coast The wars associated in British minds with the labels Kumasi and Ashanti are a reminder that the penetration from the Gulf of Guinea inland was not always peaceful.

The coast of north-west Africa, from Gabes on the Mediterranean to Port Harcourt on the Gulf, has ever had an attraction for those who fared over the waters. From the times when the Phoenicians and the Romans were interested in Tunisia, until the captains of Prince Henry the Navigator in the 15th century crept cautiously from Tangier to Benin and beyond, while Britons and others exploited the thus made known coast lands for slaves, oils and cocoa—through the centuries ships have frequented these shores.

Physically the area has three sections : the north-west, where the Atlas mountains belong in geological time to Europe of the Alpine uplifts ; the interior, slightly elevated plateau ; and the coast of the south-west and south, where the waters are surf-disturbed, the shores are mangrove swamps, the littoral an alluvial plain, and the interior rises to ranges between which the Volta and other smaller rivers flow southwards. Southern Nigeria consists almost entirely of the lower Niger and its swampy delta. Northern Nigeria, between the Niger-Benue fork and the desert frontier beyond Kano, is the boss of the Bauchi highland.

The whole area is hot, except where temperature is moderated by elevation. The seasonal differences in temperature are greater in the north than in the south, but the seasonal character of the rainfall calls into existence four regions of climatic difference : the north, which is Mediterranean, has winter rains and summer droughts, while snow is not unknown in the winter ; the definite interior, which lacks rain always ; the belt of summer rain and winter drought farther south ; and the coastal fringe, which tends to experience constant equatorial rains of considerable magnitude. The summer rains reach the latitude of Timbuktu on the great bend of the Upper Niger : the northern winter rain area is much narrower and more dependent on the sea ; south of the latitude of Biskra the area of no rains begins.

Consequently, there are four belts of natural vegetation. The Gulf Coast is almost entirely equatorial, hot, wet, jungle, forest.

The summer rain belt is savannah, park-land, where first the
trees and later the shrubs thin out towards Timbuktu, north of
which is the true desert, the Sahara. The north coast has Mediterranean vegetation, marked by fruit-bearing trees, fig, nut, orange,
lime and lemon, and drought-resisting plants of exotic character.

SKETCH MAP OF NORTH-WEST AFRICA

For long the Sahara was regarded as a barrier, but its traverses
by camel caravan, by tractor and motor-car, and by aeroplane
have brought to light unexpected possibilities, and, like the
Australian desert, the Sahara is neither useless nor impenetrable.
The north-west Atlantic coast by its trend lies for many
miles below the regularly used airway route from Europe to

Brazil. The rainy areas of the south are the home of a section of the black race, sometimes labelled Sudan negroes, of whom Kru and Fulah are well-known tribes. The people of the northern rainy area are a mixed race or a mixed populace · there the non-whites represent a relic of the Mussulman empire, which so disturbed medieval Spain. The inland is peopled by Tuaregs, Berbers and Moors. Population is nowhere dense ; the coastal fringes and the Niger valley have the largest aggregate of folk.

Numerically the total population is some fifty millions, of whom a third are in Nigeria and a quarter inhabit the French areas of the north and another quarter the French areas of the south ; the other British possessions include some five million natives. Five towns have a population in excess of 100,000 ; the largest is Algiers, with a population of about a quarter of a million, the capital of French Africa and the chief port of the area. Tunis comes next ; it is a port situated where the Mediterranean narrows to the straits between Africa and the great islands of Sardinia and Sicily. Oran in Algeria, Marrakesh and Casablanca in Morocco, complete the list. The other places, many of which are politically important, named on the map are smaller.

Algeria, Morocco and Tunisia produce wheat—together, about a quarter of the total product of France, which holds these supplies as a supplement to the French harvest. The quantity of barley grown in Algeria almost equals that grown in France. Some maize and some oats are also grown in these three states. Small quantities of rice are produced in the south, notably in Sierra Leone. Vines are typical of Mediterranean lands, and the wine produced in Algeria and Tunisia totals a third as many gallons as the production of France. The Guinea lands are the chief areas for the production of the cocoa bean. the British Gold Coast alone producing 40 per cent of the world's crop , to this must be added beans from Nigeria, the French Ivory Coast and Dahomey, as well as from neighbouring islands. They also provide the soap makers with palm oil and palm kernels. Nigeria has experimental small-scale cotton plantations and small collieries. Relatively small quantities of rubber are obtained in both French and British coastal areas round the Gulf. Algeria and Tunisia grow small quantities of tobacco. The northern coastal lands have horses and cattle and many sheep and goats.

Algeria and Tunisia supply less than 2 per cent of the world's iron ore—together, about half as much as is obtained from Spain.

CHARLES READE (1814–84). Son of an Oxfordshire land-owner, he wrote several plays before producing a number of highly successful novels.
ENGLISH LITERATURE 46

"MARK RUTHERFORD" William Hale White (1831–1913) was born at Bedford and became a Congregational minister, but resigned on account of his unorthodox opinions. He then entered the Civil Service and rose to become assistant director of contracts at the Admiralty.
ENGLISH LITERATURE 46

"GEORGE ELIOT." Born near Nuneaton, Marian Evans (1819–1880) was an agnostic from girlhood, and opened her literary career by translating Strauss's rationalistic "Life of Jesus." Her union with the critic, G. H. Lewes, began in 1854; after his death she married, in 1880, John W. Cross.
ENGLISH LITERATURE 46

ANTHONY TROLLOPE (1815–82). Born in London, he entered the postal service in 1834, and in his leisure hours produced an enormous quantity of fiction and travel books, writing daily a fixed number of words. He also wrote an Auto-biography which was edited by his son and published in 1883.
ENGLISH LITERATURE 46

SAMUEL BUTLER (1835–1902).
Born at Langar, Notts, he spent
1860–64 on a New Zealand sheep-
run, but the rest of his life in
London chambers. He was a
strenuous opponent of Darwinism,
and a keen critic of modern society.
ENGLISH LITERATURE 47
National Portrait Gallery

ROBERT LOUIS STEVENSON (1850–94). After
some experience of engineering he qualified as an
advocate, but soon deserted the law for letters.
Much of his life was spent abroad in the search for
health, and in 1889 he settled at Samoa. He was
buried on the summit of mount Vaea.
ENGLISH LITERATURE 47

Plate 34   *Volume* VI

THOMAS HARDY (1840-1928). A stonemason's son, he was born at Upper Bockhampton, near Dorchester, and became an architect. His first and latest literary activity was poetry, but it was his novels that brought him popularity. He received the O.M. in 1910. His ashes were buried in Westminster Abbey, but his heart at Stinsford.

ENGLISH LITERATURE 47

GEORGE MEREDITH (1828-1909). Born at Portsmouth he became articled to a London solicitor, but soon turned to literature. In 1849 he married a daughter of T. L. Peacock, and two years later published his first poems. His first novel appeared in 1859. He was awarded the O.M. in 1905, and died at Flint Cottage, Box Hill, his home since 1868.

ENGLISH LITERATURE 47

From the etching by Mortimer Menpes

'DARING' NOVELISTS OF THE 'NINETIES. Mrs. Humphry Ward (left: 1851-1920), née Arnold (her grandfather was Arnold of Rugby), was born in Tasmania. Coming to England, she married T. H. Ward in 1872 and published her first novel in 1881. She was keenly interested in social work. "Lucas Malet" (right: 1852-1931) was the younger daughter of Charles Kingsley and the wife of Rev. W. Harrison, rector of Clovelly.
ENGLISH LITERATURE 48

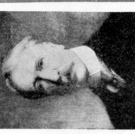

MASTERS OF STYLE AND REALISM. Left, George Moore (1852-1933), son of an Irish landowner, studied painting in Paris before embarking on a literary career. He played a considerable part in the Irish Revival, and was generally recognized as one of the greatest prosemen of his time. Right, George Gissing (1857-1903), who was born at Wakefield, and after a spell of clerking in Liverpool spent some months in America. Returning to England, he managed to exist by writing novels and coaching pupils. In 1897 he visited Italy with H. G. Wells and in 1901 settled for health reasons in the south of France, where he died.
ENGLISH LITERATURE 48

WILLIAM DE MORGAN (1839-1917). Born in London, he devoted himself to working in pottery and glass, and was 65 when his first novel appeared.
ENGLISH LITERATURE 48

Plate 36

Volume VI

These countries also mine some copper, lead and zinc on relatively small scales. Tunisia produces a quarter and Algeria and Morocco together a fifth of the world's supply of phosphates. Nigeria mines less than a twelfth of the world's tin from the Bauchi district. On the whole the area is economically unimportant. Its fifty million people produce relatively little for the world, and are not great purchasers of commodities. Their supplies are food stuffs and raw materials, and most of the latter are fortuitous ; once garnered, they do not recur. They include areas in which the white man has sunk and may sink his capital with the necessary consequence that they provide a means of livelihood for colonial civil servants and agents of business houses and traders. The total number of whites in the area is comparatively negligible, especially if the professional soldiers, always on active service in the troubled north-west, be excluded. The area is not even a white man's corridor—it is a cul-de-sac.

LESSON 35

Geographical Study of Central Africa

THE portion of the African continent included in Central Africa is an irregular area with coastlands on the Atlantic and Indian Oceans and, in the interior, the great mountains of the Central African lake district. The west coast stretches from Cameroon mountain to Mossamedes in Angola it fringes British Nigeria, French Equatorial Africa, including the enclave of Muni, and Portuguese Angola in it is the relatively narrow sea outlet of the Belgian Congo, which is almost a Belgian corridor between French and Portuguese territory. It is a plateau coast with a narrow lowland margin and a steep rise inland. At the corner is Cameroon mountain 2½ miles in elevation, a definite land and air mark. The Congo mouth differs almost completely from the Niger mouth, for there a navigable estuary narrows definitely to a semi-gorge, in which the river tumbles from its reservoir at Stanley Pool cataract fashion, seawards ; this stretch is a barrier to water communication inland, obviated by a special railway from Matadi to Leopoldville.

The north-west boundary of the area traverses the Cameroon highlands, and north of Yola drops into the depression of Lake Chad, one of the world's basins of internal drainage, into which smallish streams occasionally drain from the boss of north Nigeria. The line of the Cameroon heights is continued across the bight of Biafra by the " cocoa " islands, Spanish Fernando Po, Portuguese Principe and São Thomé, and Spanish Annobon. French Equatorial Africa has a coast from 5° N. to 5° S., and terminates at a corner near the Tibesti highlands, almost on the tropic of Cancer ; Libreville is almost on the equator. Its eastern margin on the south is first the Congo, then the Ubangi, and farther north the higher ground round the Nile valley, with the Anglo-Egyptian Sudan to the east. The southern portion drains from the Cameroon heights to the Ubangi-Congo. The northern portion is drained by the Shari, which terminates its flat marshy lower course, north of Fort Lamy, in Lake Chad ; the extreme north is a depression against the wall of Tibesti crossed by intermittent streams after infrequent rains.

Angola rises quickly to the southern plateau of Africa ; the central Bihe highlands mark an approximate watershed, whence there is drainage to the coast, to the Congo and to the Zambezi ; the eastern half slopes down eastwards to the lower levels of the upper Zambezi in Northern Rhodesia. The Belgian Congo is almost completely inland, and almost coincides with the basin of the river. In the south-east, in the Katanga district, the state reaches Northern Rhodesia ; here is Lake Bangweulu, whence flows one of the Congo headstreams. North of this the boundary lies in Lake Tanganyika, whence the Lukuga sometimes provides lake waters to increase the Congo flood. Farther north still the boundary with Tanganyika to the east penetrates into the higher ground of Ruanda, east of the mountain-girt Lake Kivu, and the larger Lake Edward, whence drainage is by Lake Albert, itself on the frontier, to the Nile. All this eastern edge of the Congo state is of interest, not only for its physical features, but as a curious passage way or corridor from the more temperate lands of the south to the Nile valley and the more useful north. The northern boundary of the state is almost wholly fluvial— the Ubangi-Congo. The state as a whole is the largest apparent depression in Africa, yet it is but a tableland depression, lacking seacoast. It is cut into valley fingers by the numerous tributaries, most of which are navigable by some sort of boat. The thousand-mile stretch of the main stream from the turn at Stanleyville, near the Stanley Falls, to Stanley Pool is used for steamer traffic.

CENTRAL AFRICA

West Central Africa is a relatively useless area of excesses; it is too hot, too wet, and vegetation is too rank. The equatorial lowlands are an area where the annual rains total 80 inches, the annual temperature fluctuates with small variations about 80° F., and where the hot wet jungle forest grows so strong that the giant trees have no room for sideways branches. Between the rivers the watersheds are more open uplands, where parkland characterizes less noxious country. The heat is mitigated by altitude here and artificial heat from fires is desirable at night.

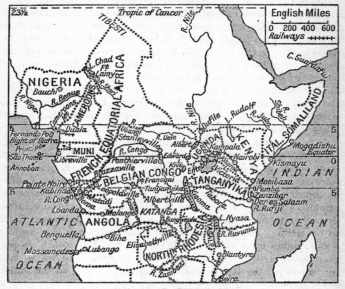

SKETCH MAP OF CENTRAL AFRICA

The rains swing with the sun. Nigeria and the land north of the Congo is wettest in July; the delta is very rainy; the Belgian Congo is wettest in January; north of Lake Chad is the rainless Sahara, and between Chad and the Ubangi a region of summer rains only. The equatorial forest has its southern limit as an east-west line along the Kasai as far as the lower eastern slopes, except near the Lower Congo, and its northern limit as an east-west line along the Uele to include a narrow coast strip in Nigeria. East Central Africa comprises the littoral of the continent on the Indian Ocean and its hinterland as far as the scarp of the African plateau and, in addition, the great boss of highland in equatorial Central Africa.

From Cape Guardafui, at the extremity of the Gulf of Aden, southwards for over 10 degrees of latitude. 700 miles, stretches the coast of Italian Somaliland : next, from just south of the equator for more than 4 degrees, 300 miles is Kenya : next. for 400 miles, 6 degrees, is Tanganyika. Inland are, from the south to the north. in the opposite direction the wide uplands of Tanganyika, which extend to Lake Victoria on the equator, and, farther north, the heights of western Kenya and the inland state of Uganda, with Lakes Rudolf, Albert. Edward and Victoria on its boundary Off the coast are the islands of Zanzibar and Pemba. Pemba Bay about 120 miles north of Mozambique, is one of the finest harbours in the world.

The Ruvuma is a frontier river ; farther north is the Rufiji, the chief stream of central Tanganyika. In Somaliland near Kismayu is the combined Juba and Shibeli, which have their lower courses in this area.

Lake Victoria differs from the other lakes. It is a water-filled depression in the plateau the others are rift gashes with some water in their lower portions. Victoria is the great Nile reservoir. The water which exudes from it traverses 2,000 miles of country, where during the cool season there is little or no rainfall, and little or no inflow of valley water ; yet the volume, despite tremendous evaporation, sends a steady flood past Cairo to the delta. The real Nile water as distinct from the summer floods, comes from Victoria ; Egypt. i.e. the Nile trench. is geographically a result of the plateau reservoir. The water falls by two steps, the Ripon and the Murchison Falls, to the valley defile from Lake Albert to Dufile.

Climatically, eastern and western middle Africa differ. The horn of Africa ending at Cape Gua dafui, i.e., the Somaliland peninsula, is as hot. as arid, and as useless as the Sahara or Arabia. Temperatures are always high, except where the elevation moderates the temperature , e.g., on the boss of Kenya the temperature is normally ten degrees lower than in similar areas inland in Tanganyika. The whole of the eastern region south of the equator has a distinct dry season from July to October, when the weather is coolest ; with the returning summer heat come the rains, which are heavier on the higher ground at mid-summer. Madagascar is wet, with a summer maximum, and in any month has more rain on the east than the west.

The consequent natural vegetation is not forest of the jungle character of the Congo basin, but parkland with a higher proportion of trees as the rainfall is heavier and with an inclination to arid steppe land where the rainfall is slight. Madagascar, however, has a forest fringe near the coasts.

The Belgian Congo is one of the most populous areas in Africa; the people are Bantu negroes. To the north-east and east are Hamites (Abyssinia), Somalis, and Masai (Kenya); the whites are few in number. For centuries the coast has been frequented by Arab and other traders, many of whom have been active in a trade in slaves, and the coastal settlements have a mixed populace. The area is about three-tenths of the continent with roughly a quarter of the population. Settlements are small. On the east, Mogadishu, Mombasa, and Dar es Salaam, on the coast, and Kigoma, Tabora, Nairobi and Entebbe, inland, have political or commercial importance. On the west coast are Duala, Kabinda, Boma, Pointe Noire and Benguella; inland are Fort Lamy, Leopoldville, Kinshasa, Elizabethville and Albertville.

Products are not numerous. About 1 per cent of the world's coffee is grown in Kenya, Tanganyika and the neighbourhood. Experimental rubber plantations in Kenya have a small yield. The wild rubber of the Congo amounted to a tenth of the world's rubber supply when this century opened; it is now but a sixth of what it was, and but a thousandth of the world's supplies. A tenth of the world's copper comes from the mines in the Katanga district and some gold from the Kivu district. Zanzibar supplies the world with cloves.

LESSON 36

Britain's Dominion in South Africa

SOUTHERN AFRICA is mainly British. It is tableland with a very narrow coastal fringe. It extends from the southern end of Lake Tanganyika, about lat. 10° S., to Cape Agulhas, lat. 35° S., about 1,800 miles. It lies between the Indian and the South Atlantic Oceans. Its extremity is one of the great sea corners. The turning of this corner by European sailors some four centuries ago was one of the great events in the history of the world.

It is the chief African area which has been sedulously penetrated by the European, and entry has been in general from the southern tip. Waves of Dutch and British, and, later, treasure hunters have lapped farther and farther inland. After a series of vicissitudes it is politically part of the British Empire, and the populace, destined to become Afrikander—except in the unlikely event of large-scale politically directed European emigration—must tend to cohere. In the west are Hottentots and Bushmen, in the east Zulus and other Bantu negroes ; throughout, the problem of the coloured races tends to be acute, and the Afrikander of mainly Aryan descent will be a minority population. There, in a seventh of the continent, is housed a fourteenth of the people of Africa. There, Durban, not so large as Stoke-on-Trent, Capetown, which is smaller than Bristol, Johannesburg, which is about the size of Leeds, are the largest urban centres, not only in Southern Africa, but generally, as a group, in all Africa, except Egypt ; Pretoria and Kimberley are smaller. In the Pretoria-Kimberley district is mined one-third of the world's gold, and thence comes the bulk of the world's diamonds.

The total white population does not exceed the population of Glasgow, Manchester and Birmingham together. Most of the area is of little worth. In the west the Kalahari is arid, a second Sahara. Practically the whole of the Atlantic coast land is desert, and almost void of settlements ; diamonds alone are the excuse for the presence there of whites. In the east are the mountains, the Drakensbergs, where the comparatively valueless Basutoland counts for as little as the arid Bechuanaland of the middle plateau area. Barotseland, the west of Northern Rhodesia, is of as little importance. Even in the Cape Province of the extreme south Great Bushman Land is relatively useless, though the presence of copper and other ores is known. The railway map is an index of utility ; main lines run roughly N.-S. through the centre and join up branch lines to mining areas or to seaports.

The political names are South-west Africa, Cape of Good Hope, Natal, and Portuguese Mozambique round the coast, Orange Free State, Transvaal, Southern Rhodesia, Northern Rhodesia, and Nyasaland inland.

SOUTH AFRICA

Physically, in the plateau there are slight depressions connected with the rivers. The lower Orange leads out from a depression in Bechuanaland ; the Limpopo flows in a depression between the Transvaal and Southern Rhodesia The Zambezi collects the drainage of a depression which fringes the western boundary from the north of Bechuanaland through Barotseland ; it emerges on to the lowland of Mozambique and terminates in a delta. It receives the drainage from Lake Nyasa by the Shire ; the lake shores are Nyasaland, a highland area, whence comes some coffee. To the south Gazaland is a coastal lowland across which flows the lower Limpopo ; farther south still is Delagoa Bay. The

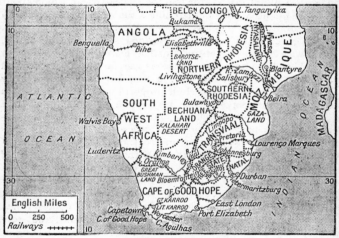

SKETCH MAP OF SOUTH AFRICA

Southern face of the plateau drops by stages—the Great Karroo and the Little Karroo (a kind of terrace arrangement)—to the narrow coastal lowland.

Climate and Vegetation. Climatically, the area has a uniformity of temperature, for elevation counteracts the effect of approach to the equator. In summer the actual temperatures exceed 70° F., and in winter the actual temperatures range between 50° and 60° F., always except near the mountainous eastern area. Rainfall tends to be slight everywhere except for the heavy summer rains north of the Zambezi. Except in the immediate locality of Capetown, where the rainfall tends to a maximum in winter, the rains come in the warmer weather—they are summer rains. The natural vegetation is veld or savannah grassland, tending to arid scrub. There is little or no forest ; timber is at a premium. Cultivation depends upon the water supply from rivers, for there are few lakes of large size.

The quantities of cereals grown vary greatly. A small amount of wheat—about a fifth of the quantity grown in England—is coupled with a large quantity of maize, locally called mealies. Except for Argentina, South Africa grows more maize than any other southern area. Other cereals are negligible.

The amount of tobacco grown in the South African Union about equals the quantity grown in Belgium ; the yield of cotton, grown experimentally, is even less important for the world at large. The Union contains half as many horses and as many cattle, nearly twice as many sheep and a fifth as many pigs, as the British Isles. The sheep are as numerous as they are in Argentina and 50 per cent more numerous than in New Zealand ; the quantity of wool which these sheep yield is proportional to the numbers of the animals themselves. The production of wool on a large scale is a recent development, and now the Union is a competitor for fifth place as a producer of wool for the world. This growth is significant, for it tends to show that, agriculturally, the country is now passing through the first of the stages of development—in the sequence wool, cattle, mutton and beef, wheat—through which the world's grasslands normally proceed. This sign of progress is coupled with an extensive growth in the fruit trade, for the Union now grows vines and makes wines, grows citrus fruits, and exports oranges, grape fruit, and stone fruits. Coal is mined in Natal, the Transvaal and Rhodesia, to about the same total as in Australia ; the quantity is important only because coal is scarce in the southern hemisphere. The amount of copper mined is but a fifth of the yield of the Belgian Congo. Small quantities of lead, tin and silver are mined.

Madagascar a large French possession, lies to the east across the Mozambique Channel. Centrally mountainous, it has a coastal forest fringe containing valuable timber. The climate is tropical and the rainfall is heavy, especially in the summer, and swings across the island from east to west as the south-east trade winds blow with greater force. Antananarivo is the capital and Tamatave the chief port.

LESSON 37

Australia, New Zealand and the South Seas

A USTRALIA is the marginal continent, the land at the edge of things, the land where, inevitably, all the activities of men are less fruitful per unit of human work employed. It is difficult to realize the Australian situation without using a globe. The globe should be unscrewed, turned upside-down, and replaced, so that Australia is roughly in the world-position normally occupied by western Europe. That is the world as the Australian sees it.

Airmen are now steadily reducing the time between London and Sydney. Landing facilities en route keep them on a sinuous line, something like a rather elongated S. Between Sydney and London lies the heart of Asia, lie Canton and Moscow. The western route from Sydney is mainly overland the eastern route is overseas.

This globe reading shows the nearness of Japan as a neighbour, and Japan is selling in a market which is of the character to suit Australia. Within the hemisphere centred on Sydney there is no part of the Americas most of India and China, all Japan and the East Indies, and Madagascar lie on the edge. World isolation could hardly be more complete.

Four-fifths of Europe in size, the continent houses less than a fiftieth of the population of Europe. But the Australian is modern ; he is a town-dweller. Coming into world history at a late date, he has missed the concept of land as the unit of desirable wealth, a concept which still controls the outlook of the bulk of the people of western Europe. The five chief capital cities of Australia contain nearly half the people. Few countries in the world have two such cities as Sydney and Melbourne, in each of which more than a million folk are gathered.

Australia produces and sells primary things, food, raw materials and minerals, and buys luxuries when they are cheap enough. Manufacturing in Australia is entirely marginal. It succeeds only when the supply of goods manufactured elsewhere is short ; it fails when the rest of the world has a surplus to sell.

Physically, the continent is mainly a plateau of old rock, somewhat similar to Africa, but with a lower average elevation ; the eastern heights are relatively near to the eastern coast, and tend to split the rural population into large-scale land-owners inland and small-scale land-workers on the littoral. The middle lowland from the Gulf of Carpentaria to the region of the mouth of the Murray is like the Mississippi valley reversed.

Climatically the continent is marginal, for, in general, rainfall tends to be insufficient, either on the whole or where needed most in the south-east during the crop-growing season. The north

SKETCH MAP OF AUSTRALIA

coast is hot with summer rains of a monsoon character ; the extreme south coast is warm with winter rains ; between them, inevitably, is the arid desert, fringed by scrublands where cultivation and usefulness for pasture are marginal. The eastern littoral has south-east trade winds on-shore and is, in places, too wet to be useful.

Australian prosperity is a result of chance. It is due to the chance that gold occurs in its rocks—the first great influx of people comprised gold-seekers—and, equally, to the chance that when gold was mined plentifully men still believed that gold was a useful commodity.

From 1890 onwards for twenty years the gold mined in Australia was from a fifth to a quarter and then to a sixth of the quantity mined in the world—roughly, as much as the gold mined in the United States and, at first, twice as much and in 1910, half as much as that mined in South Africa. Since 1910 gold-mining has steadily become less important. The quantity now is less than a third of the yield some forty years ago : it is less than 3 per cent of the world's total, and but a quarter of the yield of the United States or Canada.

The story of silver is not unlike that of gold—progress until 1910, decay since. In this case, however, competition is with America, for the United States supplies of silver have remained more or less steady and the Mexican supplies have increased . the Australian yield has declined from about 10 per cent of the world's supplies to less than half this fraction. The story of lead and zinc is similar ; the continent is losing ground against the higher yields of the U.S.A. and Mexico. Some coal is mined in the eastern littoral between Sydney and Brisbane. The town of Newcastle is a centre ; the quantity has a scarcity value by reason of the small coalfields of the southern hemisphere. Small quantities of iron, copper, and tin are mined.

Most of the middle lowland is grass-land, the downs—grass-land with summer rains and a tendency to aridity, and increasing temperature from south to north. The normal sequence—sheep for wool, sheep for meat, cattle for hides and beef, wheat on a large scale—has been followed nearer the settlements : the outlying districts are entirely marginal, with sparse sheep or cattle. Wool retains its pre-eminence ; the yield since 1900 has been doubled, and the sharp competition of that year with an almost equal yield from Argentina has lost edge, for the South American supply has declined in quantity.

Australia produces three times as much wheat as Britain and consumes a tenth as much ; the whole of the Australian surplus would supply two-fifths of what Britain buys. This surplus from Australia is in competition with a surplus from Canada—which in itself exceeds the whole consumption of Britain—with a larger surplus than that of Canada from the United States, and with a larger surplus than the Australian from Argentina.

Australian wheat in the British market is in a marginal position, inevitably precarious, and is produced in a climate noted for precocity.

Railways are numerous, notably the trans-continental railway in the south. There are air-mails, and regular steamship services along the coast and to Europe.

New Zealand. The North and South Islands, which, together with Stewart Island, comprise the Dominion of New Zealand, are in some degree in contrast. The South is compact in shape ;

SKETCH MAP OF NEW ZEALAND

the North has bays and lengthy peninsulas. The South has a backbone of mountain, the Southern Alps, snow-capped and containing some of the largest glaciers in temperate latitudes ; the North has a central plateau with volcanic peaks, a large lake, hot springs, and mud or water geysers, and every evidence of volcanic activity, punctuated at intervals by earthquake shocks. The South has smallish rivers and rock-valley moraine-dammed, long, narrow lakes and coastal fiords, with the Canterbury plains to the east ; the North has larger rivers and little real lowland, except in the neighbourhood of Auckland.

In these islands live one and a half million people, not many more than live in Sydney and its environs. Some of these people are Maoris, probably the most intelligent of the semi-indigenous races of the world. A third of the people live in the chief towns—Auckland, Wellington, Christchurch and Dunedin As in Australia, the population is enlarged by a net immigration.

New Zealand exports no cereals. Some gold and some coal are mined, in both cases roughly a quarter as much as in Australia. The country depends almost entirely on its production of wool and mutton, with the recent addition of dairy products, chiefly butter, and fruits. The relative size of the annual wool clip—a quarter of that of Australia, and two-thirds of that of Argentina, or the Union of South Africa, or the United States—is an additional indication of the marginal character of the New Zealand situation, for wool is the first product in the sequence of exploited products of the great farming areas of the world. With a more extensive and more reliable rainfall, and with a more equable and more temperate climate than Australia, the islands are more suited to a large population, probably, than Australia, and life is, on the whole, less difficult for the individual. New Zealand has been one of the pioneer states in attempts to secure the well-being of all its people. There a comparative handful of whites have managed in the mass to live and prosper with some success in a land which has many natural advantages.

South Sea Islands. The islands of the Pacific Ocean tend to be unimportant. New Caledonia at the beginning of the century produced two-thirds of the world's nickel, but the supply has declined to 10 per cent in face of the competition from Ontario, Canada, the yield now being less than a third of the former amount. The Fiji Islands produce sugar canes, copra, and fresh fruits. Nauru is noted for its phosphates ; Samoa for its copra and cocoa. Hawaii exports sugar and pineapples Many of the islands are important in connexion with the great ocean and cable routes across the Pacific Ocean.

This Lesson concludes our Course in Geography.

Crumpling World of Miocene and Pliocene Times

(See plate 41)

THE Miocene period, together with the Pliocene, is now regarded by many authorities as two series of the Neogene system of Tertiary deposits ; nevertheless, they were totally dissimilar periods, though the strata and life forms merge as a rule without distinctive break. There are scarcely any deposits in Britain of the Miocene period, the only evidence being the fossil types in the lacustrine deposits of the Bovey Tracey area in Devonshire, and in some small deposits in basaltic hollows of the west of Scotland and elsewhere.

The Miocene deposits are, however, extensively presented in the continent of Europe, more particularly in the Touraine area of France, in Belgium, over most of Germany, Austria, Switzerland between the Jura and Alps, north-east Spain, Italy, eastern Europe ; also in Syria, Egypt, Arabia, Persia, India ; in the Atlantic States of North America and in the Pacific States. Here they are known as the Monterey beds and attain a thickness of between 6,000 and 7,000 feet. The shales of this series reach to 4,000 feet, and are of great value on account of their oil-bearing properties. The Miocene beds are uplifted to high altitudes in the Rockies, indicative of the chain's recent raising.

While practically the whole of Britain, Ireland and the north of France were above sea level in Miocene times, and so have left scarcely any deposits, a general upraising of vast submerged areas continued from the Oligocene and Eocene periods. So in the course of the Miocene age—probably at least 5,000,000 years and possibly much more—the vast Ocean of Tethys was divided into what are known now as the Indian Ocean and the great Mediterranean area by the upraising of Asia Minor and the Arabian, Persian and Syrian regions of south-west Asia. Egypt and North Africa followed, while a colossal folding of the earth's crust began and continued generally in an east and west direction.

This folding extended its course from the downland of Britain to what is now China ; out of the vast sea that had existed for some hundred-million years these great folds of a shrinking earth arose to form the enormous mountain chains of the Himalayas, the Caucasus, Taurus and mountains of Persia, Arabia and Baluchistan. The Alps, Carpathians, Apennines, Pyrenees all formed part of this the most colossal fold of the earth's crust, the loftiest and most far-reaching that is known ever to have occurred. Curving southward, through the Sierra Nevada of Spain, it crossed at the place where is now the Strait of Gibraltar and formed a southern and lesser fold constituting the Atlas Mountains. Subsidiary folds accompanied the lines of the main fold in a series of thrusts and overfolds, which extended as far north as the downs of the Isle of Wight

Deep and shallow areas remained between these gigantic walls of raised sea bed ; some formed arms of the now much restricted Mediterranean or Central Sea, while one across southern France formed a wide strait connecting the sea with the Atlantic for a time. North of the ascending Alps large areas of the former sea remained and formed a series of great shallow lakes, known as basins, which gradually became freshwater lakes ; one covering an Austrian area is known as the Vienna Basin and another in the Rhine area as the Mainz basin, while Switzerland mainly formed a great lake between Alps and Jura.

The great Sarmatian Sea remained as the eastern remnant of the vast Tethys Ocean, with the recently upraised Himalayas and Baluchistan mountains dividing it from the Indian Ocean, the third and southern remnant. This Sarmatian Sea spread as a shallow waste of waters from the Carpathians to the Himalayas ; it also gradually shrank into a series of great basins, the present-day remains of which constitute the Black Sea, Caspian and Aral Seas and numerous drying-up salt lakes.

In England the extensive syncline which now forms the basin of the Thames, with the Chiltern Hills composing its northern rim and the Downs its southern, came into existence as the result of this upraising and crustal folding. At first a broad synclinal depression extended to what is now the Severn estuary, and constituted a long channel connecting the North Sea with the Atlantic Ocean, the present English Channel being then non-existent. By this means warm waters were able to penetrate into the North Sea with living forms adapted thereto. At a later date only organisms flourishing in colder waters existed in that sea, showing that the increasing upraising of the land had closed the channel. So an inlet of the North Sea was first formed, and then came the verdant valley through which the Thames and its tributaries meandered. As this upraising of the land continued into the succeeding Pliocene times, the North Sea of those days itself retreated and a broad plain took its place. The Thames then became the tributary of a much larger river flowing north and a continuation of the predecessor of the Rhine.

In the western hemisphere, as in the eastern, continental masses were approaching their modern form. Most of the colossal upraising of the Andes and Rocky Mountains occurred during this Miocene period. Salt lakes formed b^r ween the Pacific and the uplifted ranges in the extensive valleys of the synclinal folds. The Great Salt Lake is the largest of the much diminished survivals of these basins.

Africa having become united to Eurasia by the upraising of Arabia and connexions with southern Europe, Australia remained as the only segregated continent surviving from pre-Miocene times, with the result that its fauna and flora were from henceforth practically distinct. Nevertheless, it shared in the world-wide upraising of the land, as the Miocene deposits of Victoria and Tasmania testify. New Zealand also has large areas of both North and South Islands covered by Miocene deposits.

Pliocene Period. Thus it may be seen how extensive was this crumpling of the earth's strata, which continued into Pliocene times and, in many areas, still continues as an upraising process with corresponding depressions in other regions, though the conditions now appear to be stabler. A general recession of the sea continued through Pliocene times, and, except for some areas of subsequent submergence on a lesser scale, such as the North Sea and the local ravages of coastal attrition, the sea undoubtedly appears to be still diminishing.

The Pliocene period is probably not much more than a million years distant ; it is practically a continuation of the Miocene, modified by climatic and local influences, which brought about new forms of animal and plant life, with the extinction of some of the older species of animals and a transference of others to warmer latitudes. Thus a distinctive series of deposits may be recognized as constituting the Pliocene. As such they occupy in England a large tract of east Norfolk and Suffolk, with the adjoining north-east corner of Essex. They are present as sand and clay in the St. Erth district of Cornwall.

MIOCENE AND PLIOCENE TIMES

On the continent of Europe the Pliocene deposits attain a thickness of about 1,200 feet in Holland, where they are extensive. They constitute a large proportion of Italy each side of the Apennines to the sea, and reach a thickness of 2,000 feet in Calabria and Sicily. In Austria, Greece and around the Mediterranean they form a fringe of beds of varying thickness and often lacustrine origin.

The Pliocene beds in England are divided into the following series:

UPPER

Cromer Beds (uppermost): the " forest bed " of peat and tree-trunks, freshwater sands and silts. Exposed from Happisburgh to Weybourn.

Weybourn Crag: sand, loam and blue-clay, a marine shelly deposit found at Weybourn.

Chillesford Beds: finely laminated clays and sands; traced as a sinuous band from Walton-on-the-Naze to Mundesley over the underlying beds.

Norwich Crag: gravel and shelly sand deposit with laminated clays between 150 and 200 feet thick at Lowestoft and Southwold, where it appears at the base of the cliffs.

MIDDLE

Red Crag: ferruginous shelly sand, the peroxide of iron producing its distinctive colour. Covers an area between Ipswich, Felixstowe and Walton-on-the-Naze, but only well exposed in valleys and cliffs at Walton, Bawdsey and Felixstowe.

LOWER

Coralline Crag: fragments of corals, molluscs, crustaceans, with numerous remains of animals, fish and reptilian vertebrae—all apparently washed out from pre-existing beds. Found between Aldeburgh and Boyton, also in patches elsewhere.

Lenham Beds: lowest and oldest of Pliocene deposits; brown clay, red and yellow sands and flint pebbles. Only fragmentary remains exist now on the downs between Folkestone and Maidstone. Their fossil types indicate their age.

The life of the above series indicates an increasing number of northern forms adapted to colder and colder conditions, while a growing decrease in those suited to a warm climate is evident.

Fauna and Flora. The world-wide warmth of the Miocene period, which in England and throughout Europe caused a sub-tropical flora to flourish, is as difficult to account for as the subsequent glacial invasion of the Pleistocene period. Even in north Greenland within 700 miles of the Pole sub-tropical evergreens flourished ; seams of coal 30 feet thick testify to its long duration.

In late Miocene times the vegetation became of a more temperate type and a change is perceptible in the fauna. Beeches, poplars and hardy evergreens such as laurels took the place of the palms, myrtles, mimosas, fig trees and magnolias of the earlier time ; while monkeys, which had made their appearance, retreated south over a thousand miles.

The fauna of Miocene times is remarkable for the elimination of marsupials from Europe and the coming of the ape, the *Machaerodus* or sabre-toothed tiger (lion), the giant Proboscideans, Dinotherium and Mastodon, the latter developing into *Elephas meridionalis*, *Elephas antiquus* and *Elephas Jeffersonii* in Pliocene times. Bears, hyaenas and species of rhinoceros, hippopotamus and tapirs approaching present-day types, developed, together with the *Anchitherium*, an ancestor of the horse, and its near relatives the *Hippotherium* and *Moropus*. The listriodon, a pig-like creature, the giant ant-eater *Macrotherium*, and *Amphicyon*, an ancestor of the dog, had also appeared ; while, perhaps the most important, the great anthropoid apes *Dryopithecus* and *Pliopithecus* now made their appearance.

In the Pliocene period the *Mastodon tetrabelodon* had appeared, while numerous wolves and horned deer (*Cervidae*) developed from the Dicroceras of Miocene times. Wild asses, the Hipparion species, and great herds of antelopes appeared, but the Dinotherium vanished, and many of the above species retreated before the advancing cold to warmer climes, never to return.

LESSON 22

The Ice Ages

(See plate 42)

THE last period of the Cainozoic era covers what some geologists call the Quaternary era. The one in which we live, it extends back in time for something between 500,000 and 1,000,000 years, and is divided into two geological periods—the earlier being the Pleistocene, or mostly recent, and the later the Holocene, or recent. This brings the palaeontological record down to archaeological and historical times. The Pleistocene deposits are exceedingly varied and fragmentary, and indicate a method of deposition largely due to ice and frigid conditions. The Pleistocene is therefore known also as the Glacial period or the Great Ice Age, though since large temperate and tropical areas remained free from these conditions, the deposits in such areas are normal and generally resemble those of the later Pliocene period.

The evidences for these frigid Arctic conditions are chiefly the extensive masses and piles of detritus peculiar to glaciers indiscriminately spread over exposed strata of various other geological periods. Other evidence is the effect produced by the weight and movement of the enormous glaciers as they pass over the various surfaces of the underlying beds.

In Pleistocene times even mountains were buried under vast moving ice sheets compounded of numerous glaciers, which attained a thickness of between 7,000 and 10,000 feet. Their movement is facilitated by the phenomenon known as regelation, which consists of constant momentary melting and refreezing of the ice particles, due to·changes of pressure. In this way glaciers will in time remove gigantic blocks of rock and grind the surfaces over which they pass into a smooth or polished condition. Striated and ice-scratched surfaces will also result, indicating the line of the glacier's advance. Thus the rugged mountain masses and great volcanic cones of pre-Glacial times became transformed during the Great Ice Age into the rounded masses and gigantic humps which are such a familiar feature of the glaciated mountains of Britain and northern Europe, as compared with the angular ruggedness of, say, the Balkans, and the mountains of Greece, southern Italy, and Spain, which escaped any extensive glaciation.

As the glacier progresses a large quantity of material, chiefly rocks, sand and clay, is collected on each side as it erodes its way ; these are known as moraines, and the mass of detritus is carried along until it becomes heaped up as a vast and ever-growing deposit of débris at the lower extremity of the glacier, where it is known as the terminal moraine. Or it may get spread out fan-wise over a large area by the rushing streams which emerge from great glaciers, and will flood the country round.

Thus materials of strata and rocks get transported hundreds or even thousands of miles, and, while possessing a totally different character, get deposited as a compound **mixture of stones, clay,** sand and pebbles, in which are frequently great boulders and even fragments of fossils, such as bones, tree trunks and mammalian teeth and tusks, collected *en route* and eventually forming a heterogeneous mass, which may attain hundreds of feet in thickness, geologically known as Boulder Clay—the harder kinds as Till. Thus is formed the most characteristic deposit of the glaciers of Pleistocene times, proving that northern Europe was covered by a vast ice sheet, which flowed chiefly from Scandinavia and reached, when at its greatest extent, from the Urals to the Atlantic Ocean and as far south as the Harz Mountains. Two great Glacial periods can be traced as emanating from Scandinavia, though evidence is found for four periods in the Alpine area; these are known as the Günz, Mindel, Riss and Würm periods. Consequently, certain authorities regard Europe as having been subject to four Glacial periods.

Britain became involved in the second period, the Mindel, when the entire counties of Lincolnshire, Norfolk, Suffolk, Cambridge, Northampton, Leicester, Bedford, Hertford, together with most of Essex, Buckingham and Warwick, were invaded by an enormous ice sheet, which had advanced from Scandinavia across what is now the North Sea, material of the Norwegian mountains being deposited in the Boulder Clay and frequently as large erratic blocks over these areas.

Meanwhile, in Scotland both the Grampian and Gallowegian areas had developed great glaciers which, together with those of the lesser areas of Cumberland, the Cheviots, Pennines and Wales, formed an immense ice sheet, in places estimated to reach 5,000 feet thick. This ice sheet held back and diverted the course of the Scandinavian ice. The deviation appears to have occurred in the Cleveland district of Yorkshire, which, with central and south Yorkshire, remained singularly free from ice. The ice spread out over the lowlands almost as far as the Thames, while the Welsh glaciers covered Wales to the Bristol Channel. The Scottish ice poured down over most of Ireland, filling the Irish Sea area with a gigantic ice sheet, which covered even the 2,034-foot mountain of Snaefell in the Isle of Man; this glacial sheet also spread out westwards over the Hebridean area, completely covering what are now the Hebrides, and extending to the Atlantic, where it presented a wall of ice; from this great bergs floated away over the Atlantic—as they do now from

Greenland. Some of these landed as boulders on the Scilly Islands.

In North America the glaciation was even greater than in Europe, the glacial drift being spread out as far south as 37° of north latitude, whereas in Europe it reached only to about 50°. There are also evidences of extensive glaciation in South America, Tasmania and New Zealand.

The last of these glacial periods is variously estimated to have terminated in this country from 50,000 to 10,000 years ago, although parts of Europe may still be regarded as in the retreating stage which followed the temporary Bühl advance. The cause of these glacial periods is still a matter of investigation and speculation. That a change in the elevation of the land may have caused them is one theory. Another theory is that a geographical change, such as a temporary partition of North from South America, creating a diversion of the warm Atlantic Drift current, may have been the cause. Variations in the solar heat or the passage of the solar system through a region of extra low temperature have also been adduced as explanations, but a change of tilt of the earth's axis seems the most likely explanatory theory, although there is yet another favoured at present—that the Glacial periods were due to recurring meteorological changes which in some manner produced different areas of high and low barometric pressure, such as would result from, say, the warm cyclones of our latitudes taking a more southerly course and permitting the east and Arctic winds to supplant them.

Animals of the Ice Age. The fauna and flora of northern Europe, including Britain, which was then an integral part of the Continent, assumed an Arctic character over the areas preceding the advancing glaciers. Thus we find, for example, in the eastern counties, beds containing Arctic shells and fossil remains of the Arctic birch and willow, with remains of Arctic animals. Northern and central Europe as far south as the Alps and Pyrenees was inhabited by swarms of reindeer, *Cervus tarandus ;* the Arctic fox, *Canis lagopus ;* the great mammoth, *Elephas primigenius ;* the woolly rhinoceros, *Rhinoceros tichorhinus ;* together with the bison and hyaena, the great elk or deer (*Cervus giganteus*), the cave-bear, *Ursus spelaeus*, and species of musk-sheep, glutton, wolf, musk-ox and wild boar. Remains of most of these are found in the deposits of the river-valleys of England, notably the Thames.

Among the evidences of the inter-glacial periods are beds in which are found relics of quite a different fauna, one suited to a warm temperate climate. In these beds the above species give place to the elephant, hippopotamus, hyaena, leopard, porcupine, African lynx, aurochs and wild horses—present-day types of warmer climes which again are superseded by creatures adapted to colder conditions.

Most remarkable of all is the development of the human species during the Quaternary era, the evidences left of their handiwork constituting so distinctive a feature, that this era is usually designated the Age of Man, though he had unquestionably acquired some of his human attributes in Pliocene times.

LESSON 23

Geology of the Present Age

(See plate 42)

THE Holocene deposits belong to the age in which we live, an age sometimes called the Post-Glacial period. These deposits are almost entirely alluvial, peaty and loess.

The alluvial deposits are usually a continuation of the Pleistocene sands and mud, brought down by the streams and deposited along the banks of rivers in the shape of terraces. They also form the beds of rivers, and spread out great deltas at their mouths, such as those of the Nile, Danube, Ganges, Euphrates, Mississippi and Amazon. The growth of the deltaic deposits at the mouths of the Nile and Euphrates within the last four to five thousand years can be measured by the distance of the seaports of antiquity from the present-day coastline.

The peaty deposits include forest débris. These are very extensive, covering wide areas in northern and central Europe and North America, and are the remains of the vast forests which grew on the rich soil left behind by the retreating glaciers after the close of the last Ice Age. The loess deposits cover very extensive areas, chiefly in Asia, which are now steppe, prairie and tundra. In these areas the fine wind-blown sand produces a state of aridity which prevents the growth of forests ; great loess deposits exist in western China, reaching some 2,000 feet in thickness, and in the adobe area of North America, where they reach 3,000 feet.

GEOLOGY OF THE PRESENT AGE

In all the Holocene deposits are found more or less fossilized remains of animals of the most recent or present-day species. A few of the fossilized forms have become extinct, notably the mammoth, *Elephas antiquus,* frozen carcasses of which have been found in the ice-bound rivers and tundra of Siberia, and in the superficial alluvial deposits of central Europe and England. The gigantic Irish deer, *Cervus giganteus,* is another famous creature which has become extinct in recent, probably in historical, times. Numerous fossil remains have been found in Irish peat bogs, and also in the cave-earth and superficial deposits in England, Scotland, and on the continent. The woolly rhinoceros, *Rhinoceros antiquitatis,* also persisted until recent Holocene times, and entire carcasses, covered with woolly hair, have been dug out of the frozen Siberian tundra.

As regards birds, the moas, *Dinornis,* which were exceedingly numerous in New Zealand, have vanished only within the last two or three hundred years ; their remains are very plentiful in the superficial deposits of recent times. Remains are found in the marshes of Madagascar of a gigantic bird, *Aepyornis,* which reached 14 feet in height and produced eggs 30 inches in circumference. Another bird, one incapable of flight, the dodo (*Didus ineptus*), disappeared in recent times, being last seen alive about 1680 ; it inhabited Mauritius, Réunion and Rodriguez, and its remains are found in the peaty deposits of these islands. The solitaire, a gigantic flightless pigeon of the same family, vanished from Rodriguez about 1760. Finally, the great auk, *Alca impennis,* became extinct in the last century, the last pair known being killed in 1844.

Now let us turn from the geological record of the past to consider the forces that are moulding the earth's surface today, often in a manner which conflicts with Man's wishes and requirements. This conflict is seen on a small scale when a few acres of carefully tended farmland or a homestead or two vanish in a cliff fall in a single night, as happens frequently round the shores of England, particularly along the coasts of Norfolk, Suffolk, Sussex, and the Holderness coast of Yorkshire. Another aspect of the process is seen when rivers change their course, as, for instance, the Indus and the Hwang-ho. Mountains slip from time to time, destroying fields and houses, and even slipping hillsides can cause disaster, as in suburbs of Lyons in 1930 and 1932, when many people were buried alive.

In addition to these catastrophic occurrences, there are *secular movements* imperceptible to the eye—movements due to silent geological forces which are ever at work, raising a sea-bed here and lowering a whole country there—processes which are evidenced by submerged forests and raised beaches respectively. The former are very numerous around the shores of England and Wales and to a lesser degree in Scotland. The wood can scarcely be regarded as fossilized, though very ancient and usually black with age and impregnation.

Submerged forests occupy a large portion of the Thames estuary, and are obviously much later than the raised river terraces of sand and gravel deposited in the Pleistocene period, in the Palaeolithic and Eolithic ages of Man. Similar forests are found off the east coast, more particularly off Lincolnshire and Durham, in the estuaries of the Humber and the Wash, beneath the fenland, and off the south coast from Hastings to Torbay. In the Bristol Channel they extend far out beneath the sea, and are well in evidence in Porlock and Caermarthen bays. Abundant remains may be seen at very low water in Cardigan Bay, off the Wirral Peninsula, the coast of Lancashire, and as far north as the Solway Firth. This fall of the land has been proceeding for some thousands of years, judging from the remains of Bronze Age men found in the uppermost layers of these submerged forests, and from the Neolithic artifacts discovered in the lower layers. How long it will continue and to what extent it is impossible to say, and the process is so slow that many generations must pass before Man is likely to see in it a large-scale menace.

Books Recommended for Further Reading " Wonders of the Earth's Crust," H. E. Taylor (Pitman) ; " Text Book of Geology," Sir Archibald Geikie (Macmillan) ; " Extinct Animals," Sir E. Ray Lankester ; " Aids in Practical Geology," Grenville Cole (Griffin) ; J. A. Jukes-Browne's " Stratigraphical Geology " (Stanford).

This Lesson concludes our Course in Geology.

LESSON 21

Rendering of the Verbal Noun

WE have now discussed the chief types of sentence that can occur in German. When the main constructions of principal and subsidiary clauses have been learned, the rest is largely a question of familiarity with idiomatic turns of phrase. In this Course we can deal only with the translation of selected phrases and constructions of frequent occurrence.

In English the verbal form in " ing " is often used. For instance : It is too cold for swimming. Apart from certain exceptional usages the English verbal noun in " ing " is translated into German in the following ways :

1. By an infinite which then becomes a neuter noun : Fencing is a strenuous sport : *Das Fechten ist ein anstrengendes Vergnügen ;* I noticed the screaming of the child : *Ich bemerkte das Schreien des Kindes.*

2. The English " ing " is translated into German by the infinitive with *zu* when it is used as the complement of a noun, an adjective or a verb. The duty of obeying : *Die Pflicht zu gehorchen* or *Die Pflicht des Gehorchens ;* He was pleased at passing his examination : *Er freute sich, sein Examen bestanden zu haben.*

This construction with *zu* is also used after the prepositions *ohne* (without), *statt, anstatt* (instead of) if the subject of both clauses is the same. Examples : He read the book without understanding it : *Er las das Buch, ohne es zu verstehen.* The tenor was shouting instead of singing : *Der Tenor schrie, anstatt zu singen ;* He went home instead of working : *Er ging nach Hause, statt zu arbeiten.* If, however, the subject of the second clause is not the same as that of the first, the dependent clause is introduced by the conjunction *ohne dass :* The boy slept without the teacher noticing it : *Der Knabe schlief, ohne dass der Lehrer es bemerkte.*

Frequently *dadurch dass* is used followed by a dependent clause : He got away by running hard : *Dadurch dass er schnell lief, kam er davon.* By falling into the river he caught a cold : *Dadurch dass er in den Fluss fiel, erkältete er sich.* This sentence could also be translated : *Durch das Fallen in den Fluss erkältete er sich ;* or : *Er fiel in den Fluss und erkältete sich.*

When translating an English present participle into German it is best to give the English sense in some other way *in English* before venturing to translate. Thus : Walking in the forest I met a lion, is really equivalent to : Whilst I was walking in the forest I met a lion, and should be translated : *Während ich im Walde spazieren ging, traf ich einen Löwen.* Digging in the garden I found a Roman coin, is really equivalent to : Whilst I was digging in the garden I found a Roman coin : *Während ich im Garten grub, fand ich eine römische Münze.*

The English present participle can also be used instead of a temporal clause : Having been in the country for several months I returned to London. This could be : Since I have been, etc., expressing that the speaker is tired of the country and wishes to return to London. If that were so, we should have to say : *Da ich seit einigen Monaten auf dem Lande gelebt hatte, fuhr ich nach London zurück.* The participle is much more likely, however, to conceal a temporal clause : After I had been in the country for several months I returned to London : *Nachdem ich einige Monate lang auf dem Lande gelebt* (or *gewohnt*) *hatte, fuhr ich nach London zurück.* Similarly, in the sentence : Having run a mile he collapsed, we should have to judge by the context whether As he had run a mile, or After he had run a mile, was intended. If the latter, we should have to translate : *Nachdem er eine Meile gelaufen war, brach er zusammen.* But in a sentence like Having spent his whole life talking he at last died, it is clearly " after " (temporal) and not " since " (causal) that is intended. We should therefore translate : *Nachdem er sein ganzes Leben im Reden verbracht hatte, starb er endlich.*

Sometimes the present participle has to be translated by a relative clause. Consider the sentence : The man running after the tram is my father. The force of " running " is easily detected. We could just as well say : The man who is running after the tram is my father, and would therefore translate : *Der Mann, der hinter der Elekstrischen herläuft, ist mein Vater.*

After *bleiben* (to remain), *finden* (to find), *fühlen* (to feel), *hören* (to hear), *sehen* (to see), the infinitive is used without *zu.* Examples : He remained standing : *Er blieb stehen ,* He found her lying on the ground : *Er fand sie am Boden liegen ;* I heard him falling (or, fall) : *Ich hörte ihn fallen,* and so forth.

LESSON 22

Auxiliary Verbs of Mood

IN Lesson 13 (Volume 3, page 440) the forms of the auxiliary verbs of mood are given, and in this Lesson we discuss their usage. Just as in English after an auxiliary of mood a verb is not introduced by *to*, so in German there is no *zu* in such cases. Examples : I can go, *Ich kann gehen ;* I may go, *Ich darf gehen ;* I must go, *Ich muss gehen*, etc.

The past participles of the auxiliary verbs are only used when they are by themselves without another verb. Examples : I have been able to do it, *Ich habe es gekonnt.* Similarly, we can construct : *Ich habe gedurft* (I was allowed to) ; *Ich habe gemusst* (I have had to), etc. On most occasions, however, the auxiliary verb of mood will be accompanied by an infinitive, and in that case the verb of mood also has the infinitive form. Note therefore : I have been able to do it : *Ich habe es tun können ;* I have been allowed to do it : *Ich habe es tun dürfen ;* I have had to do it : *Ich habe es tun müssen*, etc.

It is quite impossible to give more than a hint of how these difficult words are employed in German. But it should be borne in mind from the very beginning that *können*, though it means *can*, has many more meanings than its English relation, and the same applies to all the other auxiliary verbs of mood. Some of the more common usages follow :

1. *Können :* expresses ability. *Ich kann es tun* (I can do it, I am able to do it. I am allowed to do it, there is nothing to prevent me from doing it). The admitted ability to do a thing leads to the extension that if I want to nobody can stop me. Which particular sense is meant will be clear from the context or, if one is listening to a speaker, from the tone of voice with which he says *kann*. *Das kann sein* (that may be so). *Er konnte es tun* (he was able to do it). *Wie konnten Sie so etwas tun ?* (how were you able to do such a thing ? how *could* you do such a thing ?). *Er kann es gelesen haben* (he may have read it). *Er könnte es gelesen haben* (he might have read it). There is far more doubt in the construction with *könnte* than in that with *kann*. But *er könnte es gelesen haben* could also be a reproach, and could then

mean : one would have expected him to have read it. *Er hätte kommen können* (he would have been able to come). Again, this statement can contain a reproach, and then it would mean : although he was quite able to come he chose not to. *Er kann schwimmen* (he is able to swim). *Er kann Englisch* (he speaks English) *Dafür kann ich nichts* (it is not my fault). If any of the above statements are negatived, the negative particle goes before the complementary verb. *Das kann nicht sein* (that cannot be).

2. *Dürfen :* expresses permission. *Ich darf es tun* (I may do it, I have been allowed to do it, I am entitled to do it). All these meanings lead quite insensibly to the farthest extension : nobody can stop me from doing it. The negative would be : *Ich darf es nicht tun. Er durfte es tun* (he was allowed to do it). *Er dürfte es tun* (he might quite possibly do that.) *Es dürfte schneien* (it might possibly snow). *Darf ich mich vorstellen ?* (may I introduce myself ?). *Dürfte ich mich vorstellen ?* (might I introduce myself ?). The second form is far more polite. *Das dürfte stimmen* (that would probably be so, might be so). *Er wird ihn sehen dürfen* (there will be no objection to his seeing him). *Darf ich so frei sein,* or *Dürfte ich so frei sein* (may I be so free, i.e. a rather polite way of saying " may I ? ").

3. *Müssen :* expresses compulsion. *Ich muss es tun* (I must do it, am compelled to do it). *Kein Mensch muss müssen* (German proverb : Nobody can be forced to do a thing against his will). *Man muss sich wundern* (one cannot help wondering). *Er musste es tun* (he had to do it, he was forced to do it). *Er müsste es tun* (he ought to be forced to do it, or he ought to feel compelled to do it). *Das musste nicht kommen* (this should not have happened, i.e., this is the last straw). *Er wird laufen müssen* (he will have to run). *Er hatte es tun müssen* (he had been obliged to do it). *Er hätte es tun müssen* (he ought to have been compelled to do it). *Er muss es getan haben* (he must have done it, there is nobody else who could have done it). *Er muss es nicht getan haben* (it is not absolutely necessary that he should be the one who has done it, i.e., he may not have done it). *Es hat so kommen müssen* (it was bound to happen in this way).

4. *Mögen :* expresses inclination. *Ich mag es tun* (I like doing it, I am allowed to do it if I want to). *Er mag es nicht tun* (he

does not like to do it). *Mag sein* (may be). This is a rather more literary form than the usual *Kann sein*. *Wir mögen kommen* (we like to come, or we are allowed to come). *Ich mochte es tun* (I liked to do it). *Ich möchte es tun* (I should like to do it). *Sie mochte zehn Jahre alt sein* (she might have been ten years old). *Sie möchte zehn Jahre alt sein* (she might be ten years old). *Er wird es nicht tun mögen* (he will not like to do it). *Er mag es getan haben* (he may have done it). *Er möchte es getan haben* (he might possibly have done it). *Mögen* is also frequently used of liking things or people, and it is this usage which is most often met with in ordinary conversation *Mögen Sie Erbsen ? Ja, ich mag sie* (Do you like peas ? Yes, I love them). Notice the different sense implied by the change of tense in the following example : *Mögen Sie Bridge spielen ?* (do you like playing bridge ?). *Möchten Sie Bridge spielen ?* (would you like to play bridge ? i.e., *now*).

5. *Wollen* : expresses volition. *Ich will es tun* (I will do it, I intend doing it). *Wer nicht will, hat schon* (German proverb : He who does not want to, is supplied already). *Was wollen Sie ?* (what do you want ?). *Willst du still sein !* (will you be quiet !). *Wollt Ihr laufen* (away with you !). *Er wollte kommen* (he intended coming). *Er wollte Offizier werden* (he wanted to be an officer). *Er würde kommen wollen* (he would be willing to come). *Er hat es tun wollen* (he has intended to do it). *Wir hätten es tun wollen* (we should have been willing to do it). Doubt is expressed in the following statements : *Er will es getan haben* (he says that he has done it). *Er wollte es getan haben* (he claimed that he did it). *Er will nichts davon wissen* (he does not wish to know anything about it).

LESSON 23

Idiomatic Usages

THERE remains one auxiliary verb which was not discussed with the others in the previous Lesson, and this perhaps is the most difficult of all in correct usage—*sollen*, which may be used to express compulsion by a third party or merely supposition that something will be done. *Ich soll es tun*, I am supposed to do it. But as the person who has told me to will not necessarily be there to see whether I do or whether I do not, it is quite likely that I will not. The two different senses will be clear from the following examples : *er soll jetzt nach Hause gehen*, he is to go home now ; *Du sollst nicht stehlen*, thou shalt not steal. It is probable that both commands will be obeyed, though there is the possibility that they will not. But in *er soll ein Dieb sein* the meaning is : he is supposed to be a thief, or they say he is a thief, and in this last example we are clearly dealing with *sollen* in the sense of supposition which arises from the fact that a command given by somebody to somebody else is not necessarily executed. *Er sollte kommen*, he ought to have come, or he was supposed to come. *Sie hat es tun sollen*, she was called upon to do it (but she probably did not). *Sie hätte es tun sollen*, she ought to have done it. *Du sollst es getan haben*, people say that you did it.

Study carefully the following sentences. *Morgen soll ich ins Theater. Ich mag nicht, und ich will nicht, aber ich werde wohl müssen. Was kann man machen? Wenn ich auch möchte, so darf ich die Einladung doch nicht ausschlagen. Man soll und man muss höflich sein, wenn man auch nicht will.* Tomorrow I am to go to the theatre. I do not feel like it and I do not want to, but I shall probably have to. What can one do ? Even if I should like to, yet I dare not refuse the invitation. One is supposed to and one must be polite even if one does not want to be.

In Lesson 17 (Volume 4, page 424) we have seen that in a subsidiary clause the verb goes to the end, and the auxiliary right to the end. There are some exceptions to this when we are dealing with auxiliary verbs of mood. The subsidiary word-order of *er hätte kommen sollen* is not *er sagte, dass er kommen sollen hätte*, as we should expect, but *er sagte er hätte kommen sollen*, or, with the *dass : er sagte, dass er hätte kommen sollen*, he said that he ought to have come. Two more examples of this are : He told me that he would not like to have done it, *er erzählte mir, dass er es nicht hätte tun mögen ;* he excused himself by saying that he had not been in a position to write, *er entschuldigte sich damit, dass er nicht hätte schreiben können.*

There are a few other verbs apart from the auxiliary verbs of mood which, when they occur together with another verb, have the infinitive form where we should expect the past participle. Similarly, these verbs, when constructed with *hätte* in a subsidiary clause, allow the *hätte* to come first. *Lassen* (to let, leave, allow),

He has let him come, *er hat ihn kommen lassen* ; He will allow him to do it, *er wird ihn es tun lassen ;* He would have allowed him to do it, *er hätte es ihn tun lassen.* (It will be noted that in the first sentence the *ihn* precedes the *es*, in the second the *es* the *ihn*. There is no fixed rule in the matter. *Ihn es* is rather more usual than *es ihn.*) He said that he would have allowed him to do it, *er sagte, dass er ihn es hätte tun lassen.*

This usage is rather more rare with *helfen* (to help), but it occurs sometimes. Instead of *Wer hat ihm geholfen, seine Stiefel anzu-ziehen ?* Who has helped him to put on his boots ? we could say : *Wer hat ihn seine Stiefel anziehen helfen ? Brauchen* (to use, to be required to). He will not be required to come, *er wird nicht kommen brauchen* or *er wird nicht zu kommen brauchen.* The second case, using *zu* before the infinitive, is more usual in modern German, though both usages are equally correct.

Occasionally this usage will still be found with *machen* (to make), *hören* (to hear), *heissen* (to bid, to command), *sehen* (to see), but with these verbs it is gradually dying out, and it is better, in modern German, to construct *ich habe ihn laufen gemacht,* I have made him run, than *ich habe ihn laufen machen*

In the following three sentences : When are you coming ? When he comes tell him to wait, and When I last saw him he had a beard, there does not seem, at first sight, to be much dif-ference in the various usages of " when " ; yet they are all three quite distinct. The first " when " is interrogative, the second refers to a future event, the third to a past event. In German, there are three different words for these three different functions :

(1) The interrogative pronoun *wann* is used for all questions, direct or indirect : When are you coming ? *wann kommen Sie ?* When did this book appear ? *wann erschien dieses Buch ?* I asked him when he was coming, *ich fragte ihn, wann er komme.*

(2) The conjunction *wenn*, in the sense of " when," is only used to refer to present or future events. When he comes tell him to wait, *wenn er kommt, bitte ihn zu warten.* When he visits me I shall be pleased, *wenn er mich besuchen wird* (or we could say *besucht* just as in English we say " visits," using the present with future meaning), *werde ich mich freuen.* Now an event which is to take place at some future time may take place, or there is a possibility that it may not. It is therefore only a slight extension of the meaning of *wenn* when we find that it is used in the sense of " if, in case." Thus : If he should come, tell him I

am not at home, *wenn er kommen sollte, sage ihm, dass ich nicht zu Hause bin*. If " when " means " whenever, every time when," *wenn* is also used for the past. When he came down the road he was always smiling, *wenn er die Strasse längs kam, lächelte er immer*.

(3) Otherwise with reference to past events *als* is used. When he came into the room I had gone, *als er ins Zimmer kam, war ich gegangen*.

LESSON 24

Passive Forms of Verbs

THE passive forms of the verbs have been given in earlier Lessons, and it now remains to give a few hints about the usage of the passive voice in German. There are no definite rules, but it may be said, on the whole, that the passive construction is more restricted in German than in English. Thus in English we may say " the angry father beat the naughty boy," or, " the naughty boy was beaten by the angry father." Except that the second construction is longer, and therefore on occasions to be avoided, both are equally usable. In German, however, it would be much more usual to say *der zornige Vater schlug den unartigen Knaben* than *der unartige Knabe wurde von dem zornigen Vater geschlagen*.

A passive can only be formed if the verb governs a direct object (an accusative). Now many verbs which govern a direct object in English govern an indirect object (a dative, sometimes even a genitive) in German, and with such verbs we cannot employ the passive voice. Thus we say " I see him," and we can therefore say " he was seen by me " : *Ich sehe ihn, er wurde von mir gesehen*. Many quite common verbs, however, govern a dative, and care must be taken when rendering them into German. The transitive verbs govern a direct object, the intransitive verbs govern an indirect object. This should always be memorized when looking up a verb in a German dictionary. Thus, " I help him " would be *Ich helfe ihm* (dative), and although we can say in English " he was helped by me," it would be definitely wrong to say in German *er wurde von mir geholfen*. Similarly we say " I met him " and " he was met by me." To meet is *begegnen*,

MAURICE HEWLETT
(1861–1923). Called to
the bar in 1891 and
Keeper of Land Re-
venue records, 1896–
1900, he established a
reputation as a roman-
tic novelist in 1898.

**EDEN PHILL-
POTTS** (b. 1862).
Turning to litera-
ture after ten years
as a clerk, he made
his name with real-
istic fiction set in
Dartmoor.

JOSEPH CONRAD
(1857–1924). Of Po-
lish parentage and
born in the Ukraine,
he was naturalized in
England in 1884. At
first a seaman, he
began to write fiction
in 1894, soon entering
the front rank of
English novelists.

RUDYARD KIPLING
(1865–1936). During 1882–89
engaged as a journalist in
India, afterwards gaining
pre-eminence as a writer
of stories in 1907 he was
awarded the Nobel prize
for literature.

ENGLISH LITERATURE 49

INTERPRETERS OF THE SOCIAL GRADIENT. Herbert George Wells (b. 1866), son of a Kent county cricketer, is a writer of versatile genius. In his novels concerning lower class suburban life the rich colour of the characterization is often greyed with the pathos of his own youthful hard times. (Centre) John Galsworthy (1867–1933), born at Combe in Surrey, educated at Harrow and Oxford, finely portrays in his fiction the wealthier English classes of his day. (Right) Arnold Bennett (1867–1931), born at Shelton, near Hanley in the Potteries, enscened this district in his panoramic series of novels dealing with the commercial life of the Five Towns. ENGLISH LITERATURE 49

Plate 38

Volume VI

THREE ACCOMPLISHED STORY-TELLERS. Left to right: Sir H. Rider
Haggard (1856–1925) was born in Norfolk and held several official posts in S.
Africa, the scene of many of his best stories. He was knighted in 1912. Sir
Arthur Conan Doyle (1859–1930), born in Edinburgh, was a doctor before he
turned to story-telling. Knighted in 1902, in his later years he was prominent
as a spiritualist. William John Locke (1863–1930), born in Barbados, was first
an architect. Commencing in 1905 he published a number of highly successful
novels of social life. ENGLISH LITERATURE 50

WRITERS OF ROMANCE AND HUMOUR. Left to right: Sir Anthony Hope
Hawkins (1863–1933) was born in London and became a barrister before winning
fame as " Anthony Hope " with his Ruritanian romances. William Wymark
Jacobs, born in 1863 in London, was a clerk in the Post Office Savings Bank
when he made a success as a short story writer. Pelham Grenville Wodehouse
(b. 1881) was a bank clerk when he began to write stories of school life. A much
wider public acclaimed his humorous creations. ENGLISH LITERATURE 50

WOMEN WRITERS OF TODAY. Left, Sheila Kaye-Smith, daughter of a St. Leonard's doctor: practically all her novels have the Sussex downland as their setting. Centre, Rose Macaulay, who since 1919 has published a number of satirically witty novels. She is also an accomplished essayist. Right, Mary Webb was the daughter of a Shropshire schoolmaster, and married, in 1912, H. B. L. Webb, also a schoolmaster. In 1924 her "Precious Bane" won praise, but it was not until after her death, in 1927, that a far wider fame came as the result of Stanley Baldwin's appreciative references to her work. ENGLISH LITERATURE 51

MASTERS OF THE 'MODERN' NOVEL. David Herbert Lawrence (left; 1885–1930) was born at Eastwood, Notts, the son of a coalminer, and won a scholarship to Nottingham High School and University College. After spells of clerking and as a school-teacher, he wrote history books under the nom-de-plume of Lawrence H. Davidson. The death of his mother in 1911 marked a crisis in his life, and in the same year his first novel appeared. He travelled much, and died at Nice. Aldous Huxley (centre) was born in 1894, a grandson of T. H. Huxley, and after Eton and Balliol joined the 'Athenaeum' and the "Westminster Gazette." Since 1921 he has produced many mordant studies of modern youth. Osbert Sitwell (right), born in 1892, the brother of Edith and Sacheverell Sitwell, served in the Grenadier Guards, 1913-19. His war experiences aroused in him a spirit of bitter satire, which has received full expression in his novels, essays and poetry. ENGLISH LITERATURE 51

Plate 40

Volume VI

and it takes a dative. Therefore, although we can say *Ich begegnete ihm* (dative), it is impossible to say *er wurde von mir begegnet*.

Care should be taken to discover whether the past participle in English is meant to express a state or an action, or, in other words, whether it is used adjectivally or verbally. Thus, in the statement " the door is closed," *closed* can describe the state of the door at the time, and the function of *closed* does not differ from that of *green* in the statement " the door is green." In German this would be given as *die Tür ist geschlossen*, just as we should say *die Tür ist grün*. If, however, we mean " the door is being closed," " someone is closing the door," then we have a true passive, and we should render this into German as *die Tür wird geschlossen*.

The Adjectival Adjunct. Instead of saying " the man who runs will get there," we can also say " the running man will get there." For " the man who runs fast will get there " it is still possible to say " the fast-running man will get there," though this is rather unusual. But when it comes to " the man who runs home fast all the way will get there first," we cannot possibly say " the all the way home fast running man will get there first." Yet this is precisely what one can do in German. *Der Mann, der läuft, wird hinkommen : Der laufende Mann wird hinkommen. Der Mann, der schnell läuft, wird hinkommen : Der schnell laufende Mann wird hinkommen. Der Mann, der schnell den ganzen Weg nach Hause läuft, wird zuerst hinkommen : Der schnell den ganzen Weg nach Hause laufende Mann wird zuerst hinkommen.* It will be seen from the examples that in this construction the verb becomes a present participle adjective and that everything that belongs to the verb in the clause comes before this adjective. When we are dealing with a verb in the perfect tense, the adjective will, of course, have past participle form. Thus : " The man who arrived from India yesterday is my father " : *Der Mann, der gestern von Indien angekommen ist, ist mein Vater : Der gestern von Indien angekommene Mann ist mein Vater.* These adjectival adjuncts can be of great length, though in more modern German the tendency is to restrict their usage severely. In the last sentence, for instance, there might have been a clause dependent on " India " : " the man who arrived yesterday from India, where he has spent many years, is my father." The normal way of translating this would be : *der Mann, der gestern* *von Indien angekommen ist, wo er viele Jahre verbracht hat, ist mein Vater.* But it would be perfectly grammatical to write: *der gestern von Indien, wo er viele Jahre verbracht hat, angekommene Mann ist mein Vater,* and such sentences will be frequently met with in older writers A fairly long separation of the article and its noun still occurs in parallel constructions. " This is the house paid for by my aunt, built by my father and inhabited by me " : *dies ist das von meiner Tante bezahlte, von meinem Vater gebaute und von mir bewohnte Haus.*

LESSON 25

Stops and Adverbial Usage

ONE of the prejudices about German is that the German sentence is far too long. This used to be true, and it may be true still of many old-fashioned authors, but it is not true of the average modern German writer. In fact, short sentences are now considered good style. This makes the study of German in one respect easier than it used to be ; but another difficulty has arisen which has not simplified it to the beginner. This difficulty is the rule that the main verb should go to the end of a statement, and it is best for the student to follow this rule. Good German writers, however, frequently break it. There are no rules discernible as yet, and the practice varies from author to author. It is still, for example, grammatically correct to say and to write : *Er sagte, dass er so alt wie sein Vetter sei,* he said he was as old as his cousin. But a good author will usually write : *Er sagte, dass er so alt sei wie sein Vetter.* Similarly : He said he was older than his cousin, *er sagte, dass er älter als sein Vetter sei,* or better, *er sagte, dass er älter sei als sein Vetter.*

In some of the examples of German we have seen that in German there is a *so* which is not in the English. This is called the correlative *so,* and it is really a way of linking the previous statement more thoroughly with what follows. We might translate this *so* by then. It is found most frequently after conditional clauses (if-clauses) introduced by *wenn. Wenn es nicht regnet, so wird er kommen,* if it does not rain, then he will come. *Wenn die Zeitung kommen sollte, so bringe sie mir auf mein Zimmer,* if the newspaper should come bring it to my room. We could equally well say : *Wenn es nicht regnet, wird er kommen* and *wenn die Zeitung kommen sollte, bringe sie mir auf mein Zimmer.* This correlative *so* also occurs frequently after a concessive clause (although-clause). It then corresponds to an English yet. Thus : Although he is a fool he is a professor, *oblgleich er ein Esel ist, so ist er ein Professor ;* and, in German, the connexion would often be still more strengthened by the introduction of *doch : Obgleich er ein Esel ist, so ist er doch ein Professor.* It is not usual to place this *so* after a temporal clause ; in fact, we can often tell whether the *wenn* is temporal or conditional by the presence or absence of the *so. Wenn er sein Examen besteht, gebe ich ihm zehn Pfund* means : When he passes his examination I will give him £10. *Wenn er sein Examen besteht, so gebe ich ihm zehn Pfund* means : If he passes his examination I will give him £10.

A puzzling feature of German is the number of little words that can be placed in a sentence without really adding anything to the meaning. Of these the most important are *ja, auch, schon, doch.* Sometimes there is no need to translate them into English ; at others, they add a certain shade of meaning to the sentence, and it is by no means always easy or even possible to find an English equivalent. *Ja* usually has the meaning " as you know very well." It is often equivalent to an excuse. *Er ist ja ein Professor,* he is, as you know, a professor, can also mean " The poor fellow can't help it—he's a professor." *Es ist wahr, was du sagst,* it is true what you say, but *es ist ja wahr, was du sagst* would usually mean something like " unfortunately, I have to admit that what you say is true." The *ja* can also be the forerunner of an *aber* that is to follow : *Es ist ja traurig, aber es lässt sich nicht ändern,* indeed, it is sad, or, I admit it is sad, but it cannot be helped. *Ja* can also be used to strengthen a negative : *Sage ihm nicht, dass ich hier war,* do not tell him that I was here. *Sage ihm ja nicht, dass ich hier war,* whatever you do, do not tell him that I was here.

The dictionary meaning of *doch* is yet, however ; but these meanings by no means cover the functions of the word. If we call *doch* an intensifier or a strengthener we are getting as near to its meaning as possible. Often it means surely, or indeed : *Es ist doch schade,* it is surely, a pity, or simply, it is a pity. *Er ist ein netter Mensch,* he is a nice fellow. *Er ist doch ein netter Mensch,* you surely agree that he is a nice fellow. These two little words are used together as an exclamation in *Ja doch !*

which is almost equivalent to our half impatient, half resigned, All right, I'm coming (or : hearing, listening, etc.)

Punctuation. There is no difficulty about the usage of the full-stop, the semicolon, the colon, the question-mark, the exclamation-mark, because they are used as in English. There are, however, fixed and definite rules which govern the placing of commas in German. A comma is placed between all attributive adjectives belonging to the same noun : *der gute, brave, tapfere Knabe*, the good, brave, courageous boy. A comma is used between all clauses in a sentence if these clauses have a verb : *Der Mann, der gestern kam, ist mein Vater.*

If two clauses are connected by *und*, place a comma if both clauses have a subject and a verb : *Der Mann schrie um Hilfe, und der Räuber lief weg*, the man called for help and the robber ran away. But : *Er kam gestern aus Paris an und fährt morgen nach Amerika weiter*, he arrived from Paris yesterday and continues his journey to America tomorrow.

In an infinitive clause a comma is placed if the sentence contains more than *zu* with the infinitive. This is the rule given, though it is not always strictly adhered to. Thus : *Ich bat ihn zu kommen*, I asked him to come. but *Ich bat ihn, morgen zu kommen*, I asked him to come tomorrow. A comma should not be placed after expressions of time or manner as is often done in English : After some time, he disappeared, *nach einiger Zeit verschwand er. Aber* in the sense of " however " is not placed between commas : It is, however, true, *es ist aber wahr.*

Inverted commas to mark the beginning and end of direct speech are placed at the bottom at the beginning of the speech and at the top at the end. *Er sagte : „Ich komme morgen."* He said : " I am coming tomorrow."

This Lesson concludes our Course in German.

LESSON 37

The Third Crusade and Innocent III

(See plates 43 and 44)

SALADIN (1137-93), an orthodox adherent of the formal khalifate of Bagdad, had succeeded in making himself master and sultan of Syria, just when the Latin kingdom in Palestine was rent by a disputed succession ; Guy of Lusignan had secured the crown, but the kingdom was divided. Unlike his predecessors, Saladin made it his aim to drive out the infidels, having already overthrown the Fatimid khalifate in Egypt. In 1187 the hosts of Saladin came down on Palestine, shattered the Latin army, and took Guy prisoner at the battle of Hattin or Tiberius ; four months later Saladin took Jerusalem. Antioch, Tripolis and Tyre held out, but practically the Latin kingdom of Jerusalem was gone. Nothing was to be hoped from Constantinople, where the line of the Comneni had just given place to the Angeli, though Isaac Comnenus (who was in correspondence with the Turks) ruled Cyprus, where he called himself emperor.

To the West, however, the call of the East was irresistible. The Church, the kings, the nobles vied with each other in their zeal. But dissensions had to be settled before a united Europe could advance upon Palestine. When Frederick Barbarossa had gathered his great German force early in 1189, the rest were not yet ready. He took the usual overland route. Next year he was marching victoriously through Asia Minor—and then came disaster ; he was drowned while trying in sport to swim a river. Without its leader the army of Germany went to pieces · many men returned home ; plague broke out among the remainder, and only a few ever reached the Crusaders in Palestine, who were besieging Acre, which had fallen to the Saracens. Saladin attempted to relieve the defenders without success, and Acre was retaken by the Crusaders in 1191.

The Crusade, however, proved a failure owing to the dissensions of its chiefs. Richard Coeur-de-Lion is a magnificent figure of romance, and in actual fact had many of the qualities of a great general—qualities which excited the admiration of the Saracens ;

but his arrogance and recklessness made him impossible as a colleague and intolerable as a chief. Kings and princes discovered an imperative need for their return home ; Philip II of France, quite unable to agree with Richard, after the taking of Acre set the example of departure. Twice Richard brought the Crusading host to within a few miles of the Holy City, but owing to the failure of the remaining German and French Crusaders to support him, he was obliged to retreat. At last, in 1192, he abandoned all hope of a reconquest, and signed with Saladin the treaty which left the Turk in possession of Jerusalem and all Palestine with the exception of certain ports. The people of the West were to be at liberty to come and go in pilgrimage to Jerusalem, exempt from taxes which the Saracen princes had been in the habit of imposing. There were several Crusades during the next century, but never again even the pretence of a united effort of Christendom. The fourth Crusade turned upon the heretical Greek empire. Nothing was achieved with regard to the recovery of Jerusalem, but the nominal supremacy of the Papal See over the Eastern Church was temporarily established.

Though the Crusades were essentially military expeditions, aiming first at conquest and then at the support of the Latin States in their struggles with Moslems, this fact should not hinder us from recognizing freely the central religious motive of these movements. At the beginning, during the 12th century, the eternal religious impulse surged up high in western Europe, showing itself in fervent zeal which gave men power to endure great hardships for their faith. Two great military-religious orders were established : the Knights Templars (1119), to protect pilgrims in the Holy Land, and the Hospitallers, which included the Knights of St. John of Jerusalem, and, later, the Teutonic Knights. This group originated about 1048 in a hospital dedicated to St. John the Baptist, for the care and cure of pilgrims to the Holy Sepulchre. Later the order became military and its members were sworn, as were the Templars, to protect the Holy Sepulchre till their death, and to war against the infidels on all occasions of meeting.

The emperor Frederick Barbarossa had procured the coronation of his son Henry as German king and king of the Romans, so as to ensure his succession, and thus left him behind, on his own departure on the third Crusade, as an indisputable viceroy —the assumption being that the king of the Romans was the recognized heir to the empire, though not technically emperor till his official coronation at Rome. Henry VI was twenty-five when his father died. During his brief reign (1190-97) he strengthened his hold on Germany. An accident delivered Richard Coeur-de-Lion into his hands on the way back from Palestine, and enabled him to extort homage from his prisoner, reducing England temporarily to vassalage, as a condition of release. In Italy Henry failed to eject his wife's illegitimate nephew Tancred from the throne of Sicily and Naples, to which he had been elected on the death of king William, but when Tancred himself died, he established his own authority as the husband of the Norman Sicilian princess, Constance, by methods as offensive to her as to the Sicilians—methods which made the German ascendancy detestable to the entire south. His career, however, was cut short by his death at thirty-two, leaving as his heir the two-year-old infant who was to become famous as Frederick II, " the Wonder of the World." At almost the same time Innocent III, mightiest of all the Popes, was elected. Constance renewed the old allegiance of the Sicilian crown to the papal suzerainty, and before her death in 1198 placed her child under the new Pope's guardianship.

The Papacy under Innocent attained the zenith of its power. Innocent claimed uncompromisingly all, and more than all, that any Pope had ever claimed—a divinely ordained supremacy over all temporal potentates. As Frederick's guardian and suzerain he ejected the German overlords whom Henry VI had forced on Sicily and Naples. He deposed king John in England, and reinstated him as his own vassal. The king of Portugal unwillingly and the king of Aragon by choice, both held their crowns as his vassals also. His influence helped to unite the Spanish monarchies for a decisive defeat of the Moors at Las Navas de Tolosa in 1212.

In another sphere Innocent in the last years of his life instituted the two great mendicant orders of the Friars of St. Francis and St. Dominic, and issued the reforming decrees of the fourth Lateran Council (1215), which, among other things, denounced and forbade, however vainly, the traditional appeal to the ordeal by battle.

LESSON 38

'Stupor Mundi': His Achievements and Significance

(See plate 45)

CRAFTY, resolute, unscrupulous, a capable soldier and a born organizer, Philip II (1180–1223) made himself king of France in a sense which had been true of none among his predecessors, though he had to wait for full success till the death of his mighty feudatory Richard, duke or count of half France, and king of England. For generations the Capet kings of France had been insidiously weakening a too powerful baronage by fostering their internecine feuds, encouraging the development of free cities or communes, choosing the clergy or minor barons for administrative posts, seizing every opportunity, whether by forfeitures or marriages, to add to the royal estates. The policy had a serious set-back when Henry of Anjou, not yet king of England, married Elinor of Aquitaine and trebled his already wide dominions. While Richard was in Palestine or a prisoner, Philip schemed against him with his brother John. But his opportunity came when John succeeded Richard on the English throne ; and at the end of a five years' conflict Normandy and Anjou became appanages of the French crown, while John was left lord of little more out of all the Angevin possessions than Guienne and Gascony. The royal estates in France were now wider than those of all the feudatories put together.

Philip's son, Louis VIII (1223–26), in his short reign, carried on his father's policy, but at his death sowed the seeds of future trouble by bestowing out of the royal domains great appanages —Artois, Poitou and Anjou—on his three younger sons. The eldest, his heir Louis IX, was only twelve ; and the successful regency of his mother, Blanche of Castile, in the face of a strong feudalist reaction, proved her remarkable abilities and efficiency as a ruler. In the son to whom she resigned the reins of government in 1135 the world found incarnated the highest medieval idea of a Christian king—a prince who, never seeking honour for himself, won it in the eyes of all men ; a knight without fear and without reproach, without touch either of feeble pietism or of fierce fanaticism.

The brilliant figure who at this period stands in the strongest possible contrast to Louis, the fine flower of medievalism, is the emperor Frederick II. Frederick was born out of due time, anticipating all and more than all, the spirit of the approaching Italian Renaissance. His versatility and his paradoxical brilliancy astonished his own age and are hardly less amazing to posterity. He was a rationalist who regulated his life by astrology; a zealous student of every known science; a poet who popularized the vernacular poetry of Sicily by his own practice; a sceptic who persecuted heresy and was in perpetual conflict with successive popes. In relation to women his principles and his practice were more oriental than European. he was no soldier, and was excommunicated for evading his promises to lead a crusade; yet he crowned himself king at Jerusalem with his own hands. He established a system of absolute monarchy in Naples and Sicily, but he deliberately turned Germany into a confederation of virtually independent princes owing hardly more than a nominal allegiance to the emperor. His university of Naples was the first founded by royal charter.

Pope Innocent III, a year before his death, had crowned Frederick emperor after receiving a solemn pledge that his kingdom of Sicily should not be united to the empire and that he would devote himself to a new crusade. Honorius III, who succeeded Innocent in the Papal chair, was less masterful. Frederick put Honorius off with fair words and plausible excuses—he must have his turbulent Sicilian kingdom in thorough order before he could take in hand such a crusade as the circumstances demanded. He had his young son Henry crowned king of Sicily as the Pope's vassal—but he also had him crowned king of the Romans. He soothed Honorius by making large concessions to the clergy, strengthening their hold on the free cities, while he avoided any measures that might perturb the German princes. Not without difficulty he suppressed the still strong Saracen element in Sicily.

Honorius died. His successor was Gregory IX, who was not to be put off by promises. To appease him Frederick had to gather a crusading force, even to set sail. But he had hardly sailed when he returned to port, and Gregory promptly excommunicated him. Frederick set out again, though he was now under the Papal ban—but he wanted the crown of Jerusalem, having just made its titular queen, Iolande of Brienne, his second wife. Saladin had long been dead; the Holy City was in the hands of the Egyptian sultan, but Frederick's diplomacy won him the coveted prize without fighting. He satisfied himself with leaving a small garrison in Jerusalem, and returned to Europe its crowned king. A few years later another sultan recaptured it.

There was a formal reconciliation (1229) with Gregory, which both pope and emperor meant to be no more than a truce ; but it lasted ten years. Frederick's son, Henry, left in Germany, had been making trouble there. Trouble in Germany was the last thing desired by Frederick, whose present aim was a free hand in Italy. Whatever his intentions for the future might be, he dropped in Germany the old policy of strengthening the clergy, the towns, and the lesser barons against the princes, whose good-will he wanted. Accordingly, he issued the Charter of the Princes, which made them all but independent sovereigns ; and when his son Henry persisted in his opposition, deposed him and procured the election of Conrad, his son by Iolande, as German king. Then he returned to Italy (1237), where the city leagues were giving trouble.

The free cities, which Barbarossa had left free republics, were constantly torn by internal factions and external rivalries, but had a common desire to free themselves from the last shreds of external control ; they were Guelph or Ghibelline, papalist or imperialist, according to the temporarily dominant faction. Frederick meant to bring them all under his own control again, and to that end encouraged the tendency to establish despotisms under despots who would seek support from him. In 1237 he won a decisive victory, which broke up the Guelph League, but brought him again into collision with his old enemy Gregory, who escaped him by dying. The conflict was renewed by Pope Innocent IV ; Germany again plunged into a struggle between Conrad and a rival German king, William of Holland ; Guelphs and Ghibellines fought and intrigued in Italy, and while the confusion was at its height Frederick died.

Notwithstanding the political degeneration of his time Frederick's reign has great historical and some literary significance. The expansion eastwards of his empire continued unchecked, mainly owing to the activities of the Teutonic Knights. It was the age of minstrels, the period of Parsifal and Tannhäuser, those far-famed German romances. There was much intellectual activity, foreshadowing that wonderful revival of learning throughout Europe, the Renaissance

Frederick's interests were always bound up in Sicily, and it was in this kingdom that he developed his revolutionary schemes, creating an absolutism, an oriental despotism beyond anything seen in the Middle Ages. In place of a theory of temporal power, dependent upon moral sanctions, an unlimited autocracy came into being. The rights of the Church in Sicily were swept away like those of the Sicilian nobles ; Frederick himself claimed to be the head of Church and State.

The religious sanction for temporal authority had no place in his scheme. Shocked at his impiety and yet admiring his audacity, his contemporaries gave him the title of Stupor Mundi, " The Wonder of the World." Setting up his notions of political authority, he sought to put reason in the place of faith, aesthetic values instead of moral doctrines in art, secular omni-potence instead of obedience to ecclesiastical and religious control. It was these modern political ideas which involved him in bitter conflict with the pope.

In the midst of the struggle a new menace descended on Europe. The Mongol Temujin, better known as Jenghiz Khan, had set up a mighty dominion in Asia from the Tigris to the Pacific. In 1240 his successor's lieutenants swept through south Russia, wiped out its embryo civilization, and poured westward, devastating, to the very confines of the Empire. Then, for no known reason except a report of the death of the Great Khan, the Tartar host rolled away again as suddenly as it had come. The menace vanished, but neither Empire nor Papacy had had even a hand in the saving of western Europe. And for two hundred years Russia was subjected to Mongol overlordship.

LESSON 39

Monarchy's Growth in Medieval Europe

(See plate 46)

THE death of Frederick II left his son Conrad fighting in Germany against a rival claimant to the title of king of the Romans. Conrad died in 1254, leaving his half-brother Manfred to defend the claims of his infant son Conradin in Sicily and Germany. Frederick's successors shared his antagonism to Papal authority, but, ignorant of his constructive policy, carried on the struggle, to end only in the complete downfall of Frederick's house, though, for a time, Manfred and Conradin maintained the imperial cause in Italy with some success.

In 1265 came the final phase of the struggle. The Papacy called from over the Alps a French prince, Charles of Anjou, the brother of Louis IX, who arrived in Italy with an army against Manfred. The Pope bestowed the crown of the Sicilies and Naples on Charles. Manfred was killed, fighting for the crown. Conradin made a final effort, but was defeated, captured and beheaded by Charles in 1268. The imperial cause was crushed by this extinction of the house of Hohenstaufen. Then, in 1273, the " interregnum " in the empire was closed by the election of Rudolf of Hapsburg, the powerful princes who formed the electoral body being satisfied that his dominions were not large enough to enable him to be more than a legal figurehead. Although he by no means proved to be this, the empire as a unit collapsed, and its collapse was permanent. The temporal leadership of Europe thus passed to the great western states, France and England, which were already beginning to apply Frederick's ideas of absolutism to their affairs.

During the last three years Louis IX in France had died, and in England Edward I had succeeded the pious but futile Henry III (1272). If Frederick II was the most brilliant prince of his time, Louis was indubitably the most admirable. His greatness, however, is to be measured rather by the loftiness of his character than by successful statesmanship—the ideal of kingship which made all men trust the man himself implicitly, and strengthened the crown by the loyalty it engendered. Provence, technically within the empire, became practically French through the marriage of his brother, Charles of Anjou, to its heiress. Twice Louis attempted to revive the crusading ideal which Frederick II had sought to twist to his own ends. In the first he was disastrously defeated ; in the course of the second he died (1270).

This was the last serious Crusade. Frederick's kingdom of Jerusalem had fallen under the sway of the Mameluke lords of Egypt, who had shattered the advance of the Mongol power westward ; and Edward of England, not yet king, who took command of the expedition on Louis' death, found the position hopeless. The Christian foothold in Asia was confined to a few

Greek stations. Cyprus was still in possession of the Lusignans, and Rhodes, held by the Knights Hospitallers, was still to remain for a long time the great naval outpost of Christendom. The Latin empire at Constantinople guttered out finally when Michael Palaeologus captured the city in 1261 and one more Greek imperial dynasty was set up ; but its power within the peninsula was very slight, while western Europe was heedless of it.

Rudolf of Hapsburg was elected by the German princes because he was lord only of some portion of Swabia, and the last thing the electors wanted was a strong emperor who could exercise effective control over them. The event was somewhat disappointing, since he raised the house of Hapsburg from a minor to a leading position, which enabled him actually to make the imperial authority felt. This he achieved by recovering and appropriating the eastern border provinces—Austria or the East Marches—of which Ottocar, king of Bohemia. had possessed himself during the interregnum. On the other hand, the pressure of the Bohemian war forced him to conciliate the Papacy by acknowledging the Pope's nominee and " vassal," Charles of Anjou (and Provence), as king of Sicily.

On Rudolf's death, then, in 1291, the princes elected not his son Albert, whom they reckoned too powerful, but another minor noble, Adolf of Nassau, for the same reason as dictated their choice of Rudolf. They were too strong for him ; but on his death Albert secured election, and continued to strengthen his position till he was assassinated in 1308.

The island of Sicily detested its foreign monarch and the Frenchmen whom he set over them. In 1282 there was a sudden and unpremeditated rising and massacre of the French in Palermo, the ghastly event known as the Sicilian Vespers ; the whole island was immediately in arms, and offered the Sicilian crown to the dead Manfred's son-in-law, Peter of Aragon, who accepted it. The island was made almost secure by Aragon's powerful fleet. Charles and Peter both died in 1285. The conflict continued between their sons until, in 1302, a composition was reached under which Naples went to Charles II of Anjou and the island kingdom of Sicily to Frederick, younger brother of king James of Aragon.

Louis IX left France enjoying a European prestige due not only to his personality, but also to the centralized administrative system inherited from his father and grandfather. His son was undistinguished, but his grandson, Philip IV the Fair, was a ruler of the same type as Philip II. In his reign (1285–1314) he did not display the brilliant abilities of his ancestor, but pursued the same policy and methods with a like freedom from scruple, and his administrative developments left a permanent mark upon French institutions. In summoning the States General he did not set up a political force such as the Parliament which Edward I was at the same time establishing in England. On the other hand, the council of lawyers, called the Parlement of Paris, which he created, though not a parliament in the English sense, was a body which, on several occasions in French history, was able to exercise a decisive political influence. His trickery in reverting to the traditional methods of absorbing vassal fiefs into crown lands brought him into collision—from which in the end he reaped no advantage—with Edward, though one issue of it was the inauguration of a Franco-Scottish alliance, which was a constant factor in the relations of the three countries for two and a half centuries to come. Similarly, his ambitions were foiled in Flanders, largely through the crushing defeat of the French chivalry by the burgher infantry at Courtrai in 1302.

But outside France the great feature of his reign was the decisive conflict with the Papacy. Weakened by the conflict with Frederick II, and robbed by his break with traditional ideas and by the subsequent downfall of the empire of its natural protector, the Papacy had played a small part in the troubles which followed. When king John had surrendered England into the hands of the legate of Innocent III (1213), receiving it back at the price of a yearly tribute of 700 marks for England and 300 for Ireland, the humiliation of Henry IV at Canossa was more than repeated ; but in less than a century after this event the Papacy received a setback to its authority from which it never recovered. Except in the too brief reign of Gregory X (1271–6), who, in happier circumstances and given a longer period, might have gone far to restore its moral prestige, the Papacy for the following twenty years was occupied with inter-necine rivalry until the election of Boniface VIII (1294–1303), who, though a man of consummate political genius, yet failed to realize that his ideas belonged to a past age. His downfall marked the rise of the new nationalism.

The great Hildebrand (Gregory VII) had promulgated the theory that subordinated the nations to the Papacy ; Innocent

III had carried this into practice. Boniface endeavoured to do so ; he intervened with an offer of arbitration between Philip of France and Edward of England, which was declined by both ; he forbade the clergy in both countries to pay taxes without his authority. Both kings compelled their clergy to submit to their demands, while Philip cut off the contributions to the Papal exchequer. Boniface threatened him with an interdict, the weapon employed by Innocent III against king John—a weapon now blunted by centuries of use.

In Edward I and Philip IV Boniface had to deal with two monarchs who, though in different ways, expressed nationalistic determinations and did not intend for one moment to allow the Pope's claims to supremacy. Philip finally took the law in his own hands, and dispatched to Anagni, where Boniface was then residing, troops who seized his person, using such violence that his death ensued (1303)—and with him perished the Hildebrandine ideal. Two years later Philip secured the election of a nominee of his own, Clement V, who found his position at Rome untenable and removed the papal court to Avignon, in the half-French Provence, where it remained, in effect, under French domination destructive of its spiritual functions.

LESSON 40

Western Europe in the 14th Century

(See plates 47 and 48)

THE thirteenth century was the great age of medievalism. The zenith of the medieval idea of the Papacy was the reign of Innocent III ; its supreme expression in art, the Gothic cathedrals ; its flower of Christianity, the ideals of St. Francis of Assisi. It was the century of Dante and Giotto, of Roger Bacon, of Thomas Aquinas and his rival Duns Scotus of Oxford, of Earl Simon the Righteous and Bishop Grossetête in England, of St. Louis (IX) in France, and of that " wonder of the world," born before his time Frederick II, the last Hohenstaufen emperor. The fourteenth century has no such array of dominant figures. Intellectually exciting, morally decadent, it was an age of pageantry, glitter and romance, when war was followed as the great game of the few heedless of the misery of the many ; it was the age of the Black Death (1348), of peasant revolts, of Jacqueries ; the age also of the reaction from which arose the reforms and views disseminated by John Wycliffe (1325–84).

When Clement V went to Avignon in 1309, Philip IV was still reigning in France, the feeble Edward II had just succeeded the great Edward I in England, Robert Bruce was gradually recovering the Scottish Lowlands from the English garrisons planted there by Edward I, and Henry VII, count of Luxemburg, had succeeded Albert I. In 1311 Henry assumed the Lombard crown, and the imperial crown in 1312. Henry died in 1313, and the electors, ignoring his young son, divided their votes between two rivals, Frederick of Hapsburg and Lewis of Bavaria, who embarked on a nine years' contest for the imperial crown. The Aragonese dynasty was at this period established in Sicily, and Robert of Anjou (1275–1343) had succeeded in 1309 to the throne of Naples, in which year his nephew, Carobert, became king of Hungary.

Almost the last acts of Philip IV before his death in 1314 were directed towards the suppression of the military-religious order of the Knights Templars, who, together with the Hospitallers and Teutonic knights, were in fact regiments of the Pope. They owed service only to Rome, and refused to pay taxes or acknowledge any king. While the Crusades lasted the Templars were endured ; with the end of these came their end also. The Hospitallers found a new field of service ; the Teutonic Knights were still fighting the heathen Letts ; but the Templars, with their enormous wealth and without an approved purpose, were a menace to Europe. Their fall was necessary if the new nations were to survive ; and, apart from the cupidity which their treasures aroused, Philip of France and Edward II of England were obliged to render impotent this great military force before it was organized in defence of the Papacy now languishing at Avignon and to create the papal dominion of Hildebrand's vision.

Ironically, the suppression of the Templars was wrung from the Papacy itself. Clement V completed thus the overthrow which had begun with Boniface. He was powerless before Philip and forced to condemn an order whose greatest crime was unswerving fidelity to Rome. For seven years torture, martyrdoms at the stake, and plunder went on, the Templars being seized and handed over to the Inquisition.

Three sons in succession followed Philip IV on the French throne, while their sister Isabella was the wife of Edward II of England, whom she succeeded in having deposed and murdered, nominally in favour of her young son Edward III. The last brother died in 1328. The direct male succession from Hugh Capet had hitherto been unbroken ; none of the brothers left a male heir ; and the Paris Parlement pronounced that by French law the heir now was Philip of Valois, son of Philip IV's brother, though Isabella put in a claim on behalf of her son which in English law would probably have been pronounced good. The question was dropped for the time, Philip VI succeeding ; but ten years later Edward revived the claim for himself and began the Hundred Years' War between England and France, really with the object of obtaining full sovereignty over the fiefs he held in Aquitaine (which French kings were constantly seeking to filch) as well as, for commercial purposes, over Flanders.

The Anglo-French war from 1338 to 1377 established the new military principle exemplified at Courtrai, and at Bannockburn in 1314, that heavy infantry, rightly handled, could hold their own against mail-clad cavalry, and could in fact annihilate it when supported by the immensely superior artillery which the English alone could bring into the field, the long-bow. It also proved the value to England of a fleet which could dominate the Channel, while the capture of Calais (1347) gave England a standing gateway into France and a centre for commercial development in Europe.

Though it enabled Edward III, his son the Black Prince, and the Breton Bertrand du Guesclin to perform astonishing feats of arms, it also demonstrated the ultimate futility of such victories in the field when strategy aimed only at successful raiding. It retarded the political development of France, while it left the Plantagenets in the end with a weaker hold on their French possessions than when the war began. After the battle of Poitiers, in 1356, Charles V (1337–80) became the real ruler of France, his father John II having been taken prisoner to England. Charles actually succeeded and was crowned at Reims in 1364.

The European position and its complications were affected by the Anglo-French war only so far as it restrained French intervention. The movements in the east were similarly without effect on the west for the time being, but only for the time. We have already seen the great Mongol or Tartar flood ebbing almost of its own accord from eastern Europe, and definitely rolled back in Asia by the Mamelukes, who dominated Syria from Egypt. The empire of the Seljuk Turks had been shattered in 1157, although they continued to be of international importance until new bands bearing the name Ottoman, from their leader Othman, took their place early in the 14th century.

Othman died in 1326, and under his son Orkhan the Ottoman power advanced rapidly in Asia Minor. In 1330 he captured Nicaea, and within a few years all that remained in Asia to Andronicus III, emperor of the East (1328–41), was a strip of coast. Stephen Dusan (1333–55), the most vigorous of the Serbian kings, was encroaching on the eastern empire at the same time, wresting from it the Balkan lands. Orkhan's successor, Murad I, captured Adrianople, which remained the Turkish capital in Europe till the fall of Constantinople in 1453.

The Serbian power, however, fell away after Stephen's death in 1355, and the Turk was now firmly footed in Europe and absorbing the peninsula piecemeal while Venetian and Genoese fleets, more intent on their own rival commercial interests than on the advance of Islam, fought each other in the eastern Mediterranean, and the apathy of Latin Christendom left the eastern Orthodox empire to take care of itself.

We return, then, to the western empire and to Italy, the greater part of which was technically within the western empire ; Bohemia being also closely connected with the former, and having for its own king John of Luxemburg, the son of Henry VII, while Hungary, with an Angevin king, Carobert, was closely connected with the Angevin kingdom of Naples.

In 1322 Lewis of Bavaria took his Hapsburg rival prisoner ; the struggle for the imperial crown seemed over, but Pope John XXII at Avignon seized the opportunity once more to assert the papal claim to decide who should be emperor Lewis rejected the claim ; the great order of the Franciscans supported Lewis, the great rival order of the Dominicans supported the Pope, the Guelph and Ghibelline factions being similarly opposed. German nationalism was all in favour of Lewis, but he threw away his great opportunities, irritated his German supporters by his greed, alienated clerical sentiment by usurping clerical functions, and thus enabled the Pope to procure his formal but not his effective deposition by the election of Charles, of Luxemburg and Bohemia, as king of the Romans. In spite of active but disunited opposition, Charles IV, on the death of Lewis in 1347, did secure the crown.

Hungary was vigorously developed under its Angevin kings, Carobert and Lewis the Great ; the latter died in 1380, having acquired also by arrangement, not by conquest, the crown of Poland. For Bohemia Charles IV (1316—78) was an entirely admirable king ; as emperor, he was promulgator of the famous decree called the Golden Bull, which he issued in 1356. This regulated the election of the imperial succession and German king. It finally established three archbishops with three German princes and the king of Bohemia as the " Electors "—bearing that title—in whom the choice of an emperor and German king was vested ; Brandenburg, the Palatinate and Saxony. Bavaria and Austria were deliberately excluded. Individually and collectively the Electors wielded a power which was an effective barrier to the development of a strong centralized government. Charles, however, succeeded in procuring during his own lifetime the election of his thoroughly incompetent elder son Wenzel as king of the Romans and successor to the throne ; while the younger, Sigismund, married the daughter and heiress of Lewis of Hungary. Charles IV died in the year in which the Great Schism (1378) was opened by the election of two rival Popes, Urban VI at Rome and the Anti-Pope Clement VII at Avignon.

LESSON 41

The Era of the Great Schism
(See plate 49)

WHEN Pope Gregory XI died in 1378, the Anglo-French war had been in suspense since a treaty in 1375 ; the king of England was Richard II ; in France Charles V, whose rule, first as regent and then as king, had done much for the salvation of the country during the last 30 years, died in 1380. His successor, Charles VI, was imbecile at the best, and definitely insane for long periods. The royal dukes, uncles, brothers or cousins of the king rent the country with the factions of Burgundy and Orleans (the latter afterwards known as Armagnacs). In Germany Wenzel, king of Bohemia and of the Romans, was a drunkard. He had not the vigour or intelligence to prevent a civil war—a " war of the towns "—during which central government in his dominions virtually ceased. His brother, Sigismund, had a prolonged struggle to secure his wife and, with her, the crown of Hungary Her sister Hedwig married Jagellon, the heathen duke of heathen Lithuania, who adopted Christianity himself, imposed it on the Letts, and founded the Jagellon dynasty of Poland.

In Italy, Venice in 1380 finally won the struggle against Genoa for supremacy in the Mediterranean. Gian Galeazzo Visconti (1347–1402), tyrant of Milan, was rapidly mastering the other cities of the north, increasing the prestige and territories of Milan, and obtained the title of independent duke of Milan from Wenzel in 1395. In the west the little kingdom of Portugal escaped possible absorption in the greater Castile by the decisive victory of Aljubarotta (1385), and peace between the two countries was secured when their respective kings, Henry III and John I of Portugal, married two daughters of John of Gaunt, whose son, deposing Richard II, became Henry IV of England (1399). The long reign of John (1385–1433) was notable for the beginnings of Portugal's activities, not as a European power, but as the pioneer of maritime exploration which opened out the New World to European peoples under the leadership of his younger son, known as Henry the Navigator (1394–1460).

Throughout the last quarter of the 14th century the Ottoman menace had been developing under Murad and his son Bajazet, who succeeded him in 1379. The Greek dominion amounted to very little outside the walls of Constantinople. John V, failing to obtain aid from the west, acknowledged himself the vassal and the tributary of the Ottoman. The Slavonic states formed a league of defence, but a crushing defeat was inflicted on them at Kossovo (1389) ; Murad's death had not checked his son's advance. The annexation of Bulgaria forced Sigismund of Hungary to take the field, but he in turn met with an overwhelming defeat, from which he barely escaped with his life, at Nicopolis (1396). Bajazet advanced against Constantinople itself, with little prospect of being stayed in his victorious career, when a storm descended on him from the east ; his power was shattered, and he himself was taken prisoner at the battle of Angora (1402) by the devastating conqueror Timur " the lame," or Tamerlaine (1336-1405), who in 1369 had overcome all rivals and seated himself on the throne of Samarkand. Timur's conquests had included Georgia, most of Persia, the Caucasian states, large portions of India, and now finally the subjugation of the Turks in Asia Minor. In times of peace Timur ruled wisely, patronizing the arts and learning and promoting social welfare. In time of war he slaughtered incredible numbers of captives. He was a zealous Mahomedan. Bajazet died in captivity next year, and for ten years more his sons fought for the succession; while the destroyer, instead of pouring his hosts into Europe, turned back to the east, intending to complete in China the conquest of Asia, a project frustrated by his death in 1405, in his seventieth year. His empire vanished with his death—nothing but his lust for conquest and bloodshed had held it together.

The west then was released from the urgent Turkish pressure. Sigismund devoted himself to Hungarian affairs with marked success, achieving thereby in the eyes of the world a reputation for efficiency higher than he deserved. Wenzel, though not unpopular in Bohemia, had neither the character nor the will to control Germany or to command respect elsewhere. In 1410 there was a fresh imperial election, at which his cousin Jobst and Sigismund were both elected. Jobst died, and from that time Sigismund, by agreement with his brother, virtually was treated as emperor, though without Wenzel's formal resignation.

The continuance of the Papacy at Avignon had become utterly impossible, but the attempt to end it involved the Papacy in another disaster, the Great Schism. Pope John, the chosen of the Council of Pisa, appealed to Sigismund for support, promising to call a General Council with the object of ending the Great Schism, a Council whose authority should be accepted as conclusive. On that understanding, Sigismund gave him his support. The plan met with general acceptance as the necessary condition precedent to the Church reform which had now become imperative; and the Council of Constance was duly assembled (1414).

Though the official business of that Council was the termination of the scandal of a divided papacy—at Avignon and in Rome—and of the schism of Christendom, the underlying need was that of spiritual and moral reformation within the ecclesiastical body, without which the authority of the Church could never be restored. Sigismund in demanding its convocation intended it also to establish the old doctrine that the emperor was the secular as the pope was the spiritual head of Christendom; while the reforming party among the Churchmen had no thought of doctrinal, but only of administrative changes, largely on nationalist lines—an attitude emphasized by the procedure, adopted in the Council, of representation by " nations." Consequently, while it successfully deposed all the three rival popes —Gregory XII at Rome, Benedict XIII at Avignon, and John XXIII—it set in their place a man of character and distinction, Martin V, and arranged for the meeting of a succession of Councils to deal with other questions of reform, in spite of Martin's uncompromising assertion of the pope's own supremacy ; it did in fact bring not peace but a sword. The explosive element had its source in Bohemia. Sigismund himself was responsible for its introduction ; and he failed most unhappily in his handling of the situation when the explosion came.

The University of Prague had risen to the highest rank under the care of Charles IV ; latterly it had in effect excluded its German elements and was fervently nationalist. Its doctors, headed by John Huss (c. 1373–1415), had gradually absorbed and disseminated the teachings of the English reformer, John Wycliffe (c. 1325–84), which cut at the roots of formal ecclesiastical authority and, from the conservative point of view, of civil authority also, while they had already been denounced in England as heretical. Orthodoxy, whether ecclesiastical or political, denounced Huss, but Bohemia was behind him. He could appear at Constance only at great peril ; but Sigismund urged his attendance, under his own guarantee of security. Huss came, was charged with heresy, condemned, and sent to the stake, Sigismund withdrawing the protection to which he had pledged himself—persuaded to that disastrous act of treachery by his ablest and most trusted adviser, Frederick of Hohenzollern, who became elector of Brandenburg three months before the sentence on Huss was carried out.

At the moment Sigismund's surrender saved the Council from immediate disruption ; it completed the work it actually had on hand, concluding with the election of Martin V, before its dissolution in 1418. The slaying of Huss had given it the solidarity for the sake of which Frederick had counselled it, since the Hussite doctrines were poisonous heresy in the sight of lay rulers no less than of the Churchmen. Outside Bohemia it did not bring even discredit on Sigismund. But in Bohemia it kindled a flame which was soon to grow to a conflagration.

LESSON 42

The Fall of Constantinople

(See plate 50)

THE Council of Constance was actually in session when the Hundred Years' War was renewed in 1415 between France and England, by the ambition of Henry V, encouraged by the factions of Burgundy and Armagnac and the imbecility of Charles VI. After the first campaign, in which Harfleur was captured and Agincourt repeated the old achievements of Crécy and Poitiers, Henry set about an organized conquest of Normandy. The assassination of John the Fearless of Burgundy at a meeting between him and the dauphin, by one of the latter's escort, drove John's son, Philip the Good, to alliance with the English, and the treaty of Troyes disinherited the French king's only surviving son in favour of the English king, who married his daughter. Both the kings died in 1422, but the two-thirds of France which had not been conquered and garrisoned acknowledged the Dauphin Charles, not the baby Henry VI.

For a time the English arms made slow progress, till the tide was checked by St. Joan of Arc. She was taken prisoner eventually and burnt as a heretic in 1431. But a breach developed between England and Burgundy ; the alliance was finally dissolved in 1435. England in turn was torn with factions which were later to issue in the Wars of the Roses ; Joan had rekindled the spirit of France ; Normandy was lost ; in 1453 everything was lost except Calais, and the Hundred Years' War was over. France could turn once more to the interrupted task of constructing a strong central government, a task made none the easier by the expansion of Burgundy under its Valois dukes.

The Netherlands, over which by their marriages these dukes held sovereignty, possessed great trading cities and consequently were extremely wealthy. The second Philip of Burgundy had become, though still a feudatory of France in respect of Burgundy itself, a practically independent potentate with the best filled treasury in Europe, standing to the French crown in a very similar relation to that of the Angevin kings of England in the 12th century.

After the betrayal and martyrdom at the stake of John Huss, Bohemia and the Bohemian government were stubbornly and angrily Hussite. Wenzel's death in 1419 left Sigismund sole king of the Romans, and we may call him emperor, though he was not actually crowned till thirteen years later. Bohemia, however, declined to submit to him. The reformers in 1420 issued their demands, the " Four Articles of Prague," which were moderate enough In the same year Pope Martin, with the emperor's concurrence, proclaimed a crusade against the heretics. A German army, under no clear leadership, was raised and was ignominiously routed by the brilliant Hussite captain Ziska.

There was a pause in the Hussite wars, during which Bohemia offered its crown to Ladislas of Poland, who refused it, thereby missing the chance of uniting Slav nationalism against German domination. The collapse of the German armies had emphasized the need for reorganizing the military system of the empire, but no improvement was effected, and two more crusades against the Hussites were even more ignominious than their predecessors. In 1431, at the moment when he had summoned another General Council to meet at Basel (finally dissolved in 1449), Martin died and was succeeded as Pope by Eugenius IV. The Council took the Hussite problem in hand. It invited the Hussites to send delegates to Basel, and a compromise, the *Compactata*, was arrived at which satisfied the more moderate Hussites, who were willing to acknowledge Sigismund, provided he secured to them religious liberty.

Next year Sigismund died, and the electors chose as his successor—for he had no direct heir—the Hapsburg Albert of Austria, his daughter's husband, who consequently succeeded him also, though not without opposition, as king of both Bohemia and Hungary. But Albert died in 1439 (his son, Ladislas Postumus, being not yet born) and another Hapsburg, Frederick of Styria, was elected king of the Romans : after him, in practice though not in theory, the imperial succession became hereditary in the house of Hapsburg. When the baby Ladislas was born Bohemia and Austria recognized him ; the Hungarians, however, offered their kingdom to Ladislas of Poland, though, when he was killed at Varna four years later, Hungary reverted to the child who bore the same name.

End of the Eastern Empire. The Ottoman advance had been suspended by the ruin of Bajazet at Angora in 1402 by

Tamerlaine, whose retirement left Bajazet's sons fighting for the succession. One son, Mohammed I, secured the sole sultanate, but still was too much occupied in Asia to make trouble in Europe. But in 1427, when Murad II had succeeded Mohammed I and the particularly futile John VI (1425–48) was at Constantinople, Serbia and Bosnia revolted. Belgrade was ceded to Sigismund to gain Hungary's aid. Notable successes were gained by the coalition, led by the Hungarian hero Janos (John) Corvinus Hunyadi : these successes extorted from Murad the very favourable treaty of Szegedin (1444), Ladislas of Poland being then king of Hungary also. But the Christians, over-elated and urged on by Pope Eugenius, promptly invading Bulgaria, met with a crushing defeat at Varna, where Ladislas was killed. Hunyadi was one of the few to escape and reach his own country. All that had been gained by the treaty was lost. Hunyadi, who had opposed the ill-starred campaign, continued the fight.

John VI had kept the peace throughout his feeble reign, ignored by Murad, though he had made a despairing effort to get aid from the West by appealing to and accepting the offer of the Ferrara or Florence Council, flatly rejected by his own subjects, which in effect required the Greek Church to submit itself to the Latin. John was succeeded in 1448 by the last of the Greek emperors, his brother Constantine, who knew that the decisive crisis was at hand and was determined to fight to the last, though there was none to help him save Venetian, Genoese or other shipmen. By confirming his brother's agreement he only alienated his own subjects and procured no aid. In 1451 Mohammed II succeeded Murad II, bent on winning Constantinople, which had hitherto been besieged often enough but had always defied capture. Throughout 1452 he was preparing. In the spring the siege opened. A Genoese squadron forced an entry, bringing supplies to the scanty garrison. Then the toils closed on the doomed city. On May 29 the walls were breached ; in irresistible swarms the Turks poured through and overwhelmed the little garrison of 10,000 or so. Constantine was slain fighting at the head of his last desperate band, and the Crescent in place of the Cross floated over the great Cathedral of St. Sophia. The mightiest empire the world had known was no more, though it had survived its severance from its birthplace for more than a thousand years.

LESSON 43

Hungary's Stand Against the Turks

(See plate 51)

IN the years following the capture of Constantinople (1453), Mohammed was consolidating both his Asiatic and his European empire and completing his subjugation of the Balkan peninsula. Western Christendom might be shocked at the disaster ; but in spite of the fervent efforts, warnings and arguments of Pope Pius II, no steps were taken by the western monarchs to help the stubborn resistance of Christianity against Islam, which was being offered by Slavs and others from patriotic motives within the peninsula.

In Albania, the national hero, George Castriot (1403–67), universally known as Scanderbeg (in complimentary reference to Alexander the Great, i.e. Iskander Bey), had remained invincible. Carried off by the Turks as a child, he had early attracted the attention of Murad, under whom he had won military distinction. Later he preferred the rôle of patriot to that of commander in the sultan's service, and in 1443 had deserted with a company of Albanian soldiers. For some twenty years he valiantly inspired and successfully headed resistance against Turkish aggression. The immediate collapse of his country after his death proves the value of his leadership.

Hungary stood as the bulwark of the west, keeping hold on the key-fortress of Belgrade. Though the Hungarian patriot, Janos Corvinus Hunyadi, entrusted with the governorship of the country after the death of Ladislas at Varna, was defeated at Kossovo (1448), the Turks had not followed up their victory —they had the greater prize of Constantinople in view. After its fall Hunyadi realized that the best he could do. without assistance from western Europe, was to hold the line of the Danube against their assaults. South of the river was the great fortress of Belgrade, which, he foresaw, the sultan would make every effort to capture. He therefore put it in a state of defence.

Mohammed arrived before Belgrade with an immense force of 300,000 men and the most formidable siege artillery of the age. Hunyadi relieved the town. and all the sultan's efforts to carry the fortress by storm failed ; having lost 40.000 men, he retreated (1456), leaving behind much of his artillery. Soon after this great service to Hungary and to Europe Hunyadi died, worn out by strain of war and defence. His son Matthias Corvinus (1443–90) was elected king in his stead in 1458.

Famed for the splendour of his embassies, Matthias was chiefly concerned with revising the laws, promoting literature, the arts and education, and supporting the general interests of the people against oppression from the nobles. In 1465 he founded the university of Pressburg, adding later an observatory. He introduced printing into Hungary, which through him participated in the progress of the Renaissance.

Venice dared to enter single-handed on a valiant fifteen years' struggle with the Turks by sea, though in the end forced to own defeat and make terms with Mohammed. It was only when, in 1480, Europe was startled by the conqueror's seizure of Otranto that the west awoke to an imminent menace; but the menace passed with Mohammed's death next year, the accession of his feeble son Bajazet, and the evacuation of Otranto. The Ottoman advance was postponed for a generation, and, on the other hand, no attempt was made to extrude the Turks from Europe, though in the farther west Islam as a power was on the point of being eliminated as an immediate result of the union of the crowns of the two major Spanish kingdoms of Castile and Aragon, a union which laid the foundation of the Spanish power which was to play such a prominent part in the 16th century.

In 1469 Ferdinand, the crown prince of Aragon, married Isabella of Castile, who a year before had been officially recognized as heiress to her brother, Henry IV, the reigning king of Castile; she succeeded him on the throne in 1474, while Ferdinand succeeded to the thrones of Aragon and Sicily in 1479, the year from which dates the joint rule over Spain of Ferdinand and Isabella, though, technically, they were not king and queen of Spain but king of Aragon and queen of Castile.

Though Ferdinand had succeeded to Sicily he had not obtained Naples. In 1442 Alfonso V of Aragon had acquired the latter crown, the reigning Angevin house having died out. The last queen, Joanna II, had nominated as her heir, at different times, Alfonso and her own very remote kinsman Louis of Anjou. In the conflict which naturally ensued Alfonso won, and he was himself succeeded in Naples, but not in Aragon, by his illegitimate son Ferrante, whose title might at any time be challenged either by his legitimate cousin Ferdinand of Aragon (whose claim was made good in 1504) or by the head of the house of Anjou—as we shall presently see actually happening—though for the time Ferrante's title was not disputed. In another quarter Milan too became a bone of contention, the French house of Orleans having a provisional claim there by descent from the daughter of Gian Galeazzo Visconti, the first duke. In both cases the claim ultimately reverted to a French king, because Anjou lapsed to the crown in 1480, and a later Louis of Orleans himself succeeded to the French throne in 1498 as Louis XII.

In Milan, on the death of the last Visconti duke, his place had been taken after a short interval, in 1450, by Francesco Sforza, who rose to be a dominant figure in medieval Italy. In Florence the Medici family had established a personal ascendancy, which was definitely confirmed when Lorenzo " the Magnificent " became its head in 1469 at the age of twenty-one. A many-sided ruler, this crafty and able politician towered by reason of personality. In the Renaissance he was the patron and protector of all artists.

The close alliance between Matthias Corvinus and George Podiebrad, the elected king of Bohemia, which had at first seemed probable, would have been an invaluable defence against Ottoman aggression, but they were divided by religious antagonism, Podiebrad being a Hussite ; and on his death in 1471 Bohemia elected Ladislas of Poland to the crown which Matthias had hoped to acquire. We may here note that the three crowns of Bohemia, Hungary and Poland were temporarily united by the election of Ladislas in Hungary on the death of Matthias in 1490, after he had added to his kingdom extensive Hapsburg territories, which were later recovered from Ladislas by Frederick III's son Maximilian. Ultimately the crowns of both Hungary and Bohemia, though remaining elective in theory, did in fact pass to the Hapsburgs, much as did the imperial crown itself.

The Council of Constance had removed a great scandal but had not restored the spiritual authority of the Church or dethroned the papacy in favour of conciliar supremacy. In effect, Eugenius had defeated the Council of Basel ; while, curiously enough, Pius II (1458–64) was the only pope who was inspired by anything resembling the ideals of the great popes of old. But it was with the election of Sixtus IV (1471–84) that the positive degradation of the papacy set in, though it did not reach its nadir till the accession of Roderigo Borgia as Alexander VI in 1492. For while each pope had pursued the old fatal policy of aiming first at political ascendancy, it was reserved to Sixtus to use his sacred office as a means to the advancement of his own kinsmen, and openly to ignore moral and spiritual considerations in the development of a purely secular policy.

LESSON 44

A Glance at the Medieval East
(See plate 52)

BEFORE concluding the medieval history of the West, we turn aside in this Lesson to touch upon that of the East— that is, of that great portion of Asia which lay practically outside the ken of the peoples of Europe from the days of Trajan to the close of the 15th century : India, China and Japan, which were all the homes of civilizations older than those of Greece and Rome ; and central Asia, occupied from time immemorial by hordes, nomadic or semi-nomadic, of Mongols, Turks, Huns, Tartars—none of whom ever created a national civilization, but from whom issued, westward, southward and eastward, periodical waves of destruction.

Those were the days of the Gupta empire (*see* Lesson 25, Volume 4, page 436) in northern India. Immediately afterwards came a great incursion of the White Huns into India. In the 7th century a great monarch named Harsha appeared who subjugated and restored order throughout northern India.

Islam had now entered on its conquering career ; presently we find the Arabs establishing themselves in Sindh, but not extending their conquests or Moslem influence. The conflict between Mahomedans and Hindus begins with the long series of incursions conducted by Mahmud of Ghazni, spread over the first thirty years of the 11th century, when Persia and Afghanistan were provinces of the Bagdad khaliphate, though Afghanistan was virtually an independent kingdom under a Turkish dynasty. Mahmud was, however, a plunderer rather than a champion of the Moslem faith. He smote and pillaged mercilessly, his attacks being fiercest against the descendants of the Arabs in

Sindh, who opposed him, while the Hindus of the Punjab, the only Indian province which he definitely annexed to the Ghazni sultanate, were usually left to observe their religious rites in peace. Nevertheless, the Mahomedan invasions introduced for the first time into India a permanently alien element, which could not be absorbed. To the fanatically monotheistic Moslem, with his definite faith, Hinduism was an abomination of polytheism and idolatry, which admitted of no compromise.

The actual Mahomedan conquest or domination of northern India began only about a century and a half after Mahmud's death, with the invasions of Mohammed of Ghor (1175–1206), whose arms were carried victoriously as far as Bengal, which never again escaped the grip of the Moslem sultans. The armies of the Indian princes were no match in organization, discipline or armament for the professional fighting men, mainly Turk or Afghan, of whom the Moslem troops were composed. A victory was usually a very decisive rout followed by a merciless massacre.

Mohammed of Ghor subdued much of northern India himself, but the greater part of the conquest, including the taking of Delhi, which he made his capital, was performed by his slave Kutb-ud-Din. He, when his master was slain in 1206, leaving no heir, became the real founder of Moslem rule in India and of the dynasty of the Slave kings, which endured till 1294, when its place was taken by the Khilji dynasty.

Ala-ud-Din Khilji distinguished himself by enunciating the general principle that Hindus were to be allowed nothing more than a bare subsistence. His armies ravaged far into the Deccan, and he also subjected to Islam Rajputana and Madura. The Rajputs held out in their stronghold of Chitor until further resistance was obviously hopeless ; then all the women gathered together to perish in a vast holocaust, and, the fires having been kindled, the men sallied forth to fight till all were killed.

The succeeding Tughlak dynasty (1320–88), founded by Tughlak Shah, who built a new suburb to Delhi as his imperial residence and named it Tughlakabad, was continued by Mohammed, whose reign was an orgy of cruelties, and ended with Firoz Shah (1351–88), a better ruler than his predecessors, who strove to restore sound government. But the foundations of the empire were so sapped by Mohammed that the Moslem empire declined, and ten years after his death came the invasion of Timur—the Tamerlane of western literature.

The Delhi empire, though not the Mohammedan domination, was thus already moribund when the century closed. Tamerlane completed its downfall by turning aside, on the way to the overthrowing of Bajazet at Angora, to devastate the Punjab and upper Hindostan, sack Delhi, and indulge his predilection for miscellaneous slaughter. In the 15th century the empire disintegrated into a number of warring Mahomedan kingdoms ; towards its close an Afghan dynasty was establishing itself at Delhi when the Europeans were on the point of making their first landing. But it was a new conqueror from beyond the mountains of the north-west, one who could reckon among his ancestors the Mongol Jenghiz Khan, conqueror of central Asia in the 13th century, and the Turk Tamerlane, Babar the founder of the Mogul dynasty, who in the next century was to re-create the Mahomedan empire.

Japan from time immemorial has dwelt in a splendid isolation, in spite of a recurrent attraction to enterprise in Korea. In Japan, under the sacred imperial family of the Mikados, a sort of feudal system, the lordship of a land-owning military caste, developed as in Europe in the early middle ages. In the 13th century a baronial leader assumed the imperial functions, though not the title. The Shogun, or commander-in-chief, became the effective head of the state, and the government remained the government of the Shogunate, despite periodical attempts on the part of Mikados to recover control, until the 19th century. The other outstanding event of Japanese history in the Middle Ages was the triumphant repulse in 1265 and 1274 of the invasion of the mighty Mongol emperor of China, Kublai Khan—a repulse which is the equivalent in Japanese history of the Greek overthrow of the Persians at Marathon and Salamis.

China under Kublai Khan. In the early medieval period China appears to have enjoyed what was traditionally one of her " Golden Ages " under the Tang dynasty—tempered by attacks of the Khitai Tartars, from whom the Europeans derive the name of Cathay. But in the 13th century China was conquered by the successors of Jenghiz Khan, who gave her a very famous ruler in that Kublai Khan (1214-94) who failed to extend his dominion over Japan. Unlike most Mongols, he was not a destroyer, but a constructive statesman. His picture has been left us by the Venetian traveller, Marco Polo, who set out to visit China in 1271 and arrived at Kublai Khan's summer residence, Chandu (none other than the Xanadu of Coleridge's poem) in 1275, when the Mongol conquest of China had been completed. Kublai Khan's capital was at Cambaluc, which occupied much the same site as Peking. Polo gives inimitably graphic details of the emperor, his court, its feasts and festivals, the splendour of his palaces, gardens and pavilions, and of the most beautiful and attractive of his four empresses, the Great Consort Jamui Khatun, who exercised an amiable influence over Kublai.

The Mongol dynasty, however, degenerated after Kublai Khan's death, and was overthrown by the Chinese patriot Hung Wu, monk, soldier, statesman and reformer, who delivered China from the foreign oppressor. Though again, after his death in 1399, the Ming dynasty which he founded did not maintain its first vigour, it was still surviving when the 15th century closed.

LESSON 45

Western Europe at the Close of the Middle Ages

(See plates 53 and 54)

DURING the 15th century the European political system based on feudalism was, as we have seen, breaking up. Volcanic forces, intellectual and religious, were in operation against the rigidity and " communism " of the Middle Ages ; reconstruction was already taking place from which individualism, nationalism and humanism emerged to separate medieval from modern history. In England the breakdown of the Lancastrian monarchy after the death of Henry V brought about the collapse of the prestige he had won for her as a military power on the Continent, and culminated in the collapse of the Lancastrian monarchy itself, in the faction wars of the Roses, which at the same time exhausted the baronage. Thus after the accession of Henry VII (1485–1509) and his marriage to the heiress of York, that astute prince was able to give the *coup de grâce* to the threatened development of baronial domination, and to establish the effective supremacy of the Crown for three generations of Tudors.

The great French nobles had always been more in the position of almost independent princes than had the barons in England.

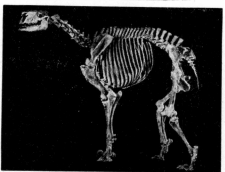

FAUNA OF THE MIOCENE.   Fossilized skeletons of :
top, Mastodon ; centre, Hippotherium or Lipparion ;
bottom, Moropus ("sloth-foot ").   **GEOLOGY 21**

American Museum of Natural History, New York

MONSTERS OF THE ICE AGE. Above, the woolly rhinoceros, and (left) a mammoth—two animals which the cave-men hunted in the dawn of human history, but which have long been extinct. GEOLOGY 22

Courtesy of American Museum of Natural History

A SUBMERGED FOREST. In addition to the catastrophic disturbances produced by volcanic eruptions, the earth's crust is subject to secular movements, evidenced by raised beaches and submerged forests, both of which are illustrated in Britain. This photo is of a submerged forest at Leasowe Castle on the Cheshire coast. GEOLOGY 23

Plate 42   *Volume VI*

SALADIN. Born 1137, son of a Kurdish general who was governor of Damascus, he was so successful in war with the Egyptians that he was made vizier in 1170; and in 1175, after the death of Nur-ed-din, sultan of Syria, made himself master of the realm. In 1187 he attacked the Latin kingdom in Palestine and by his capture of Jerusalem evoked the Third Crusade. He died at Damascus in 1193. HISTORY: MEDIEVAL 37

TRAVELLING TO THE HOLY LAND. The Crusades were responsible for a flood of literature, historical and descriptive. One manuscript, the " De Passagiis in Terram Sanctam," a Venetian work produced in the thirteenth century just after the crusading age was over, gives admirable pictures (of which this is one) of crusaders and pilgrims en route for the Holy Land. HISTORY: MEDIEVAL 37

From Kügler, "Geschichte der Kreuzzüge"

JUDICIAL COMBAT IN NORMAN ENGLAND. Ordeal by battle was a Frankish custom introduced into England by the Normans. In criminal charges accuser and accused fought in person, and the accused, if vanquished, was forthwith hanged or mutilated. If the accuser lost he was fined sixty shillings and became " infamous " as a perjurer. Innocent III attempted, though not with entire success, to suppress the custom.

HISTORY : MEDIEVAL 37

From the Curia Regis Roll, No. 216. Record Office

INNOCENT III (1160–1216) Educated at Rome, Bologna and Paris, he held various offices in the papal court before he succeeded Celestine III in the Chair of St. Peter in 1198. He devoted himself unremittingly to the restoration of the temporal power of the Papacy, and was very largely successful in reducing the monarchs of Europe to a state of vassalage.

HISTORY : MEDIEVAL 37

Church of the Sacro Speco, Subiaco; photo. Moscioni

Plate 44

Volume VI

The Hundred Years' War itself had opened as a struggle between the French monarchy and its powerful feudatory England. Its renewal in the 15th century had been made practicable because Burgundy sided with the Plantagenet against the reigning Valois, and the Plantagenet was finally defeated, inevitably, because Burgundy reverted to its French allegiance for the purposes of the war. The expulsion of the English enabled Charles VII and his ministers to carry out administrative reforms—notably the creation (1439) of a royal force under strict discipline and control of the Crown, independent of the feudal levies under control of the feudatories, and absorbing or suppressing the " free companies," which had, when not in fighting service, plundered and menaced the peace of citizens— thus strengthening the central government against feudal disintegration. Philip of Burgundy was more concerned with the great and wealthy dominions which had accrued to him outside France, and with erecting the whole into a first-class principality, than in resisting the centralizing process within France.

The practice which had arisen in the 13th century of distributing among the royal princes the great fiefs which passed to the crown by lapse or forfeiture, had originally been intended to strengthen the royal family as against the old feudal baronage ; but it had created a new nobility of " Princes of the Lilies," or blood royal, who were as jealous of their own privileges as the dukes and counts of old, and as resentful of the royal encroachments thereon. The reforms of Charles VII set the Dauphin Louis at the head of the " Princes' " active resistance, and Louis himself was driven to take refuge at the court of Burgundy. But when in 1461 he ascended the throne as Louis XI, he set himself to break the power of the " Princes of the Lilies," while his young cousin, Charles the Bold, dominated by hostility to France, became their leader. In the long duel which followed Charles was no match for Louis in craft. Louis' diplomacy implanted discords and broke up the combination of the " Princes," directed against the royal usurpations in the Civil War of the Public Weal, though there were moments when the defeat of Louis seemed all but inevitable.

Charles, however, developed the more ambitious objective of reviving the old Middle Kingdom of Burgundy between France and Germany stretching from the Rhine mouth to the Rhône mouth. The intrigues of Louis undermined his schemes ; but in the pursuit of them he set about development of his ambitions on the other side of the Rhine, laying claim to sovereignty over the Swiss confederation. The Switzers defied him, defeated him, and finally overthrew and killed him at the battle of Nancy in 1477. With his death perished his project His daughter and heiress Mary was married in the same year to Maximilian, the son and heir of the emperor Frederick III of Hapsburg. The Burgundian dominions remained under her sovereignty not that of her husband and passed not to him, but to their son Philip, and after him to his infant son Charles, who himself, as Maximilian's grandson was heir to the Hapsburg dominion, and through his own mother, Philip's wife, Joanna of Castile, to the crown of Spain. This aggregation of sovereignties in the hands of one prince, who also succeeded to the imperial crown, was not completed, however, till Maximilian's death in 1519.

On the death of Charles the Bold, Louis tried in vain to claim the Burgundian succession. but had to be satisfied with retaining the French duchy as well as Artois and Picardy, while the Netherlands and the trans-Rhenish county remained with the duchess and continued to be known generally as Burgundy. The crown absorbed the French duchy, Champagne, and other major fiefs, Brittany alone retaining some of its old independence : by the deliberate employment of ministers who were not of the nobility at all, but were wholly creatures of his own, he had gathered into his own hands complete control of the administration. The regency for his infant son Charles VIII was conducted by his very capable elder daughter, Anne of Beaujeu ; and there was no recrudescence of the feudal disintegration. Later the marriage of Charles to the young duchess of Brittany brought that fief, too, into the royal control.

Frederick III of Hapsburg, mainly by good luck, kept the imperial dignity from his accession in 1440 till his death in 1493 ; during his life he succeeded to the inheritances of his Hapsburg cousins, heretofore divided between different branches of the family. His son Maximilian had secured the ultimate addition of Burgundy by his marriage to the daughter of Charles the Bold, and his own succession to the imperial throne by his election as king of the Romans in 1486, during his father's lifetime ; and he at once set about recovering the territories of which his father had been deprived by Matthias (Corvinus) of Hungary.

CLOSE OF THE MIDDLE AGES

We turn now to the consolidation of Spain and the beginning of her expansion in the New World, under Ferdinand and Isabella, which opens with the actual union of the crowns of Castile and Aragon in 1479. This enabled the two monarchs each to lend support to the other in their respective kingdoms, since jealousy prevented their subjects from making common cause against the rulers, so that the Crown was greatly strengthened in both. In the main, however, their subjects were with them—in the establishment of the Inquisition as an engine for the suppression of heresy, since Spain had always been clergy-ridden ; in the persecution of the Jews and Mahomedans ; and in the war which destroyed the last relic of Moorish independence in the peninsula of which they had once been masters and into which they had introduced so much culture.

But six years before the conquest of Granada the Portuguese Bartholomew Diaz opened the ocean route to the East by rounding the Cape of Good Hope ; and in the year of that conquest, 1492, the Genoese Christopher Columbus, in the service of the Spanish monarchs, voyaged across the Atlantic expecting to land on the shores of India, and found the West Indies instead. These discoveries produced during the Renaissance period a vast and sudden change in economic conditions. Next year the new Pope, Alexander VI—Roderigo Borgia (1431-1503)—issued a bull bestowing all the lands which might be or had been discovered —upon Portugal those east, and upon Spain those west of a line drawn down the Atlantic from north to south, the papal authority being as yet unchallenged.

And then in 1494 young Charles VIII of France invaded Italy to assert his claim as head of the historic house of Anjou to the crown of Naples, now worn by Ferrante, the illegitimate son of Alfonso V of Aragon, raising hopes in some patriotic Italians of a coming unification of Italy—doomed to blank disappointment. But here our narrative of the Middle Ages closes, for these last events mark the starting-point of Modern History.

This Lesson concludes our Course in Ancient and Medieval History.

LESSON 42

On the Geometric Mean

THE geometric mean M between two quantities A and B must satisfy the equation $M^2 = AB$, which may take the form $A/M = M/B$. Let $A/M = k$, then $A = kM$ and $M = kB$, whence $A = k^2B$, i.e. $A/B = k^2$.

Hence $A/B - 1 = k^2 - 1$; whence $(A - B)/B = k^2 - 1$, etc. This is the general case which is illustrated geometrically in Fig. 1. There MN is the diameter of a circle with centre O. RS is any semi-chord at right angles to MN, then $RS^2 = MR.RN$, i.e. RS is the geometric mean between MR and RN. The geometric condition here is that the sum of the two quantities given shall be used as the diameter of the circle.

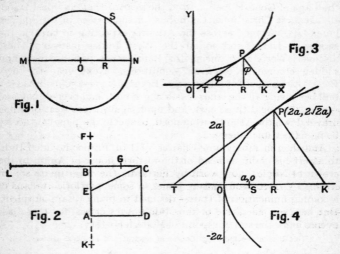

Fig. 1

Fig. 3

Fig. 2

P(2a, 2√2a)

Fig. 4

A special case of the geometric mean occurs when the geometric mean plus the smaller quantity add to equal the larger quantity. Using the values A and M and B, the condition has been specially added that M, when found, must be such that $M = (A - B)$. This condition implies that the constant k must be such that it equals $(k^2 - 1)$; for if $M = (A - B)$, then $M/B = k = (k^2 - 1)$. This constant is therefore unique; for when $k = (k^2 - 1)$, $k = (\frac{1}{2} + \frac{1}{2}\sqrt{5})$.

The geometrical construction depends upon the square. In Fig. 2 ABCD is a square, E is the mid-point of AB; then if AB = 1, EC = $\frac{1}{2}\sqrt{5}$. EB is produced to F so that EF = EC. BF = $(\frac{1}{2}\sqrt{5} - \frac{1}{2})$; BG is taken in BC such that BG = BF. Then GC = $1 - (\frac{1}{2}\sqrt{5} - \frac{1}{2}) = 1\frac{1}{2} - \frac{1}{2}\sqrt{5} = (\frac{1}{2}\sqrt{5} - \frac{1}{2})^2$. Whence GC.CB = BG^2, i.e. G divides BC into a mean ratio.

EA is produced so that EK = EC, i.e. BK = $(\frac{1}{2}\sqrt{5} + \frac{1}{2})$. CB is produced to L so that BL = BK, then CL = $1\frac{1}{2} + \frac{1}{2}\sqrt{5} = (\frac{1}{2} + \frac{1}{2}\sqrt{5})^2$, whence BC.CL = BL^2, i.e. L divides BC into extreme ratio. But, as was shown in connexion with the carving of a cube, the following ratios are equal:

$$(1\frac{1}{2}\sqrt{5} + \frac{1}{2}\sqrt{5}) : (\frac{1}{2}\sqrt{5} + \frac{1}{2})$$
$$(\frac{1}{2}\sqrt{5} + \frac{1}{2}) : 1$$
$$1 : (\frac{1}{2}\sqrt{5} - \frac{1}{2})$$
$$(\frac{1}{2}\sqrt{5} - \frac{1}{2}) : (1\frac{1}{2} - \frac{1}{2}\sqrt{5})$$

i.e. LC : LB = LB : BC = BC : BG = BG : GC.

The order of values beginning with the largest is LC, LB, BC, BG, GC; let the length of LC = k, then the values are, using the P notation of Volume 3, page 511, where P = $(\frac{1}{2}\sqrt{5} - \frac{1}{2})$ and $(1 + P) = (\frac{1}{2}\sqrt{5} + \frac{1}{2})$ k, kP, kP^2, kP^3, kP^4; let the length of GC, the smallest, be m, then the values are

$m(1 + P)^4$, $m(1 + P)^3$, $m(1 + P)^2$, $m(1 + P)$, m; and the following equations hold: LC = LB + BC; LB = BC + BG; and BC = BG + GC; and LC = 2BC + BG = 3BG + 2GC, etc.

The rate of increase of expanding spherical volumes such as spherical balloons, soap bubbles, etc., may now be investigated.

If V = volume and x = diameter, V = $(\pi/6)x^3$. If x increases slightly to $(x + \delta x)$ and the corresponding increase in volume is δV, then

$$V + \delta V = (\pi/6)(x + \delta x)^3 = (\pi/6)(x^3 + 3x^2\delta x + 3x(\delta x)^2 + (\delta x)^3)$$

whence $\delta V/\delta x = (\pi/6)(3x^2 + 3x.\delta x + (\delta x)^2)$

whence the average rate of increase of volume, indicated by $\delta V/\delta x$, when δx is sufficiently small to be negligible, is $(\pi/6)(3x^2)$.

Practically, when the diameter is 4 inches and the diameter increases by 1% of itself per second the volume increases ($(\pi/6) =$

0·5236), by 1% of 4 times 0·5236 (48), i.e. 1·005 cubic inches per second.

Obviously, if the diameter is 7 inches and the increase in the diameter is 0·1 in. per second, the vol. increases 0·1 times 0·5236 (147), i.e. 7·7 cubic inches per second.

Of course, it is obvious that this problem is the problem of finding the volume of metal of exceeding relative thinness which makes a hollow sphere. The difference between the outside and inside areas of the metal skin is so small as to be of no account, hence the volume of metal is the surface area of the sphere, which is practically constant within the limits of the experiment, times its thickness. In the first case a diameter of 4 inches is increased to 4·04 inches; the radius of the sphere is 2 inches, the thickness is 0·02 inches; the surface is 16 = 50·24, the volume of the skin is 1·005 cu. in. In the second case the radius is 3·5, which increases to 3·55; the surface $49\pi = 153\cdot86$, the vol. = 7·69 cu. in., when $\pi = 3\cdot14$.

In Fig. 3 a point P is taken on a curve so that PT is tangent to the curve at P, the curve being expressed by $y = f(x)$, the code for " y is a function of x." Obviously, the rate of increase of y in terms of x at P is indicated by dy/dx; i.e. PR/TR = $\tan\phi$ = dy/dx.

The intercept between the foot of the perpendicular from P, i.e. R, and T is labelled the sub-tangent; whence
$$\text{sub-tangent} = RT = y(dx/dy).$$
PK perpendicular to the tangent at P is labelled the normal at P, and the corresponding intercept KR is the sub-normal, whence sub-normal = KR. PR tan φ = y (dy/dx).

By Pythagoras: (i) (normal)^2 = PK^2 = $y^2(1 + (dy/dx)^2)$
(ii) (tangent)^2 = PT^2 = PR^2 + RT^2 = $y^2(1 + (dx/dy)^2)$ = $y^2(1 + (dy/dx)^2)/(dy/dx)^2$.

The curve $y^2 = 4ax$ is a parabola with focus, s, at the point (a,O). Such a curve is drawn in Fig. 4.

Differentiating $y^2 = 4ax$, $2y(dy/dx) = 4a$,
whence $(dy/dx) = (2a/y)$ and $(dx/dy) = (y/2a)$,
whence subnormal = $y(dy/dx) = 2a$,
subtangent = $y(dx/dy) = y(y/2a) = 2x$,
(normal)^2 = $y^2(1 + (2a/y)^2) = (y^2 + 4a^2)$,
(tangent)^2 = $(y^2 + 4a^2)/(4a^2/y^2)$.

In order to draw the tangent at P, take T so that OT = OR and join TP.

GEOMETRIC MEAN

To draw the normal at P, make RK = 2a.

Check : (tangent) by formula = $(8a^2 + 4a^2)/(4a^2/8a^2) = 24a^2$
by Pythagoras = $8a^2 + 16a^2 = 24a^2$
(normal) by formula and by Pythagoras = $8a^2 + 4a^2 = 12a^2$.

Drill. 1. Using the P notation, find the geometric mean between P and $(1 + P)$, and between P^3 and $(1 + P)^3$. Evaluate $P^2 + (1 + P)^2$, and $P^2 - (1 - P)^2$, numerically.

2. Draw the graph of the curve $x^2 + y^2 = 12$. Draw the tangent and normal at the point $(2, 2\sqrt{2})$, and find their lengths.

Revision. 1. Differentiate the following functions (the angle = x radians) :

Group C (i) sin x ; (ii) cos x ; (iii) tan x.
Group D (i) $\sin^{-1}x$; (ii) $\cos^{-1}x$; (iii) $\tan^{-1}x$.

2. Find the volume of a piece of circular wire 4 mm. thick used to make the circumference of a circle of a metre radius.

Expansion. Imagine a regular tetrahedron made of glass placed with its base horizontal in the rays of the noonday sun on the summer solstice in lat. $53\frac{1}{2}°$ N., with one face facing south.

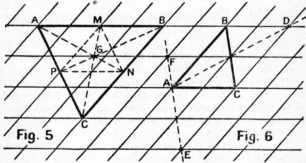

Fig. 5   Fig. 6

Assume that a ray of sunlight which has once passed through the surface remains within the tetrahedron, being completely reflected inwards each time it reaches a surface. Investigate what happens to various rays which enter the glass at different levels.

Solutions to Problems in Lesson 41

Drill (a) ABC is scalene. MP is parallel to BC, and half of it, etc. G is the centroid, and 2GM = GC, etc. (Fig. 5).

(b) ABC is isosceles, AB = AC ; then BC is either a cross diagonal or is parallel to a cross diagonal, *i.e.* is perpendicular to

(359)

AD, angle ABC = angle ACB. The out-centres lie in AD, AE, and AF respectively, and DA is perpendicular to EF, etc. (Fig. 6).

2. Cone $\frac{1}{3}(3\cdot03)\pi(2\cdot997)^2\frac{1}{4}$. Sphere $\frac{1}{6}\pi(3\cdot003)^3$.

Ans. :

$$\text{Weight} = 59\cdot994 \times {}^{12} \times \frac{(3\cdot033)^3}{(3\cdot03)(2\cdot997)^2}$$

$$= 60 (1 - \cdot0001)\frac{3}{2} \frac{(1\cdot011)^3 \cdot 27}{(1\cdot01)(\cdot999)^2 \cdot 27}$$

$$= 90 (1 - \cdot0001)(1\cdot033 + \cdot002 - \cdot01)$$

$$= 90 (1 - \cdot0001)(1\cdot025) = 90 (1\cdot025)$$

$$= 92\cdot25 \text{ i.e. } 92 \text{ correct to two fig.}$$

Expansion. $\alpha = \beta$ and varies from $0°$ at A and B to $90°$ half way between them.

LESSON 43

The Parallelogram in Mathematics

THE parallelogram is a quadrilateral with a minimum of regularity. If attention be first directed towards the shape of the figure, regularity appears in the fact that the figure is due to the intersection of two pairs of parallel lines ; if attention be first directed to size, then regularity appears in the fact that the figure is composed of two pairs of equal lines set in opposition and not in juxtaposition, as in the diamond shape. The facts about the figure are immediately obvious when use is made of parallelogram ruled paper. The figure has two unequal diagonals, which bisect each other. The lengths of these diagonals depend on the set of the sides of the figure, i.e. upon the angle of the parallelogram which controlled the ruling machine. In Fig. 1, ABCD is a unit parallelogram with unit sides connected by the relation AD = m AB, so that a units along AD are equal to ma units along AB set at an angle, θ, so that BAD = BCD = θ. Let AD = a, AB = b, AC = c, BD = d, then $d^2 = a^2 + b^2 - 2 ab \cos \theta$ in the triangle BDA, and $c^2 = a^2 + b^2 + 2ab \cos \theta$ in the triangle CDA ; whence $d^2 = m^2b^2 + b^2 - 2mb^2 \cos \theta = b^2(m^2 + 1 - 2m \cos \theta)$,

THE PARALLELOGRAM

and $c^2 = b^2(m^2 + 1 + 2m \cos \theta)$,
and $d^2/c^2 = (m^2 + 1 - 2m \cos \theta) / (m^2 + 1 + 2m \cos \theta)$,
also $d/a = \sin \theta/\sin ABD$, and $c/a = \sin \theta/\sin BAC$,
i.e. $d/c = \sin BAC/ \sin ABD$, which also follows from any one
of the four triangles into which the parallelogram is divided,
since the diagonals bisect each other.

AD may represent in strength, by its length, and in direction
a force acting at A along AD ; AB may represent, similarly, the
strength and direction of a force acting at A along AB ; hence
AC determines, similarly, the strength and direction of a force
acting at A compounded of the two forces, so that at A a force
represented in strength by the length of AC and acting in the
direction CA would balance the two forces acting at A.

The most interesting practical problems in this connexion
arise in reference to the drift in ships and aeroplanes due to wind
action. If a ship should reach D
from A during a period, while a
wind blowing in the direction AB
is acting upon it, and AB represents relatively the strength of the
wind, then the ship will travel
along the path AC, and reach C
instead of D, and the angle of
deviation from the intended

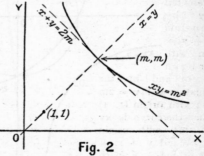

Fig. 1

Fig. 2

course will be CAD.
A ship steaming at 16
knots eastward by com-
pass while a wind is
blowing at 4 knots from
the south - west would
travel at a speed of ap-
prox. 19 knots in a
direction approx. 8° N.
of E. Smoke from the
funnel would steadily
point N.E. and its angle to the ship's course would gradually decrease from 45° to 37°.

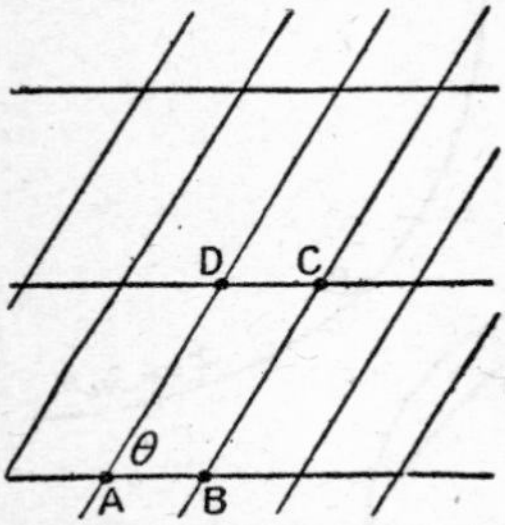

When $xy = m^2$, $y = m^2/x$, whence $dy/dx = - m^2/x^2$. Since
the variable y is not expressed directly as a function of x, the

expression $xy = m^2$ is labelled an implicit function; in the equivalent form $y = m^2/x$ the function is explicit. Using the form $xy = m^2$, where xy is the product of two functions of x, and differentiating both sides of the expression, then $y + x (dy/dx) = 0$, i.e. $dy/dx = - y/x$, which is equivalent to $dy/dx = - m^2/x^2$, for $y = m^2/x$.

In Fig. 2 the graph of $xy = m^2$ is drawn; it is a rectangular hyperbola, with an axis of symmetry $x = y$.

This axis cuts the graph at the point (m, m). The tangent to the graph at this point is the line $x + y = 2m$, and the tangent of the angle of slope is 1, which agrees with $dy/dx = -m^2/x^2 = - 1$ when $x = m$.

If the origin be shifted to the point $(1, 1)$, then this line is indicated by $x + y = 2m - 2$; and the curve is indicated by the expression $(y + 1) (x + 1) = m^2$; i.e. $y + x + xy = m^2 - 1$. For this function $dy/dx = - m^2/(x + 1)^2$, but $x = m - 1$, so that $dy/dx = - (m - 1)^2/x^2$.

Hence the same line, tangent to the same curve, is represented by the equation $x + y = 2m$ with origin $(0, 0)$ and by the equation $x + y = 2m - 2$ with origin $(1, 1)$ when the curve is $xy = m^2$ with origin $(0, 0)$ and $y + x + xy = m^2 - 1$ with origin $(1, 1)$. In the expression $x + y + xy = 3n^2$; $y = - \frac{1}{2} x \pm \frac{1}{2} (12n^2 - 3x^2)^{\frac{1}{2}}$.

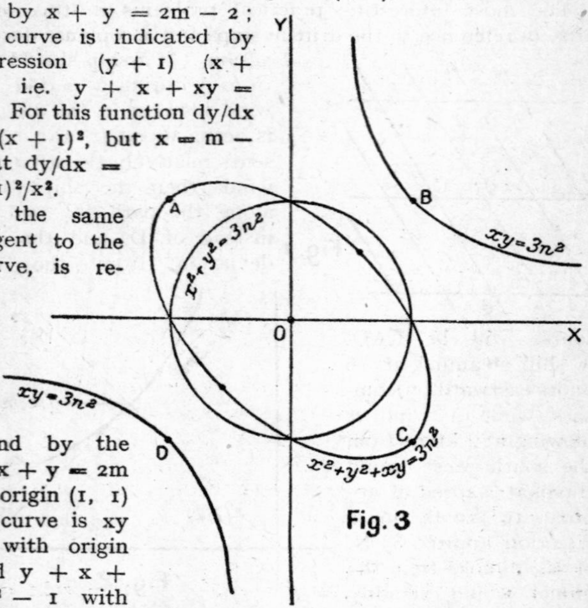

Fig. 3

In Fig. 3 the square ABCD has corners at B $(\sqrt{3}n, \sqrt{3}n)$, C $(\sqrt{3}n, - \sqrt{3}n)$, D $(- \sqrt{3}n, - \sqrt{3}n)$, A $(- \sqrt{3}n, \sqrt{3}n)$.

THE PARALLELOGRAM

The curves $xy = 3n^2$, a rectangular hyperbola, and $x^2 + y^2 = 3n^2$, a circle, and $x^2 + y^2 + xy = 3n^2$, an ellipse, are drawn.

The line $x = y$ cuts these curves at the points : (hyperbola) $(\sqrt{3}n, \sqrt{3}n)$ and $(-\sqrt{3}n, -\sqrt{3}n)$, (circle) $(\frac{1}{2}\sqrt{6}n, \frac{1}{2}\sqrt{6}n)$ and $(-\frac{1}{2}\sqrt{6}n, -\frac{1}{2}\sqrt{6}n)$, (ellipse) (n, n) and $(-n, -n)$. The tangents to the curves at these points are respectively $x + y = 2\sqrt{3}n$ or $-2\sqrt{3}n$ (hyperbola), $\sqrt{6}n$, or $-\sqrt{6}n$ (circle), or $2n$, or $-2n$ (ellipse).

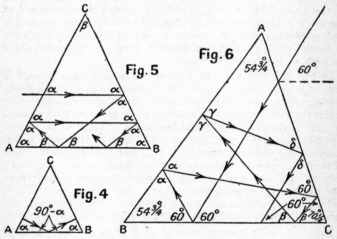

Fig. 5　Fig. 6　Fig. 4

The major axis of the ellipse is the line $x + y = 0$, which cuts the ellipse at two of the corners of the square, where the tangents to the ellipse are the lines

$$x - y = 2\sqrt{3}n \text{ or } -2\sqrt{3}n.$$

The lines $x + y = 2n$, etc., are parallels, with the tangent of their angle of slope $= -1$.

When $xy = 3n^2$, $dy/dx = -3n^2/x^2$, whence $dy/dx = -1$ at the point where $x = \sqrt{3}n$.

When $x^2 + y^2 = 3n^2$, $y = \pm(3n^2 - x^2)^{-\frac{1}{2}}$, $dy/dx = -x(3n^2 - x^2)^{-\frac{1}{2}}$, and again $dy/dx = -1$ at the point where $x = \pm\frac{1}{2}\sqrt{6}n$.

When $x^2 + y^2 + xy = 3n^2$, $y = -\frac{1}{2}x \pm \frac{1}{2}(12n^2 - 3x^2)^{\frac{1}{2}}$, $dy/dx = -\frac{1}{2} \pm 1\frac{1}{2}x(12n^2 - 3x^2)^{-\frac{1}{2}}$ and again $dy/dx =$

— 1, when $x = \pm$ n. Also $dy/dx = +$ 1, when $x = \pm \sqrt{3}$n ; and the lines $x - y = \pm 2\sqrt{3}$ have a slope of which the tangent $= +$ 1 and are the tangents to the ellipse at the points where $x = \pm \sqrt{3}$n.

In Fig. 4, in the triangle ABC, CA = CB. A line perpendicular to AC meets AB at the angle $(90 - a)$, is reflected from AB at an angle $(90 - a)$ and meets BC perpendicularly. If BC is a reflector, then the line is reflected back again along its original path. In Fig. 5 the incident line leaves AC at an angle a, equal to the angle CAB or CBA, is reflected from CB to meet AB at the angle β, is reflected at the angle β (= ACB), and meets CA and is reflected from CA at angle a, and continues the cycle until it meets CA at A. If A is a reflector, it returns backward along its path in the reverse direction.

In Fig. 6, AC = CB and ABC is the cross section through a regular tetrahedron of which AB is an edge and C the opposite corner. A ray of sunlight falls on AC, the median of a face, and enters the tetrahedron ; it is assumed to continue its path to meet BC, the median of a horizontal face at 60°. Angle ACB = $70\frac{1}{2}$°, and ABC = CAB = $54\frac{3}{4}$° approx. The path of the ray which is continuously reflected from AB, BC, and CA is shown. The respective angles of incidence and reflection are 60°, $a = 65\frac{1}{4}$°, 60°, $\beta = 49\frac{1}{2}$, $\gamma = 75\frac{3}{4}$, $\delta = 49\frac{1}{2}$, 60, when the cycle begins again. The ray can never reach either B or C, and cannot reach AB or BC or CA perpendicularly, hence the path is never reversed, and the plane ABC is illuminated except a small piece near B.

Drill. 1. Solve simultaneously $x^2 + y^2 = 3n^2$ and $x^2 + y^2 + xy = 3n^2$. Check your solutions against the solution in Fig. 3 above.

2. A ship is sailing N.E. at 16 knots. An E. wind is blowing at 4 knots. Find (a) the speed of motion ; (b) the course of the ship ; (c) the distance at 5.10 p.m. between its funnel and a particle of smoke (assumed to be continuously visible) which leaves the funnel at 5 p.m.

Revision. 1. Graph the equation $x^2 + xy + y^2 = 12$. What happens to all the straight lines through the origin which are terminated at the curve ? Shift the origin to (2, 1) and find the equation of the curve.

2. Graph the equation $x^2 + xy + y^2 = 6$. Find the equation of the major axis. Slew the curve until the major axis is (i)

$y = 0$, (ii) $x = 0$, (iii) turned through 90. Find the three new equations of the curve.

3. On the same axes graph (i) $y = x^3 + 2x^2 + 3x + 4$; (ii) $y = 3x^2 + 4x + 3$; (iii) $y = 6x + 4$.

4. Draw the triangle ABC inside a circle. Bisect angle BAC by AD meeting the circumference in D and cutting BC in X. Prove that the rectangle BA.AC = the square on AX plus the rectangle BX.XC.

Expansion. When a square or a rectangle ABCD is taken away from a larger square or rectangle AEFG the six-sided figure left, BEFGDC, is called a gnomon. Find expressions for the relative areas of the gnomon in terms of the original square or rectangle. Find the pattern wherein the small square is $\frac{1}{4}$ the original square and wherein the remainder ($\frac{3}{4}$) is divided into 4 equal gnomons. Apply this to the rectangle. Examine whether the pattern holds when $1/n^2$, $(n^2 - 1)/n^2$, and n^2 be substituted for $\frac{1}{4}$, $\frac{3}{4}$, and 4 respectively.

Solutions to Problems in Lesson 42

Drill. 1. 1, 1, 3, ($\sqrt{5} - 2$).

2. Normal = radius = $2\sqrt{3}$. Tangent = $2\sqrt{6}$.

Revision. 1. Group C (i) cos x; (ii) — sin x; (iii) sec^2 x.

Group D (i) $1/\cos$ $y = (1 - x^2)^{-\frac{1}{2}}$; (ii) — $1/\cos$ $y = -(1 - x^2)^{-\frac{1}{2}}$; (iii) $\cos^2 y = (1 + x^2)^{-1}$.

2. $y = \pi x^2$, where y = the area of the circle and x = the radius; $dy/dx = 2\pi x$, assuming that the increase in the diameter is negligible, $2\pi x$ = the length of wire, and its vol. = 2π metres times 4π sq. mm. = 79 c.c.

Expansion. See above.

LESSON 44

A Study in Averages

A NUMBER of small tetrahedra, identically equal and each with a blue and a green and a red and a black face, were mixed and thrown on a perfectly horizontal table. They were examined and note was made of the colour of the face which was in contact with the table. This is a description of a hypothetical experiment. If there were a million tetrahedra, we should expect the result to be almost exactly a quarter of a million of each colour. Were we to find a definite preponderance of one colour we should seek for a special explanation of the anomaly.

If there were one tetrahedron and it were thrown a million times, we should expect almost exactly a quarter of a million cases of each colour.

Were the tetrahedra numbered from one to a million serially and were they thrown a hundred times we should not expect that each of the tetrahedra would be recorded thus : black 25, red 25, blue 25, green 25.

If we paid attention solely to the records for the red colour we should expect that out of a million some would score for the red all the 101 possible scores, from the minimum zero to the maximum 100. In the mass we are entitled to expect an average uniformity, but when the individuals are considered as identities —having been appropriately labelled—an average uniformity is not expected ; on the contrary, we expect a small number of performances which depart from the average as widely as possible.

Were we to use icosahedra instead of tetrahedra, we add to the labour of counting up the results of the experiment. We reduce the scale of frequency of any happening because we have enlarged the range within which the happenings may occur, but we may expect analogous results : a small number of extreme cases, and a steadily increasing frequency up to a maximum frequency for the average performance.

We may now suppose that we introduce a bias into the experiment. We may suppose that the material of which the solids are made is not uniform throughout, with the consequence that the C.G. of each solid does not always coincide with the centre of the shape. It is not necessary to suppose that the C.G. is very far away from its theoretical position for a uniform solid. In a million solids we should expect to find the distance out of position to be repeated in much the same sort of way as the red colours happened—few freaks and many averages. We should expect also that the position of the C.G. relative to specific faces of the solid would be almost uniformly repeated, i.e. the C.G. would be nearest to a black face as often as it would be nearest to a red face, and so on for each of the 20 faces.

When these biased solids are thrown down we should expect that they would come to rest usually on the face nearest to the

C.G., but we should expect also a number of cases when the solid came to rest on faces adjacent to the nearest face, and this tendency to departure from the normal habit of stopping on the nearest face would be least marked in those cases when the C.G. was least removed from the geometrical centre of the solid.

Obviously, the frequency of the red colour would be disturbed. The number of reds would depend, normally on the normal distribution in relative position of the C.G. nearest to red but, abnormally on the number of times red was recorded when a colour adjacent to red should have been normally recorded and abnormally also, on the number of times red was not recorded when red should have been normally recorded : we should expect that the two abnormalities would tend to neutralize each other. The total number of reds in the mass would be normal or there-abouts, but when we attend to the individuals we should find a relatively large number of reds which should not have been reds and probably an equal number of non-reds which should have been reds.

If the bias is distributed by chance then the totals should be normal in frequency, but the individuals comprising the totals would be often in their wrong compartment. Consequently, when the throw was repeated we should not expect to find the totals different, but we should expect to find the individuals differently labelled, we should expect as many reds as before, but we should not feel justified in saying " once a red, always a red." This statement—" once a red, always a red "—represents an ideal towards which the results would converge as the distance between the C.G. and the red face was diminished.

Behaviour of a precise character tends in the mass to recur with uniform regularity, but in the individual its frequency depends upon the relation of the individual and the bias. The world is not uniform ; bias is to be expected ; individual behaviour varies. Obviously, both the range of individual variation and the relative frequency of the individual's red and non-red behaviour depend upon the number of times when behaviour has been recorded and also upon the sharpness of the delimitation of red from non-red. But it also depends upon another factor. One individual may have a sequence of r r r nnnnnnnnn rrnnnrnnnnnnr rrrrrn happenings : another may have a sequence of rrnnnnrrrrrrrrrrrrr-nnnnnnn. Both have the same proportion of r to n happenings, but if by chance the period of observation of both be limited to coincident happenings over a short period, then the record of the one might be rrnnnrnnnnn (i.e. ¼ r) and of the other rrrrrrrrrrrr (i.e. all r) ; the time-dimension matters greatly.

From this point of view, we should expect, in the long run—

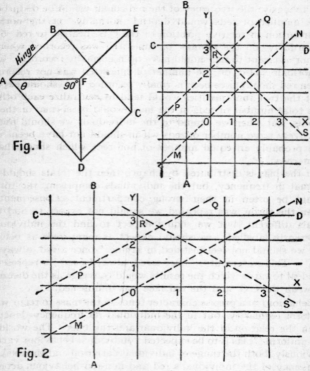

Fig. 1

Fig. 2

provided the run be long enough—Oxford and Cambridge to score an equal number of wins in the Boat Race. We should also expect, on the assumption that the U.S.A., having more people, have more golfers than Britain, (i) the average ability at golf in the two countries would be very little different ; (ii) freak Bobby Jones would be better than freak Roger Wethered, or freak Hagen would beat freak Cotton ; and (iii) that in a given year one of the freaks would fail to manifest freakish ability in between two years of much more successful golf.

Any scale of measurement of behaviour, animate or inanimate, inevitably means freakish behaviour at the extremes of the scale and different judgements of individuals at different times.

A rectangle may be projected into a square. In its simplest form the projection occurs when the square and rectangle are hinged at a common edge and the plane through the two edges parallel to the hinge is perpendicular to the plane of the square (Fig. 1). In this case dimensions parallel to the hinge are unaltered, dimensions perpendicular to the hinge are changed; the measure of the change is $\cos \theta$, where θ is the angle at the hinge between the plane of the square and that of the rectangle; when $\theta = 90°$, the rectangle projects to a line, for $\cos 90° = 0$. Fig. 2 shows squared paper on which certain lines have been drawn, and rectangle paper on which projections of these lines have been drawn, the hinge being the y-axis (line OY). Scales along the y-axis are identical and equal; scales along the x-axis are unequal, but in correspondence by projection. For convenience it is desirable to indicate distances on the squared paper by x and on the rectangle paper by X, when $x = X \cos \theta$.

The equations are :

line	on squared paper	on rectangle paper
AB	$x = -1$	$X = -1$
CD	$y = 3$	$y = 3$
MN	$x = y$	$X = y$
PQ	$y - x = 2$	$y - X = 2$
RS	$y + x = 3$	$y + X = 3$

MN and PQ are parallel in both cases, for $y - x \cos \theta = 0$ and $y - x \cos \theta = 2$ satisfy the condition of parallelism. $ay \pm bx = n$ represents a system of parallel lines for all values of n.

Line MN bisects the angle XOY on the squared paper for $y = x$, but not on the rectangle paper for $y = x \cos \theta$.

RS is perpendicular to MN on the squared paper, for $y - x = 0$ and $y + x = 3$ satisfy the conditions of perpendicularity, but not on the rectangle paper, for $y - x \cos \theta = 0$ and $y + x \cos \theta = 3$ do not satisfy the conditions of perpendicularity, since the coefficients have not been interchanged. The more difficult case of projection occurs when no edge of the square is parallel to an edge of the rectangle; this case may be considered in two steps. Project the rectangle ABCD on a hinge AD into a rectangle ADEF such that AF is equal and parallel to one edge of the square; then project ADEF on a hinge AF into the square; this process involves two angles, one at each hinge.

Drill: Draw axes suitable to a double projection involving $\cos \phi$ and $\cos \phi$. Set up lines corresponding to AB, etc., in Fig. 2: and note the results.

Revision. Differentiate these functions. Logs are to base e. Angles are in radians.

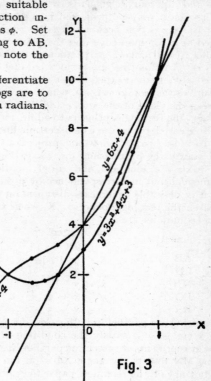

Fig. 3

(i) $(bx)^{n+1}/(n+1)$; (ii) $(bx+c)^{n+1}/b(n+1)$; (iii) $a(bx)^{n-1}/b(n-1)$; (iv) $1/x$; (v) $(n+1)/(bx)^{n+1}$; (vi) $b(n+1)/(bx+c)^{n+1}$; (vii) b^x; (viii) $\log x$; (ix) $b \log x$ (x) $b \log (x+c)$ (xi) $\sin x$; (xii) $\sin \frac{1}{2}x$; (xiii) $\cos x$; (xiv) $\cos (x/n)$ (xv) $\tan (x/n)$ (xvi) $(x+b)/(x+c)$; (xvii) $(x^n-b)/(x^n-c)$ (xviii) $\sin x - x . \cos x$.

Expansion. Graph on squared paper the curve $x^2+y^2=9$.

Project the curve on to
rectangle paper where
Y = y and X = 2x, i.e.
paper hinged along
OY at an angle cos
$\theta = \frac{1}{2}$.

Find the equation of
the curve.

Project a second
time on to rectangle
paper where Y = 2y,
i.e. cos $\phi = \frac{1}{2}$ and

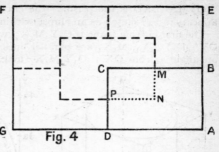

Fig. 4

X = 3x, i.e. cos $\theta = 1/\beta$. Find the equation of the curve.

Solutions of Problems in Lesson 43. *Drill* 2. (a) $13\frac{1}{2}$
knots approx. (b) 33° E. of N. (c) 2·6 sea miles = 3·0 miles
approx.

Revision. 1. The lines are bisected at the origin. The new
equation is $x^2 - 5x + xy + y^2 - 4y = 5$.

2. Major axis x + y = 0. Equations: (i) $x^2 + 3y^2 = 12$; (ii)
$3x^2 + y^2 = 12$; (iii) $x^2 - xy + y^2 = 6$.

3. Fig. 3.

4. $AX + BX.XC = AX^2 + AX.XD = AX.AD$; for two chords
divide each other so that the rectangles of the pairs of parts are
equal; because triangles AXC, ABD are similar AX.AD =
BA.AC.

Expansion. See Fig. 4, where the rectangle pattern is given.
If n be other than 2, it must be 4, 8, etc., for CMNP taken from
AEFG leaves 5 gnomons each subdivisible into 4 gnomons
each $\frac{3}{4}$ of CMNP.

LESSON 45

Another Study in Averages

EVERYTHING depends on the point of view. Imagine a
square prism, the typical three dimensional form, standing on its square base. Imagine that it be made of glass,
so that the cylinder which it just contains is visible. Imagine
that the solid is sliced by two cutting planes and that the edges
where the cutting planes cut the prism and the cylinder are
marked by painted lines. The result will look like Fig. 1.

OYMXCBAD is the prism, the circular end of the cylinder appears in the sketch as an ellipse within the square OYMX.

The first cutting plane is $O_1Y_1M_1X_1$, which is arranged so that OY, MX, O_1Y_1, M_1X_1 are parallel lines, with O_1X_1 dropped at an angle α from OX. $O_1Y_1M_1X_1$ looks like a parallelogram;

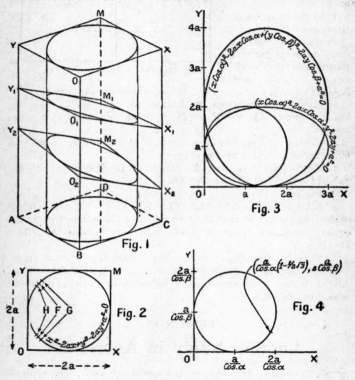

Fig. 1

Fig. 2

$$x^2 - 2axy + y^2 - 2ay + a^2 = 0$$

H F G

Fig. 3

$$(x\cos\alpha)^2 - 2ax\cos\alpha)^2 + (y\cos\beta)^2 - 2ay\cos\beta + a^2 = 0$$

$$(x\cos\alpha)^2 - 2ax\cos\alpha)^2 + 2axy\cos\alpha = 0$$

Fig. 4

$$\left(\frac{a}{\cos\alpha}\left(1 - \tfrac{1}{2}\sqrt{3}\right),\, a\frac{a}{\cos\beta}\right)$$

It is really a rectangle within which is an ellipse where the plane cuts the cylinder.

The second cutting plane is $O_2Y_2M_2X_2$, so arranged that Y_1M_1, O_1X_1, Y_2M_2, O_2X_2 are parallel, and that O_2Y_2 is dropped from OY at an angle β. $O_2Y_2M_2X_2$ looks like a parallelogram; it is a rectangle containing an ellipse, as before.

ANOTHER STUDY IN AVERAGES

The two rectangles are unequal and are different from the square. The two ellipses are unequal and are different from the circle. $O_1X_1 = OX/\cos \alpha$; $O_2Y_2 = OY/\cos \beta$.

In the first ellipse, $O_1X_1 =$ the major axis, $O_1Y_1 =$ the minor axis. In the second ellipse O_2Y_2 is the major axis if β exceeds α. Fig. 2 shows the top. Let $OX = OY = 2a$. The equation of the circle is $x^2 - 2ax + y^2 - 2ay + a^2 = 0$. On the circle are the following points :

$$F \left(\tfrac{1}{4}a, \ a(1 \pm \tfrac{1}{4}\sqrt{7}\right) ; \quad G \left(\tfrac{1}{3}a, \ a(1 \pm \tfrac{1}{3}\sqrt{5}\right)) ;$$
$$H \left(\tfrac{1}{5}a, \ a(1 \pm \tfrac{3}{5}\right)).$$

On the first ellipse and referred to rectangle paper the co-ordinates are unaltered ; hence the points F, G, H, are indicated as above, and the equation of the curve is :

$$X^2 - 2aX + y^2 - 2ay + a^2 = 0.$$

Hence the equation of this pattern represents a circle on squared paper and an ellipse on rectangle paper ; this is equally true of the second ellipse, of which the equation is :

$$X^2 - 2aX + Y^2 - 2aY + a^2 = 0.$$

The real shapes of the circle and the two ellipses are shown in Fig. 3, where the equations (referred to squared paper) are :

$$x. \cos \alpha)^2 - 2 \, ax \cos \alpha + y^2 - 2 \, ay + a^2 = 0 \text{ and}$$
$$(x. \cos \alpha)^2 - 2ax \cos \alpha + (y. \cos \beta)^2 - 2ay \cos \beta + a^2 = 0.$$

For purposes of drawing, $\cos \alpha = \tfrac{2}{3}$ and $\cos \beta = \tfrac{1}{2}$ in Fig. 3.

Hence if the units of the scale along OX (Fig. 3) be reduced from a to $(a/\cos \alpha)$, $2a$ to $2(a/\cos \alpha)$, etc., and the units of the scale along OY (Fig. 3) be reduced from a to $(a/\cos \beta)$, $2a$ to $2(a/\cos \beta)$, etc., the curve representing the equation

$$(x \cos \alpha)^2 - 2 \, ax \cos \alpha + (y.\cos \beta)^2 - 2ay \cos \beta + a^2 = 0$$

would be circular and not elliptical in shape.

In Fig. 4, on the scales given, the circle is a locus of a point (x, y) such that

$$x^2. \cos^2\alpha - 2ax \cos \alpha + y^2.\cos^2\beta - 2ay \cos \beta + a^2 = 0$$

e.g., the point $a(1 + \tfrac{1}{2}\sqrt{3}/\cos \alpha, \ a/2 \cos \beta$.

Since the area of a circle is $\tfrac{1}{4}\pi$ of the area of the square which contains it, it follows that the area of an ellipse is $\tfrac{1}{4}\pi$ of the area of the rectangle which contains it, i.e. $\frac{1}{4}\pi$ of the area of the rectangle made by the major axis and the minor axis.

The scales in Fig. 4 are determined from Fig. 3.

In Fig. 3 the semi-minor axis is $1\frac{1}{2}$a, i.e. a/cos α, which is the unit along OX in Fig. 4 ; the semi-major axis is 2a, i.e. a/cos β, which is the unit along OY in Fig. 4, and is drawn in the figure the same length as a/cos α. The centre of the circle Fig. 4 is the point (a/cos α, a/cos β), and the distance from this centre to the curve is a variable quantity when expressed in terms of the two scales in use.

A happening may occur t times out of p equally likely possibilities, e.g. an unbiased icosahedron may come to rest when thrown or rolled upon its single red face once in 20 cases. The chance of uniform recurrence of the happening is t/p (1 in 20). Let t/p = f ; the chance of non-recurrence is (p−t)/p (19 in 20). Let (p−t)/p = g ; f + g = 1. The odds in favour are f to g, the odds against g to f ; in favour 1 in 19, against 19 to 1. An independent happening may occur T times out of P equally likely possibilities. Let T/P = F, etc.

Then in the case of pP possibilities the first happening may be expected tP times and the second happening will occur in tT cases out of tP possibilities ; hence both events will happen together in tT cases out of pP possibles, and the chance of the "double" is fF. Two unbiased icosahedra will come to rest both on red faces at the same throw once in 400 throws and the odds against are 399 to 1.

The chance that an unbiased icosahedron will continually and successively come to rest on the red n times is 1 in 20^n. If the chance that a bowler send down a ball to rebound from a fixed spot on the pitch and hit the wicket is 1 in 6 and the chance that a batsman is beaten by this particular type of ball is 1 in 3, then the chance that this bowler will get this batsman out is 1 in 18, provided that the bowler attempts in these 18 balls to reproduce the flight under consideration. The bowler may be biased ; he may find that if he tries to reproduce this ball twice, then sends down a ball of a different kind, and repeats this sequence of three balls, then his chance of hitting the wicket becomes 1 in 4 instead of 1 in 6 ; the batsman may be biased so that he is only beaten once in 5 times ; or the preparation of the wicket may neutralize all the chances.

ANOTHER STUDY IN AVERAGES

Biased icosahedra may be thrown on a horizontal table so that they obey the rule " once a red, always a red " ; yet the bias might be counteracted by a slope of the table coupled with a rod placed across the table to impede the free movement of the solids, even to the extent of reducing the chance of a red to 1 in 20. Obviously a 1 to 1 chance may be theoretically certain and yet may never occur or may occur once in 400 times, if the chance that the theoretical conditions happen coincidently is but 1 in 400.

A slab of butter may weigh 1lb. in fact. On scales that weighed accurately to the nearest ounce the chance that this slab's weight was recorded as 1 lb. would be 1 in 1 ; if the scales weighed accurately to the nearest millionth of an ounce the chance that the weight of the slab was recorded as 16·000000 ounces would not be 1 in 1, but would be 1 in X, which is the chance of the bias of the scales against accurate weighing. Obviously, measurement of an individual depends not only on the sequential or time factor, but also upon the space factor which determines the chance that the theoretical conditions are operative.

Drill. 1. Find the chance that four cards dealt successively from a pack of 52 cards will be the 1, 2, 3, 4 of hearts. 2. Find the odds against the king and queen of diamonds being the first and second cards dealt. 3. A horizontal section of a right cone is a circle ; an oblique section across the curved surface is an ellipse. The elliptical cross-section of a cone and cylinder is the lower ellipse of Fig. 2, and a circular projection of this ellipse on the conic surface is in the plane of the upper circle of Fig. 2. The vertical angle of the cone is 2γ. The vertical distance between the nearest points on the circular and elliptical sections is d. Find the equation of the circular conic section.

Revision. 1. Let AD be the diameter of the circum-circle of the triangle ABC, and let AN be perpendicular to BC ; prove that the rectangle BA.AC is equal to the rectangle DA.AN. 2. Let ABCD be any quadrilateral. Prove that the DB.AC is less than the sum of the rectangles AB.CD and AD.BC. Investigate possible corollaries to this.

Expansion. Let P be any point on the surface of a cone. Investigate the shape of cross-sections to the cone through P when the cutting plane is (i) vertical and (ii) parallel to the slope of the cone. Find the character of the equations for the curved edges of the sections.

Solutions to Problems in Lesson 44. *Drill.* Examine Fig. 2 in Lesson 44 (page 368). In the rectangle paper imagine that the scale along OY is increased by the fraction 4/3. The positions of the lines MN, PQ, and RS will be altered with reference to OX and OY, but MN and PQ will still be parallel, and RS will not be perpendicular to MN.

Revision. (i) $b^{n+1} x^n$; (ii) $(bx+c)^n$; (iii) $a(bx)^{n-2}$; (iv) $-1/x^2$; (v) $-b(n+1)^2/(bx)^{n+3}$; (vi) $-b^2(n+1)^2/(bx+c)^{n+2}$; (vii) $b^x \log b$; (viii) $1/x$; (ix) b/x ; (x) $b/(x+c)$; (xi) $\cos x$; (xii) $\frac{1}{2}\cos\frac{1}{2}x$; (xiii) $-\sin x$; (xiv) $-(1/n)\sin (x/n)$; (xv) $(1/n)$ $\sec^2 (x/n)$; (xvi) $(c-b)/(x+c)^2$; (xvii) $nx^{n-1} (b-c)/(x^n-c)^2$; (xviii) $x \sin x$.

Tabulate the functions printed in Lesson 44 as the integrals of the expressions in the above list, adding in each case the constant C.

Expansion. See above.

LESSON 46

Effects of Distortion

A SQUARE may circumscribe a circle. A square distorted in the direction of one edge becomes a rectangle, and the circle within becomes an ellipse. A square distorted in unequal proportions in the directions (opposed at right angles) of two edges becomes also a rectangle. A square distorted in unequal proportions in the directions (opposed at right angles) of the two diagonals becomes a parallelogram, which lies within a rectangle with sides respectively equal in length to the distorted diagonals. In each case the circle is distorted to an ellipse. The square has an edge $= 2c$. The circle is represented by the equation $x^2/c^2 + y^2/c^2 = 1$, where the origin is at the centre of the square and the circle, and the axes are parallel to the edges of the square.

Distortion may be enlargement or diminution ; the distorted edge $= mc$, where m depends on the angle between the distortion and the edge distorted measured in a right-angled triangle of which the third side is opposite this angle. In both cases in Fig. 1 the angle is a : for enlargement $m = \sec a$ and for diminution $m = \cos a$.

EFFECTS OF DISTORTION

Enlargement along the x-axis means that every x-value becomes mx. The rectangle is 2 mc by c; the equation of the ellipse is $x^2/(mc)^2 + y^2/c^2 = 1$; when $a = mc$ and $b = c$ this equation takes a standard form $x^2/a^2 + y^2/b^2 = 1$. Here $m = a/b$; $b^2/a^2 = 1/m^2 = (1 - e^2)$, where $e^2 = (m^2 - 1)/m^2$, and e is less than unity, for $e = \sin a$.

This type of distortion may happen in connexion with a square prism, cut obliquely by a plane making an angle a with the horizontal square base of the prism. In Fig. 2 a square prism is shown in elevation, the square base ABCD becomes the rectangle AEFD, and a circle within ABCD—the base of a cylinder within the prism—becomes an ellipse within AEFD; i.e. the oblique

Fig.1

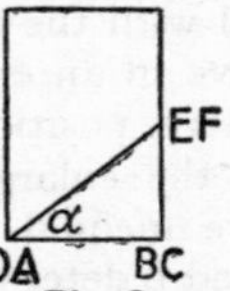

Fig.2

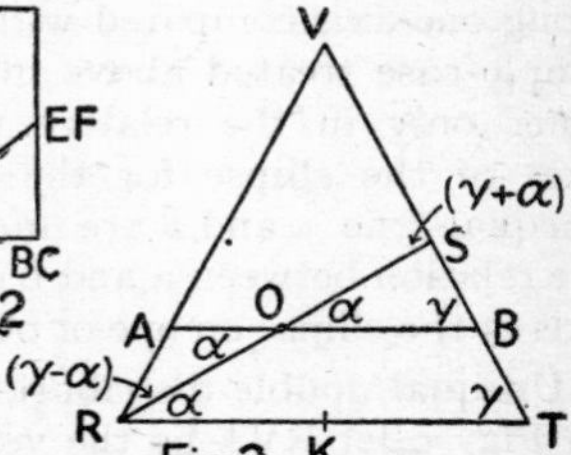

Fig.3

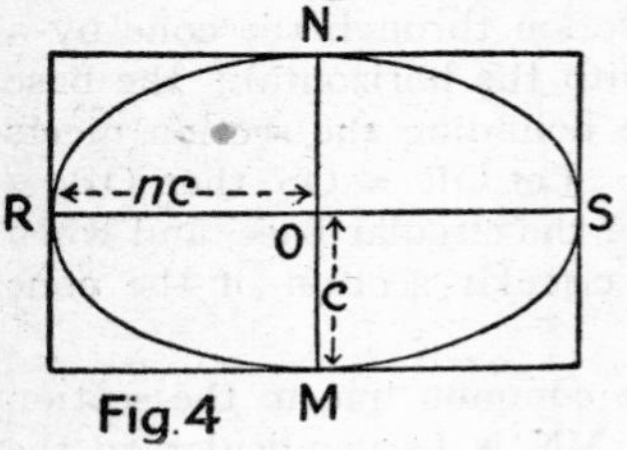

Fig.4

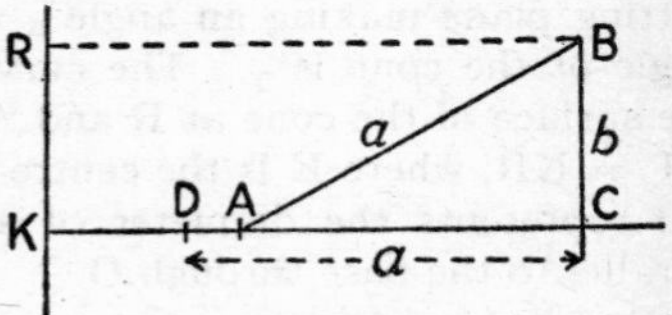

Fig.5

section of a cylinder is an ellipse. In the case of diminution the only change is that $m = \cos a$, whence $e = \tan a$, and a is less than 45°.

Equal double enlargement (or diminution) retains the circular and square shapes; unequal double distribution means that the square c by c becomes the rectangle mc by nc where $m = \sec a$ (or $\cos a$) as above and $n = \sec \beta$ (or $\cos \beta$). The equation of the curve is then $x^2/(mc)^2 + y^2/(nc)^2 = 1$; i.e. $x^2/a^2 + y^2/b^2 = 1$, when $c = a/m = b/n$; whence $b^2/a^2 = n^2/m^2 = (1 - e^2)$. This new e^2 expresses the result for both enlargement and diminution. Four cases arise:

$n = \sec \beta$ and $m = \sec \alpha$, whence $e^2 =$
$$1 - \sec^2 \beta / \sec^2 \alpha = 1 - \cos^2 \alpha / \cos^2 \beta \ldots \ldots (1)$$
$n = \sec \beta$ and $m = \cos \alpha$, whence $e^2 =$
$$1 - 1/\cos^2 \beta. \quad \cos^2 \alpha \ldots \ldots (2)$$
$n = \cos \beta$ and $m = \sec \alpha$, whence $e^2 =$
$$1 - \cos^2 \beta. \quad \cos^2 \alpha \ldots \ldots (3)$$
$n = \cos \beta$ and $m = \cos \alpha$, whence $e^2 =$
$$1 - \cos^2 \beta / \cos^2 \alpha \ldots \ldots (4)$$

In (2) and (3) an enlargement is coupled with a diminution which is equivalent to either a greater enlargement (or diminution) along one axis compared with the other ; hence the result is the simple case treated above in an exaggerated form. (1) and (3) differ only in the relative positions of the major and minor axes of the ellipse for the enlargements (or diminutions) are unequal ; i.e. α and β are unequal, and a and b are unequal, and the relation between a and b determines the position of the major axis of the ellipse on one or other of the axes of coordinates.

Unequal double distribution occurs in connexion with a cone. In Fig. 3, let RVT be the vertical section of a cone through the vertex V. RS is an axis of the section through the cone by a cutting plane making an angle α with the horizontal ; the base angle of the cone is γ. The curve bounding the section meets the surface of the cone at R and S. Let OR = OS, then OB = KT = KR, where K is the centre of the circular base, and when AB represents the diameter of a circular section of the cone parallel to the base through O.

Let OM = ON, when MN is the common line to the section and the circle through AB ; then MN is perpendicular to the plane of VRT and is a chord of the circle through AB/(MN cannot be shown in the Fig.) $OM^2 = OA \cdot OB$; i.e. $OM^2/RO \cdot OS = AO \cdot OB$. $RO \cdot OS = (AO/RO) \cdot (OB/OS)$.

Whence $OM^2/OR^2 = \sin (\gamma - \alpha)/\sin \alpha$ times $\sin (\gamma + \alpha)/\sin \alpha$
$$= \sin (\gamma - \alpha) \cdot \sin (\gamma + \alpha)/\sin^2 \alpha$$
$$= (\sin^2 \gamma - \sin^2 \alpha)/\sin^2 \alpha$$
Let $1/n^2 = (\sin^2 \gamma - \sin^2 \alpha)/\sin^2 \alpha$
then $n^2 = \sin^2 \alpha/(\sin^2 \gamma - \sin^2 \alpha)$

S may be anywhere in VT. Hence O lies within the cone and OM is always less than RK ; also γ always exceeds α, so that when α is large, n is large, and MN becomes very small ; in the limit when $\alpha = \gamma$, MN vanishes; when α is small, n becomes small, and in the limit when α vanishes, OM = RO = RK.

As the angle α grows, RS gets smaller slowly until RST is a right angle, and then RS grows; but MN rapidly gets smaller. MN is the minor and RS the major axis of the curve of the section. The section lies within a rectangle, Fig. 4, and is an ellipse. In Fig. 5 let ABC be a right-angled triangle, with hypotenuse = a, perpendicular = b, and in the base CA produced take D, so that CD = a. Let AD = k. Let RK be perpendicular to CD produced such that DK = mk, at the same time as the perpendicular, BR = ma. Then: $AC^2 = (a^2 - b^2)$; $AD = a - (a^2 - b^2)^{\frac{1}{2}}$; $KD = am - m(a^2 - b^2)^{\frac{1}{2}}$. $= RB - KD = am - a$. Hence $am = (a^2 - b^2)^{\frac{1}{2}}$; whence $b^2/a^2 = (1 - m^2) = (1 - e^2)$ where m = e.

An ellipse is defined as a curve such that the distance of any point on the curve from a given point is always the same fraction of the perpendicular distance of the point on the curve from a given straight line. The curve is two-dimensional. The fraction is denoted in code as $e < 1$.

In Fig. 5; e = m and when $e < 1$, $m < 1$, and D and B are the termini of the axes of an ellipse centered at the origin C; whence the equation of the ellipse is $x^2/a^2 + y^2/b^2 = 1$. The given point is A, the focus, the point $(a^2 - b^2)^{\frac{1}{2}}$, o. The given line is KR, the directrix, $x + a$ $(i - e) = 0$. In the ellipse of Fig. 4, the foci are the points $\pm c$ $(n^2 - 1)^{\frac{1}{2}}$, o; i.e. $\pm /ce(1 - e^2)^{\frac{1}{2}}$, o; the directrix is $x + c$ $(i - e^2)^{\frac{1}{2}} = 0$ where $e^2 = (n^2 - 1)/n^2 = 2 - (\sin^2\gamma/\sin^2\alpha)$.

When $\alpha = \gamma$, then e = 1; this is the special case when RS coincides with RV, Fig. 3, and the ellipse has vanished; and eccentricity has vanished. If it be imagined that the cone RVT fits into a larger cone TV^1R^1, then RV is parallel to R^1V^1, and the cutting plane through RV to the larger cone would not reach the line R^1V^1, but would be a curve which became more distant from RV as it went away from V; this is a parabola.

When $\alpha = 90°$, there is no curve; the edges of a section of a cone by a cutting plane perpendicular to the circular base form with the chord of section of the base an isosceles triangle. When α exceeds γ, RS falls outside the cone RTV and must be considered as within the larger cone R^1V^1T.

Drill. Graph the rectangle made by the four points $(\pm 3, \pm 2)$. Find the equation of the ellipse within the rectangle; its focus and its directrix. Slew the rectangle and its ellipse through 60°. Find the coordinates of the corners, and the equations of the sides of the rectangle, and of the ellipse, and of its major and minor axes, in the new position.

Revision. 1. On the same base a number of triangles have been constructed of equal perimeter (i.e. isoperimetrical triangles). Prove that one of these triangles is isosceles and has the largest area of them all.

2. Within an angle RAM a point B is taken. Through B a number of lines are drawn terminated at both ends on the arms RA and MS of the angle. One of these lines may make with the arms an isosceles triangle : prove that this line is the smallest possible of the set of lines so drawn.

Expansion. Examine Fig. 5. Reconstruct it with these changes : (i) BA is unequal to CD : (ii) KD = d ; (iii) AD is larger than KD, i.e. AD = f · KD, where F exceeds 1 ; (iv) AB = f · BR. Find the equation of a curve through B and D of which KC is the axis of symmetry.

Solutions to Problems in Lesson 45.

Drill. 1. Ans.: the continued product of 1/52, 1/51, 1/50, 1/49 ; i.e. 1/6497400.

2. $(52 \times 51 = 2652)$. Ans.: 2651 to 1.

3. The equation would be $xy = c$, where $(a - c)/d = \cos \gamma$, i.e. $c = a - d \cos \gamma$.

Revision. 1. Triangles ABN and ADC are similar : BA/AN = DA/AC ; BA . AC = DA . AN.

2. When angles BDC and BAC are unequal, BDC being the larger ; draw CDE equal to BAC and DCE equal to BCA, making the triangle DCE, Fig. 6. Triangles CDE and CAB are similar ; CD/DE = CA/AB, i.e. AB.CD = CA.DE ; also CD/CE = AC/CB. Since, also, in the triangles ACD and CEB angles DCA and ECB are equal, these triangles are similar ; and AD/AC = EB/CB, i.e. AD. BC = AC.EB : whence AB.CD and AD.BC together = AC(DE + EB) and are greater than AC . BD.

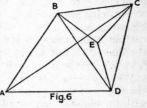

Fig. 6

Corollary (*a*) : E will fall on BD when BAC and BDC are equal angles and the quadrilateral is cyclic ; hence ABCD must be not any quadrilateral, but any non-cyclic quadrilateral.

Corollary (b) : Any two of the three rectangles are together greater than the third, for they are proportional to the sides of the triangle BDE ; they are equal to the rectangles contained by the length AC and the sides of the triangle BDE in turn.

Expansion. See above.

LESSON 47

Rectangles and Ellipses

THE relation between a rectangle and its inscribed ellipse is indicated by the fact that when the ellipse is represented by the equation $x^2/a^2 + y^2/b^2 = 1$, the four corners of the rectangle are represented by ($\pm a$, $\pm b$). These four corners are shown as N, P, Q, M, in Fig. 1. O is the centre of the rectangle and OA is parallel to MN, and OB to NP.

In OA, S is taken such that BS = a. Let OS = ma.

Produce OA to K so that OK = a/m. Then SK = a $(1-m)/m$; and AK = a$(1-m)/m$; and SA = a $(1-m)$. i.e. SA = m. AK, and SB = m.OK = m.BD.

Also $m^2 = 1 - b^2/a^2$.

Whence A and B are on an ellipse, eccentricity = m, of which S is one focus and KR one directrix.

Repeat the rectangle MNPQ in Fig. 2. Let $n^2 = 1 + b^2/a^2$.

Find R in OA such that OR = na, and AR = a $(n-1)$.

OL = BE = a/n. Let C be the point (a$\sqrt{2}$,b) ; then RC^2 = (na − a$\sqrt{2}$)^2 + b^2 = a^2 (n^2 − 2$\sqrt{2}$n + 2 + n^2 − 1) = a^2 (2n^2 − 2$\sqrt{2}$n + 1) = a^2 ($\sqrt{2}$n − 1)^2. But CE = a$\sqrt{2}$ − a/n = ($\sqrt{2}$n − 1) a/n ; i.e. CR = n.CE.

Hence both C and A lie on a hyperbola of which R is the focus. LE is the directrix, n is the eccentricity, and the equation is $x^2/a^2 − y^2/b^2 = 1$.

Since $m^2 = 1 - b^2/a^2$ and $n^2 = 1 + b^2/a^2$, $m^2 + n^2 = 2$ and $n^2 − m^2 = 2b^2/a^2$.

RS = a $(n-m)$. KL = a $(n-m)/mn$. BR = $(2b^2 + a^2)^{\frac{1}{2}}$.

Obviously OB is an axis of symmetry.

The line QN is $x/a − y/b = 0$; the point (ka,kb) is on this line for all values of k. On the hyperbola when y = kb, x = a $(k^2 + 1)^{\frac{1}{2}}$. Hence the curve will never meet the line until at the limit k is so great that the difference between k and $(k^2+1)^{\frac{1}{2}}$ is immaterial, i.e. the curve and the line meet at infinity. The curve lies wholly between the lines NQ and MP, which are labelled the asymptotes of the curve.

But the equation $x^2/a^2-y^2/b^2=1$ suggests another curve $-x^2/a^2+y^2/b^2=1$ within the area outside the rectangle and situated within the same asymptotes and having chords parallel to MN or PQ.

In Fig. 3, the necessary

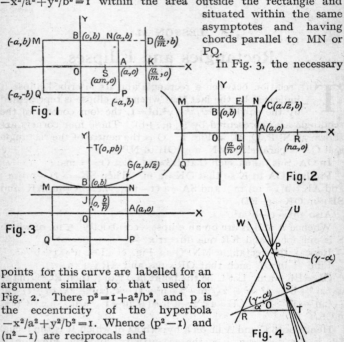

Fig. I

Fig. 2

Fig. 3

Fig. 4

points for this curve are labelled for an argument similar to that used for Fig. 2. There is $p^2=1+a^2/b^2$, and p is the eccentricity of the hyperbola $-x^2/a^2+y^2/b^2=1$. Whence (p^2-1) and (n^2-1) are reciprocals and

$$p^2n^2=p^2+n^2=2+a^2/b^2+b^2/a^2.$$

(p^2-1) and $(1-m^2)$ are reciprocals, whence $p^2m^2=p^2+m^2-2$.

The relation between the ellipse and its two hyperbolas is such that the common tangents to the curves at the points of contact make the rectangle which circumscribes the ellipse. This fact can now be used in connexion with Fig. 3 of Lesson 46. In that Lesson the relation between an ellipse and a conical section was investigated. In Fig. 4, VRT is a cone to which the cone UVW is added. RT is the diameter of a circular section of RTV, and RS is the major axis, middle point O, of an elliptical section of the cone. O is the centre of the hyperbola of which RS is the axis of symmetry.

The angle SRV = $(\gamma - \alpha)$, in VU take the point P such that the angle VPS = the angle VRS.

Imagine the set of curves belonging to RS swung on a hinge which is the common tangent of the curves at the point S until R coincides with P; then the ellipse lies outside the cone, where is the hyperbola?

The angles were given and are constants for the argument. Hence RS is fixed. Hence the minor axis of the ellipse is fixed. Hence the rectangle of reference for the ellipse is fixed in position and size by SP. The hyperbola must be the outline of the section of the double cone by a plane cutting the solid in the plane of the rectangle and its set of curves.

Sin 2 A = 2 sin A.cos A.

Hence sin B = 2 sin $\frac{1}{2}$B.cos $\frac{1}{2}$B = 2 (sin $\frac{1}{2}$B/cos $\frac{1}{2}$B) . cos^2 $\frac{1}{2}$B

$\qquad$ = 2 tan $\frac{1}{2}$B/(1 + tan $\frac{1}{2}$B)

Cos 2A = 1 − 2 sin^{2}A = 2 cos^{2}A − 1

Hence cos B = 1 − 2 sin^2 $\frac{1}{2}$B = cos^2 $\frac{1}{2}$B − sin^2 $\frac{1}{2}$B

$\qquad$ = cos^2 $\frac{1}{2}$B (1 − tan^2 $\frac{1}{2}$B)

$\qquad$ = (1 − tan^2 $\frac{1}{2}$B)/(1 + tan^2 $\frac{1}{2}$B)

Whence tan B = 2 tan $\frac{1}{2}$B/(1 − tan^2 $\frac{1}{2}$B)

Sin (M−N) . sin (M+N) = (sin M cos N)^2 − (cos M sin N)^2

$\qquad$ = sin^2 M − sin^{2}N = cos^2 N − cos^2 M

Cos 3A = cos A cos 2A − sin A sin 2A

$\qquad$ = cos A (2 cos^2 A − 1) − sin A . 2 sin A cos A

$\qquad$ = 4 cos^3 A − 3 cos A

Sin 3A = 3 sin A − 4 sin^3 A

Tan 3A = (tan A + tan 2A)/(1 − tan A tan 2A)

$$= \left(\tan A + \frac{2 \tan A}{1 - \tan^2 A} \right) \Big/ \left(1 - \frac{2 \tan A \tan A}{1 - \tan^2 A} \right)$$

$\qquad$ = (3 tan A − tan^{3}A)/(1 − 3 tan^2 A)

In the radian measurement of angles, $\pi/2$ = a right angle. Trigonometrical equations are solved in radian measurement: e.g.:

Sin A + cos A = $\sqrt{2}$

Sin A . $1/\sqrt{2}$ + cos A . $1/\sqrt{2}$ = 1;

sin A . cos $\pi/4$ + cos A . sin $\pi/4$ = 1

(383)

i.e. $\sin (A+\pi/4) = 1 = \sin \pi/2$; whence $A=\pi/4$: i.e. (in degrees) 45°, 135°, 225°, 315°.

Sin $3B+\cos 5B=\cos B$

Sin $3B=\cos B-\cos 5B=2 \sin 3B . \sin 2B$; whence $\sin 3B=0$ or $1=2 \sin 2B$, i.e. $\sin 2B=\frac{1}{2}=\sin \pi/6$.

Either $3B=0$ or π or 2π, i.e. $B=0$ or $\pi/3$, $2\pi/3$ or $B=\pi/12$, etc. Angles are (in degrees) 0°, 15°, 60°, 75°, 120°.

Definition. A and B are the centres of two unequal circles. In the line AB, M and N are taken such that MA/MB = NA/NB = (radius of circle A)/(radius of circle B). M and N are centres of similitude, if N lie between A and B, it is the internal (c.s.) and M is the external (c.s.).

In Fig. 5 let M and N be (c.s.); D, E, F, G, M are collinear, P, Q, N, R, S are collinear. MBG and MAE are similar triangles, then BG is parallel to AE. Similarly, the following are pairs of parallels : FB and DA, PA and SB, AQ and RB.

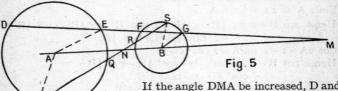

Fig. 5

If the angle DMA be increased, D and E approach each other, and, in the limit, coincide, and then the line DM is a tangent to both circles; hence a tangent to one circle from either (c.s.) is also a tangent to the other circle.

MB/MA = rectangle MG.MD/rectangle ME . MD

MA/MB = rectangle MD . ME/ rectangle MF . ME

Hence rectangle MG . MD = rectangle MF . ME

But rectangle MG . MF = square on tangent to circle B from M = k times the square on MB; similarly rectangle ME . MD = k times the square on MA from M, hence the product of these rectangles = k^2 times the product of these squares = k^2m^2, where m = the rectangle MA . MB, i.e. MG . MF . ME . MD = k^2m^2; whence MG . MD = MF . ME = km, a constant, and this constant is independent of the size of the angle DMA, so long as DM cuts each circle twice.

This demonstration indicates an important relation between the parts of a line which makes chords in two circles and starts at a centre of similitude.

YELLOW PERIL OF THE MIDDLE AGES. Temujin (1162–1227), son of a petty Mongol chieftain, built up a great empire in Asia, from China to Georgia and south to the Indus valley. In 1206 he proclaimed himself Jenghiz Khan, or " peerless warrior emperor "—an event which is depicted in this illustration from a MS. of Rashid-ed-Din, written about 1310. HISTORY: MEDIEVAL 38

From Blochet, "Manuscrits orientaux de la Bibliothèque Nationale; and H. Lamb, "Genghiz Khan"

CHARLES I OF NAPLES AND SICILY (1226–85). Brother of Louis IX of France, Charles count of Anjou was crowned king of Naples and Sicily in 1265. His tyranny, however, resulted in the rising known as the Sicilian Vespers, when his French followers were almost all massacred, and in the collapse of his dominion (1282).

HISTORY : MEDIEVAL 39

RUDOLF I OF HAPSBURG (1218–91). Head of the Hapsburg family, he secured for himself and his House after him Austria and the headship of Germany. This equestrian portrait is on the façade of Strasbourg cathedral.

HISTORY : MEDIEVAL 39

Courtesy of Chapter of Strasbourg Cathedral

Plate 46

Volume VI

CHARLES IV (1316–78). Grandson of Henry VI and son of king John of Bohemia, he became king of Bohemia after the death of his father at Crécy, and in 1355 was crowned emperor at Rome. He is known as the founder of the university at Prague and as the author of the "Golden Bull," by which the imperial succession became regulated. This portrait of him with his son Wenzel, king of the Romans, is taken from a transcript of the bull.

HISTORY : MEDIEVAL 40

From O. Jäger, "Weltgeschichte"

HENRY VII (c. 1270–1313). Though French in speech and sympathies, he was elected German king in 1308. Three years later he went to Italy, where his advent aroused high hopes of political stabilization in Dante, and was crowned emperor in 1312. He proved, however, quite unequal to the task of controlling his great domain. He died near Siena.

HISTORY : MEDIEVAL 40

Codex Balduineus; from Irmer, "Die Romfahrt Heinrich's VII"

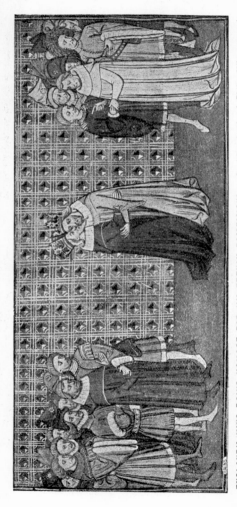

ENGLAND'S KING DOING HOMAGE FOR HIS FRENCH POSSESSIONS. On the death of Philip IV's youngest son, Charles IV, in 1328, the senior male line of the Capets became extinct, and by a decision of the French peers—to which, much later, the term Salic Law was attached—the succession was given to Philip of Valois. Edward III, as son of Philip IV's daughter, Isabella, disputed this decision, but ultimately consented to do homage to Philip VI for his possessions in Guienne. The incident is thus illustrated in a fourteenth-century French chronicle.

HISTORY: MEDIEVAL 40

Plate 48

Volume VI

Drill. Solve the following equations : (i) $\tan B + 3 \cos B = 4$: (ii) $\tan B . \tan 2 B = 1$; (iii) $\cos d + \sqrt{3} \sin d = 1$.

Revision. Solve the equations : (i) $9 = 4x + y$, when $8 = 3x^2 - 4y^2$; (ii) twice the sum of x and y equals the sum of their reciprocals and equals the reciprocal of the expression $\frac{1}{17}(4\frac{7}{12} + (x+y))$; (iii) $(x+y)^{\frac{1}{2}} + (x-y)^{\frac{1}{2}} = 7$, when $(x^2 - y^2)^{\frac{1}{2}} = 12$.

Expansion. Draw three circles. Find their centres of similitude. This gives nine points in all. These nine are collinear in threes. Find the lines of collinearity and investigate the proof of your discovery.

Solutions of Problems in Lesson 46.

Drill. (a) Original : ellipse $4x^2 + 9y^2 = 36$
focus $(\sqrt{5}, 0)$
directrix $x = 9/\sqrt{5}$

(b) Slewed : ellipse $9x^2 + 4y^2 = 36$
focus $(0, \sqrt{5})$
directrix $y = 9/\sqrt{5}$

Revision. 1. In Fig. 6 PMN is right-angled at M ; PO = ON, PL = LM. MON is isosceles, let MAN be of equal perimeter

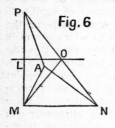

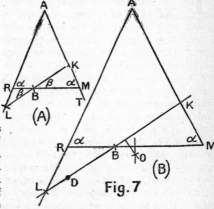

Fig. 6

(A)

(B)

Fig. 7

with MON. PN is less than PA and AN. PN = (MO and ON) = (MA and AN). Hence PA exceeds MA ; hence A is on the other side of LO from P. Hence the vertical height of MAN is less than the vertical height of MON. Hence MON has the maximum area of all the isoperimetrical triangles on MN with a perimeter equal to that of MAN.

(385)

2. In Fig. 7 RAM is isosceles, KL is any other line through B. (A) In the solid ; RAM is the section of a cone through the vertex A and perpendicular to the circular base of which RM is a diameter. KL is the major axis of an ellipse into which the circle is distorted on the conical surface : KL exceeds RM. (B) In Fig. 7 (B) in the plane ; RM and DK are two equal straight lines which intersect at any common point B ; hence R, D, K, M are concyclic with a centre at O. Join KM and make angle TRM equal to angle KMR. TR cuts KD produced in L. MK and TR will meet in A and RM is less than KL. Obviously, since the rectangle RB . BM = the rectangle DB . BK, the rectangle RB . BM is a minimum rectangle made by the segments of lines through B terminated on AR and AM.

Expansion. See above for the equation of the hyperbola.

LESSON 48

Collinearities and Concurrencies

THE method of rectangular coordinates may be used to investigate the relations between centres of similitude for pairs of circles. Let the points A and B be on the y-axis and respectively the centres of circles of which the radii are r and s (Fig. 1). Let A be the point (O, a) ; then B is the point $(O, as/r)$, when the internal centre of similitude (c.s.) is at the origin. The external c.s. is at C, whence C is the point $(O, 2as/(r-s))$. At any other point D, (d,e) let a third circle be drawn of which the radius is t ; where d and e and t are quite independent of r and s and a, making altogether six independent values. E is the internal c.s. in AD and F the external c.s. Let E be (f,g) ; then $(d-f)/d=t/(r+t)$, whence $f=dr/(r+t)$ and $(g-e)/(a-e)=t/(r+t)$, whence $g=(at+er)/(r+t)$. Let F be (l,m) ; then $d/l=(r-t)/r$, whence $l=dr/(r-t)$ and $(e-m)/(a-m)=t/r$, whence $m=(er-at)/(r-t)$. Let G be (h,k) ; then $(d-h)/d=t/(s+t)$, whence $h=ds/(s+t)$ and $(k-e)/(e+as/r)=t/(s+t)$, whence $k=(esr-ast)/(s+t)r$. Let H be (n,p) ; then $(d+n)/n=t/s$, whence $n=ds/(s-t)$ and $(e+b)/(e+p)=(s-t)/t$, whence $p=s(er+at)/(s-t)r$. Note the symmetry of the expressions for the pairs E and G, and F and H.

The drawing suggests that the following sets of points are

collinear : OGF, EOH, EGC, FCH. O is (O,O) and G is (h,k), whence the tangent of the angle XOG is k/h, which equals s(er—at)/drs. But the tangent of the angle XOF is m/l, which equals (er—at)/dr. OGF is one line.

The tangent of the angle XOE is g/f, which equals (at+er)/dr, which equals p/n, which is the tangent of the angle at which HO meets XO. EOH is one line.

g/f = (at+er)/dr

(2as/(r—s)/f = (2ars + 2ast) / (r—s)dr

Adding these, the result is (er(r—s) + 2ars + ast + art)/dr (r—s) ; k/h = (er—at)dr

(2as/(r—s)/h = (2ars + 2art)/(r—s)dr

Adding these, the result is the same as the sum above ; whence the cotangent of OCE equals the cotangent of OCG, CGE is one line. Let FQR be the line y = m, and Q be (O,m) and R be (n,m) whence QC = (p — m) l/(1+n) ; then the equation of the line FH is

(p—m)x — (1+n)y = lp+mn which cuts the y-axis at y = — (pl+mn) / (1 +n).

(pl + mn) = (drs (er+at) + drs (at — er))/(r — t) (t—s)r

=2 dsat/(r—t) (t—s)

(1+n)   =dt(r—s)/(r—t) (t—s)

whence y = — 2as/(r—s) = the y — value for the point C. FCH is one line.

The drawing suggests that AG, OD, and BE are concurrent.

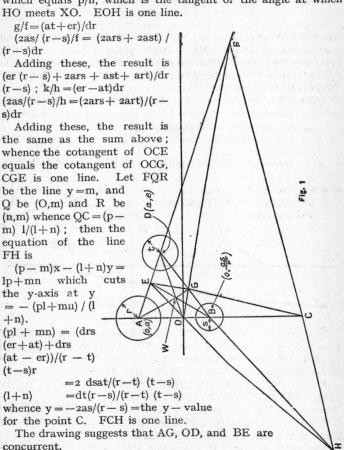

Fig. 1

Line OD ex = dy

Line BE x(at+er)/(r+t)+asx/r−dry/(r+t) = ads/(r+t)

i.e. x(atr+er²+asr+ast) − dry = adrs.

Line AG (a+k)x+hy = ah,

i.e. x(ars+art+ast−esr) + drsy+adrs.

These three equations solve simultaneously when

$$x(rt+rs+st) = drs$$
$$y(rt+rs+st) = ers$$

which fix W in position, for when z = rs/(rt+rs+st), x = zd, and y = ze, whence OW = z.OD. Hence arises a quick method of obtaining the figure. From the values of the three radii, evaluate z. Determine O the internal c.s. for the two circles. Join OD. Find z . OD = OW and fix W in relative position; the rest follows. The line FH is the external axis of similitude for the three circles and the three intersecting lines are the internal axes of similitude.

In plane geometry the demonstration depends upon the theorems of Ceva and Menelaus.

Ceva's theorem. In a triangle MNP take any point O and MO meets NP in X, etc., as in Fig. 2; then (NX/XP) (PY/YM) (MZ/ZN) = 1, and conversely.

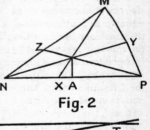

Fig. 2

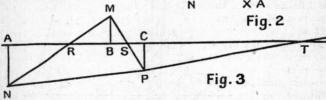

Fig. 3

Consider the triangles MON and NOP and the triangles AON and AOP, where A is any point in NP. When A coincides with X, NX/XP = area N XM/areaPXM = (areas NXO and NOM)/(areas PXO and POM) = area NOM/ area POM, and conversely.

Areally (NOM/POM) (POM/PON) (PON/NOM) = 1,

whence (NX/XP) (MZ/ZN) (PY/YM) = 1.

Whence in Fig. 1; since (AO/OB) = r/s, (BG/GD) = s/t, and (DE/EA) = t/r, (AO/OB) (BG/GD) (DE/EA) = 1, and W is the point of concurrency of AG, BE, and DO.

Menelaus' theorem. In a triangle MNP a line TSR cuts the

sides MN, etc., as in Fig. 3 ; then (RM/RN) (TN/TP) (SP/SM) = 1, and conversely. Take A and B and C in RT ; then (MB/NA) (CP/MB) (NA/CP) = 1.

But when NA and MB are parallel (MB/NA) = (MR/RN), and conversely. Whence, when NA, MB, and PC are parallel, the continued product (MR/RN), etc. = 1.

Whence, in Fig. 1 ; since (BC/CA) = s/r, (FA/FD) = r/t, and (DH/HB) = t/s, the continued product (BC/CA), etc. = 1, and FCH are collinear.

The whole is, in both codes, an exercise in the properties of similar triangles, and follows from the fact that scale drawing involves a constant linear ratio between corresponding lines.

It is a useful exercise in thinking to take the arithmetical conception of ratio, apply it to the triangular shape, and from this basis work out examples of concurrency of lines in the flat and in the solid, as in pyramids.

Imagine you have a pair of dodecahedra, each of which has four red and four green and four black faces. If either were thrown a large number of times on a horizontal table and the record kept of the colour on the table when the solid stopped, it would be expected that once in three throws would be the porportion in which each colour were recorded. If both were thrown and the pairing of colours recorded the record might be summarized as in the diagram, Fig. 4. Each letter a, or b, or c represents a number ; a represents the number of times when red on the first solid appeared simultaneously with green on the other ; both were black f times. x is the number of times red appeared on the first solid. After a large number of throws x = y = z = m = n = p would be the record expected, each being equal to a third of the number of throws ; and a = b = d = g = e, etc. (each equal to a ninth of the number of throws) would be expected for the pairings of colours. The arrangement of the colours would not matter.

Now suppose that the solids were not uniform, but each had a definite bias towards one particular face. The equality of the sets of numbers would vanish ; one of the letters a, b, c, etc., would emerge as a number much larger than the others, and other of these numbers would tend to be small. Let h be very large and a be very small. It would be concluded that No. 1 solid was biased towards a green face and away from a red face, and No. 2 solid was biased towards a red face and away from a green face ; and we should expect to find in both solids a red face opposite a green face. If we did not find this we should be set a problem, that of discovering by other means where the bias lay. Here the arrangement of the colours matters, for it might happen that the three greens of No. 1 were on adjacent faces, thus increasing the probable frequency of green being recorded, and it might happen that the bias of No. 2 was to a particular red face which had four of its adjacent faces black, thus tending to increase the value of n at the expense of p. If also the total number of throws were smallish the inequalities of the numbers recorded would be less important and our inferences less sure.

Hitherto it has been assumed that there are no difficulties in observing the facts ; suppose that the colouring is a series of

No 2 ↓		R	G	B	Total
	G	a	b	c	$m = a+b+c$
	B	d	e	f	$n = d+e+f$
	R	g	h	k	$p = g+h+k$
Total		$x = a+d+g$	$y = b+e+h$	$z = c+f+k$	All the throws

No 1 ⟶

Fig. 4

shades of yellow and that R represents the darkest shade and B the lightest. Suppose also that the experiment were carried out under various lighting conditions which increased the difficulty of determining whether the shade on a particular face was to be recorded as R or G or as G or B ; i.e. the borderlines were relatively indeterminate. Suppose also that the bias in both was towards the darkest shade and away from the lighter shades, x would exceed y and y would exceed z ; also p would exceed m and m would exceed n ; with the result that the numbers would tend to range from g, the largest, down to f, the smallest. Suppose the bias were not in the solids, but in the thrower, e.g. he might place both solids symmetrically in his hand, then we should expect b and f and g to be large and the others small.

COLLINEARITIES AND CONCURRENCIES

Suppose further that the thrower becomes skilled in throwing and can secure more green records than the others, then b would emerge as the largest number, and the more skilled he is the less likely are g and f to be large. Obviously, all differences from equality in a, b, c, etc., are indications of bias, and the character of the differences is suggestive of where the bias lies.

Drill. 1. The selling price of an article is x shillings. The article is sold at a profit of x per cent. Find an expression for the cost price when profit is reckoned per cent on cost and find suitable values in integers for x. Repeat the process when profit is reckoned per cent of selling price.

2. A man left A at 3 p.m. G.M.T. He reached B at 3.45 p.m. registered by the local time at B. He travelled back from B to A at a speed half as fast again as that of the outward journey by a route a third as long again and reached A at 4.30 G.M.T. Assuming that no time was spent at B, what is the difference between G.M.T. and local time at B ?

Revision. 1. Given that $d^2y/dx^2 = A + Bx + Cx^2 + Dx^3$ . . . and that $y = m + nx + (A/2)x^2 + (B/6)x^3 + (C/12)x^4$ . . . where m and n are constants of integration. Find dy/dx, and demonstrate that the two expressions are related.

2. Proceed similarly with the pair : $d^2y/dx^2 = -Ky$, where K is a constant ; and $y = M \sin \sqrt{K}x + N \cos \sqrt{K}x$, where M and N are constants of integration.

3. Proceed similarly with the pair : $d^2y/dx^2 = Ma^2e^{ax}$ and $y = Me^{ax}$.

Expansion. In Fig. 1 regard A and B as fixed points ; and D as a point such that $DA/DB = OA/OB = CA/CB$; show that the locus of D is a circle with OC as diameter. This is a particular case of Apollonius' Locus.

Solutions to Problems in Lesson 47.

Drill. (i) B = 45 or $71\frac{1}{2}$ (approx.) ; (ii) B = 30 or 150 ; (iii) d = 120 or 0.

Revision. (i) x = 2 or $2\frac{44}{61}$, y = 1 or $-1\frac{54}{61}$; (ii) x = $\frac{3}{4}$ or $\frac{1}{2}$. $(\sqrt{34} - 6)$, y = 2/3 or $-\frac{1}{2} (\sqrt{34} + 6)$; (iii) x = $12\frac{1}{2}$, y = $3\frac{1}{2}$

Expansion. See above.

LESSON 49

Perspective and Anti-Parallelism

A TRIANGULAR pyramid has four triangular faces. Fig. 1 is the plan of such a pyramid, of which the base ABC is horizontal and the vertex V is elevated so that the three faces which meet at V are sloping. Since the solid is irregular the edges are unequal and the faces are unequal. Fig. 2 shows the pyramid again in plan. The pyramid is cut by a plane which leaves the horizontal plane along the line MNP; the cut face is a triangle of which EDF is the plan. The line DE in the air will meet the line BA in the plane of the face PBA at M, which is in the line MP common to the horizontal plane and the cutting plane. Similarly, CA, FE, and MP intersect at N; and BC, FD, and MP at P. These points M, N, and P are collinear whether the triangle be the triangle DEF in the air or the triangular plan of DEF in the horizontal plane. Obviously, the

Fig. 1

Fig. 2

joins of A and E, and of C and F, and of B and D, the corners of the triangles, are concurrent in V, the vertex of the pyramid, when DEF is in the air, and in the plan of V when the plan of EDF is taken.

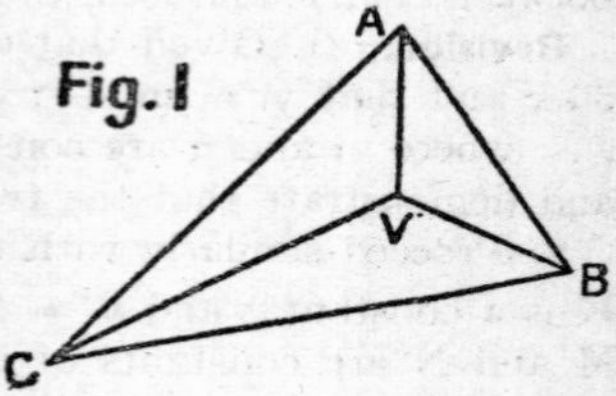

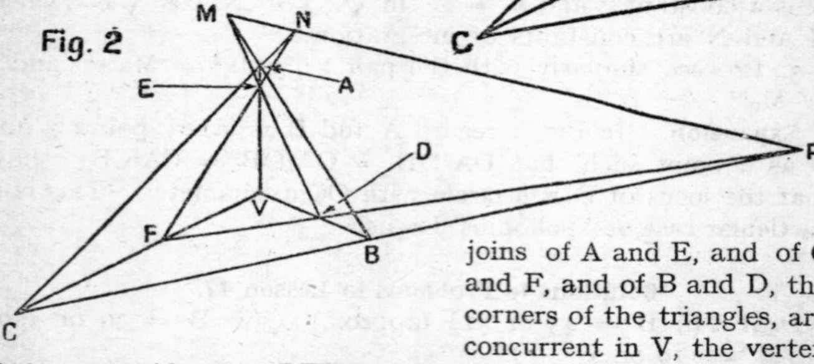

Hence EDF can be any triangle the section of the pyramid, and a different position for EDF merely means a different position for MNP. Hence if two triangles are so arranged that the joins of corresponding corners are concurrent, the intersections of their corresponding sides are collinear.

PERSPECTIVE AND ANTI-PARALLELISM

This is the Desargues' Theorem in plane geometry. Such triangles in one plane are said to be in perspective, and the point of concurrency, V in plan, is the centre of perspective and the line of collinearity. MNP, is the axis of perspective.

A parallelogram can be split into two similar triangles, ABCD, Fig. 3. Let the split be along BD. The triangle BCD may be kept in the plane of ABCD and rotated round O, the mid-point of BD, until it fits the triangle BAD.

If the angles at O are right angles the figure is a rectangle; if, also, the figure is equilateral it is a square.

Similar triangles comprise the diamond figure ABCD, Fig. 4, along the diagonal AC but not along BD. Also ACD cannot be rotated without removal from the plane of ABCD to fit ABC. Also the diagonals do not bisect each other. To make the similar triangles fit is necessary to turn one of them over; when turning over is necessary the triangles are said to be inversely similar.

Without turning ACD over, it may be rotated until CD falls along CA, Fig. 5, where CDE is the new position of CDA. In this case M, the intersection of BA and DE, is on the axis of symmetry of the figure and MC bisects the angle ACE.

The line DE thus obtained is said to be an anti-parallel of AB. Any line parallel to DE is anti-parallel to AB. In Fig. 6 let DE be anti-parallel and unequal to AB, and let N be the mid-point of DE; then NC is a median of the triangle DEC; hence all the parallels to DE in DEC are bisected by the line NC; hence all the anti-parallels to AB in the triangle ABC are bisected by NC; hence NC is the median of CDE and the symmedian of the triangle ABC with regard to AB; hence each triangle has three medians and three symmedians. A symmedian is the locus of the mid-points of the anti-parallels.

In Fig. 7 let DE be anti-parallel to AB, and $KE = KD$, then KC is the symmedian of ABC. $KE = KB \sin \gamma / \sin \alpha = KD = KA \sin \alpha / \sin \gamma$, whence $BK/KA = \sin^2 \alpha / \sin^2 \gamma$. Using the customary notation for the angles of ABC: $\sin \alpha = \sin A$, $\sin \gamma = \sin B$. $BK/KA = \sin^2 A / \sin^2 B$. Similarly, if HB be the symmedian, then $AH/HC = \sin^2 C / \sin^2 A$; and if GA be the symmedian, then $CG/GB = \sin^2 B / \sin^2 C$. Whence $BK/KA . AH/HC . CG/GB = 1$, whence KC, HB, and GA are concurrent (Ceva). The three symmedians, like the medians, are concurrent; their point of concurrency is known as the Lemoine point: the point of concurrency of the medians is the C.G. or centroid. Obviously, a side of a triangle and any anti-parallel are the joins of four concyclic points; ADBE is a cyclic quadrilateral. C is the centre of inversion and D and E are a pair of points inverse to the pair of points AB in relation to the centre C.

When the triangles are identically equal, as in Fig. 5, the line CM is both a median and symmedian for ABC and for EDC.

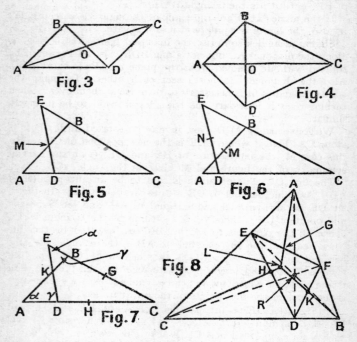

When the triangles are similar, as in Fig. 7, then K and M do not coincide, for if B exceeds A the order of size is AK exceeds DK (and also KE), which exceeds KB, the foot of the symmedian is nearer the larger of the two angles.

In Fig. 8 R is the orthocentre of the triangle ABC and DEF is the pedal triangle of ABC. The sides DE, EF, and FD are respectively anti-parallel to AB, BC, and CA; let H, G, and K be their mid-points, then CH, AG, and BK produced meet in L, the Lemoine point of ABC.

In Fig. 8 let DEFGHK be a cyclic hexagon in which the opposite sides are equal and parallel in pairs. The angles of the figure are indicated.

In Fig. 9 diameter GD is anti-parallel to AB, HE is anti-parallel to AC, and KF is anti-parallel to BC. Hence L is the Lemoine point of ABC. The circle is known as the second Lemoine circle of the triangle ABC. If the radius of the circle be R then DE = 2Rcos a, FG = 2Rcos β, and HK = 2R cos γ; so that the intercepts of the second Lemoine circle on the sides are proportional to the cosine of the opposite angles of the triangle, the complete sides being proportional to the sines of the opposite angles. The circle is hence known as the cosine circle.

Fig. 9

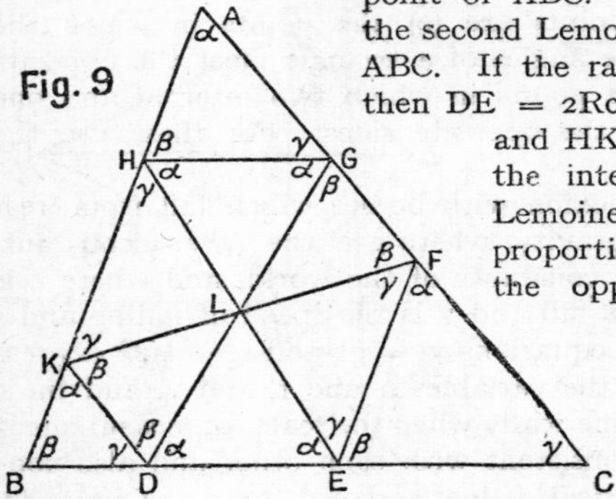

DE = 2Rcos a; DK = GF = 2Rcos β; EF = KH = 2Rcos γ;
DE + DB + EC = 2Rcos a + 2Rcos β. sin a/sin β
$$+ 2R\cos \gamma . \sin a/\sin \gamma$$
$$= 2R(\cos a + a \cos \beta/b + a \cos \gamma/c)$$
$$= a$$
i.e. abc = (ab cos γ + bc cos a + ca cos β) 2R
i.e. $1/2R$ = cos a/a + cos β/b + cos γ/c

Obviously, the distances from L to BC = R sin a, to CA = R sin β, and to AB = R sin γ; hence these distances are proportional to the respective sides of the triangle.

Drill. 1. Integrate with respect to x (m, n, p, being constants)
(i) x^n; (ii) $1/x$; (iii) e^x; (iv) sin x; (v) cos x; (vi) sec² x; (vii) cosec²x; (viii) $(1 - x^2)^{-\frac{1}{2}}$; (ix) $(x^2 \pm 1)^{-\frac{1}{2}}$; (x) $(1 + x^2)^{-1}$.

2. Integrate with respect to x: (i) $(mx + p)^n$; (ii) $(mx + p)^{-1}$; (iii) e^{px}; (iv) sin (mx + p); (v) cos (mx + p); (vi) sec² (mx + p); (vii) cosec² (mx + p); (viii) $(m^2 - x^2)^{-\frac{1}{2}}$;

(ix) $(x^5 \pm m^2)^{-\frac{1}{3}}$; (x) $(m^2 + x^2)^{-1}$; (xi) $(x^2-m^2)^{-1}$; (xii) $(-x)^{-1}$; (xiii) $(m-x)^{-1}$; (xiv) $(m^2 + (-x)^2)^{-\frac{1}{3}}$.

Revision. In any triangle the concurrent lines are (a) the three altitudes; (b) the three medians; (c) the three bisectors of the angles; (d) the lines joining the corners to the point of contact of the opposite side and the inscribed circle. It is an interesting simplification of previous methods of proof to establish proofs dependent upon the theorem of Ceva.

Similarly, collinear points are (e) the points in which the external bisectors of the angles of a triangle meet the opposite sides produced; (f) the points in which two internal and one external bisector meet the opposite sides. For these use the theorem of Menelaus.

Expansion. In connexion with bodies which fall from rest under the influence of gravity, where g is the gravity constant, one of the fundamental constants of the world, and where t is the time occupied in the fall and v is the speed of falling and s is the length fallen, the equations $v = gt$ and $s = \frac{1}{2}gt^2$ express valid relations between the variables s, and t, and v, and these relations can be used numerically when the scales of measurement of s and v and t are consistent with each other and also consistent with the numerical value assigned to g. Obviously $ds/dt = v$, where g does not appear in the equation. Consider other scientific or other formulae after this fashion.

Solutions to Problems in Lesson 48.

Drill. 1. (a) If c = cost, $c(100 + x) = 100 x$; whence when x = 25 c = 20. (b) If c = S.P., $100c = x (100 - x)$; whence when x = 50 c. = 25. Both sets of related figures depend on the ratios 1 : 2, 2 : 3, etc., read in different places:

ratio	1 : 2	2 : 3	3 : 4	4 : 5
(a) c : x	50 : 100	$33\frac{1}{3}$: 50	25 : 33	20 : 25
(b) c : x	25 : 50	$22\frac{2}{3}$: $33\frac{1}{3}$	$18\frac{3}{4}$: 25	16 : 20

2. Let the outward journey take x minutes, G.M.T. The double journey took 17x/9 min. G.M.T. = 90, x = $47\frac{11}{17}$. Then local time at B was $2\frac{11}{17}$ minutes slow on Greenwich.

Revision. 1. $dy/dx = n + Ax + (B/2)x^2 + (C/3)x^3 \ldots \ldots$

2. $dy/dx = K(\cos \sqrt{K}x - \sin \sqrt{K}x)$.

3. $dy/dx = Mae^{ax}$.

Expansion. In the triangle DAB, O lies between A and B and DO is the internal bisector of the angle BDA ; C lies beyond B from A and CD is the external bisector of the angle BDA ; whence ODC is a right angle, and the locus of D is on the semi-circle with OC as diameter. In Fig. 1, Lesson 48, the ratio of DA to DB is not fixed, but should DA : DB = OA : OB this result holds.

LESSON 50

Volumes and Surfaces of Revolution

LET BDFK (Fig. 1) be any curve and BA, DC, FE, be ordinates of the points B,D,F, on the curve. Let OX be an axis of revolution ; when the curve BD is revolved round OX the surface which is generated by the curve BD contains a volume ; let V be that volume.

Let $OC = x$, and $DC = y = $ a function of x.

Let $OE = x + \delta x$, where δx is very small ; then the volume V increases by δV, the volume of the slab contained by DF revolved.

This slab is not cylindrical ; its volume lies between the volumes of cylinders of equal height along OX, i.e. CE, and with radii of their circular bases DC and FE ; whence $\delta y/\delta x$ lies between πDC^2 and πCE^2. Hence the limit for $\delta x = 0$

$$D_x V = \pi CD^2 = \pi y^2 ; \quad dV = \pi y^2 dx.$$

Hence the volume V is that integral of πy^2 which is zero when $x = OA$.

A. When BD is such that $y = k$, (i.e. a straight line)
$D_x V = \pi k^2 ; \quad V = \pi k^2 x + W$, where W is a constant of integration ; $V = 0$ when $OA = x - h$, where $h = $ the length of AC. Thence $W = -\pi k^2 x + \pi k^2 h ;$ whence $V = \pi k^2 h$. The volume of the cylinder of revolution is the product of the area of the circular end and the distance between the circular ends.

B. Let BDK be a curve $y^2 = 2Rx - x^2$; where R is the radius of the curve, which is a circle through the origin.
$D_x V = (2Rx - x^2)\pi ; \quad V = \frac{1}{3}\pi x^2(3R - x) + W ;$ when $V = 0$, $x = 0$ and $W = 0$; therefore $V = \frac{1}{3}\pi x^2(3R - x)$.

The volume required is the value for V when $x = 2R$ and is therefore $\frac{1}{3}\pi\ R^2(3R - 2R) = \frac{4}{3}\pi\ R^3$.

The volume of the solid which is a sphere is $\frac{4}{3}\pi$ (radius)^3.

C. Let BDK be a part of a curve $y^2 = R^2 - x^2$ for values of x greater than $(R - H)$.

$D_xV = \pi\ (R^2 - x^2)$; $V = \frac{1}{3}\pi\ x\ (3R - x^2) + W$; $V = O$ when $x = (R - H)$; therefore $W = -\frac{1}{3}\pi\ (2R^3 - 3RH^2 + H^3)$: and $V = \frac{1}{3}\pi\ x\ (3R - x^2) - \frac{1}{3}\pi\ (2R^3 - 3RH^2 + H^3)$.

The volume of the solid is the value for V when $x = R$, and is, therefore, $\pi\ H^2(R - \frac{1}{3}H)$. This is the volume of a spherical cap of height H in a sphere of radius R.

Obviously, when $H = R$, the volume is that of a hemisphere.

D. Let BDK be part of a curve $b^2x^2 + a^2y^2 = a^2b^2$, when x is positive. When $V = O$, $x = O$, $W = O$.

$D_xV = \pi b^2(1 - x^2/a^2)$;

whence $V = \pi b^2 x(1 - x^2/3a)$.

The volume required is when $x = a$; i.e. $V = 2\ ab^2/3$.

This volume is a solid formed by the revolution of half an ellipse ; hence the volume of the spheroid generated by the rotation of a whole ellipse about the axis, which is $2a$, is $4\ ab^2/3$. In this formula, when $2a$ is the major axis, the spheroid is labelled prolate. Obviously, the formula when the revolution is about the minor axis, i.e. when the spheroid is oblate, is $4\ a^2b/3$, when $2b$ is the minor axis.

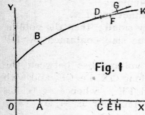

Fig. 1

Reverting to Fig. 1, let DG be tangent to the curve and let the length of DG equal the length of the curve DF, and let GH be an ordinate. When AC increases by CE, i.e. when x increases by $\delta\ x$, then BD increases by the portion DF, i.e. $\delta\ s$. The surface of the slab with thickness $\delta\ x$, and the curve DF as its edge of revolution, has an area in between the areas of the surfaces of the slabs (i) with thickness $\delta\ x$ and line DF as its edge of revolution, and (ii) with thickness CH and line DG as its edge of revolution. Let the surface of revolution traced out by the curve DF have an area S, and let BD $= s$.

Then $\pi(CD + EF)DF/\delta\ x$ and $\pi(CD + GH)DG/\delta\ x$ are the two values between which lies the value $\delta\ S/\ \delta\ x$.

VOLUMES AND SURFACES OF REVOLUTION

The limit for x = O of $DF/\delta x$ and of $DG/\delta x$ is $D_x s$: and the limit of (CD + EF) and of (CD + GH) is 2CD.

Hence $D_x S = 2\pi CD \cdot D_x s = 2\pi y D_x s$.

i.e. $dS = 2\pi y \, dx$. $(ds/dx) = 2\pi y (ds)$.

The area S is that integral of $2\pi y (ds/dx)$ which is zero when x = OA. Also $(ds)^2 = (dx)^2 + (dy)^2$; or $(ds/dx) = (1 + (dy/dx)^2)^{\frac{1}{2}}$

A. $y = k$; $ds/dx = 1$; $dS/dx = 2\pi y = 2\pi k$; $S = 2\pi kx + W$; when OA $= x - h$; $W = -2\pi k(x - h)$ when $x = h$, $S = 2\pi kh$.

i.e. the surface area of a cylinder = the product of its height and the circumference of its circular base.

B. $y^2 = 2Rx - x^2$; $dy/dx = (R - x) (2Rx - x^2)^{\frac{1}{2}}$; $ds/dx = R/(2Rx - x^2)^{\frac{1}{2}}$; $dS/dx = 2\pi R$; $S = 2\pi Rx + W$; when S = O, x = O, and W = O; and when x = 2R, $S = 4\pi R^2$.

i.e. the area of the surface of a sphere $= 4\pi$ (radius)^2.

C. $y^2 = R^2 - x^2$; $(dy/dx)^2 = x^2/(R^2 - x^2)$: $ds/dx = R/(R^2 - x^2)^{\frac{1}{2}}$; $dS/dx = 2\pi R$;

$S = 2\pi Rx + W$; when $x = (R - H)$, S = O and $W = -2\pi R (R - H)$; when x = R, then $S = 2\pi R - 2\pi R + 2 RH$ i.e. $S = 2\pi RH$.

i.e. the area of the surface of a spherical cap of height H in a sphere of radius R $= 2\pi RH$. Obviously, when R = H, the area is that of the surface of a hemisphere.

D. $a^2y^2 = b^2(a^2 - x^2)$; $(dy/dx)^2 = b^2x^2/a^2 (a^2 - x^2)$; $(ds/dx)^2 = (a^4 - a^2x^2 + b^2x^2) a^2 (a^2 - x^2)$. Since the curve is an ellipse $b^2/a^2 = (1 - e^2)$, where e = eccentricity, and

$dS/dx = 2\pi y(a^2 - x^2e^2)^{\frac{1}{2}}/(a^2 - x^2)^{\frac{1}{2}}$

$= 2\pi (1 - e^2)^{\frac{1}{2}}(a^2 - x^2e^2)^{\frac{1}{2}} + W$

When S = O, x = O, W = O; hence S $= \pi a^2(1 - e^2 + (1 - e^2)\frac{1}{2}/e. \sin e)$, which is the surface area of half a prolate ellipse.

In testing the native capacity of children, use is made of considerations of chance, when chance is affected by observed bias.

By experiment with large numbers of children a set of questions is obtained such that, on the average, beginning with the most difficult question, when an average group of P children are set to answer the P questions in the test, question 1 is correctly answered by 1 child, questions 1 and 2 both correctly answered by 2 children, the first N questions are all correctly answered by N children. This means that 1 child scores full marks, i.e. P; a second child scores (P − 1), a third child (P − 2) and so on

This is a hypothetical case due to averaging, for children do not behave thus uniformly. In fact, the K children who answer K questions and score K marks out of the possible P rather rarely answer a sequence of K questions. They miss one or two and make up their total by answering a question here or there of the more difficult type. This circumstance has been smoothed out in the averaging when the test as a whole was constructed, but when the test is applied to a group of 10,000 children this circumstance reappears. Assuming that P = 100, theoretically, if each child scored at least 1, 100 children would score each of the marks between 1 and 100. This would not happen. It would probably happen that, taking the questions and ignoring the capricious individualities of the children, question 1 would be correctly answered 100 times, questions 1 and 2 would be, in total, correctly answered 200 times, and so on; if not, the averaging would be at fault. But each child who answered No. 1 correctly would not also have answered the other 99 correctly, and so on. Consequently, the scores would tend to "pack" towards 50, the mean. The farther away the score from 1 and 100, the greater the number of children who totalled the score. In itself, this tendency towards the mean is evidence of the fact that children do not perform uniformly.

Experience indicates an inevitable bias of this character. This bias is accentuated when the jumps between the questions are large, and tends to disappear when the jumps are small; when the jumps are very large the experiment breaks down. Such jumps between the questions are evidence of a bias in the observer; they may be also evidence of a bias in the subject matter of the questions. Obviously, such experimentation is likely to provide valid conclusions about the child in general, but doubtful conclusions about individual children. Hence is evolved the primary conclusion in examining: the central portion of the score sheet, i.e. the portion which contains the mean score and nearly mean scores, is ineffective; children with such scores have not been adequately examined. Averaging tends to smooth out the effects of bias; averaging may be an adjustment to secure a distribution of scores corresponding with the theoretical pattern outlined above, or it may be to secure a distribution of scores corresponding with any other theoretical pattern judged suitable; a decision in this connexion involves practical considerations strictly related to the purpose of the examining.

VOLUMES AND SURFACES OF REVOLUTION

Drill. Find the value for the volume of a cone, vertical height A and base radius B. Find the value of the area of the surface of this cone, neglecting the area of the base circle.

For A substitute $(R - H)$ and for B substitute $\sqrt{H\,(2R - H)}$. To each of these values now altered add from C above the values for a spherical cap, and so find expressions for the volume and surface area of a spherical sector in a sphere of radius R· with the height of the spherical cap portion of the solid $= H$.

Revision. 1. Divide $(m \pm n)$ by $(m^{\frac{1}{3}} \pm n^{\frac{1}{3}})$.

2. Find the value of $(0.03541)^{\frac{1}{2}}\,(0.00002648)^{\frac{1}{4}}$.

3. Show that $a/b = c/d = (a^n + c^n)_n^{\frac{1}{n}}/(b^n + d^n)_n^{\frac{1}{n}}$.

4. Find the middle term and the thirteenth term of the expansion of $(a^3 + 3/a^3)^{16}$.

5. Find the remainder when $x^4 + 6x^3 - 9x^2 - 3x + 4$ is divided by $x - 3$. Find a method of answering this question without performing the division.

6. Solve $x^2 - 8ax + 15a^2 = O$; hence write down the roots of : $-x^2 - 8x + 15 = O$; $x^2 - 80x + 1500 = O$; $10x^2 - 8x + 1\frac{1}{2} = O$.

7. Solve $(1·05)^x = 1$.

8. Solve $(25)^{x-2} = (4)^{3x+1}$.

Expansion. Apply the dictum "In any examination the candidates who are ranged at or about the mean mark have not been adequately examined" to your own experiences and draw the inevitable conclusions.

Solutions to Problems in Lesson 49.

Drill 1. (i) $x^{n+1}(n + 1)^{-1}$; (ii) log x (a special case of (i) when $n = -1$); (iii) e^x;
(iv) $-\cos x$; (v) $\sin x$; (vi) $\tan x$;
(vii) $-\cot x$; (viii) $1/\sin x$ or $-1/\cos x$;
(ix) $\log(x + (x^2 \pm 1)^{\frac{1}{2}})$; (x) $1/\tan x$ or $-1/\cot x$.

2. (i) $(mx + p)^{n+1}(n + 1)^{-1}m^{-1}$;
(ii) $m^{-1}\log(mx + p)$; (iii) $p^{-1}e^{px}$;
(iv) $-m^{-1}\cos(mx + p)$; (v) $m^{-1}\sin(mx + p)$;
(vi) $m^{-1}\tan(mx + p)$; (vii) $-m^{-1}\cot(mx + p)$;
(viii) $-1/\sin(x/m)$; or $-1/\cos(x/m)$;
(ix) $\log(x + (x^2 \pm m^2)^{\frac{1}{2}})$; (x) $m^{-1}\tan^{-1}(x/m)$
or $-m^{-1}\cot^{-1}(x/m)$;
(xi) if x exceeds m : $(\log(x - m)$
$- \log(x + m))\,(2m)^{-1}$;

if m exceeds x : $(\log(m - x)$
$- \log(x + m)) (2m)^{-1}$;
(xii) $\log(- x)$; (xiii) $\log(m - x)$;
(xiv) $- \log(- x + (m^2 + (- x)^2)^{\frac{1}{2}})$.

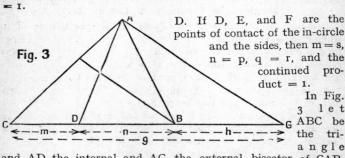

Fig. 2

Revision. Let ABC (Fig. 2) be a triangle and D, E, F, be the points in the sides. AD, BF, CE are concurrent whenever the continued product of m/n, p/q, and r/s is 1.

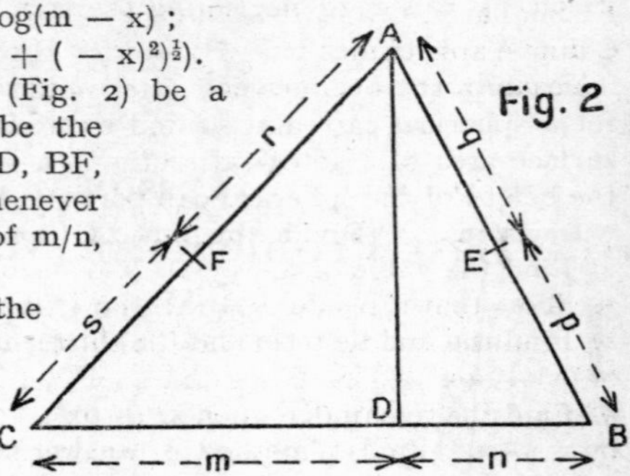

A. If D, E, and F are the feet of the altitudes, m = b cos C, n = c cos B · whence the continued product is (b cos C/c cos B) times (a cos B/b cos A) times (c cos A/a cos C), which cancels to 1.

B. If D, E, and F are the feet of the three medians, m = n, p = q, r = s ; and the continued product = 1.

C. If D, E, and F are the crossing points of the bisectors of the angles, then D is symmetrically placed regarding AD and the perpendiculars from D to AC and to AB are equal , let these be denoted by w. Then w = m sin C = n sin B, and the continued product is (sin B/sin C) times (sin A/sin B) times (sin C/sin A) = 1.

D. If D, E, and F are the points of contact of the in-circle and the sides, then m = s, n = p, q = r, and the continued product = 1.

Fig. 3

In Fig. 3 let ABC be the triangle and AD the internal and AG the external bisector of CAB. m/n (by C above) = sin B/sin C, and so, m/n = b/c. Since DAG is a right angle. then, by Apollonius Locus, g/h = m/n = b/c.

E. Whence, since (b/c) (c/a) (a/b) = 1, by Menelaus' Theorem, G and its corresponding points on external bisectors are collinear.
F. Similarly, G and the points E and F in the positions for case C above are collinear.

Expansion. See above.

LESSON 51

Last Problems in Mathematics

IN Lesson 50 it was shown that in a test on a single paper of questions—or, of course, any test with a number of scoring points, such as an interview before a board of N interviewers—mean scores were valueless, except as an indication that the test had not served to differentiate the ability of the P % candidates who scored round about the mean mark. The examining was defective ; the amount of the defect due to the bias of the paper of questions and to the examiner's point of view may be " corrected," but the bias due to the candidates remains. Let this bias be expressed, in terms of the number of candidates, as x %, then the chance in favour of the correct examining of a candidate is (100 — x) to x. A particular candidate may be of such a type that his personal factor alters the general x to kx ; his chances are then (100 — kx) to kx. If his k reduces kx to a small percentage, he is a good examinee, but not necessarily an able child ; if his k enlarges kx to 50%, he cannot be examined at all, although he may be an able child.

An examination often averages the result of two tests. Akx and Bkx are the probable errors on the tests A and B, the average is ½(A + B)kx, k and x are independent of A and B, and the probable error is not changed. Averaging merely reduces the bias due to the questions set and the personality of the examiner ; it does not alter the fact that candidates whose scores range near to the mean have not been examined.

The result of an examination is therefore, for the individual, a fluke ; it indicates whether the candidate and the examiner were in agreement in a particular manner and on a particular occasion. A candidate who just scrapes through Matriculation has no more justification to be admitted as a student of a university than one who has just failed to scrape through. On the other hand, a comparison of the results of two tests may supply some information about the probable values of x and k. It is observable, for example, in arithmetic and English tests of a general and presumably unbiased character that a candidate who is in the top 10 % of the list in arithmetic has an even chance of being in the top 10 % in English and conversely ; this tendency is observable throughout the lists and is observable on many occasions with different ages of children. This suggests that children stand an even chance of equal performances in arithmetic and English ; a good examinee has a bias in favour of equal performances.

This line of thought may at this point be left, not because it cannot be pursued further with considerable profit, but because it has served its immediate purpose to emphasize the fact that a mathematical argument is merely a form of analysis and statement which in the end must be capable of statement in language and capable of verification in common experience. When a mathematical summary statement disagrees with experience, the mathematical argument is in the air or else observation is at fault. Mathematics is a code, a consistent code, consistent within itself ; its consistence with experience is not determinable mathematically.

The mathematical argument is not : Because A is valid therefore B is valid, but that A and B are both consistent with each other because they are consistent with the mathematical code. $AB = M$ is a statement in code of a mathematical relation. For our purposes we may start with A, determine in fact a relation $xA = M$, determine a second relation that $x = B$, or we may commence with B or even with M ; it is solely a matter of convenience where we begin and end our demonstration of the relation $AB = M$.

$$Zero + A + A + A + A + \ldots . N \text{ times} = NA$$
$$Zero - B - B - B - B - B - \ldots . M \text{ times} = - MB$$
$$Zero = (A - A) = (B - B), \text{ etc.}$$

$NA/A = N$; $NA/N = A$; merely begin with NA.

A and B are independent ; but $e^a = A$, and $e^n = N$, $e^b = B$, $e^m = M$; where e provides a link between A and B they are still independent, for a and b are independent, yet $NA = e^a$ added e^n times $= e^{a + n}$; and when N and A are multiplied n and a are added · the form of expression has been changed, the facts remain.

$(dy/dx) = 3x^2$, and $y = x^3$, state the same factual relation in a different form. But x^3 suggests the fact called volume and x^2 suggests the fact called area; it is a matter for observational investigation to discover the thing for which y represents the volume when (dy/dx) represents the area. If, for example, y represents the volume of a sphere of radius x, then (dy/dx) represents the surface area of that sphere, both on a scale of which the unit is $4\pi/3$.

With reference to the zero, or beginning, of rectangular coordinates the following summary is obtained :

Codal expression	Verbal expression
(i) $x/a = 1$	(i) a line parallel to the y-axis and distant a from it.
(ii) $\pm y/a = 1$	(ii) both lines parallel to the x-axis and distant a from it.
(iii) $\pm x/a = 1$ or $\pm y/a = 1$	(iii) perimeter of a square of side 2a, with sides parallel to the axes of reference.
(iv) $\pm x/a = 1$ and $\pm y/a = 1$ i.e. $\pm (x \pm y) = a$	(iv) perimeter of a square of side $a \sqrt{2}$ with corners on the axes of reference symmetrically.
(v) $\Sigma(\pm x/a = 1) = \Sigma(\pm y/a = 1) = \Sigma(\pm x/a \pm y/a) = 1$	(v) for all values of a, the plane of reference.
(vi) $(x^2/a^2 = 1) = (\pm x/a = 1)$	(vi) both lines as above.
(vii) $x^2/a^2 + y^2/a^2 = 1$	(vii) circumference of a circle, radius a, centre origin.
(viii) $\Sigma(x^2/a^2 + y^2/a^2 = 1)$	(viii) for all values of a, the plane of reference.

In the above, the facts are lines of a certain character in certain relative positions such that the summation of all lines of this character is the plane of reference which is an area ; this area can be limited by putting a limit to the value of a ; all these lines and the plane of reference may be described as the loci of points which satisfy certain conditions.

(ix) $x/a + y/a + z/a = 1$ (ix) in general, the surface of a plane which is tangential to the sphere centred at O with radius $\frac{1}{2}\sqrt{3}$ a, at the point $(\frac{1}{2}a, \frac{1}{2}a, \frac{1}{2}a)$.

(x) $\pm x/a \pm y/a \pm z/a = 1$ (x) the surface of an octahedron, centred on O, with edge $a\sqrt{2}$, with each face an equilateral triangle area $2\sqrt{3}$ a and with volume $4a^3/3$.

(xi) $x^2/a^2 + y^2/a^2 + z^2/a^2$ (xi) the surface of a sphere
      $= 1$ centred on the origin, radius a, volume $4\pi a^3/3$.

So far, the constant has been retained as a, without change throughout ; the condition of equality of distance from the origin. Now let a and b be unequal constants.

(iii b) $\pm x/a = 1$ OR $\pm$ (iii b) the perimeter of a rectangle
         $y/b = 1$ 2a along the x-axis by 2b along the y-axis.

(iv b) $\pm (x/a \pm y/b) = 1$ (iv b) the perimeter of a parallelo-gram, diagonals 2a and 2b with corners on the axes of reference.

(vii b) $x^2/a^2 + y^2/b^2 = 1$ (vii b) the elliptical curve centred at O, with axes 2a and 2b, and turning points on the axes of reference.

(ix b) $x/a + y/b + z/c = 1$ (ix b) the surface of a plane which passes through the points (a, O, O), (O, b, O) (O, O, c).

(xi b) $x^2/a^2 + y^2/b^2 + z^2/c^2 = 1$

(xi b) the surface of an ellipsoid centred at O, and passing through the points specified above in (ix b).

Here we may pause. Such a pause is characteristic of this line of thought, for the possibilities are not exhausted ; it is equally typical both of this course in Mathematics, which now is ended, and of Mathematics as a code, for its farthest limit depends solely upon the ingenuity of the human mind. This ingenuity works in two directions—the direction of apparent simplification by convenient summaries, and the direction of real complexity in the stringent analysis of the growing complexities of a man's interpretation of the universe of which he is but a fragment. When all that may be done is done, he will not know how his interpretation is related to the real universe he thinks he has interpreted ; the end is not the goal, it is the joy of endeavour.

Solutions to Problems in Lesson 50

Drill. With the vertex of the cone as origin and the axis of the cone as the x-axis, and as the axis of revolution $y = Bx/A$.
$D_x V = \pi B^2 x^2/A^2$. $V = (\tfrac{1}{3}\pi B^2 x^3/A^2) + W$.
When $x = O, W = O$.
When $x = A, V = \tfrac{1}{3}\pi AB^2$.
Also, $(dy/dx)^2 = B^2/A^2$: $ds/dx = (A^2 + B^2)^{\frac{1}{2}}/A$; $dS/dx = 2\pi x(A^2 + B^2)^{\frac{1}{2}}B/A^2$
$S = (\pi x^2(A^2 + B^2)^{\frac{1}{2}}B/A^2) + W$.
When $x = O, W = O$. When $x = A, S = \pi B(A^2 + B^2)^{\frac{1}{2}}$.
Substituting ; $V = \tfrac{1}{3}\pi(R - H)H/(2R - H)$ $S = \pi R\sqrt{H}(2R - H)$ or $\pi R\sqrt{R^2 - (R - H)^2}$. Vol. of cap $= \pi H^2(R - \tfrac{1}{3}H)$. By addition, total vol. of spherical sector $= \tfrac{2}{3}\pi HR^2$. But the surface of the cap $= S = 2\pi RH$, hence the vol. of the sector $= \tfrac{1}{3}$ RS.
The total surface area of the sector
$$= \pi R(2H + \sqrt{R^2 - (R - H)^2}).$$

Revision. 1. $m^{\frac{2}{3}} \pm m^{\frac{1}{3}} n^{\frac{1}{3}} + n^{\frac{2}{3}}$.
2. 0.005608.
3. $K = a/b = c/d = (b^n K^n + d^n K^n)^{\frac{1}{n}}/(b^n + d^n)^{\frac{1}{n}} = (K^n)^{\frac{1}{n}}$.
4. $m = a^3$; $n = 3/a^3$. Middle term $12870m^8n^8 = 12870 \cdot (3^8)$
   Thirteenth term $= 1820 m^4 n^{12} = 1820 (3^{12})/a^8$.

5. If R = the remainder, the expression − R = O. When
x − 3 = O

R = the result of substituting 3 for x in the expression;
i.e. R = − 167.

6. Expression = (x − 5a) (x − 3a) = O ; i.e. x = 5a or 3a.
    x = 3 or 5 ; x = 30 or 50 ; x = 0·3 or 0·5.

7. (using logs) x = 47·18

8. (using logs) x = − 8½ (approx.).

Expansion. See above.

This Lesson concludes our Course in Mathematics.

LESSON 27

American Nations in the Making

(See plate 55)

W E now turn to review American developments from
the beginning of the 19th century until the end of
the Civil War in 1865—dealing with the division of
Latin America into independent republics and the consolidation
of the United States. At the peace of 1815, Brazil, the largest
country in South America, was still attached to Portugal, and
the rest of Latin America, including Mexico, to the restored
Spanish monarchy, which had been suspended by Napoleon.
The population—pure Spanish, Creoles, half-castes, Africans
and Indian natives—were ruled by governors sent from Spain.

Brazil effected a peaceful change. From 1808 till 1821 Rio
was the residence of the Brazilian court, and after the king's
return to Portugal, his son Pedro, the Portuguese crown prince
and regent of Brazil, declared himself emperor of an independent
Brazil (1822) and resigned the Portuguese succession in favour
of his daughter on his father's death in 1826. The Brazilian
monarchy existed until converted into a republic in 1889.

With the instability of the Spanish crown—the one link
which held together Spain's scattered dominions—during the
Peninsular War, thought in Spanish America was changing
towards independence, though traditional royal authority
partially prevailed for some years. Spanish American emancipation was effected by a series of revolutions which swept away
existing institutions. With the fall of the monarchy in Spain
the separatist and regional tendencies characteristic of Spaniards
were increased by the geographical distances and large areas
of the South American dominions. Emergency governments
were set up in every Spanish-American capital to replace fallen
authority, to resist French aggression, and in nominal support
of the Spanish crown. These efforts at local self-government
finally led to the creation of independent states.

In the temperate regions of Buenos Aires and of Chile the
revolution was carried through by fairly constitutional methods.
In 1816 the emergency governments formed in 1810 abandoned
the theory of Spanish dependence : Argentina came into existence

as a republic, and in 1817 the Argentine general San Martin led his army over the Andes to liberate Chile from the invading Royalists of Peru and recovered her independence. A Chilean war fleet, under Thomas Cochrane (afterwards Lord Dundonald), and chiefly manned by English sailors, landed large Chilean and Argentine forces under San Martin in Peru, where they defeated the Royalists.

In tropical Latin America, violent turmoil preceded emancipation. Carácas was twice retaken by Royalists. Bolivar the Liberator enlisted a British legion in England and Ireland, and in a series of astounding campaigns defeated the Spanish Royalist forces. Cochrane had already cleared the Pacific of Spanish ships. In 1824 Bolivar's army was victorious at Ayacucho, and the independence of South America was secured, though the various states scarcely acquired stability until the end of the 19th century.

The Americas were not practically involved in the political complications of Europe, especially after the enunciation of the Monroe doctrine (1823) that Europeans must not concern themselves with political complications in America. For Americans international questions meant disputes between American states with which European states had nothing to do, except so far as the security of the lives and property of their own nationals might be involved. Meanwhile, the attitude of George Canning, British Foreign Minister, had averted the complication of French aid for the Spanish scheme of reconquest : in 1825, Great Britain recognized the independence of Buenos Aires (Argentina), Colombia and Mexico. Venezuela was established as a republic in 1830. Bolivia and Peru had separated before the death of Bolivar in that year. Notwithstanding revolutions, strife and political set-backs, freedom of commerce and of intercourse with Europe now steadily progressed. The influx of European, and particularly of British, capital, together with the demand for South American raw materials, etc., greatly aided development.

Affairs in Mexico. In Mexico, and the five small provinces to its south-east in Central America, emancipation had been delayed. With the acknowledgment of independence, these five provinces separated from the Mexican republic and broke off into the five independent republics of Guatemala, Honduras, Salvador, Nicaragua and Costa Rica. Mexico continued to be menaced by Spanish attempts at reconquest from the Spanish island of

Cuba. Frontier questions led to the war with the United States (1845-8), during which Mexico was invaded and the capital occupied ; as a result, one-third of its nominal territory. California and New Mexico, was ceded to the United States. This opened up the westward expansion to the Pacific Ocean, with important effect on the U.S. system.

In 1855 there began a period of civil war, and in 1861 Spanish, British and French troops landed to enforce foreign rights. After the withdrawal of the British and Spanish in 1863, the French remained and installed Maximilian of Austria, younger brother of the emperor Francis Joseph and son-in-law of Leopold I of Belgium, as emperor of Mexico under the aegis of Napoleon III. For some years the new emperor maintained his position, but in 1866 the supporting French troops were withdrawn and in 1867 Maximilian was taken and shot. After this, turmoil prevailed until General Diaz seized the government and ruled the republic as autocratic president till 1911.

The United States had disputes with Great Britain over ill-defined boundaries, which were settled by a complaisant British Government very much in favour of the American claims and to the displeasure of Canada. The States had also their own problems to solve. They had, after the severance of the Thirteen Colonies from the British Empire, set up a common authority for the whole Union side by side with individual state authorities. From the beginning antagonistic views were held as to the extent to which the common authority could override state rights.

Now, both social traditions and economic traditions made a dividing line between the northern and the southern states of the Union. The southern planters, mainly of English descent and with the traditions of English gentry, lived on large estates run by negro slave labour, in a semi-tropical climate ; the northerners were mainly traders and agriculturists descended from the Puritan settlers with Puritan religious convictions. They neither required nor desired to employ slave labour ; as they would have derived no economic benefit, they had no interests to blind them to its moral degradation. The southerner, who found it easy to believe in slavery as a divine institution, had nothing to fear, as a producer, from the imports of foreign competitors, while he wanted to buy the goods he required in the cheapest market and to export his own produce. The northern producer, on the other hand, wanted to shut out the foreign competitor. In other words, the southerner found his interest in free trade and slave labour, while the northerner found his

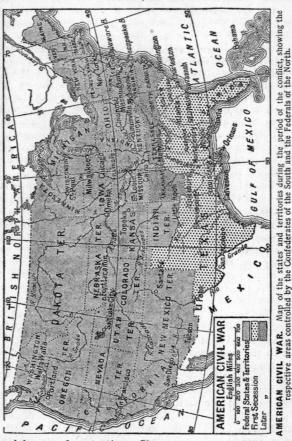

AMERICAN CIVIL WAR. Map of the states and territories during the period of the conflict, showing the respective areas controlled by the Confederates of the South and the Federals of the North.

AMERICAN CIVIL WAR.
English Miles
0 100 200 300 400 500 600 700
Federal States & Territories
First Secession
Later "

in free labour and protection. Slavery was an established system in the south; in the north it was prohibited, but the northerners for years recognized its existence in the south as a matter of state right.

The more numerous northern states were preponderant in the common central government; if that preponderance should become excessive the southern states were in danger of finding their interests overridden—their chance of economic salvation would turn on the open question of their right to secede from the Union. But the westward expansion at the middle of the century gave the question a new character. It meant that as sufficient territory was occupied, new states would continue to be formed. Were they to be slave states—that is, attached to the southern economic system of slave labour—or free states attached to the northern system? Among the new occupants northerners would inevitably outnumber the southerners. The South claimed that the existing " Missouri Line " dividing slave from free states should not be crossed by new free states; northern sentiment demanded in effect that all new states should be free; compromises were adopted in spite of hot opposition and some fighting. John Brown, an extreme type of abolitionist, was actively engaged in anti-slavery enterprises and as a leader in border conflicts in Kansas; after the episode of his raid on the United States armoury at Harper's Ferry he was taken prisoner, convicted, and hanged for treason and murder in 1859. The full effects of John Brown's fighting spirit and example were felt during the next few years.

American Civil War. When Abraham Lincoln, who abominated slavery, was elected to the Presidency, to take office in 1861, the South was convinced that its interests were doomed to be swamped. It was time to secede from the Union, as the only way of escape, and in February of that year seven of the southern states drew up for themselves a constitution for the " Confederated States of America," assuming the right of secession implied in that term, as opposed to Federal, which implies indissoluble union. Nearly all the slave states joined them at once, electing Jefferson Davis president of the Confederate States. Lincoln proclaimed his intention of enforcing the laws of the Union in all the states; the Confederates seized the arsenal Fort Sumpter in April; and the great Civil War began. In the northern view the Confederates were rebels; in their own view they were fighting for political freedom.

The immediate issue of the war was not abolition, but the right of one portion of the republic to separate itself from another portion—a highly debatable question of law. Europe, remaining neutral, recognized the south as *de facto* belligerents, not rebels. The war was fought between volunteer citizen armies, the southern Confederates being numerically much weaker, while the northern Federals had so much the stronger fleet that they were able to blockade the Confederate ports and cut off the commerce on which the South was dependent. Nevertheless, for a long time the balance of military successes was with the South, which put all its forces into the field from the beginning, which the North did not.

At Bull Run, in Virginia, the first big battle, the Confederates were victorious; again, in 1862, General Robert Lee put the northern troops to flight in the same neighbourhood. But the South had no reserves, whereas the North could not only make good its losses, but continuously multiply its armies. A destructive blow was dealt in January, 1863, when Lincoln, for the federal government, proclaimed the emancipation of all slaves. In that summer the South met its decisive check in the great three days' battle of Gettysburg. In the campaigning of 1864, when Ulysses Grant had been placed in general command of the Federal forces, the southern armies under Lee were gradually enveloped; next April the Confederate army was overwhelmed, and Lee was forced to surrender at Appomattox Court House. The war was finished; slavery was no more, and the American nation was at last an established fact; five days later, while viewing a play with his family at Ford's Theatre, Washington, Lincoln was shot by J. W. Booth—an unsuccessful actor, who had become involved in a conspiracy to revenge the defeat of the Confederates—and died the next morning, April 15, 1865.

LESSON 28

Creation of the German Empire

(See plates 55 and 56)

THE unpopularity of the Bismarck régime in the past was forgotten in the general jubilation at its triumphant success, and after the Peace of Prague (1866) the Government was strengthened (as before it would have been weakened) by popular concessions and ostentatious deference to constitutional practice. Austria was deprived of no territory but Venetia, and subjected to no humiliations, so that friendship could be restored without soreness. The Hungarian leaders had established a claim on the imperial government by their judicious attitude, with the result that the " dual monarchy," which united the imperial Austrian and Hungarian crowns, was established, under distinct administrative systems, the one German and the other Magyar, but with a common supreme government ; the Slav populations were subject to one or the other of the pair.

France had failed to snatch any advantages out of the complications. From this time Bismarck was rather preparing than awaiting the opportunity to deal with the remaining obstacle to Prussian ascendancy—the rivalry of France, whose unfailing policy since the days of Richelieu had been prevention of the consolidation of Germany ; yet the opportunity was not, in fact, of his making. It was provided by Spain, which ejected Queen Isabella and sought a foreign prince to whom her crown might be offered. One possible candidate was a prince of a junior branch of the house of Hohenzollern. Here was a menace to French influence in the Peninsula. King William and Bismarck were at odds on the question. Prince Leopold's acceptance would almost certainly bring on the war which Bismarck desired. The offer was made, but rejected by Leopold on July 12, 1870. The German candidate was disposed of ; France had won the diplomatic duel. But Napoleon's hand, to Bismarck's deep satisfaction, was forced by the war party. On July 14 he demanded a pledge from William that he would in no event support Leopold's candidature. There was an interview between the French ambassador and king William at Ems, the king declaring that the incident was closed, but that he could give no pledges as to the future. His telegram reporting the interview to his minister was published that night in German newspapers, but in a condensed form, which set both France and the whole of Germany ablaze with the war fever. Napoleon declared war. South as well as North Germany threw in its lot with Prussia.

Franco-Prussian War. The fighting began on August 2 at Saarbrücken Then in the course of a fortnight the Germans won a series of costly victories—Wörth, Colombières, Mars-la-Tour and Gravelotte—and shut up Bazaine with 170,000 men in Metz and drove Macmahon to join the emperor at Sedan, where, after fierce resistance, on September 1, Napoleon surrendered with his whole force, and the second French Empire vanished. Paris proclaimed the Third Republic with a government of national defence under General Trochu, Jules Favre and Léon Gambetta; the empress Eugénie, whom Napoleon was afterwards permitted to join, took refuge in England.

The Republic was willing to treat, but not to surrender territory. Bismarck demanded Alsace and Lorraine. On September 19 the siege of Paris began. On the 27th Strasbourg fell; a month later Bazaine at Metz surrendered with all his huge army. Meanwhile, Gambetta escaped from Paris in a balloon and organized the government from Tours. The struggle was maintained by raw levies fighting desperately against the mightiest military machine yet known. Since 1866 Moltke and Van Roon had been organizing the general German army up to the Prussian standard of efficiency. There could be only one result. The war party had rushed the French people into a conflict for which, owing to corrupt administration, they were totally unprepared. The Germans had vanquished the regular army; fervid patriotism and dauntless courage could not hold their own against perfect training and consummate organization. On January 28 Paris was starved into capitulation; the last forces in the field were already crushed. The victors dictated the terms of an armistice and the Treaty of Frankfort was signed on May 10, 1871.

Other important events had, however, taken place since Sedan. The Italian kingdom regarded Rome as its rightful capital, but there the Pope, under the aegis of Napoleon, was temporal as well as spiritual sovereign. After Sedan Victor Emmanuel did not hesitate to march on Rome, occupy it, and make it his own secular capital, while the Pope, no longer a temporal sovereign, remained in the Vatican (September, 1870). The German demand for Alsace-Lorraine had threatened the intervention of Russia as the constant champion of the permanent inviolability of treaties, but the Czar wanted to abrogate the Black Sea treaty of 1856; if that treaty might be revised, so also might the treaty of Vienna. So Bismarck approved the demand for a conference to revise the Black Sea treaty, which after a new treaty of London (1871) became waste paper; and the results of the Crimean war were virtually washed out.

During the Franco-Prussian war the states of the South German Confederation were successively coming into the North German; by the end of the year they had all agreed to transform its president, the king of Prussia, into the hereditary German emperor, and as such William I was acclaimed on January 18,

JOHN HUSS ON THE WAY TO EXECUTION. John Huss (c. 1373–1415) was a Bohemian peasant who became a priest and rector of Prague university. Falling under the influence of John Wycliffe, he became critical of the Church's doctrine and discipline, and a champion of Czech nationalism. Summoned to the Council of Constance, and given a safe-conduct, on his arrival he was arrested, tried for heresy condemned to death and burnt alive. This picture from the account of Ulrech von Reichenthal, an eye witness of the proceedings, shows Huss crowned with a paper mitre on his way to the stake.

HISTORY : MEDIEVAL 41

TAMERLANE, Tamburlaine or Timur (1336–1405). This Tartar king of Samarkand, after conquering Persia and northern India, subjugated Asia Minor. Fortunately for Europe he then turned eastward again to China. On his death his vast empire collapsed into fragments.

HISTORY : MEDIEVAL 41

From Martin, "Miniature Painting of Persia, India and Turkey" (Quaritch)

HENRY THE NAVIGATOR (1394–1460). Son of king John I of Portugal and grandson of John of Gaunt, he early interested himself in geographical discovery, and during nearly 50 years financed, organized and occasionally led exploring expeditions to the islands and coasts of Africa. He had an observatory and a college of navigation at Sagres, near Cape St. Vincent.

HISTORY : MEDIEVAL 41

MOHAMMED II (1430–81).
Born at Adrianople, he succeeded his father, Murad II,
in 1451. Two years later he
led an army of 150,000 men
against Constantinople, captured it after a siege of 53
days, and made it his capital.
He then overran much of the
Balkans. This portrait was
painted by Gentile Bellini.
HISTORY : MEDIEVAL 42

National Gallery, London

ASSASSINATION OF JOHN OF BURGUNDY. At a meeting held on the
Bridge of Montereau, September 10, 1419, to effect reconciliation with
the dauphin (later Charles VII), John the Fearless of Burgundy was
felled with an axe by Tanneguy du Chastel, one of Charles's escort, as
seen in this almost contemporary miniature. HISTORY : MEDIEVAL 42
Bibliothèque Nationale; from Larousse, "Histoire de France"

Plate 50　　　　　　　　　　　　　　　　　　　　　　*Volume VI*

1871, in the Hall of Mirrors at Versailles—which during the siege of Paris had been occupied as a German military hospital.

Germany—or Bismarck—dictated the terms at Frankfort, the main features being the cession of Alsace-Lorraine, and the retention of German troops in Paris till France should have paid off an indemnity so huge that the process seemed certain to occupy many more years than, in fact, it did. The French showed a power of resuscitation which astonished the world, though it was not till near the end of the decade that France was really able to resume her place in the front rank of the European powers. The Government and administration needed complete reorganization, and for some time it was uncertain whether the provisional Republic would give way to a monarchical restoration; the possibility of this was frustrated by the hopeless division of the monarchists between the rival claims of the three dynasties of Bourbon, Orleans and Bonaparte.

Bismarck's policy had turned France into an irreconcilable but for the present powerless enemy; to keep France powerless was therefore with him a primary object. Russia was powerful and might become an enemy if Russian interests should clash with those of Germany; a clashing of interests must therefore be avoided. Austria, having accepted separation from Germany, had no interests antagonistic to those of Prussia, and was desirable as a powerful ally. Unison among the three emperors would guarantee the peace of Europe and the consolidation of the German imperial system. Italy was not yet consolidated and England was as unlikely to be attracted either to Russia—the conviction that India was the Czar's objective being more strongly rooted than ever—or to France. A mutual understanding between the emperors—the informal *Dreikaiserbund*—was the result. But the " little rift " revealed itself in the Balkan peninsula, since there Russian and Austrian interests clashed.

Russo-Turkish War. The Porte on principle omitted to carry its promised reforms into effect. In 1875 Herzegovina revolted against Moslem oppression. The Porte made more promises; the insurgents demanded something more substantial and appealed to the powers. The emperors proposed joint action; England refused, the matter being within Turkish sovereignty. The Bulgarians rose and were savagely crushed; Serbia and Montenegro declared war. England urged a conference on the Sultan, who accepted it and then proposed reforms without guarantees. Russia's patience was exhausted. Rumania gave free passage to the Russian troops which crossed the frontier. The other powers, for varying reasons, made no move (April, 1877). For three months the Russians were held up on the Danube. Then, after a rapid advance, they found themselves opposed by the Turks under Osman Pasha before Plevna, where they suffered disastrous defeats. But the fall of Plevna in December turned the scale. In January the Russians were in Adrianople.

Austria and England demanded a congress for the settlement of peace terms. Russia assented, but, nevertheless, on March 3, without waiting, signed with Turkey the Treaty of San Stefano, which in effect would have converted the Turkish empire in Europe into a collection of Slavonic principalities under the protection of Russia. For three more months war and peace hung in the balance. But in June the congress of the powers met at Berlin under the presidency of Bismarck.

LESSON 29

Russian Diplomacy in the 'Eighties

(See plate 57)

Russia's scheme for giving an overwhelming preponderance in the Balkans to Bulgaria as a virtual dependency was quashed under the Berlin Congress treaties (1878), while a much smaller Bulgaria than the Czar had contemplated was made an independent principality. Serbia and Montenegro were also independent but Macedonia and Rumelia remained under the Turkish government. Russia kept Bessarabia, to the disgust of Rumania, which had expected to receive it as a reward for valuable assistance given in the war. Austria acquired a temporary protectorate of Bosnia. Every one of these states, with Greece added to them, was desperately jealous of the others, which they regarded as having received territory to which they themselves were entitled. Russia had bitterly offended Rumania, and very soon alienated Bulgaria by trying to subject its government to Russian control ; and the Balkan peninsula, liberated from Turkish rule, became under the new conditions an even more serious menace to European peace than in the past.

Whether Beaconsfield's policy was or was not in itself wise, there was no question that he carried it through triumphantly defeating Russia all along the line. Russia retorted by advancing in Central Asia towards India, which for some years to come intensified the British suspicions of Russian aims ; though after the agreed boundary delimitations in 1887 Russia turned her attention to the east of Asia, unconscious—like the rest of the world—of a new obstacle, a new power arising there.

Japan's Awakening. Japan had awakened from the prolonged trance of medievalism, realizing as China still refused to realize, that for good or evil the East could no longer keep itself isolated from the West, and that, unless the oriental peoples made ready to meet the occidentals on something like an equal footing, they would be broken. The result was that since the middle of the 19th century, the Japanese nation, headed by the feudal nobility, the Samurai, and by the young Mikado—to whom on his accession in 1868 the Shogun Kokei deliberately resigned the imperial functions, thus ending the system of rule by hereditary military leaders, appropriated to the Shogunate in the 13th century—initiated and carried through an unprecedented revolution, abolishing the old feudal system—after an unsuccessful rebellion of malcontents and irreconcilable conservatives in the Satsuma clan—reconstructing the Japanese polity from top to bottom, reorganizing army and navy on the basis of a scientific study of European methods and principles, and adopting those institutions to which Europe seemed to owe its competitive superiority to every eastern people with which its peoples had come into conflict. In 1871 the old-time clans were finally abolished by imperial decree and prefectures created instead. At the same date the feudal chieftains and court nobility became one class, while the warriors or clansmen (the Samurai) were merged in the new gentry class and forbidden to wear arms. These changes were voluntary on the part of those chiefly concerned.

Bismarck's Foreign Policy. The Berlin Congress had been conducted under the presidency of Bismarck in the character of wholly disinterested friend of all the parties concerned, Germany having no stake at all in the Balkans. Nevertheless, it had materially increased the difficulties of his policy. His primary aim was to maintain a close accord between Germany and Russia on the one hand and Austria on the other ; a breach between those two powers, especially one which might force Germany to side with one against the other, was therefore to be strenuously avoided. The Balkans provided a permanent point of possible friction. The Congress there gave Austria the desired protectorate of Bosnia, while the Russian project had been balked. As a matter of fact, Austria was more necessary to Bismarck than Russia, and he could not afford to placate Russia at Austria's expense, though it suited him very well that hostile feeling between Russia and Britain, as possible allies of a permanently alienated France, should be intensified.

Moreover, France was now at the close of the period during which full recovery from the war was delayed by uncertainty whether the country would revert from republic to monarchy under one of the three dynasties—Bourbon, Orleanist, or Bonapartist, which had rival claims and supporters. The Prince Imperial, son of Napoleon III, was killed in Zululand in 1879 ; the Orleanist renounced his own claim, and the Bourbon eliminated his otherwise promising chance of a restoration by his uncompromising refusal to shed any of those traditional principles of his house which had driven it into exile in 1830. Therefore, to keep France isolated was, from the German point of view, more imperative than ever, though any attraction between France and Great Britain was made the more improbable by the friction between the two powers engendered by the establishment of a British protectorate in Egypt in 1882. Africa was most useful in this programme, since France's ambitions there did not square with Great Britain's in Morocco as well as in Egypt, while both France and Italy were casting covetous eyes on Tunis. In 1881 France annexed Tunis, encouraged by Britain and Germany ; and Italian jealousy made it the easier for Bismarck to attach Italy, in spite of traditional friction with Austria, to the informal Three Emperors' league.

Nihilism. Meanwhile Russia was at grips with the revolutionary movement known as Nihilism, which was in various ways a preparation for the Bolshevism of a future generation. Alexander II, like Alexander I before and Nicholas II after him, was a visionary with high ideals, unaware that he was working blindfolded by tradition and by the deadly system of cast-iron tyranny embodied in the bureaucracy of the czardom. The effect of his well-meant reforms had been destroyed by the agents who never intended them to succeed, and by the merciless iniquities of the law ; and the " Czar-Liberator " was murdered by the bomb of a nihilist in 1882. His son Alexander III was only hardened by the crime ; all thoughts of reform vanished and the tyranny of the government and its officials became more grinding and ruthless than ever. Attachment to Germany cooled ; things were not going well for Russia in the Balkans.

Government in Bulgaria. The prince nominated to Bulgaria was another Alexander—of Battenberg—a kinsman of the Czar, who expected to find in him a subservient tool. The principality had an admirable constitution on paper ; in practice, the Czar provided it with a Russian executive, while Bulgarian patriotism seethed. Just before the murder of Alexander II the prince effected a *coup d'état*, suspended the constitution, dismissed the Russians, and worked through Bulgarian ministers—to the great joy of his people and the wrath of the Czar. Two years later (1883) he was able to restore the constitution. Then in 1885 Rumelia revolted against its Turkish governor, and offered itself to Bulgaria. Alexander accepted the offer ; Serbia was at once up in arms, demanding an equivalent. There was a short war, Bulgaria being victorious at Slivnitza ; but Austria intervened to stop the fighting, while the Porte offered Alexander the governorship of Rumelia under its own sovereignty.

Then occurred an exceedingly curious episode. Russian agents kidnapped the prince, carried him over the border, and forced him to abdicate (1886). Bulgaria under the dictatorship of Stambulov, the indomitable Bulgarian minister of Alexander, stood defiant—Russia having worse than no case for intervention —and accepted a new prince (1887), Ferdinand of Saxe-Coburg, who for the present was content to reign while Stambulov governed. The remnant of profit in the Balkans that Russia had saved from the victory over Turkey when the Berlin Treaties took the place of that of San Stefano had thus been thrown away by overbearing activities, while the Balkan states were still seething with their jealous antagonisms, and Serbia was rent by dynastic rivalries. Bosnia was, however, enjoying unwonted prosperity under Austrian rule, while Turkey, under Abdul Hamid, held firmly to the time-honoured policy of propounding programmes of reform which were always left unfulfilled.

But in 1888 the aged Kaiser William I died ; his son Frederick I, already a dying man when he ascended the throne, followed him to the grave three months later. Bismarck's day was over. In 1890 the man who had created the German Empire was retired into private life. The new autocrat, William II (emperor 1888— abdicated 1918), had no use for a tutor in statecraft.

LESSON 30

Expansion of the Great Powers

(See plate 57)

WILLIAM II inaugurated his reign by a departure from precedent which appeared at the time to be eccentric rather than significant. He paid a state visit to the sultan (Abdul Hamid II), which no other European monarch had done before. Actually, it meant that he had adopted a new outlook on the East and eastern questions. The development of German influence or power in Asia was an idea so new that it was not readily assimilated by the world at large (later it revealed itself as an integral part of the Kaiser's policy), since the method adopted was that of " peaceful penetration " by way of commerce, not the blatancy of the mailed fist.

It was hardly due, however, to desertion of Bismarck's policy that one of its aims was conspicuously worn out. In 1891 Russia and France were manifestly drawing together, though as yet without the formal alliance which was to follow ere long. Austria and Germany were drawn together the more closely, having no divergent interests, while it was difficult to see what interests were common to the czardom and the French republic apart from a common hostility to the two Central empires. The Dreikaiserbund was dead ; Europe was settling down to a very uneasy equilibrium between two pairs of powers, each pair in constant dread of aggression by the other, while neither was sufficiently confident of its own military superiority to be willing to force a duel. The peace was not likely to be broken so long as both groups felt the chances of decisive victory to be so uncertain, and neither could count on active support from any other power. The theory of general cooperation was, however, preserved under the name of the " Concert of Europe," a term which came into vogue after the Berlin Congress.

Colonial Expansion. Acute causes of quarrel were evaded, but in many quarters there was friction. The magnitude of the British empire was a constant source of jealousy ; and in the last decade Europe generally—as well as France, to whom the idea was by no means a novelty—had awakened to the existence of vast unexploited territories in Africa which were in danger of being absorbed by the British unless other countries made haste to secure a share for themselves. Great Britain was already in control of Egypt, and sovereign in South Africa, except in the small section which had for centuries pertained to Portugal. A scramble for African territories began, Germany for the first time taking active part in spite of the coldness with which Bismarck—concentrating on European hegemony—contemplated colonial expansion. France, having foiled Italy in Tunis and been foiled by the British in Egypt, annexed Madagascar, which attracted no other power ; Belgium planted a colony on the Congo, with a French colony hard by ; Germany occupied territory both in East and West Africa.

A series of treaties partitioned Africa into " spheres of influence," consummated by an Anglo-German agreement in 1890 which the colonizing parties in both countries regarded as a miserable surrender on the part of its own government. (At this date Lord Salisbury's cession of Heligoland to Germany also met with some adverse criticism.) French sentiment received a painful shock in 1898, when Kitchener with British and Egyptian troops wrested from the Khalifa by the Omdurman campaign the Sudan, which had been abandoned in 1885, politely declining to recognize the claim to prior occupation asserted by a party of French who had reached Fashoda. But the French government, recognizing that there was no sound case for protest, declined to make the incident a serious cause of quarrel. The anti-British sympathies of the European nations were sufficiently demonstrated when the South African War broke out at the end of the next year, but the supremacy of the British navy was a guarantee against foreign intervention.

The importance of the British fleet as a political factor during this decade was manifested on two other occasions. Turkish misrule and Greek excitability compelled the intervention of the Concert in 1894-7. The Turkish government, of course, explained that it was only the unruliness of the sultan's Christian subjects in Armenia that had interfered with the projects of reform which the Porte, according to promise, was on the point of carrying out. But Crete, anxious to form part of the kingdom of Greece and escape Moslem rule, revolted ; Greece attacked Turkey, but was decisively defeated ; the Concert intervened to restore order and save Greece from the penalties of defeat ; and it was a demonstration by the British fleet, acting for the Concert

—from which Germany and Austria withdrew—that brought the contending parties to reason. The second event was outbreak of war between the United States and a European power.

Spanish-American War. A quarrel between the western republic and Spain about Cuba issued in a four months' war (1898), in which the Americans were completely victorious ; but the fact that the conflict was a simple duel was owing to the certainty that any intervention on behalf of Spain would bring the British fleet into play. But there was a much more fundamental significance attaching to the episode. It broke through the barrier of isolation which the States had hitherto been resolute to maintain, by adding them to the number of colonizing and expanding powers ; so that in the Chinese war of 1900–1 America as well as Europe was an active participant.

For, besides Africa, eastern Asia was opening up new problems for the West, where, on the one hand, it seemed to offer a hitherto unworked field for exploitation, while, on the other, the idea was gaining ground that China, with its enormous population and possible resources, might be awakening and, awake, might become not a prey but a menace to Europe—that a " Yellow Peril " against which the West must arm itself was in sight. The whole Far Eastern Question was forced to the front by the unlooked-for outcome of a war between China and Japan in 1894, in which, to the general amazement, the Chinese were ejected from Korea, over which they had claimed suzerainty, and were thoroughly defeated by the reorganized and efficient Japanese army.

But if Japan were allowed to reap the natural fruits of victory, the Russian scheme of expansion to ice-free ports in the Pacific would be choked off, because those ports would pass into Japan's hands. Under pressure from Russia and France, with support from Germany, Japan with dignified self-restraint reduced territorial claims to a minimum, content for the time being to have established a title to be treated on an equal footing with the European powers. These powers generally now began to scramble for concessions from the Chinese government in return for their good offices as peace-makers.

Boxer Rebellion. Then in China itself broke out the great Boxer Rebellion, inspired by hate of foreigners at large and all their ways, but connived at if not encouraged by the dowager Empress, the real ruler of China. Two German missionaries were murdered ; anti-foreign riots took place ; the government did nothing, and the official representatives of the powers were besieged in the Legations at Peking. All the interested powers, including Japan and the United States, sent an international force with a German general in command to deal with the situation. They relieved the Legations and occupied Peking (1901), and there was a renewed scramble for concessions by way of compensation. Germany was granted Kiaochau, while to Britain was leased Weihaiwei—restored to China in 1921.

Russo-Japanese War. In the new conditions thus created the conflicting interests of Japan and Russia in Manchuria and Korea became critical. Japan invited compromise ; Russia's idea of compromise was Japan's concession of all points in dispute. In 1902 Japan and Great Britain had made an open alliance binding each to come to the aid of the other in the event of attack by a combination of two or more powers, but not otherwise ; therefore it was practically certain that if Russia and Japan should go to war they would be left to fight out their duel alone. In January, 1904, Japan's final proposal that Russia should have a free hand in Manchuria and Japan in Korea was left unanswered ; Japan declared war. Russia had enormously underrated both the efficiency and the numbers of the Japanese army, and still more Japan's advantages in a naval struggle. Huge as were the Russian resources in men, there was but a single-line railway, not yet completed, to carry them across Siberia, whereas the Japanese were fighting close to their base. The Japanese fleet, commanded by Admiral Togo, outclassed and shattered the Russian, and in a series of engagements on land, more destructive and on a bigger scale than those even of the Franco-German war, the Japanese armies forced back the Russians under Kuropatkin. The victory of the Japanese at Liao-yang was, however, modified by their terrible losses. Port Arthur, the fortified seaport in Manchuria leased by Russia from China, was blockaded from the beginning of the war. It surrendered in January, 1905, and a few weeks later Oyama attacked the Russian positions at Mukden, the capital of Manchuria. Though the Russians fought well, Kuropatkin was at length forced to order a retreat, which soon became a rout.

Both sides had suffered tremendous losses, and in August a peace was negotiated at Portsmouth, U.S.A. Japan had firmly established a position in the first rank of world powers.

LESSON 31

The Drift to World War
<small>(See plate 58)</small>

I T will be well to grasp the significance of sundry events which took place between 1895 and 1905. In the former year the world knew that some understanding—an *entente*—was established between Russia—where Nicholas II had not long succeeded Alexander III, and the old friction with England was lessening—and France, which was not on the best of terms with either England or Italy. In 1897, however, these three powers acted together in the Turkish imbroglio, mainly through the instrumentality of the British fleet.

In 1898, as we saw in the last Lesson, the fleet was again in reserve, as it were, when war broke out between the United States and Spain, a war resulting from the conviction of the American public that the blowing up of the U.S. warship " Maine " in Havana harbour was a hostile act on the part of Spain, and not a pure accident, as the Spanish government maintained. The war, on the one hand, improved Anglo-American relations —it lasted less than four months during which Porto Rico and the Philippines were annexed by the United States, any disposition to intervention by European powers being squashed by certainty of the British fleet's cooperation with the United States ; and, on the other hand, suggested that the States would not for long be able to maintain their cherished isolation— which in turn was emphasized when they joined the other powers in coercing China in 1901.

The Fashoda incident troubled Anglo-French relations in 1898, and the South African War marked the isolation of England, but also surprised the world by showing the unexpected solidarity of the British Empire, while again manifesting impressively the strength of the navy. This may or may not have been the Kaiser's reason for greatly extending the German naval programme during the progress of the war—an unprecedented development hard to separate from the idea of rivalry between Germany and Great Britain as the leading maritime power.

It was also significant, though in another direction, that the first Hague Conference was called in 1898 on the Czar's initiative, with a view to checking by international agreement the incubus of growing armaments, humanizing the methods of civilized warfare, and establishing an international court of arbitration. On all these matters some general and some partial agreements were reached—and acted upon both in the South African and Russo-Japanese wars. The Hague Tribunal was set up, and some progress was made at subsequent conferences, but the reduction of armaments was virtually vetoed by the German refusal to participate.

Anglo-French Entente. On the death of Queen Victoria and the accession of Edward VII in 1901 a far-reaching change was inaugurated. Diplomacy succeeded in reconciling the differences which had so long maintained friction between Great Britain, on the one hand, and France and Russia, on the other. In German eyes this *entente*—it was not an alliance—appeared to be precisely the consummation which Bismarck had successfully combated, intensifying the growing belief that the three powers were scheming for the destruction of the two Central empires. It therefore behoved Germany and Austria to make ready to meet, and it might be to anticipate, the attack of the three powers by the methods which had proved so successful in the hands of Frederick the Great and Bismarck. But none of the three *entente* powers, least of all England, would have admitted at any time that there was any sort of justification for such apprehension, sedulously fostered in Austria and Germany until it took form as solid conviction, although Russia's failure in the Japanese war showed that Russian effective military power was far less than had been imagined. The impression was, however, confirmed when friction arose between France and Germany concerning German interests in Morocco, which was dealt with by an international conference at Algeciras in 1906, where no one but Austria supported Germany's claims. Yet the Kaiser's government professed satisfaction with the outcome of the conference, while France's position in Morocco was confirmed.

Unrest in the Balkans. In 1908 the Balkans were once more in commotion, born of the rise of the " Young Turk " reforming party, which successfully imposed on the Sultan its demand for a long-promised constitution. But Ferdinand of Bulgaria seized the opportunity to assume full sovereign authority, with the old historic title of Czar, while Austria simultaneously announced annexation of Bosnia, where the Berlin treaty had given her only a temporary protectorate. Slavonic sentiment was alarmed and irritated; the action was, in effect, a challenge to Russia and Russia's influence and prestige among the Slavs, who both within and without the Austrian empire detested the Austro-Magyar domination. But Russia was warned in unmistakable terms that Austria could count on unqualified support from Germany, so that the Czar had no choice but to acquiesce. The Central powers had recovered anything they might have lost at Algeciras.

The Young Turks, vehemently nationalist in sentiment, but encouraged by Germany, whether for commercial or strategic reasons, were masters of the Turkish government, and had substituted a feeble-minded brother for the crafty but unpopular Abdul Hamid, as Sultan of Turkey, and orthodox Mahomedan Khalif. The weakness of Russia was manifest. Great Britain was rent by a constitutional struggle between the two Houses of Parliament and a revival of the perennial Irish problem, besides having entered on the anxious experiment of restoring full citizenship to recent antagonists, the South African Boers, while British difficulties were complicated by the death of Edward VII and loss of his diplomatic wisdom.

It was easy to see in these facts the motive for what looked like an explicit threat to France when, in 1911, the Kaiser sent the gunboat " Panther," to be replaced by the German cruiser " Berlin," to Agadir to safeguard German interests in Morocco, on the plea that they were endangered by recent action on the part of France in that country. It appeared, however, on the one hand, that Great Britain had no intention of deserting her informal ally, and on the other, that no threat was intended, and the matter was easily adjustable. Then at the moment when it was being amicably settled a slight discord arose between the Central empires and Italy, which loosened the doubtful bonds holding the last country to the Triple Alliance. Italy entered on a somewhat desultory naval war with Turkey to extort from the Porte the cession of full sovereignty in Tripoli, where Italy had for some time past been seeking an equivalent for the French annexation of Tunis. In October, 1912, peace left Italy in possession of Tripoli and the captured Aegean islands.

This war, however, was the prologue to a fresh eruption in the Balkans. The Greek minister Venizelos had been secretly working for an unprecedented accord between the Balkan states which in 1912 issued in the formation of the Balkan League between Greece, Serbia, Bulgaria and Montenegro, with liberation of Macedonia from Turkish rule as its primary object—very disturbing to the Concert of Powers, to which it came as a surprise. Albania revolted against Turkish rule and won unexpected successes ; the league appealed to the powers to intervene, and dissatisfied with their hesitation, declared war on its own account. The Turks were in process of reorganizing their army under German tuition, but the process was incomplete, and the result was a Turkish *débâcle*, in effecting which the hardest and most successful part was played by Bulgaria, in threatening Constantinople and investing Adrianople. Then the powers intervened and called the London Conference, which evolved a scheme of settlement in the Treaty of London (May, 1913).

Second Balkan War. This pleased no one, and Bulgaria, considering that she had been robbed for Serbia's benefit, attacked Serbia. The latter state was promptly supported by Greece, and then Rumania joined them against Bulgaria, who was badly beaten and penalized for her tragic blunder. Now were revived in full measure the old vindictive jealousies which Venizelos had succeeded for a short period in pacifying. In July, 1913, Adrianople was recovered from the Bulgarians by Turkey. Nominally over the question of its surrender, the Young Turks, headed by Colonel Enver Bey, overthrew the existing cabinet by a *coup d'état* and set up in its place a Young Turk government intent on the reconstruction of their empire. Across the Danube, Rumania, though she had attacked Bulgaria on her own account, had never joined the Balkan League. Ruled by a prince of the house of Hohenzollern, she repudiated Slavonic affinities. The Balkan state which had derived the most direct profit out of the wars was not Greece—Hellenic and not Slav by tradition—nor Bulgaria, but the practically pure Slav Serbia, whose humbling Austria most desired.

Outbreak of the Great War. Serbia blocked the way for Austrian expansion to the Aegean, and in Serbia was focused the Slavonic anti-Austrian feeling which was the most disintegrating force within that heterogeneous empire for Austria and Hungary both held large Slav populations. Serbia, in Austria's belief, was a hotbed of Slav conspirators out of reach of the Austrian government. On June 28, 1914, the Austrian heir presumptive,

Archduke Francis Ferdinand, and his wife, were assassinated
in Serajevo, the chief town of Bosnia, near the Serbian border.
Austria declared that the murder was a Serbian plot and that
the Serbian government was responsible. Serbia protested
and wished to appeal to the impartial Hague tribunal. Austria,
the accuser, claimed to be also the sole judge—sending the
Serbian government a series of demands, acceptance of which
would completely cripple their state's sovereignty—and to execute
judgement by her own authority. Germany declared that Austria
could do no less. If Russia admitted that view and surrendered
Serbia to the will of Austria, Russian humiliation would be disastrous and complete ; there would be an end to all Russian influence
in Balkan affairs. England offered mediation, but Austria
rejected all proposals of peaceful intervention, and on July
28 declared war on Serbia. On the 31st both Austria and Russia
were mobilizing. On that day Germany sent an ultimatum
to Russia and to France, who was bound by treaty to come to
Russia's aid. On August 1 Germany declared war on Russia—
and next day on France. So far it was reasonably debatable
whether there was a moral obligation—as there was no treaty
pledge with France and Russia—for Britain to come in ; but
that was settled by Germany's invasion of Belgium, as an open
road to France on August 3, ignoring the treaty guarantee of
Belgian neutrality, to which all the powers were pledged ; and
on August 4 Great Britain declared war on Germany.

LESSON 32

The Great War in Outline

(See plates 58 and 59)

ON August 3 1914, the two central empires side by side and
both under the single guidance of Berlin, had ranged
against them Russia with Serbia on the east, and on the
west France and Belgium, supported by Great Britain. The
empires had their war-plan fully shaped, their armies ready for
immediate action, a fleet powerful but much less so than that of
Great Britain. They held the interior lines, so that they could
mass their troops on either front at will, and it was very soon to
be seen that they were much more powerfully armed than their
adversaries, while they had been prepared to violate the neutrality
of Belgium—guaranteed by treaty and faithfully observed in the

war of 1870—because the section of France which marched with
Belgium was nearly defenceless, so that it could be swiftly
penetrated by troops rushed through Belgian territory.

There was no reason for Germany to suppose that the Russian
armies on the eastern front were more efficient than they had been
ten years before, when Japan had so decisively held her own against
them and Berlin took no account either of Belgium or of the few,
if efficient, British troops which were all that could be available
for some time to come. It was therefore a reasonable expectation
on the part of Germany that by leaving Austria to hold up any
attack on the eastern front, the Germans, concentrating on the
west, could smash their way through to Paris in a few weeks,
shatter France as a fighting force, and deal at leisure afterwards
with Great Britain and Russia.

The plan was foiled. The unexpected, stubborn and heroic
resistance of Belgium—the invasion of which hastened Great
Britain's entrance into the war—just gave time for the British
force to take its place on the French left. The whole line was
nowhere broken, but was swung back, always covering Paris.
Almost at the gates of Paris the impetus of the rush was exhausted.
The French reserves had been accumulating ; on Sept. 6 the
French opened the counter attack ; then it was the German line
that swung back, the battle of the Marne developing into the
battle of the Aisne (Sept. 13), each line striving and failing to
turn the other's northern flank till both had stretched up to the
Belgian coast at Nieuport and Ostend respectively, so that about
the middle of October both were stabilized. The war on the
western front took shape as an interminable siege, a ceaseless
battle for the capturing and recapturing of a trench here and a
trench there in the hope of forcing a penetration which would
create a flank to be turned, with periodical concentrations upon
particular points, while neither side succeeded in effecting the
necessary break-through.

Japan's accession to the Allies in the first month of the war
helped to clear the seas of German raiders, and her fleets convoyed
Indian and Australian troops to the west. On the other hand,
Turkey joined the central powers at the moment when the
western front was stabilized, giving new occupation for both
Russia and Britain. The momentum of the German rush had
doubtless been sapped by the unexpected vigour of a Russian
onslaught on East Prussia, though it was disastrously shattered,

after initial successes, at the battle of Tannenberg. In spite of this defeat Russia moved a second army on Galicia, driving the Austrians before them. The Germans, obliged to help Austria, answered with a series of rushes into Poland, followed by successive evacuations, always failing to bring the Russians to a decisive engagement and compelled to fall back when they had advanced too far from their base. Thus for more than a year the adversaries stood at death-grips in the west, hammering, attacking, counter-attacking, each occasionally gaining a mile or two of ground, but neither able to make any substantial advance, still less to penetrate the opposing line ; while in the east they did not stand but swung backwards and forwards over a vast expanse of territory which neither could hold continuously. The Germans never forgot the lesson of Napoleon's Moscow disaster.

On the western front, after six months of war, it had been realized that infantry alone was powerless in trench warfare. The tactical theories of previous years had been reduced to zero and the great artillery phase of the war began in 1915. At Neuve Chapelle (March) and at Loos (September) fierce gunfire preparation preceded the attack. At the second battle of Ypres (April, 1915) the Germans made first use of poison gas, which had been repudiated as a permissible instrument of war at The Hague Conference.

But there were other developments in 1915. Italy entered the war on the side of the Allies—the Entente was sympathetic to her historical claims on the east of the Adriatic, and on May 23 she declared war on Austria ; there were also the British and Russian campaigns against the Turks in Asia. There was the splendid but tragic British attempt to take the Central powers in the rear and establish concert with Russia by capturing the Dardanelles, an adventure which had to be abandoned before the year was out. Germany began her submarine war and the torpedoing of non-combatant ships, signalized by the sinking of the passenger liner Lusitania in May, Great Britain having retorted by declaring a general blockade (which incidentally annoyed America more than the Lusitania affair). The failure of the British on the Dardanelles encouraged Bulgaria to join the Central powers in October, and with Austria to fall upon Serbia, while with the assent of one half of Greece an allied force occupied Salonica. The prospect of a decisive end seemed remoter than ever.

In 1916 a shattering German attack was hurled upon the French at Verdun. Four times in four months onslaught after mighty onslaught drove the French lines in with terrific massacre in both armies ; but Verdun held. The German offensive forestalled a great Allied push designed for the summer of 1916. In order to relieve the French, the latter was started on July 1, before preparations were quite complete. The attack, not concentrated like that of the Germans at Verdun but along an extended line, is known as the first battle of the Somme. A tremendous artillery bombardment preceded it, lasting for seven days. Some ground was gained, but without practical effect on the general situation, though at huge cost to both sides.

In May, 1916, was fought the great naval engagement of the war, the battle of Jutland (see British History, Lesson 26, page 121). The German fleet came out and engaged a portion of the British fleet, but on the approach of the main fleet escaped skilfully to the cover of its mines, and never again ventured to take the seas—except under water.

While the Verdun struggle was in progress Austria struck at Italy in the Trentino, but found the adventure too much for her— the more because the Russians developed a new offensive in Galicia ; this in turn encouraged Rumania, hitherto neutral, to take the field against Austria. The result was, however, disastrous to Rumania, as the Germans came to the rescue of their ally, drove the Rumanians back, and invaded Rumania itself in irresistible force. Bukarest, the capital, fell before their onslaught on Dec. 5, 1916.

In the new year, 1917, the Allied " push " in the west continued to make slow progress, but the operations known as the battle of Messines (June 7) for the capture of the Messines ridge were a continuation, followed by the last of the great allied artillery offensives on the western front known as the third battle of Ypres (July 31, 1917). In the spring two developments of the highest importance took place ; the United States declaration of war in April, which made it imperative for the Germans to achieve victory before the Americans could take the field in force, and the Russian Revolution which paralysed Russia as an effective force in the war—despite a desperate effort under General Brussilov in Galicia in July—and also led to the liberation by the end of the year of German troops, hitherto tied to the eastern front, to reinforce the German armies in the west. In November the Bolshevik Government, headed by Lenin and Trotsky, negotiated the withdrawal of Russia from the war.

The Communist infection had already spread to the Italian army pressing on the Austrian front, so that it was routed at Caporetto (October, 1917) and driven back in headlong retreat till it was able to make a desperate stand on the Piave. In January, 1918, preparations began for the decisive life-and-death struggle. In March Foch was appointed commander of the Allied armies ; the arrival of the Americans was imminent.

On the morning of March 21, 1918, began the battle of St. Quentin, or the second battle of the Somme. The Germans hurled themselves at the centre of the Allied line on the Somme, and for a week the British were swept back. But the line was not actually snapped, and was at last able to turn at bay and repulse the exhausted onslaught. The attack was renewed on the British left in April, but was again held up.

American troops were already in France when the Germans staked all on a final throw. The thrust was launched against the French left on May 27, and throughout June. Then on July 18 the initiative passed to Foch, when he opened his victory offensive. Sector by sector the line was pushed back, till by the middle of September it stood again where it had stood at the beginning of March before Ludendorff's offensive.

The last phase opened before the middle of September. The Germans were driven by the British out of the Hindenburg line, by the Americans out of St. Mihiel. On every other front their allies were tottering. Bulgaria went first, while the Turks were being defeated everywhere. Austria was exhausted ; on November 3 she obtained an armistice, following in the wake of Bulgaria and Turkey. Germany, now alone, fought on stubbornly ; but demoralization was spreading among the German troops and in the civilian population, broken by the long pressure of the blockade. On October 26 Ludendorff resigned ; a week later the Americans accelerated their push down the Meuse ; the French were pressing hard on the centre ; on the left the British captured Valenciennes, and on November 9 were over the Scheldt. The strain had reached breaking point. Mutiny had broken out in the fleet at Kiel, and red revolution in Berlin. The Kaiser fled to neutral Holland. On November 11 the delegates of the Socialist provisional government signed the dictated armistice which ended the most shattering war known to history.

Europe Since 1918

THE " Cease Fire " that closed the Great War sounded in a world that was exhausted, devastated, and disillusioned. Victors and vanquished alike had been bled white of their blood and treasure. The idealism with which the great struggle had opened had long since been drowned in the sea of slaughter, and it is hardly surprising that the peace treaties which at length put a formal end to the hostilities—the Treaties of Versailles, Trianon, St. Germain and Sèvres—were all alike conceived in hatred and revenge, and made the future dark.

Out of the desolation and anguish of the war years there was one good thing which seemed to have emerged—the League of Nations. Geneva enshrined the hope of a new order in human affairs, and in its earlier years, at least, it had many successes to its credit in the shape of peaceful readjustment of frontiers and the avoidance of wars between certain of the smaller states ; and its work on behalf of the millions of refugees from Russia, Turkey, Greece and elsewhere, in the suppression of the white slave and drug traffics, and in the improvement of conditions of labour effected through the International Labour Office, was beyond praise. When Germany and the other ex-enemy countries were admitted to membership, the future seemed bright indeed, and the Pact of Locarno (1925) and the Briand-Kellogg Pact outlawing war (Pact of Paris, 1928), promised to banish still further the threat of war. It was a false hope, however, as we shall see. Nationalism, armed by political unrest, economic loss, and social disorder, tore holes in the fabric of post-War idealism.

Post-War Britain is the subject of another chapter in this volume (British History, No. 27, page 125). France, though nominally victorious, was sorely wounded, and despite her victory and the return of Alsace-Lorraine, was still fearful of the menace from across the Rhine. For years to come her foreign policy was dictated by the determination to keep Germany in a position of definite inferiority, and to maintain the hegemony of the Continent by a great French standing army and a system of alliances in which the newly created or extended states— Czechoslovakia, Jugoslavia, Poland, and Greater Rumania—had their place. Enormous indemnities were demanded of Germany in the hope of making her pay the full cost of the War, and when the reparations were not forthcoming in 1923 the government of M. Poincaré sent a French army to occupy the Ruhr.

For some time after the end of the War Germany trembled on the brink of social dissolution. Kaiserism and all that it stood for had been swept away in a fit of angry disgust, and the new Socialist government had to meet a situation in which unemployment on a vast scale was rife, the Left Wing Socialists and Communists were for a time in open revolt, and huge payments in money and in kind had to be made to the victorious Allies. The situation improved somewhat with the formation in 1923 of a policy of co-operation with the Allies, initiated by Stresemann, when he became Foreign Secretary. A new currency was also introduced in substitution for the mark which had depreciated into worthlessness. In 1925 Germany was a partner to the Pact of Locarno, and in the following year she joined the League of Nations. The burden of reparations, originally fixed at an impossibly high figure, was also successively lifted by the Dawes Plan of 1924 and the Young Plan of 1929, until in 1931 payments were postponed by the Hoover moratorium, while in 1932 they were almost cancelled at the Lausanne Conference.

Italy, though one of the victorious powers, entered upon the period of peace in almost as bad a case as Germany. Thoroughly disappointed with the results of the War, politically corrupt, and socially disorganized, the country became the battleground of extremist factions. For a time, and particularly in the north, the Socialists were predominant. Then, after the factories which they had seized had been returned to their owners, came the turn of the ex-Socialist, ex-Serviceman, Benito Mussolini, who had founded his first Fascist group on March 23, 1919. Although Mussolini's first programme was radical in the extreme, he was a fervent patriot and nationalist, and in a country distressed by something approaching to civil war, his movement seemed the natural rallying ground for all who believed in order and social stability. In 1921 Mussolini and 32 other Fascists were elected to Parliament, and on October 27, 1922, bands of his supporters marched on Rome, and their leader was called to the premiership by King Victor Emmanuel. The Fascist Revolution then proceeded step by step. The new régime was badly shaken for a time by the murder of Matteotti, a Socialist deputy, in 1924, but each subsequent year saw a diminution in the opposition. Parliament was virtually superseded in favour of the Grand Fascist Council; capitalism became severely controlled, and plans were drawn up for the reorganization of the country's economic life on corporate lines; and at the head of this Corporative State is *Il Duce*, Mussolini himself, who controls, directly or indirectly, all the powers, civil and military, of the State.

Meanwhile, a revolution inspired by a very different ideology was taking its course in Russia. In March, 1917, food riots in Petrograd led to a political upheaval which involved the abdication of Nicholas II. Czarism had proved itself to be as inefficient as it was corrupt, and there was practically no resistance to the new Liberal-Socialist government. In July the power passed to Alexander Kerensky, a moderate Socialist, whose efforts to continue the War on behalf of the Allies were countered by the propaganda of the extreme section of the Socialists, the Bolsheviks, who promised to the soldiers peace, to the peasants land, and to the workmen bread. On November 9 the Bolsheviks under Lenin and Trotsky overthrew the government and substituted for it a system of Soviets or local councils of soldiers, peasants and workers. A reign of terror ensued, in which not only the Czar and his family perished, but also many of the supporters of the old régime. Bitter civil war, in fact, broke out between the Bolsheviks, or Reds, and the forces of the Czarist commanders—the Whites. Despite the active assistance of Britain and France, the Red Army organized by Trotsky was everywhere successful, and the Bolshevik or Communist party became the dominant power in the State. Until his death in 1924 the country found its natural leader in Nikolai Lenin, who did not hesitate in 1921, when the people were on the verge of starvation, to abandon strict Communist principles in favour of the " New Economic Policy " (N.E.P.), which permitted the re-introduction within certain limits of private trading and of the wage system. After Lenin's death there was a clash of personality and policy between Trotsky and Josef Stalin, which eventually resulted in the banishment of the former and the elevation of Stalin to the position of virtual dictator. In 1928 Stalin inaugurated the first Five-year Plan which called for the production of all that was necessary to build a complete machine-age civilization. In the process, the more conservative peasants (Kulaks) were " liquidated," as had been the middle classes before them. In 1933 a second Five-year Plan was announced, and this was followed in due course by a third

Plan. Together the Plans have resulted in the complete transformation of the political, social, and educational system of Russia.

By 1929 it seemed as if the wounds of war were really being healed, and that the new order—the Weimar Republic in Germany, the Soviet State in Russia, and its Fascist counterpart in Italy—was at length taking permanent shape. In that year, however, America was struck by an economic blizzard, and the ensuing slump had repercussions of the most violent kind in Europe. Particularly in Germany was its effect felt, for the German economic system had for long been dependent on the credits supplied by the United States. When these were withdrawn, the financial system was deprived of its foundation, and the political and social structure built up since the War seemed to be tottering to its fall. As in Italy years before, the masses of Germany were stirred by the agitation of extremists—of the Communists on the one hand, and of the National Socialist Party (Nazi) led by Adolf Hitler on the other. The Liberal régime virtually ended in June 1932, when President Hindenburg dismissed Chancellor Brüning in favour of a Nationalist nominee of his own, and six months later, in January 1933, Hitler became Chancellor.

Then in Germany, as before in Russia and Italy, everything savouring of democratic liberalism was scornfully suppressed, and it was not long before Germany, already relieved of the burden of reparations, set herself to throw off the other shackles imposed at Versailles. Rearmament, forbidden by the Treaty, was begun, at first surreptitiously, then openly ; in 1936 the Rhineland was reoccupied by German troops and again militarized ; military conscription was re-introduced. When the former Allies hesitated to accept Germany's claim to equality in armament as well as in disarmament, Hitler announced Germany's resignation from the League of Nations, denounced the Peace Treaties, and effected a political and military alliance with his fellow dictator in Italy. Within a very few years, German military might was such that she was able, in 1938, to seize Austria (thus effecting the Anschluss which had been sought by Austria herself in 1919, but which had then been vetoed by France) and also to compel the surrender of the German-speaking districts of Czechoslovakia to the Reich.

Within 20 years of the close of the War the political situation was, then, radically transformed. The democratic powers which in 1919 were enjoying a triumph such as never before had been seen in history, were now on the defensive. The totalitarian powers—renascent Germany and Italy—had seized the initiative, and the Berlin-Rome Axis dominated the politics of the Continent. Germany, rearmed and reorganized, dominated Central Europe. Italy, having completed the conquest of Libya, successfully challenged the full concourse of League of Nations powers, and in 1935 invaded and overran Abyssinia. In Spain, which since 1931 had been a Liberal republic, Germany and Italy openly supported with troops, ammunition and aircraft the Nationalist revolt begun by General Franco in 1936—a revolt which after years of the most sanguinary fighting was brought to a close by the complete triumph of the Nationalists in 1939.

In 1938 the old order of Europe, as established by the Peace Treaties of 1919, collapsed into ruin. Austria, as already stated, was absorbed by Germany, and Germany's support of the allegedly-oppressed German elements in Czechoslovakia threatened the peace of the world. When war seemed imminent, Mr. Neville Chamberlain, Britain's Prime Minister, flew to Germany to see Herr Hitler, and from across the world President Roosevelt, Democracy's stalwart champion in the United States, addressed appeal after appeal to the leaders and peoples of Europe to consider afresh before the war dogs were again unleashed. Still the preparations for war continued, until at the eleventh hour it was announced that a conference between Herr Hitler, Mr. Chamberlain, Signor Mussolini and Premier Daladier of France, was to be held at Munich ; and there, on September 30, 1938, the dismemberment of Czechoslovakia was agreed upon.

An immense sigh of relief went up from all the peoples of the world, but it was soon found that the hopes of the dawn of a new era of peace and goodwill were premature. The great powers continued their arming on an ever-increasing scale. In the new year the rump state of Czechoslovakia was completely absorbed by Germany, and shortly afterwards Memel was restored to the Reich as a result of a similar demonstration of armed force. Ere long Danzig was threatened, and Britain and France hastened to form a Peace Front which involved the guarantee against aggression of Poland, Rumania, and Greece. The drift to war continued, however. On September 1, 1939, Germany delivered an unprovoked attack on Poland, and two days later Britain and France declared war against the Reich.

This Lesson concludes our Course in Modern History.

LESSON 25

Bergson's Vitalist Philosophy

THE materialist theory of the universe which was considered in the preceding Lesson is open to criticism from a number of different points of view. From the side of biology data have been accumulated which make it difficult to believe that the behaviour of living organisms can be adequately interpreted on the assumption that they are merely highly complicated automata reacting to the stimuli of their environment. In psychology, although materialist interpretations have recently, under the name of Behaviourism, achieved a wide vogue, it is, nevertheless, the case that an adequate account of consciousness in terms of the movements of the brain and the nervous system is as far from being successfully given as it has ever been. The researches of modern physicists into the nature of material things have resulted in a concept of matter at once too vague and too intangible to form any longer an adequate foundation for literally everything that exists. Finally, materialism is exposed to various difficulties of a logical order. If what it asserts is true, thought is only a reflection of, or function of, the brain. I think what I do, not because I am constrained by any external evidence to which I have paid attention and which determines my view, but because my body and brain are in a certain condition. An idea is, therefore, an event of the same type as any other bodily event. It follows that it is meaningless to ask whether an idea is true—as meaningless as to ask whether one's blood pressure is true.

Now materialism is a system of ideas. If, therefore, what materialism asserts is true, materialism is not a statement to the effect that the universe is of a certain kind, it is only evidence that the brains of materialists are in a certain condition. It is, therefore, meaningless to ask whether materialism is true. All that we are entitled to say is that the mental reflections of brains in a certain condition, namely the brains of materialists, produce or are that system of ideas to which we give the name of materialism. Hence, if materialism is true, materialism does not give us information about the universe.

BERGSON'S VITALIST PHILOSOPHY

Vitalist Philosophies. In the light of these considerations there has arisen a movement in modern philosophy which, while taking fully into account the fact of evolution and all that it implies, affirms the primacy of mind or spirit in evolution. The movement takes various forms, of which, perhaps, the most celebrated is that which finds expression in the philosophy of Bergson ; another, which will be found in the writings of Samuel Butler and Shaw, has been developed into a general system of philosophy in C. E. M. Joad's " Matter, Life and Value " ; another is in Professor S. Alexander's famous book, " Space, Time and Deity " ; a fourth is to be found in the works of the Italian philosophers, Croce and Gentile, who, combining the conclusions of Hegel as to the primary reality of mind with the evolutionary conception of mind as a developing dynamic process, find in the experience of the individual spirit of Man, which is conceived as active and changing, a model on which to interpret the universe as a whole.

Theories of this type may, perhaps, most conveniently be studied in the writings of Bergson, an original expositor of the modern vitalist point of view with the advantage of a capacity for persuasive presentation unequalled since Plato.

The Élan Vital. The main features in Bergson's philosophy are the following. The process of evolution cannot, he holds, be satisfactorily explained in terms of adaptation to environment. A degree of physical adaptation, which is far superior to that exhibited by human beings, was achieved thousands of years ago by the elephant and the tortoise. Why, then, does evolution go on to produce Man, unless it is the embodiment of some purposive force which aims at developing higher *quality* life ?

Such a force, called by Bergson the *élan vital*, is affirmed by him to be the fundamental reality of the universe. It is pictured as an ever-active, ever-changing developing urge, which expresses itself in all the phenomena which constitute the universe.

Bergson is led to this conception by a consideration of the nature of change, and his conception of change is, in turn, derived from an examination of our own consciousness. At first sight our consciousness seems to consist of a succession of psychic states or conditions strung out along the thread of a continuing personality, the ego, much as beads are threaded on a necklace. Closer inspection, however, shows this view to be erroneous, and the error consists in supposing that each particular psychic state or condition remains constant while it persists. In fact, says Bergson, there is nothing in any psychic state but a constant flow of change. Take, he says, "the most stable of internal states, the visual perception of a motionless object. The object may remain the same. I may look at it from the same side, at the same angle, in the same light; nevertheless, the vision I now have of it differs from that which I have just had, if only because the one is an instant older than the other. My memory is there, which conveys something of the past into the present." The conclusion is that "we change without ceasing and the state itself is nothing but change." The conception that we are beings who endure by change—that we are, in fact, simply elements or currents in a stream of change—is then developed into an account of the universe as a whole. This, too, is conceived as a vast vital surge or activity without beginning or end, the movement of which we know as consciousness in ourselves and as evolution in the external world.

Matter and the Intellect. The appearance of solid, static objects extended in space, which the universe undoubtedly presents, is, says Bergson, a figment of the intellect. The intellect is a practical faculty evolved by life to assist the individual in the business of living. Since life in an all-pervasive homogeneous vital surge would present difficulties, the intellect makes cuts across the living flow of reality as a result of which it appears congealed as a number of separate static objects.

Hence, matter is the way in which the intellect represents reality to us. Matter is also envisaged as the backward flow of life. If life is pictured as a fountain jetting into the air, matter is the spent drops that fall back.

Intuition. The faculty by virtue of which we come to realize the nature of reality as it is, is not intellect but intuition. This faculty, which is most highly developed in insects, is more akin to instinct than to intellect, and may be best described as instinct guided and informed by intelligence. By means of it, Bergson claims, we can, while attending to the pulse of life within ourselves and sensing the flow of our own consciousness, come to realize that this is but a part or aspect of the same dynamic stream that constitutes the universe itself. The flow of our consciousness is the reality of which we are most indubitably aware, and it is in terms of this psychical flow that reality as a whole is to be conceived.

LESSON 26

Problems of Ethical Philosophy

GENERALLY treated as a separate branch of philosophy, the province of ethics is, however, no less difficult to define than that of philosophy as a whole. Philosophers are commonly agreed that it is concerned with the meaning of such words as " right " and " good," with the nature of duty, and with the validity and character of the obligation which we feel to do our duty. Ethical philosophers have also been concerned to find a criterion by means of which to distinguish right actions from wrong and to lay down the principles of right living. It is very difficult to separate the treatment of these questions from the problems of philosophy as a whole, since the view which a particular philosopher takes in regard to them is largely determined by what may be called his general philosophy. For example, if he is a Materialist he is bound to deny the freedom of the will, since on a Materialist view either the mind is itself a form of matter, or it is determined in respect of all its activity by the movements of the brain. These movements are themselves determined according to the laws of physiology, which can theoretically be derived from physics, and the apparent freedom of the mind must, therefore, be an illusion. If there is no freedom, ethics becomes meaningless. Ethics is a structure built upon the twin pillars of praise and blame, and if a man is not free, it is as irrelevant to praise him for doing what is right as it is impertinent to blame him for doing what is wrong. Thus ethics falls to the ground.

Utilitarian Theories. For the purpose of this brief treatment, ethical philosophies may be broadly divided into two types : (1) those which assess the morality of an action in terms of some intrinsic property or properties alleged to belong to the action, or, sometimes, in terms of the motive from which the action was performed, or the will from which it proceeded ; (2) those which assess the rightness or wrongness of an action in terms of the consequences which follow from that action. Theories of the second type, usually known as Utilitarian theories, will first be considered.

(439)

The theory of Utilitarianism was first advanced in its modern form by Jeremy Bentham, the socio-legal reformer. It involves two separate sorts of assertions : (a) the ethical value of actions depends entirely on their consequences ; (b) of these consequences only pleasure or happiness is to be regarded as valuable. The doctrine involved by this second assertion is Hedonism.

With regard to the first of these assertions, according to Bentham and J. S. Mill, a right action is one that has the best consequences on the whole. Two points may be noticed (1) By best consequences is meant best actual consequences, not best expected consequences. If, therefore, an action done with the best possible intentions unexpectedly turns out badly, it is a wrong action. It follows that it is sometimes our duty to do actions which are ethically wrong. (2) As we can never know all the actual consequences of an action, it is impossible to tell with absolute certainty whether an action is right or wrong. Thus Utilitarianism, while it assigns a *meaning* to the words " right " and " wrong," only provides a rough and ready test for measuring the rightness or wrongness of particular actions.

Psychological Hedonism. The doctrine of Hedonism, that " pleasure is the only good," is of great antiquity in philosophy. Unconscious appeal is often made to it by the young and the sceptical in revolt against morality and authority. The theory derives its strength from the fact that, in the case of any action, it is always possible to advance reasons for thinking that it was undertaken with the object of obtaining pleasure for the agent. Thus, the unselfish person who prefers giving pleasure to others to obtaining pleasure directly for himself, when he is not taking a morbid satisfaction in making a martyr of himself, may be said to be one who gets his greatest satisfaction from pleasing other people. The fanatic goes to the stake for his convictions because he prefers an eternity of bliss prefaced by ten minutes torment in an earthly fire to humbling himself before his enemies, abandoning his most cherished convictions and suffering an eternity of torment in an infernal one. The man who saves a child from drowning at the risk of his own life prefers the Royal Humane Society's medal and the approval of his friends to the possibility of a coroner's censure and the stings of his conscience. Stating the theory shortly, we may say that we always do what, after calculating the probable consequences, we think we shall like most. We may, of course, and no doubt often do, make mistakes as to what consequences we shall like most—success in the art of life consists in knowing in advance what is likely to please us, and most of us only too often fail—but the fact that we make such mistakes does not, it is said, invalidate the general truth of the thesis that we do always in fact act in the way which we *think* will give us most pleasure.

With the statement that pleasure is a good in the sense of being an ultimate good, it seems difficult to quarrel. Whether it is so or not can only be determined by inspecting our own consciousness and finding out whether we do in fact desire it for its own sake. If we do desire it for its own sake, it is clear that no reasons can be given for so desiring it.

The things which we desire fall into two classes—those which we desire for the sake of something else, and those which we desire for their own sake. Those which we desire for the sake of something else always ultimately imply a desire for one of the things which we desire for its own sake. Thus, if I am about to have influenza, and say I desire quinine, the reason why I desire quinine is in order that I may avoid influenza. Why do I desire to avoid influenza ? Because, let us say, I think health is better than disease, and I desire health. Why do I desire health ? Either I can say that I realize health to be a good in itself, in which case I desire it for its own sake, or else I shall say that I desire it for something else, for example, happiness or well-being. In this event I must consider why I desire happiness or well-being. Once again I shall desire them either for themselves or for the sake of something else ; but clearly I must stop somewhere. I must, that is to say, postulate *something* that I desire for its own sake, and not for the sake of something else. This something will be an ultimate good, and if it is really ultimate, I cannot give any reason for desiring it, since any such reason would take the form of specifying some other good for the sake of which I desire it, in which event the first good would not after all have been ultimate.

Thus, if pleasure is an ultimate good, no reasons can be given for thinking it to be so. Nevertheless, it seems fairly clear from an inspection of one's own consciousness that it probably is ultimate. It does not therefore follow, as the Hedonists assert, that it is the sole ultimate good, that it is The Good.

LESSON 27

A Critique of Hedonism

IT seems fairly clear that the assertion which Hedonists make to the effect that pleasure is the *sole* good is mistaken.

In the first place, if pleasure is *The Good*, in the sense that everything which is good is pleasure, and *vice versa*, and that there is no good, therefore, except pleasure, then for the word " good " we may read the word " pleasure " without any change of meaning. Now, the statement " pleasure is the good " may be right or it may be wrong, but it can at least be intelligibly discussed with a view to determining whether it is right or wrong. But the statement " pleasure is pleasure " has no meaning. It is the assertion of an identity. Therefore the statement " pleasure is the good " cannot mean the same as the statement " pleasure is pleasure." Therefore good, or The Good, cannot be absolutely identical with pleasure, from which it follows that good must mean something other than, or at any rate additional to, pleasure.

In the second place, the argument for Hedonism rests upon a false psychology. We can see this by taking a concrete instance. If Hedonism is true, we must all have starved in infancy. If an infant did not suck at the breast, it would starve. On the first occasion on which it sucks it cannot be motivated by the expectation of pleasure or the desire to obtain pleasure, since, if the occasion were *really* the first, it could not know whether it would obtain pleasure from the action or not. Consequently, if, as the Hedonists assert, the only possible motive for any human action is to obtain pleasure, it is impossible to understand why the infant should have sucked on the first occasion—that is to say, it is impossible to understand why it did not starve.

The psychology of Hedonism is based upon two truths which may be stated with some degree of confidence. The first is that the satisfaction of any desire brings some pleasure ; the second, that the value of actions depends upon, is indeed ultimately assessable only in terms of, their effect upon some human consciousness. But while it embraces these truths, Hedonism makes assertions which go far beyond them. Because all satisfaction of desire brings pleasure, it does not follow that the motive for all our actions is the desire to obtain pleasure.

In actual experience we desire specific things without really considering whether we shall experience pleasure by obtaining them, and we obey particular impulses without considering whether the results of giving way to them are likely to be more pleasant than those of resistance. The fact that pleasure enriches our mental state when we have obtained the thing or satisfied the impulse does not justify us in saying that, *as a matter of actual experience*, it was our desire to obtain this pleasure which prompted our action. To make this assertion is to put the cart before the horse. Hedonism rests on the assumption that human beings are always rational and purposive, that they always deliberate about the results of their actions and act in order to secure certain specific ends. This belief is a delusion. Many of our actions are purely impulsive in character and are not done with the object of securing any end. When a man breaks the furniture in a rage, boasts, ducks to avoid a flying cricket ball, or shrinks from a ghost, he is not acting with any object at all—certainly not with the object of obtaining pleasure.

Bentham's Utilitarianism. In addition to the psychological doctrine described above, Jeremy Bentham advocated the ethical doctrine that we ought always to promote the greatest happiness of the greatest number. This is not, as would first appear, necessarily inconsistent with the psychological doctrine that we can act only so as to promote our own greatest pleasure, since, according to Bentham, to promote the greatest happiness of the greatest number was also to obtain the greatest possible amount of pleasure for oneself. The reason for this is that society has taken care to secure the performance of those acts which benefit it, by arranging that they shall automatically conduce to the pleasure of the agent. The brave man, for example, is happier than the coward because society rewards bravery, which benefits it, and discourages cowardice, which endangers it.

Mill's Modifications. J. S. Mill introduced two important qualifications into the doctrine of psychological Hedonism, which in effect amount to the abandonment of the view that the pleasure of the agent is the only possible object of desire, and hence that pleasure is the sole good. He introduces a distinction between different types of pleasures. Bentham had said, " Quantity of pleasure being equal, pushpin is as good as poetry." Mill, however, held that we ought always to prefer a smaller quantity of a higher pleasure to a large quantity of a lower, that, in short, it is " better to be Socrates dissatisfied than a pig satisfied." But, it may be asked, why should we prefer a smaller quantity of higher pleasure, unless that smaller quantity contains some element of value which makes it more desirable than the larger quantity of lower pleasure ? This element of value cannot itself be pleasure, since, if it were, the smaller quantity of higher pleasure would be just *more pleasure*. Hence we are driven to admit elements of value which are not pleasure. In the second place, Mill held that it was our duty to promote what he called Social Good, that is to say, the greatest happiness of the greatest number, even when other courses of action more conducive to our own individual happiness are open to us. He abandoned, that is to say, Bentham's contention that the greatest happiness of the individual *always* lies in promoting the greatest happiness of the greatest number, and held that, where they conflict, the latter *ought* to be preferred to the former. Thus, though Utilitarianism may succeed in establishing the validity of the assessment of the ethical value of actions in terms of their consequences, the attempt to establish pleasure as the only consequence of value breaks down.

Books Recommended. " Utilitarianism," J. S. Mill ; " Methods of Ethics," Alfred Sidgwick ; " Principia Ethica," G. E. Moore. In " Elements of Ethics," J. H. Muirhead gives a general survey of ethical philosophies.

LESSON 28

Do We Possess a Moral Sense?

MANY writers on Ethics have held that actions possess in themselves some intrinsic quality in virtue of which they have ethical value. This quality is recognized as belonging to the action by a special faculty known as the moral sense or conscience. The deliverances of conscience are intuitional —that is to say, though they may be defended by, they are not based upon, reason ; they are also final. The moral sense, that is to say, is arbiter over all that pertains to the moral sphere, just as the sense of sight is arbiter over all that pertains to the visual sphere. Our eyes tell us what is beautiful, the moral sense tells us what is right ; and there is no appeal against either verdict.

In some forms of the moral sense theory it is maintained that good actions are those which spring from or are motivated by a particular part of our nature, and in the most famous form of this theory the particular part of our nature in question is held to be in some sense continuous with, or an expression of reality.

This latter view was advanced in an extreme form by Kant (*see* Lessons 15 and 16). It is only in so far as he acts morally, willing to do his duty whatever the cost, that, according to Kant, a man is free. As a moral agent he escapes from the law of cause and effect which governs the phenomenal world, and acts freely as a member of the real or noumenal world. Translated into psychological terms, the theory may be stated as follows. Man as a member of the phenomenal world is a creature of desire. A complete knowledge of his temperament, past history and dominant impulses at any given moment would enable an observer to predict exactly how he would act in any given situation, *in so far as he acted according to his desires*. In so far, therefore, as he acts according to his desires he is not free. But his moral self, which is expressed in a free will, prescribes for him what is right irrespective of his desires, and, in so far as he follows its dictates, he is acting freely because he is acting in accordance with his own real nature.

Kant's doctrine, then, amounts to this, that we should act in every case in accordance with general principles which the will intuitively recognizes as binding. Unfortunately, this doctrine affords little practical guidance in the doubtful moral situations that arise in everyday life. The general principles which the will lays down are, indeed, rational enough ; Kant points out, for example, in regard to them that they can be universalized, whereas conduct in accordance with the contradictory principles cannot.

It is possible, for example, for everybody to tell the truth, but, if everybody lied, nobody would believe anybody else, and there would be no point in lying. It is, however, obvious that in practice all general principles admit of exceptions—e.g., it is sometimes right to lie to a lunatic—and for these Kant's system does not provide.

Intuitional Judgements. The important part of Kant's doctrine, which is embodied also in that of the other writers of the moral sense school, is his insistence on the special and unique character of the " feeling "—to use a non-committal word—that we have in regard to certain actions or classes of actions. We recognize instinctively and immediately, it is said, with regard to those actions and classes of actions that they are right and ought to be done, even if we, in fact, do the contrary. It is because of the *directness and certainty* of this feeling that the deliverances of the moral sense are sometimes called intuitions. Thus children and uneducated persons have direct intuitions with regard, say, to the wrongness of lying or cruelty, in virtue of which they condemn lies and cruel actions, even while they practise them, without taking any cognizance of the effects of cruel or dishonest conduct upon society.

That people's moral intuitions differ in different ages and countries is admitted ; it is admitted also that analysis may show a close relation between what the moral sense of a people pronounces to be right, and what conduces on the whole to the advantage of the society to which they belong. These facts do not, however, it is said, diminish the authority of our moral judgements. On the contrary, they strengthen it. We should not expect the moral intuitions of savages to be the same as those of highly civilized Man, and, as the evolution of the race progresses, there is no reason why Man's moral sense should not have developed together with his other faculties. As a matter of fact, such progress can be traced in the history of religion. Compare, for example, the high moral code of the New Testament with the savage cruelty of that of the Old. What the moral sense theories assert is, then, that with regard to certain classes of actions and also on occasion with regard to certain individual actions, we experience feelings of approval and disapproval which are ultimate and immediate. These feelings pronounce upon the ethical rightness and wrongness of the actions in question without reference to their social utility, and, though we may not be able to explain or to defend them, we know that they are such as we ought to follow.

Intuitionism of Ends. To these arguments Utilitarians reply that an action divested of its consequences is a mere figment. If dishonesty, for example, did not produce injurious effects both upon the dishonest man and his victim, why should we

DO WE POSSESS A MORAL SENSE ?

censure it ?   Hence it is essential to take into account the social effects of actions when assessing their ethical value, those actions, and only those, being right which produce good social effects.

What are good social effects ?   As we have seen, the Utilitarian attempt to identify good exclusively with pleasure or happiness broke down.   Now when we come to ask what is ultimately good—good, that is to say, in itself and not for the sake of its consequences—there may be a legitimate field for intuition. We cannot give reasons for thinking a thing ultimately good, since such reasons would take the form of showing why it is desirable—i.e. for the sake of what other thing it is desired— and what is ultimately good is by definition desirable in itself.

On the whole, the intuitions of Mankind seem to be in favour of the view that truth, goodness, beauty and, possibly, happiness are all of them ultimately good in this sense.   This doctrine, sometimes known as the " intuitionism of ends," has been advocated in G. E. Moore's " Principia Ethica."

Books for Further Study.   The Dialogues of Plato, particularly " The Republic."   Berkeley's " Three Dialogues between Hylas and Philonous " (Everyman Library).   Hume's " Treatise of Human Nature " (Everyman Library).   F. H. Bradley's " Appearance and Reality."   Bergson's " Creative Evolution."   Bertrand Russell's " Problems of Philosophy " (Home University Library), and his later books, " Our Knowledge of the External World," and " An Outline of Philosophy." C. E. M. Joad's " Guide to Modern Thought," " Guide to Philosophy," and " Guide to the Philosophy of Morals and Politics."

This Lesson concludes our Course in Philosophy.

LESSON 21

More About Electrical Units

IN the preceding Lesson 20 (Volume 5) we discussed the law of force between charges and saw that it was similar to the law of force between magnetic poles. If a sphere is charged, the effect on outside charges is as though the charge was concentrated at the centre; for example, if a large region of space has a charge Q spread evenly throughout a volume of radius R, then at any point outside the sphere the force is the same as if Q were at the centre of the sphere. If a charge q units of the opposite sign be placed a distance d away, the attraction is $\frac{qQ}{d^2}$, so long as d is greater than R. For points within the distance R, the force is no longer governed by this net result. The fact is that when within a charge there is no force from that charge. So we see in Fig. 1 (p. 450), which illustrates this, there is no force on q at P due to the part of the charge Q which is in the vertical shading, and the force is given by the inverse square law as:

$$q \times \frac{\text{(charge within sphere of radius d)}}{d^2}$$

Now the enclosed volume is $\frac{4}{3} \pi d^3$, which is a fraction of the total volume, $\frac{4}{3} \pi R^3$, which is obviously $\frac{\frac{4}{3} \pi d^3}{\frac{4}{3} \pi R^3} = \frac{d^3}{R^3}$ and therefore, since Q is uniformly spread throughout the volume, the charge within the small sphere is $\frac{d^3}{R^3} \cdot Q$, and so the force on q is

$$\left(\frac{d^3}{R^3} \cdot Q\right) \frac{q}{d^2} = d \left(\frac{Qq}{R^3}\right)$$

that is, the force within the charge is directly proportional to the distance from the centre. This is again analogous to what happens in the gravitational case for any two portions of matter.

The second idea which was introduced in Lesson 20 was the important electrical term, " potential." We saw that an electric charge raises the electric potential of a body just as a quantity

MATTHIAS CORVINUS (1443–90). Son of Janos Hunyadi, he was elected king of Hungary in 1458 and warred successfully against the Turks, Bohemia and Austria. HISTORY : MEDIEVAL 43

From Franknoi, "Matthias Corvinus"

FRANCESCO SFORZA (1401–66). By military genius and political acumen he made himself duke of Milan in 1450 and fostered learning and the arts. HISTORY : MEDIEVAL 43

Relief by Romano in Florence

LORENZO DE' MEDICI (1448–92). Succeeding to the headship of the Florentine republic in 1469, he raised Florence to the pinnacle of its greatness. Himself a scholar and poet, Lorenzo the Magnificent welcomed to his glittering court the leading artists and literary men of his age. HISTORY : MEDIEVAL 43

Panel by Vasari; Uffizi Gallery, Florence

KUBLAI KHAN AT LUNCH. This illustration, taken (like the one below) from the "Livre des Merveilles," a MS. written about 1351 containing the narratives of Marco Polo and Sir John Mandeville, shows the Great Khan lunching in a kind of summer pavilion. His chief wife is seen sitting on his left hand. HISTORY: MEDIEVAL 44

Bibliothèque Nationale, Paris

MARCO POLO ON HIS TRAVELS. A Venetian of noble parentage, Marco Polo (c. 1254–1324) set out with his father and uncle for China in 1271. Travelling across Persia, Tartary and the Gobi desert, they arrived at Chandu, Kublai Khan's summer residence, in 1275. Marco Polo won the favour of the Great Khan, was employed by him on several missions, and appointed a provincial governor. HISTORY: MEDIEVAL 44

From the Livre de Merveilles, Bibliothèque Nationale, Paris

Plate 52   Volume VI

of heat raises the temperature of a body, or a quantity of water raises the level or pressure in a container. The "electric temperature," or "electric pressure" as we sometimes call potential, exists in stationary charges and also by our definition is present to cause a movement of charges, when we say that a current flows, and further it must be maintained so long as we require the electricity to pass.

Consider first the stationary charges. When a sphere of radius r cm. is given q units of electricity we saw that the potential may be calculated to be q/r. It will be apparent that, if we divide the charge by the potential, we obtain the radius (q ÷ q/r = r). We find in all cases that if a body is fixed in space the ratio of $\frac{charge}{potential}$ is a constant which we call the *capacity* of a body.

In our example above we see that the electrical capacity of a sphere is equal to the radius. Now the capacity can be increased by increasing the area of the body, by bringing another earth-connected body near the first, and by displacing the air between the two bodies by inserting shellac, glass, mica, etc. This arrangement is called a *condenser*, and is usually made by taking parallel plates which are separated by waxed paper, or sheets of mica. In the *air* condenser the plates are separated by air. In wireless variable air condensers the capacity is changed by rotating the plate so that a change in the area of the facing plates is brought about.

If we now consider the movement of charges due to a difference of potential, we find that if two stationary charges at different potentials are joined a current flows and equalizes potential and then the current ceases. This is almost instantaneous in action. To maintain the current we must maintain the potential difference. The friction methods are abandoned for most practical purposes, and we utilize the fact that when any two dissimilar metals are placed in a dilute acid, suitably chosen, a potential difference is set up which is maintained even when a current flows, as shown in Fig. 2, which illustrates a typical *simple cell*.

In practice it is found that the cell soon polarizes and runs down, and special modifications are introduced to overcome the difficulty. Otherwise accumulators are used.

If we take any form of cell or battery and allow a current to flow by joining the poles, + and −, by means of a wire, we find several effects are produced by the current.

There are : 1. Physiological effects. 2. Magnetic effects. 3. Heating effects. 4. Chemical effects, etc.

In addition we find that when acted on by a magnetic field we produce an important interaction.

The physiological effect referred to is most marked when several cells are joined together. Cases are reported in the newspapers of the fatal results of applying the ends of such a battery

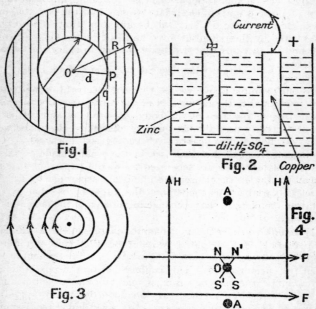

Fig. 1

Fig. 2   Copper

Zinc   *dil.* H_2SO_4

Current   +

Fig. 3

Fig. 4

ELECTRICAL POTENTIALS. Fig. 1. Electrical capacity of a sphere; the lettering is explained in the text. **Fig. 2.** Typical simple cell. **Fig. 3.** Magnetic field set up by an electric current. **Fig. 4.** Principle of the galvanometer; AA, section of a coil of wire; NS, magnet pivoted at O; H, the earth's magnetic field in horizontal plane; F, field due to current in coil; N'S', position of magnet when currents pass.

either by accident or design (U.S.A. electric chair). In fact, the physiological effect observed on a freshly killed frog led to the discovery by Galvani of the simple cell, which was developed by Volta.

When a current is passed along a wire the region about the wire has a magnetic field set up in it in the form of circular lines of force. In Fig. 3 the dot represents the section of a wire conveying a current into the plane of the paper; the magnetic field is represented by the circles. If the current is reversed the magnetic field is reversed. There is a simple useful rule to determine the relative directions of the magnetic field and the current. This was given by Clerk-Maxwell, formerly professor of Physics at King's College, London, and subsequently appointed the first Cavendish professor of Physics at Cambridge. His main work was the electromagnetic theory, the importance of which is of first rank. His simple little rule is called the *corkscrew rule*. If you imagine that a corkscrew is being driven in the direction of the current, the direction of rotation gives the direction of the magnetic field.

If a wire is bent into a circular coil and a current passed through it, the magnetic field is still in circles about the wire; i.e. if we draw planes at right angles to the *wire* the field is in circles in the plane. So that at the centre of the coil of wire the magnetic field is at right angles to the plane of the coil, and is made up of the effects produced by each bit of current in the wires. Our mental picture of the magnetic field is somewhat like the smoke in a smoke ring. Now we can make use of this magnetic effect to define current, so that we have a unit for measurement. We define it in terms of the strength of the magnetic field it sets up.

It was found by experiment that the magnetic field due to a short length l of conductor conveying a current was proportional to the length and inversely proportional to the square of the distance, r, away from the wire as well as to the current itself, and therefore at the centre of a circular coil of wire of radius r the magnetic field, F, is proportional to $\frac{2\pi r}{r^2} \times$ strength of current, i.e. $F = \text{constant} \times \frac{2\pi}{r} i$, where i is the current in some units.

Now we define unit current in terms of the magnetic effect (called the electromagnetic unit, or E.M.U.) by saying that if it flowed in a circle of radius 1 cm. it produces a magnetic field of 2π dynes per unit pole at the centre. This makes the constant equal to unity, and we write.

$$F = \frac{2\pi i}{r}.$$

where i is in E.M.U.

The theoretical unit is too large for many practical purposes, so we use the *ampère*, which is one-tenth part of the unit we have defined. Not only does this give us a definition of a unit current, but the same ideas are underlying a practical method of measuring current in an instrument called a galvanometer, the principle of which is shown in Fig. 4. A coil of wire shown in section at A, A, and of a known number of turns is placed in the magnetic meridian and at its centre a small magnet is pivoted. When a current is sent round the coils a magnetic field F is set up which is $n \times \dfrac{2\pi i}{r}$: this moves the needle through an angle θ, which is given by $F = H \tan \theta$ (*see* last Lesson), so that $\dfrac{2\pi n i}{r} = H \tan \theta$ or $i = \dfrac{Hr}{2\pi n} \tan \theta$.

If we know H, r, and observe θ we can calculate i in theoretical units, or, if we multiply by 10, we obtain i in ampères. This is the principle of the tangent galvanometer (or current measurer), and is the fundamental idea in all galvanometers using a moving magnet. We see at least from this that if we *define* current in terms of the magnetic effect it produces, we can also *measure* the current by similar means. The ammeter generally used for current measurement makes use of another principle, which is discussed later in these Lessons, but all moving magnet instruments are based on the above theory.

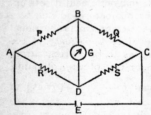

Fig. 5. Scheme of the Wheatstone bridge: the lettering is explained in the text.

The unit of quantity of electricity in E.M.U. is obtained by considering the amount of electricity which is conveyed by the current in unit time. For example, if an ampère flows for one second the quantity of electricity passing any point is a *coulomb*, which is 1/10 of the quantity conveyed past a point in one second when a theoretical unit of current flows. Of course, the current flows because a potential difference exists. From a theoretical point of view we define unit potential difference as being set up between two points when 1 erg of work is done by the current in taking one unit of quantity of electricity from the point at higher to the point at lower potential. This is much too small a unit for practical purposes, so we select a suitable number of this unit and call it a practical unit—just the same as in measurement of length, 1 inch is a suitable unit for some measurements, whereas for long distances we take 63,360 of these and call them a mile. The practical unit of potential is called the *volt*, and this is 100 million (10^8) theoretical units.

It was found by Ohm that if a wire was maintained at constant temperature there is a constant relation between the potential applied to its ends and the current which results. Thus if i is the current and E is the potential Ohm found that $\dfrac{E}{i} = $ constant.

This constant was called the resistance, R, and the relation above, which is called Ohm's Law, may be written $\dfrac{E}{i} = R$.

If E and i are in theoretical units R is also in theoretical E.M.U. of resistance. This unit has many advantages in calculations, as have i and E, but for practical purposes it is much too small, so we take what is a convenient large number of these units, 1,000 million (10^9) and call this the *ohm*.

In terms of practical units we have, where i is in ampères, and E is in volts,

$$R = E/i.$$

Thus if the mains are at 100 volts and a current of 5 ampères passes through an apparatus, its resistance is $\dfrac{100}{5} = 20$ ohms.

Actually, the resistance of a wire is not constant, but in most cases goes up with an increase of temperature, so that if the resistance at O°C. is R_o and at t°C. is R_t we have a relation connecting the two of the form

$$R_t = R_o (1 + at + \beta t^2) ;$$

for small ranges of temperature this becomes

$$R_t = R_o (1 + at)$$

because the constant β is small. The constant a for pure metals has a value of about ·0036. The change in resistance of a wire which has been carefully measured at three known temperatures can be used to measure unknown temperatures.

This is used, for example, in the measurement of furnace temperatures. The wire is encased in a porcelain cover and inserted in the furnace. The measurement of resistance can be carried out in a cool office some distance away, using a modified form of Wheatstone bridge.

The Wheatstone bridge is really a simple enough scheme. Two fixed resistances P and Q (usually equal, or P is 10 or 100 times Q) are connected as shown in Fig. 5. R is a known resistance which may be varied, and S is the unknown. A battery sends a current via ABC or ADC and R is adjusted until the galvanometer G shows no deflection, when it can be simply shown that the following relation holds :

$$\frac{P}{Q} = \frac{R}{S}$$

from which the unknown S may be calculated.

LESSON 22

Electric Energy and its Effects

WHEN a current flows between two points where a unit of potential difference exists, the work done on each unit of quantity of electricity passing is, by definition, equal to one erg. Now the quantity, q, of electricity is given by $i\,t$ where i is the current and t the time in seconds for which it flows. Therefore the work done by the current when flowing between two points where the potential difference is E is q E or $i\,t$ E ergs. This work is done in overcoming the resistance, etc., in the wire, and the energy appears as heat in the wire unless some definite extra work is done by the current. In Lesson 8 (Volume 3, page 573) we saw that as a result of Dr. Joule's experiments we are able to find the thermal equivalent of the work done, using the mechanical equivalent of heat J ($=4\cdot2 \times 10^7$ ergs per calorie). We therefore anticipate that an amount of heat H cals. is given when the current i flows for a time t between two points at potential difference E, where

$$J = \frac{W}{H} \text{ or } H = \frac{E\,i\,t}{4\cdot2 \times 10^7}, \text{ cals.}$$

When we measure the electrical quantities in practical units we remember the relations given in Lesson 21, and we then say that for i in ampères we have $i/10$ theoretical units ; for E volts, 10^8 theoretical units, and therefore we have $i \times E \times 1/10 \times 10^8$ ergs or $= i\,E\,t \times 10^7$ ergs, i.e. the heat is

$$\frac{\text{amps.} \times \text{volts} \times \text{secs.}}{4\cdot2} \text{ cals.}$$

We see that the energy supplied *per second* is amps × volts × 10^7 ergs, or *amps × volts* joules (since the joule is the large unit of work which is equal to 10^7 ergs). The *rate* of working in the electric circuit is $E\,i$ joules per second.

Now in the C.G.S. system we have a unit for measuring the rate of working, just as in the British System we employ a unit, the *horse power*. When the energy is used at the rate of 1 joule per second we say the rate of working is one watt ; therefore in our case the rate of working is volts × amps watts. When the energy consumed is at a large rate, comparable with a horse power, we use a larger unit—in fact, 1,000 watts—called a kilowatt. Obviously, the rate of working in kilowatts is $\dfrac{\text{volt} \times \text{amps}}{1000}$ kilowatts. For the purpose of illustrating this point we may consider a well-known example. The ordinary electric lamp is rated at so many watts. A 60-watt lamp on a 100-volt mains passes a current, i, given by $100 \times i = 60$ or $i = 0.6$ ampère. On a 240-volt main a lamp made for *this* voltage, and called a 60-watt lamp, takes i', where

$$240 \times i' = 60 \qquad i' = \tfrac{1}{4} = \cdot 25 \text{ amp.}$$

In the first case of 100-volt mains the resistance of the lamp is given by Ohm's Law

$$R = \frac{E}{i} = \frac{100}{\cdot 6} = 166\tfrac{2}{3} \text{ ohms.}$$

In the second case (240 volt)

$$R = \frac{E}{i} = \frac{240}{\cdot 25} = 960 \text{ ohms.}$$

Obviously, if we put the lamp marked 60 watt 100 volt on the 240 volt mains, the current which would pass would be, by Ohm's Law :

$$i = \frac{E}{R} = \frac{240}{166\tfrac{2}{3}} = 1\cdot 44 \text{ ampères,}$$

assuming there is no change in the resistance of the lamp. It is important to avoid this in practice. In all electrical apparatus the voltage of the mains must be that marked on the apparatus.

Consider the second case a little further. The lamp wrongly used on 240-volt mains has a current 1·44 ampères. In proper use it should take ·6 ampère. The heat produced in normal running on its correct voltage is :

$$\frac{\cdot 6 \times 100}{4 \cdot 2}$$ cals. per second, and in the second case is

$$\frac{1 \cdot 44 \times 240}{4 \cdot 2}$$ cals., i.e. $\frac{345}{60} = 5 \cdot 7$ times as much.

The obvious will happen—the heat developed is nearly 6 times the normal, so the metal wire will melt and the lamp becomes useless.

This kind of thing happens when a wire is overloaded. In wiring a house the electrician uses wires which are sufficiently thick, and therefore sufficiently low in resistance. He ensures that when the full load is taken the heating of the lead wires will be negligibly small, as it would not be safe to allow these encased wires to heat up. In ordinary use this is sufficient. But, especially nowadays, when so many electrical devices are easily obtainable, it is not certain that the consumer will not add considerably to the load by using electric fires, irons and the like.

To safeguard the house against possible fire, *fuses* are placed in each circuit. At the point near the meter where all the wires are branching off to the various floors in the house, a glass-faced box contains these fuses. They are simply lengths of wire made of alloys or *thin* copper strands, which join the outgoing and ingoing wires. When the current in any of the circuits exceeds the safe current in that circuit it is arranged that the fuse becomes so hot that it melts. A 5-amp. fuse melts when 5 ampères are passed continuously through it, so if the wiring is safe up to 5 ampères and a 5-amp. fuse is in circuit, any increased load would break the weakest link—the fuse—and save overheating of the rest of the circuit. If the fuse " blows " it is easily replaced by first switching off the main switch and then inserting a new length of fuse wire of the same kind. Do not try thicker fuse wire unless you know that the wiring will stand heavier currents. Repeated " blowing " of the fuse suggests a short circuit or an overload of the circuit, which should be overhauled.

The method of charging for electrical supply is to charge for the *energy* " consumed," as the supply is ultimately from energy used at the power station. Now if we use at the rate of 1 kilowatt for one hour we use energy equivalent to $(1000 \times 10^7) \times 60 \times 60$ ergs. This method of calculating the ergs introduces too many noughts ; we simply say 1 kilowatt hour, the Board of Trade unit of supply.

Suppose we use four 60-watt lamps for four hours per night

for one week, the energy in kilowatt hours is $\dfrac{4 \times 60 \times 4 \times 7}{1000}$

In addition, one electric fire rated at 1 kilowatt (a 1-bar fire) for the same time consumes $1 \times 4 \times 7 = 28$ kilowatt hours, and the bill at 3d. per unit is $(6.72 + 28) \times 3$ pence $=$ $\dfrac{34.72 \times 3}{12}$ shillings $\dfrac{104.2}{12} = 8s.$ 8d., of which 7s. is for the fire !

The above heating effects are referred to as the Joule-heating effect. The expression for the energy, E i t, can be changed, by Ohm's Law, substituting $E = i R$, to i^2Rt, and the engineer usually refers to energy " lost " in this way as " the i^2Rt loss."

Mechanical Effects. When a current passes along a wire there are other ways in which the energy may be practically used. If a straight wire AB, Fig. 1 (a), conveys a current i as shown, and is in a magnetic field set up, in this case, by two magnets, it is found that the wire is acted upon by a force tending to move the wire in the direction of the arrow. If either i or the magnetic field, H, is reversed the direction of movement is reversed. If we extend the first two fingers and thumb of the left hand so that they are mutually at right angles, and then point the first finger in the direction of the magnetic field and the second finger in the direction of the current, the direction of the thumb indicates the direction of the resulting motion of the conductor (Fig. 1 b). This *left-hand rule* summarizes the results of observation on the interaction between magnetic field and current.

The movement, of course, takes energy from the source of supply of the current in addition to the i^2Rt energy, which is a loss if our main object is to produce movement. From a simple observation of this kind the modern electric motor has been developed. We will consider one stage in this development as illustrated in Fig. 2. A rectangular coil of wire is mounted to rotate about a central axis, shown as a broken line in Fig. 2, and a uniform magnetic field, H, is applied at right angles to this axis. The side AB is acted upon by an upward force, as may be seen by applying the left-hand rule, and the side DC is acted upon by an equal downward force. This causes the coil to rotate. When, as in Fig. 2 (b), the coil is at right angles to the field, the forces are parallel to the plane of the coil and do not tend to turn the system. Actually, when the coil turns it overshoots this position, but the upward force on AB rotates it back to the position shown in Fig. 2 (b). If, however, we reverse the current as the coil passes the position of Fig. 2 (b), the coil rotates half a turn, when the reversal of the current will cause a continued rotation. If this reversal is done each time the plane of the coil is at right angles to the field, the rotation becomes continuous.

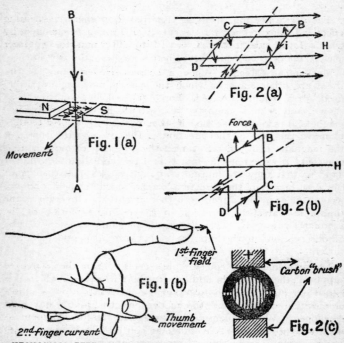

MECHANICAL EFFECTS OF CURRENTS. Fig. 1 (a), showing movement of an electric wire in a magnetic field. **Fig. 1 (b),** illustrating the left hand rule (*see* text). **Fig. 2 (a)** and (b), illustrating the behaviour of a coil of wire relative to magnetic forces. **Fig. 2 (c).** Principle of a commutator, by means of which current is reversed twice for each revolution of the coil.

This reversal is brought about by the use of a commutator, seen in Fig. 2 (c), which shows the section of the axis. Two metal sectors, shown in black, are joined to the ends of the coil, and the current is led from the carbon brushes. When the coil

(458)

is in the " dead centre " position of Fig. 2 (b) the gaps between the metal sectors are against the brushes, and a slight continued movement reverses the current automatically. So much for the physics of the motor. Development of this idea is the province of the electrical engineer.

Galvanometers and Voltmeters. If we hang up a coil of wire by means of a very thin wire between the poles of a magnet, as in Fig. 3, we find that when a current is passed the coil moves through an angle and so twists the wire XY which supports it. When the wire is twisted it sets up a turning effect, tending to restore the coil to its original position. If now we fix a soft

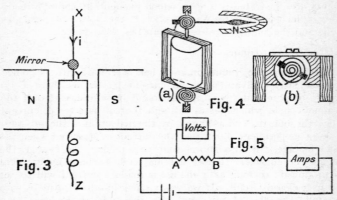

GALVANOMETERS AND VOLTMETERS. Fig. 3. Diagram showing principle of mirror galvanometer. **Fig. 4 (a) and (b).** Moving parts of an ammeter or voltmeter. **Fig. 5.** Voltmeter in parallel and ammeter in series.

iron core by means of a screw to a piece of brass as shown in the section diagram given in Fig. 4 (b), and let the coil move in the space between the magnetic poles and the soft iron cylindrical core, we find that the angle of twist is proportional to the current. This constitutes, therefore, a simple galvanometer with a moving coil, where i is proportional to θ, the angle of deflection, and forms the basis of ammeters and voltmeters. Instead of the supporting wires XY and the flexible lead Z, the coil is mounted on two jewels and the current is led in and out by two hair springs, which also act as control. When used as an ammeter, the two ends of the hair springs are connected to a low resistance (called a shunt), which allows most of the current to be sidetracked and which makes the net resistance of the instrument very small. The instrument is then placed in series with the circuit in which the current is to be measured. Instead of using a mirror, as in the galvanometer, a pointer N moves over a scale graduated in ampères, and so the instrument is direct reading.

When used as a voltmeter a very high resistance is placed in series with the coil, so that the total resistance of the whole instrument becomes so high that only a small current is passed through it ; therefore the instrument is always used in parallel with the circuit in which the potential is to be measured. These points are illustrated in Fig. 5, which incidentally shows a ready way of measuring a resistance AB. If the voltmeter reads 15 volts and the ammeter reads 1·5 ampères : Resistance

$$AB = \frac{15}{1\cdot5} = \text{10 ohms.}$$

Electromagnetic Induction. When a coil of wire is joined to a sensitive galvanometer no current passes, as there is no source of potential. Now it was found by Faraday that if the magnetic field which passes through the coil is altered, current flows through the coil as shown by the deflection of the galvano-meter. Experiment shows that the current is produced when the field changes ; it also shows that the quicker the change the bigger the current. It does not matter how the magnetic field is produced ; so long as a change is made a current will be set up in a closed circuit. If we wrap a few hundred turns of wire around a cardboard tube and join the ends of the wire to a sensitive (moving coil) galvanometer, and then slowly introduce the north pole of a magnet, a small deflection is produced in the galvanometer, which persists so long as the magnet moves in the same way. When the magnet goes out at the other end the current reverses, but is present so long as the magnet moves. If we introduce a magnet south pole first the *direction* of the current is reversed, but the current is there.

Now if we do the same two experiments at a quicker rate the deflection is bigger, i.e. the current is bigger, but, of course, lasts for the smaller time taken to move the magnet.

If we find the direction of the current we see that the induced currents set up a magnetic field in opposition to that which has caused them. For example, when the north pole is introduced, the current which is set up in the coil produces a magnetic field which tends to push the north pole out of the coil. When the north pole is taken out the current reverses and so sets up a magnetic field tending to bring the north pole back again. This is summarized in the Law of Lenz, which says that "when an induced current is produced it is in such a direction as to oppose the motion which causes it." The first observations are summarized in Faraday's Law of Electromagnetic Induction, which states that "an induced current is set up in a closed circuit whenever there is any change in the magnetic flux in that circuit. The induced electromotive force (potential) is proportional to the rate of change of the magnetic field (i.e. change per second)."

LESSON 23

Electric Induction and Conduction

THE laws of electro-magnetic induction, discussed in the preceding Lesson, summarize the results of a very important set of experiments, and we find many useful applications of the principles involved in them. So long as there is a change in the magnetic field threading through a circuit, an electric pressure (potential) is set up which will drive a current through a closed circuit (i.e. one in which there is a complete conducting path). We saw that with a fixed coil we can produce this effect by bringing a magnet up to, and into, the coil. Another way is to have a second coil within the first, as in Fig. 1. When a current is sent in coil AB, which is called the *primary coil*, a second current passes through the circuit C G D, containing a galvanometer G, which shows that the current only passes when the key in the primary circuit is being closed or opened. When the key remains down or up there is no "secondary current."

This is consistent with what we saw in the previous Lesson, for when the current passes in AB it sets up a magnetic field in AB. If we apply the corkscrew rule to each turn of wire in the primary coil, we find that the field produced by all the turns is along the axis of the coil (called a *solenoid*). If the current is set up in the direction of the arrows, the magnetic field runs in the coil from left to right. Therefore, as far as the secondary coil is concerned, we have introduced a magnetic field in this direction, and therefore, to be consistent with Lenz's law, a current will be induced in the secondary in the opposite direction, in order to make a transient magnetic field to oppose the motion which causes the induction. When the current in the primary coil is established, the magnetic field becomes fixed, and since there is now no movement of the field there is no induction and, therefore, the secondary current ceases. When the current in the primary is stopped, by opening the key, the magnetic field goes, and so again a transient current is induced in the secondary coil, this time in the reverse direction from the last. In the secondary coil the electric pressure set up depends on the

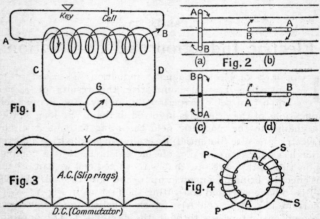

ELECTRO-MAGNETIC INDUCTION. Fig. 1. Current produced in secondary circuit. **Fig. 2.** Current production by movement of coil in a magnetic field. **Fig. 3.** Diagram of alternating and direct current: X Y is one cycle of A.C. **Fig. 4.** Transformer: A, soft iron ring; P, primary winding; S, secondary winding.

number of turns. Each turn has a definite pressure, so that the total potential at the ends of the secondary is proportional to the total number of turns in the secondary. In the device known as the *induction coil* we can produce very high potential by automatically or otherwise " making " and " breaking " the primary current.

For example, if 100 volts are used in the primary it is possible to obtain, with ease, 80,000 volts in the secondary. Of course, to do this we use large currents in the primary and only obtain small currents in the secondary, because the power put in is never exceeded by the power taken out, i.e., $i_p \times E_p = i_s E_s$ under ideal conditions, where i and E are the currents and potentials, and the suffix *s* refers to the secondary and suffix *p* to primary. Suppose that, using 100 volts mains, the current that is taken is 15 ampères, and that 75,000 volts are produced in the secondary, then the maximum theoretical current (which is never quite obtained) in the secondary is $i_s = \dfrac{100 \times 15}{75,000} = \dfrac{1}{50}$ ampère. These small currents are usually measured in a smaller unit called the milliampère ($=1/1000$ amp.). Therefore, the current is 20 milliampères. This kind of device has been largely used in X-ray practice.

An alternative method of producing a current by relative movement of a magnetic field and a coil is to leave the field fixed and rotate the coil. Fig. 2, in Lesson 22 (page 458), illustrates this case. When the plane of the coil is at right angles to the field (2b) there is a maximum number of lines of magnetic force through the coil. When the latter turns through a right angle there are no lines of force through the coil. Therefore, in the act of turning, an electric current goes through coil and the external wires which join its ends. Let us examine this case a little further with the help of the diagrams here given in Fig. 2.

Starting with the coil shown in section in Fig. 2 (a) with a maximum magnetic flux passing through it, we pass to Fig. 2 (b), where the position of the coil after moving through a right angle is set out. During this movement lines of magnetic force have been taken out of the left-hand face, and as the coil moves on to position (c), lines of magnetic force are pushed into the former right-hand face, which amounts to the same thing. Therefore, a potential is set up always in one direction. The rate of cutting the lines is very small in positions (a) and (c), but is quick at position (b) ; therefore there is a big potential at (b), and as a matter of fact, there is no potential in the exact positions (a) and (c). As the coil continues to rotate for the next half revolution the potential reverses in direction, for in going from (c) to (d) lines are now taken out of the face into which they were previously inserted. We see, therefore, that this method of producing potential results in the direction being reversed every half revolution, and if the ends of the coil are each connected to a separate circular ring (called a slip ring) on the axis of rotation, a current may be caused to pass through an external circuit by allowing carbon brushes to press on these slip rings. If, on the other hand, the ends of the coil are connected to a commutator (as illustrated in Fig. 2 (c) of Lesson 22) the current in the circuit is reversed every half revolution and so becomes unidirectional.

The first type of current is called alternating current (A.C.), and the second, direct current (D.C.), which has similar properties to that type of current already discussed. These are illustrated in Fig. 3. A.C., which is more generally supplied by the electric lighting undertakings, has certain advantages over D.C. It can be " transformed " from high to low potential, or *vice versa*, by using a transformer. This is to be expected from our previous considerations of induction. The transformer is a closed iron core on which are two windings of wire. When an alternating current enters P P (*see* Fig. 4) it is continually changing direction. In usual commercial supply there are 50 cycles per second. This means the current goes first one way, then the other, completely 50 times per second, and so the magnetic field, set up in this core, performs similar reversals. This reversing field induces a potential in the secondary S S of the same frequency (i.e. 50/sec.). If the number of turns in S S is 20 times that in P P, the potential set up is about 20 times as big, and the transformer is said to be a " step-up " transformer. If the secondary has less turns than the primary, the potential is less (and therefore the current can be bigger) and the apparatus is called a " step-down " transformer. The student who wishes to follow this further should study wireless telephony, where understanding of these ideas is of fundamental importance.

Electrolysis. When a current passes through a liquid which conducts electricity, we find that its passage is accompanied by a chemical decomposition of the liquid. This chemical effect is of importance to the chemist, who has been enabled to isolate substances by its aid. An account of the process of electrolysis is given in Lessons 21 and 22 in Chemistry (Vol. 3, pp. 181-191).

Study of these Lessons will show that electricity is conveyed through liquid by means of *ions*, which are charged particles of matter. By the mere act of dissolving a salt in water the molecule breaks up into groups of atoms with equal positive and negative charges. Thus a solution of common salt (NaCl—sodium chloride) contains molecules of NaCl together with positively charged sodium atoms called sodium ions, also negatively charged chlorine atoms called chlorine ions. The number of molecules which dissociate or break up into ions depends on the concentration of the solution. The main point is that the solution contains the ready-made ions. When two electrodes are inserted in the liquid and a potential difference is applied, the + ions are conveyed down the electric field and reach the − ive electrode, and the − ive ions move up the field and reach the + ive electrode. When they arrive at their destination they give up their charge to the electrodes. The current, therefore, depends on the number of ions passing, on their velocity, and the charge on each ion. By finding the total mass of an ion deposited and the total quantity of electricity passed, the charge per ion (e) can be calculated, if we know the number of ions per gram. If the mass (m) of the ion is known the ratio of e/m can also be found.

When the charged ions reach the electrodes it sometimes happens, for gaseous ions, that they form layers on the electrode and, as they are charged, they set up a back electrical potential. Thus if E^1 is the value of this potential when a current i flows as a result of the application of a potential E, the resistance of the liquid, as stated by Ohm's Law, is not

$$\frac{E}{i} \text{ but } \frac{E - E^1}{i}.$$

It seems, therefore, that Ohm's Law holds for liquid conductors as well as solids, provided we state the law as

$$\frac{\text{effective potential}}{\text{net current}} = \text{total resistance.}$$

In finding the resistance of a liquid it is customary to use alternating current to overcome the electrode effect just referred to. The experiment is simply conducted using the arrangement of Fig. 5 in Lesson 21 (page 452). Alternating current is used instead of the cell E, and a pair of telephones instead of the galvanometer. The adjustment of R is then made until the buzz in the telephone is reduced to a minimum when $P/Q = R/S$ as before.

Conduction in Gases. If we remove the two electrodes from the electrolyte through which a current has been passing, and fix these—say, 1 cm. apart in air—we find that no current passes. We say that, for the potential applied, the air is an insulator or non-conductor. Similarly, if the electrodes are placed in really pure water no current passes. We need the introduction of some ions to the liquid to allow the current to pass. The question arises, is it possible to introduce ions to the air in the space between a pair of metal plates to which a potential difference is applied? Obviously we cannot do this by the same means as for the liquid—solids will not dissolve in the air. Ions of positively and negatively charged *gas* molecules can be introduced, and we can make the air conducting in that way. Before discussing this, let us consider the ordinary air between two metal plates A B (Fig. 5). If we attach one cell and have a very sensitive recorder of current at Q, we find no current passes. By adding cell by cell we can build up quite a high potential and still find no current. It is clear that Ohm's Law is not obeyed in this case. If we continue adding cells we finally reach a potential sufficiently high to break down the air resistance, and a spark

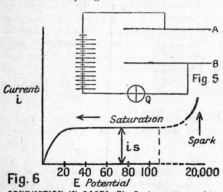

passes. When we replace the plates by two pointed rods the spark passes at much lower potentials. Once the spark has passed the air seems to act as though it were a conductor—a poor one, it is true. The air in the spark seems to have taken on conducting properties. It is in fact *ionized*, or split up into +ive and —ive molecules of air which convey the current.

CONDUCTION IN GASES. Fig. 5. Apparatus used to investigate the conductivity of gases. **Fig. 6.** Conductivity of gases which are ionized. Note that Ohm's Law does not hold in this case.

If the potential is cut off and then, after a short interval, once more applied, the spark appears to pass more easily, because some of the gaseous ions are present from the last spark. If a little time elapses before switching on we must again raise the potential to be as high as in the first case. The reason is that the ions have opposite charges, and being readily movable, attract each other and recombine to be neutral air molecules.

We see from the above that the formation of gaseous ions is possible by raising the potential to " sparking potential " for the gap. There are other means available. For instance, if we send a beam of X-rays through the gas, or allow the radiations from radio-active substances to pass, we find that the air is ionized and that even with such a low potential as 2 volts a current will pass, so long as the ionizing agent acts on the gas. Both the ionizing agents, X-ray and radioactive bodies, are able to produce a definite number of ions per second, and when a potential sufficiently high is applied to the electrodes, all the ions produced per second are carried across the space in that time and no more can be carried, i.e. the possible current will reach a maximum, and for any increase in potential there will be no increase in current simply because there are no more ions produced to be conveyed across the space. This maximum current is called the saturation current. In Fig. 6 the relation between E and i shows that, except for small potentials, the Law of Ohm is again not applicable to conduction through gases. Incidentally, the " strength " of a beam of X-rays or the rays from a radioactive body are often compared by measuring the saturation currents which they produce in the air between two plates.

The effect of the applied potential is, of course, to direct the ions, the +ive ions to the —ive electrodes, and —ive ions to the +ive electrodes. As the potential is increased the speed of travel of the ions becomes bigger, and, finally, when a sufficiently high potential is applied, the ions attain such a speed that in their course between the plates they collide with other uncharged air molecules and ionize them. This process is called ionization by collision. The very large number of ions so formed repeat the process, and the result is that a very large current passes, again as a spark, between the plates.

LESSON 24

X-Rays in Surgery and Laboratory

(See plate 60)

WHEN we consider a gas at ordinary atmospheric pressure, the conductivity is not in accordance with Ohm's Law. Now a very interesting and important sequence of observations may be obtained from a study of what happens to the conductivity of a gas when the pressure of the gas is reduced.   Fig. 1 shows a section of a glass apparatus, which can be exhausted in slow degrees by connecting to an exhaust pump.

When ordinary atmospheric pressure prevails, the discharge does not take place until the potential is raised to be sufficient to cause a spark to pass between the anode and cathode within the tube.   If there is an alternative spark gap as shown, the spark will all take place at this place, as there is a shorter air path in the gap.   Now when the pressure is reduced we find that the spark ceases to pass at the spark gap, but at the same time there is evidence of a current passing through the tube in the form of a thin, line-like glow.   As the pressure decreases there is a wide glow with a beautiful colour extending from the anode and almost

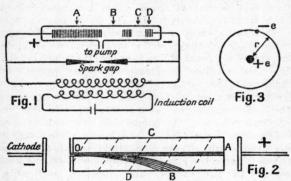

CATHODE RAYS. Fig. 1. A, glowing positive column ; B, Faraday's dark space ; C, Crookes' dark space ; D, glow around cathode ; **Fig. 2.** OA, path of cathode rays when no magnetic field acts ; OB, path of cathode rays when a magnetic field acts into the plane of the paper. **Fig. 3.** Hydrogen atom and one electron.

reaching the cathode.   This is called the positive column and takes on a colour which is characteristic of the gas in the tube. With air it has a pinkish hue.   As the pressure is decreased the colour scheme and the distribution of the glowing colours within the tube alter.   A dark space is apparent between the cathode and the positive column, which now recedes towards the anode. This is followed by the appearance of Crookes' dark space, and then a glow about the cathode, as indicated in Fig. 1.   For a further diminution of the pressure the resistance of the tube decreases, and the Crookes' dark space advances towards the cathode.   Finally, the Crookes' dark space fills the tube and the resistance gets bigger, as evidenced by the appearance of spark in the spark gap.

In the early stage the positive column and previous thin glow represent the actual path of the current. We can deflect this glow by using a magnet, and so on, just as we have been able to deflect wires conveying current. But when the Crookes' dark space fills the tube there is naturally no glow to deflect. The glass walls of the tube at this stage, however, take on a greenish glow. This represents a new phase in the gaseous discharge.

The electricity is conveyed through the tube by gaseous ions, which are made obvious in the early stages by the glow produced. In the later stages no glow is apparent to mark the ionization, but the actual electric current is still conveyed by ions.

When the positive ions hit the cathode they give rise to what was called the "cathode rays" or the "cathode stream." At one time it was thought that this stream was, like light, an electromagnetic radiation. The English school of physicists led by Crookes, however, maintained that the cathode stream consists of discrete particles, or corpuscles as Sir J. J. Thomson called them. This point of view seems to be the correct one.

Cathode "Rays." Let us see what experiment showed to be the case. The cathode stream on hitting the glass wall opposite the cathode caused a vigorous green glow ; also when certain crystals were placed in the beam (which leaves the cathode at right angles and goes in straight lines) fluorescence, and in some cases phosphorescence, is produced.

For example, certain sulphides glow when placed in the beam. These crystals, when powdered and gummed to a sheet of cardboard, form an excellent screen for detecting the cathode ray beams. If a solid cross is placed between the cathode and such a screen placed within the tube, it is found that a "shadow" is formed, just as if the fluorescence were caused by a light shining from the cathode ; i.e. the cathode rays travel in straight lines.

If the cathode is cup-shaped, the "rays," leaving at right angles to the cathode, all converge to the centre of the cup. If a thin sheet of platinum is placed there, it is found to be heated to a bright red glow by the bombardment of the cathode rays. A light windmill placed on horizontal rails is caused to rotate by the cathode rays hitting the vanes. It is clear, therefore, that these "rays" are capable of showing their energy by the heat produced or, indirectly, by the rotation of the vanes.

A most important piece of information may be obtained as to the nature of cathode rays by applying a magnetic field. In Fig. 2 is a section of a suitable apparatus. A sheet of card covered with powdered zinc sulphide, CD, serves to indicate the path of the cathode rays which pass from the cathode through the slit O towards the anode, making a line of fluorescence OA. When the magnetic field is applied into and at right angles to the plane of the paper, the line OA is displaced into the splayed out line OB.

Applying the left-hand rule, we see that this is what would happen to a current going from A to O, and since the effect has its origin at O, we are led to speculate that the cathode stream is made of negative charges going from O to A. In other words, a wave theory for the beam appears to be wrong, and we have excellent grounds for supposing that the stream consists of negatively charged corpuscles. At this stage of exhaustion of the tube, therefore, we are led to visualize the current passing by means of ions, and where the positive ions bombard the cathode we have a cathode stream of negative charges moving off at right angles to the cathode. These negative charges are additional to the negative ions which go from cathode to anode.

Sir J. J. Thomson, by a most ingenious set of experiments, was able to measure the speed of the cathode corpuscles and also to obtain a value of the ratio of the charge to the mass (e/m). The essence of the experiment was to deflect the corpuscles by a magnetic and an electric field. From the amounts of the deflections he calculated the quantities mentioned. From the value of e/m which was found, and a knowledge of the probable value of e, it was calculated that m was approximately one two-thousandth part of the mass of a hydrogen atom.

Now the hydrogen atom is the smallest particle of matter which can exist alone, and the conclusion was reached that the corpuscles, which were called *electrons*, were a " fourth state " of matter—actually they were considered to be " discrete particles of negative electricity " free from all matter. They are, indeed, the " atoms of electricity." Modern theory suggests that atoms are built up of a central core of positive electricity of a definite value with one or more of these electrons moving about it in orbits. The charge on the electron is taken as a fundamental unit, and is usually written as e. Thus Fig. 3 represents the hydrogen atom with a core of $+ e$ and one electron moving about it. The possible orbits for the electron have been the subject of much theoretical speculation, and certain paths or orbits are regarded as being possible. In the case illustrated the attraction which would result would be $\frac{ee}{r^2}$ (according to the inverse square law). This is balanced by the effect of the rotation. When the electron jumps to an orbit nearer the core, the potential energy is less, and the difference in these energies is regarded as being spent in radiation. The characteristic lines of the line spectrum of the elements are regarded as originating in this manner. The ionization of the element is produced by the removal of the electron from the atom.

From this brief statement of the theory of the atom it becomes clear that if the theory is at all correct, the electron which was " isolated " by J. J. Thomson in the very artificial manner in the discharge tube should be available in all forms of matter, since it is the fundamental brick from which the matter is made. This conclusion has since been verified. We can produce electrons in a variety of ways, and from all forms of matter.

When any matter is bombarded by X-rays or γ-rays from radioactive bodies, such matter becomes a source of electrons. When ultra-violet light falls on polished zinc plates a copious supply of electrons is given out. A most important method of obtaining electrons was discovered by O. W. Richardson. When a wire is raised to incandescence it emits an electron stream which is stronger the higher the temperature of the wire. This pheno-menon was called " thermionic emission," and has been utilized in the thermionic " valve " or vacuum tube, where it is noticed that the thermionic current, i, is bigger the higher the temperature, T, of the wire, which is controlled by the heating current or filament current. In fact i, by Richardson's law, is equal to $AT^{\frac{1}{2}}e - \frac{b}{T}$ when A and b are constants.

X-Rays. But let us return to our discharge tube where the electron was first discovered, as there is another property of the electron to discuss. When the electron is stopped by a platinum foil we saw that heat was produced. In addition to this a very small fraction of the energy of the electron stream is changed into a radiation which is called *X-rays*. This was accidentally discovered by Röntgen when he was investigating the properties of the cathode ray stream. Röntgen had a discharge tube covered entirely with black paper. Outside the tube was a screen covered with crystals of barium-platino-cyanide. When the potential was applied to the tube in a dark room it was found that the screen lit up, owing to a fluorescence of the crystals. When solid bodies were placed between the tube and the screen the shadows enabled him to locate the origin of the radiation. This he traced to be the spot where the cathode rays were arrested. The energy of the cathode rays which were so changed was small, but the radiation was relatively penetrating. It was further found that the radiation passed through substances like flesh and tissue, but was absorbed by bone. The denser and the higher the atomic weight of a substance, the more it absorbed the rays. When a hand was placed between the tube and the screen the latter showed a faint outline of the fingers, at the centre of which was a shadow picture of the bones. The medical application of the discovery was very soon realized and many used it for the location of foreign

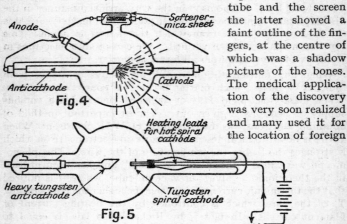

X-RAYS. **Fig. 4.** Tube originally used for the production of X-rays. **Fig. 5.** Coolidge tube which has now practically replaced it for the purpose.

bodies—e.g. a needle in the hand, etc.—and for the diagnosis of fractures, and so on. The physicists developed a special tube for the more efficient production of the rays. Fig. 4 shows a section of one of the tubes universally used before 1914, and still used by some research physicists.

The cathode is cup-shaped, and at the centre of the sphere of which the cup is part is placed a massive lump of copper, faced with tungsten or similar hard metal. As shown by the broken lines, the X - rays set up on this " anti-cathode " radiate out in all directions in the hemisphere nearest to the cathode ; the other half is absorbed in the mass of the anti-cathode. The tube is excited by connecting to the secondary of an induction coil. The higher the potential which is applied to the tube the quicker the speed of the electrons, and consequently the more sudden is their stoppage when they hit the anti-cathode. In these circumstances it is found that the rays are more penetrating—they are said to be " hard X-rays." With small potentials the rays are " soft," i.e. easily stopped.

About 1914 a new type of tube, called the Coolidge tube, was introduced, and has now largely replaced the ordinary gas tube which was described above. The new ideas involved aim at complete control of the radiations given out, both as to penetrating power and strength or intensity of the beam. These ideas may be readily understood, for if we return to our glass vessel (Fig. 1), we find that when the tube is exhausted of the gas beyond the stage when the cathode rays appear, the more the gas is exhausted the bigger the resistance becomes. The current is conveyed by ions ; when an ion travels down the tube it hits the gas molecules and produces more ions by the collisions. As the pressure gets less, the number of the gas molecules gets less, and so the longer is the path any molecule or ion can go without hitting another molecule or ion. When, finally, the pressure is so low that an ion can go from one electrode to another without hitting a molecule, that is, when " the mean free path " is longer than the distance between the electrodes, it goes from one end of the tube to the other without producing more ions. Instead of the thousands of ions normally produced, only one goes through the tube. The current is, therefore, reduced to practically zero value, and the resistance of the tube becomes enormous.

This is the state inside the Coolidge tube, which is shown in Fig. 5. Even when very high potentials are applied no current passes ; and as there is no appreciable number of ions passing there are no electrons produced and consequently no X-rays.

To produce the necessary electron stream, the cathode is made in the form of a spiral of wire which can be made incandescent by a heating current, just as in the more modern thermionic valve. To make the electrons so produced go down the tube at a high speed and set up X-rays when stopped at the anti-cathode, a potential is applied from an induction coil or a large step-up transformer. By making the potential high, penetrating X-rays are produced ; by making the filament current high, an intense beam is produced.

The use of X-rays in medicine is fairly apparent for diagnosing fractures of the bones, whose shadow picture can be produced on a screen. A permanent record of these shadow pictures can be made by allowing the rays to cast a shadow picture on to a photographic plate instead of the fluorescence screen. The plate, when developed, produces photographs as shown in Plate 6o.

When photographs are wanted there must always be a difference in density of the materials, otherwise the shadow picture produced will not show any difference. For example, when used to help in diagnosis in the alimentary tract, the patient is given a " meal " of bread-and-milk containing a heavy barium salt, which fills the stomach, etc., and allows the radiologist to determine, both from the shape and the time the meal remains, whether or not the patient is normal ; without the meal nothing could be gained in the case quoted.

In addition to the more obvious medical applications, X-rays have been of extreme importance in helping the physicist to obtain information about the structure of the atom.

LESSON 25

What is the Quantum Theory?

PRODUCED in a manner described in the preceding Lesson, X-rays have been most fruitful of results in investigations on atomic structure. When the rays were first discovered the theories as to their nature also led to much physical research, which yielded results of importance. In the early years of this century the speculations on the nature of X-rays were very similar to those which were advanced in Newton's time to account for the nature of ordinary light. In those years two serious theories were rivals in the field. The first postulated that light was produced by " corpuscles " shot out from the source and travelling in straight lines at great speed to the receiver, in much the same way as bullets from a machine-gun. A light source, on this theory, was analogous to a machine-gun nest firing its " corpuscle " bullets in all directions. This led to results which were contrary to experimental findings, and was abandoned. The other theory, which has held the field from that time until recently without serious challenge, is that light is a wave motion. This theory we have discussed in previous Lessons.

Many X-ray properties were such that support was apparently given in turn to each theory. Reflection, refraction, interference, diffraction, etc., which are to be predicted on a wave theory, and occur with light, were not found with X-rays, and so some support was forthcoming for a corpuscular theory.

Now when we discussed diffraction of light we saw that the amount of diffraction to be expected depended on the relative size of the wave and the slit used. Also in such a simple thing as reflection, the *regular* reflection of the wave only occurs if the surface is free of irregularities of the size of the wave. A sheet of white paper does not reflect light in the same way as a mirror,

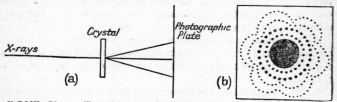

X-RAYS. Diagram illustrating experiments in connexion with the nature of X-rays.

simply because the surface is not smooth to the order of a wave length of the light used. It merely gives a diffuse reflection in most directions. This was the kind of result obtained in the early experiments with X-rays. However, a theory which was new about 1908, called the Quantum theory, led to the suggestion that X-rays were waves of a *very* short wave length—something of the order of one hundred millionth part of a centimetre (10^{-8}cm.). This is of the same order as the distance between the molecules in a solid. It was then suggested that in crystals the molecules are arranged in regular patterns as evidenced by the constant shape of crystals of all sizes, and that if crystals were used, some sort of diffraction or interference should be made apparent. The experiments performed to check this theoretical pointer were successful.

The scheme of the first experiment is shown at (a) in the diagram. A narrow beam of X-rays was sent at right angles to a thin piece of crystal, and a photographic plate, arranged as in the diagram, was found to have a pattern on it when developed, showing a symmetrical set of images about the central area which marked the direct beam, as shown in (b). This pattern was produced by the diffraction of the X-rays at the regularly arranged molecules within the crystal.

The idea was developed by Sir W. Bragg and his son Prof. W. L. Bragg; it was found that the equivalent of reflection could be obtained.

Further, they were able to calculate the distance between the molecules and also the wave length of the rays used.

This settled the point, in outline at least; X-rays are of a wave character of measurable wave length. They are found to be $\frac{1}{1000}$ part of the wave length of visible light, but are of the same general nature as light—a very dwarf member of the family of radiations which we have previously discussed. Incidentally, the crystal methods have led to a very certain way of investigating the arrangement of molecules and atoms within crystals and powders.

As technique has advanced it has been found possible to produce reflection at polished metal surfaces and also to produce refraction by thin prisms which in the early days was not obtainable.

Incidentally again, the consequences of such refraction show that a beam of X-rays is bent in the opposite way from light, i.e. towards the refracting angle of the prism. The refraction is small, but measurable. Diffraction by diffraction gratings has also been obtained in the last few years, and it is safe to say that in nature the rays are very similiar to light waves.

Photo Electrons. When light falls on certain metals it causes the emission of electrons from the metal. If an electric field is set up by arranging a positive charge near the metal, these electrons are attracted to the charge and consequently a current passes. The electrons ejected as a result of the action of light are called photo electrons. The photo electric cell, which now has a wide application, is based on this principle. The current passing fluctuates with fluctuation of intensity of the light falling on the metals.

In this respect, too, X-rays strongly resemble visible light. If a beam of X-rays falls on any substance it ejects electrons from that substance. By analogy with the photo electrons with light, these ejected electrons are called X-ray photo electrons. When X-rays are used the speed of the photo electrons is much greater than when they are excited by visible or ultra-violet light, and when hard X-rays (i.e. short wave length X-rays) are used the velocity is greater than for soft X-rays (longer wave length X-rays). These photo electrons cause ionization in gases, which, in the case of X-rays, is almost entirely due to such secondary action.

The result of investigations on the velocity of photo electrons for different wave length X-rays led to similar conclusions as in the case of visible radiations. A beam of one wave length gives out electrons at one speed. Whatever the strength of the X-ray beam, the speed of the electron is the same so long as the wave length is the same.

Now the classical, established theory would not predict this sort of result. If, for example, we think of the electron as being ejected by the incoming wave we would anticipate that the stronger the beam, the bigger the force and, consequently, the quicker the speed of ejection.

The Quantum Theory. About 1908 Prof. Max Planck propounded a theory, called the Quantum theory, to explain the results of observations on the radiation of energy from a hot body. In this case there was the first serious example of results obtained with radiation which did not agree with deductions based on the established or classical ideas. According to these ideas if a body is giving out radiations—and in so doing is really converting its energy into radiation—it may do so in a continuous manner. In the same way it presupposes that an atom may absorb energy continuously. Unfortunately, this apparently obvious assumption leads to results contrary to experience. Planck postulated that when there is an interchange of energy from matter to radiation or *vice versa* this interchange takes place in multiples of a unit of energy, and that the size of the unit is different for each wave length in the radiation. He did not use *wave length*, however, but *frequency*. As we know, these are *simply* related, for frequency $= \dfrac{\text{velocity}}{\text{wave-length}}$. The unit of energy used in these interchanges was called the quantum of energy for the particular frequency used. It is really equivalent to saying that when a radiation is falling on a body the latter is not taking in the radiation continuously, but in small packets or quanta ; for a fixed frequency the number of quanta received per second depends on the intensity of strength of the beam. The size of the quantum for any frequency n was postulated to be a constant $h \times n$, i.e. $= hn$. This constant is called Planck's constant and is very small. When we are dealing with a large scale effect removed from critical regions we find that, since the quantum is small, the effect is similar to the classical ideas, but when we consider *individual atoms* absorbing energy, there is a sharp demarcation in the results of the application of two theories.

In the case of X-ray photo-electricity, for example, where we are ejecting single electrons by absorbing energy incident on a material, we find, by Planck's Quantum theory, that if the X-rays have a frequency n, the unit of energy absorbed is $hn = W$, say, and this energy is given to the electron which is emitted. The kinetic energy acquired, $\frac{1}{2}mv^2$, is therefore given by

$$W = hn = \tfrac{1}{2}mv^2 \ldots \ldots (i)$$

and so we have a relation between frequency, n, and v, the velocity of the electron, assuming that all the energy is used in imparting movement to it. By measuring v for X-ray photo electrons an estimate of n and, consequently wave length of X-rays was made before crystal analysis was first introduced.

Applying this theory to the X-ray case in all stages, we find that the photo electron emitted has the same velocity as the electron in the X-ray tube, for suppose that the velocity of the electron in the cathode ray beam in the X-ray tube is v, the energy of the electron is $\frac{1}{2}mv^2$. If this changes to X-radiations, causing the formation of radiation of one quantum, we anticipate that the ray will have a frequency n given by

$$\tfrac{1}{2}mv^2 = hn.$$

When this radiation ejects a photo electron from matter it causes the latter to move with a velocity given by

$$hn = \tfrac{1}{2}mv^2,$$

therefore this velocity is the same as that of the parent cathode ray electron—a fact which had been shown experimentally to be the case before the Quantum theory was developed.

The Rutherford-Bohr Model of the atom considers it to be made up of a positive nucleus with electrons rotating about it in orbits. The higher the atomic weight the larger the number of electrons. When an electron from an outer orbit is removed—say, by being hit with another electron or by impact of a radiation—the atom which is left without one of its negative charges is ionized. When an unattached electron is attracted to the incomplete atom it loses potential energy with respect to the positive nucleus or core. Suppose this energy lost as potential energy is W, then, according to the Quantum theory, there will be radiated from the atom a radiation of frequency n given by $W = hn$, where again h is Planck's constant. Accordingly, if n comes to be within the limits of the visible spectrum the radiation will be what we call light.

On older ideas we were content to think that the radius of the orbits of the electrons may have any value (considering circular orbits for simplicity) within the limits of the atom. But the Quantum theory postulates that only relatively few radii are permissible. The radii are of such magnitude that the energy of the electrons in these orbits is a simple multiple of a unit value. Therefore, when we consider the electrons in the atom, we have only to visualize possible paths, which are relatively few.

Suppose we return to the atom again and consider the removal of an electron from the orbit next to the outer one. We find that the atom can be made complete once more, this time either by an electron from the outer orbit or alternatively from outside the atom. In each case there is a specific amount of energy lost as potential energy and, consequently, radiated out as a radiation of one of two frequencies given by equation (i) above. It will be apparent to the student, at least in a general way, from what has been said, that in the way briefly outlined a set of radiations of definite frequencies will be radiated from the disturbed atom. For a different atom a similar set of frequencies will be possible, but of different absolute values—each atom can give out its own waves of frequencies, which can be calculated. If these frequencies come within the visible range they correspond to the line spectra discussed in Lesson 16 (Volume 4, page 546).

When very fast electrons bombard the atoms it is possible to remove electrons from the orbit next or near to the nucleus itself. These electrons move out as photo electrons. The incomplete atom which is left gets back to normal by the falling in of electrons from the outer orbits and, finally, from outside the atom itself. In processes of this kind the energy change may be as much as 1,000 times that visualized above. Consequently, the frequency n of the radiation emitted is 1,000 times as great, or the wave length 1,000 times smaller. It is in fact no longer a light wave but an X-ray wave which is given out.

There are in the X-ray regions as in the light regions, many possibilities of replacing the " lost " electron. Consequently, there is radiated a range of wave lengths, and X-ray spectra result. The most penetrating X-rays have their origin in the removal of an electron from the orbit nearest the nucleus, and the consequent completion of the atom by the falling in of an electron to that orbit.

Radioactivity. In Lessons 31 and 32 in Chemistry (Volume 4, pages 211 and 215) an account is given of the physics of radio-activity, and in Lessons 30, 33 and 34 (ibid., pages 206, 220 and 224) are summaries of the theories of the atom, together with an account of the work of such physicists as Lord Rutherford. From these accounts it will be realized that in a radioactive disintegration of an atom it is possible to obtain α, β and γ " radiations." It is realized that the α and β " rays " are not rays, but are charged helium nuclei and swift electrons respectively. The γ radiation is a true radiation of the same nature as X-rays. The question which may perhaps occur to the student is, " What is the source of origin of the γ ray, if this is shorter in wave length than the most penetrating X-ray which can be excited in the element, say, radium ? " It seems that the γ ray is due to some cause within the nucleus itself, as also is the origin of the α and β rays.

The chemical property of an atom depends among other factors on the number of positive charges on the nucleus. Therefore if this charge is altered, either by altering the weight of the atom or otherwise, the chemical nature of the residue will be charged. Now when an α particle is removed there is a removal of a helium atom of atomic weight 4 and also a removal of two positive charges, so the net charge is two units less, and on both counts it is clear that the atom has been spontaneously transmuted to a lighter atom having entirely different properties.

When a β particle is shot out of the nucleus, the effect is an inappreciable loss of mass—i.e. the atomic weight remains the same, but since there is a loss of one unit of negative charge, the net positive charge left on the nucleus is one more than before. We have, in fact, an entirely different atom in spite of the fact that it has the same atomic weight.

A study of the family tree of the radioactive series of uranium in Volume 4, page 219, will make these points clear ; the fact to notice here is that in these emissions of β particles in particular

AN ARABIAN PHYSICIAN. During most of the Middle Ages the Mahomedan world was far ahead of Christendom in science and culture generally. Medical learning, in particular, was highly developed amongst the Arabs, and the European doctors received most of their knowledge through Latin translations of the Arabian textbooks. This picture of a consultation with an Arab doctor occurs in an Arabic version of the Materia Medica of Dioscorides, dated 1222.

HISTORY : MEDIEVAL 44

From Martin, "Miniature Painters and Paintings of India, etc." (Quaritch)

LOUIS XI OF FRANCE (1423–83). Succeeding his father, Charles VII, on the French throne in 1461, he encouraged the middle class at the expense of the feudal nobility, averted the last menace of an English invasion, and became the consolidator of modern France. This portrait was painted by Jean Fouquet.

HISTORY : MEDIEVAL 45

Bibliothèque Nationale, MS. français 19,819

CHARLES THE BOLD (1433–77).
Succeeding his father as duke of
Burgundy in 1467, his reign was
spent in warfare with his neigh-
bours. He was defeated and
killed by the Swiss at Nancy.
HISTORY : MEDIEVAL 45
Dijon Museum

FERDINAND AND ISABELLA. Ferdinand V (1452–1516) succeeded
his father as king of Aragon in 1479. In the same year his queen,
Isabella (1451–1504), daughter of the king of Castile, was established
on the Castilian throne. Two of the four Spanish kingdoms were thus
brought into union, and before Ferdinand died he had conquered the
third, Granada of the Moors, and acquired almost all of the fourth,
Navarre. HISTORY : MEDIEVAL 45
National Gallery, Madrid

Plate 54

Volume VI

we have a phenomenon similar to the photo electron we have discussed above. If the β particles are stopped they give rise to radiations according to the equation (i) above. In these naturally occurring, quickly moving charges, however, we have material from which we are able to consider the application of another of the modern theories, the theory of relativity.

LESSON 26

The Theory of Relativity

THE so-called radiations from a radio-active body include, as we saw in the preceding Lesson, the β " radiation," which is merely a stream of very rapidly moving electrons which are ejected from the nucleus itself. According to the particular source of the β particles it is found that their velocity has distinct values, and these velocities, although very great, have been measured by deflecting the particles in strong magnetic fields. From the deflection produced, calculation has yielded the values of v. Combined with the magnetic deflection experiments, the deflections produced by strong electric fields have given data from which the ratio of e/m has also been calculated for the electrons from different sources.

The velocities have been found to be very great indeed. For example, from Radium B, velocities of 1 to 2 × 10^{10} cms. per sec. have been allotted to the β particles.

The interesting fact emerges that e/m has smaller values for the higher velocity β particles, and we are led to one of two obvious alternatives to account for these results—either the mass of the electron has a bigger value, or the charge becomes less when the speed is increased.

Now e has been determined by a very large number of varied experiments, and invariably its value comes to the same number. At the same time we remember that one of the fundamental concepts of our older mechanics is that mass is constant.

This latter notion is the basis of the older mechanics founded by Newton, and it has been adequate to account for all observed facts from his day to the present century. In 1905 Einstein first formulated his celebrated principle of relativity, and this provides an explanation of the variation of e/m with velocity.

In dealing with movement we have to realize that all measurements are of motion relative to some " system of reference." The speed of a car, e.g., is measured with respect to the ground, which may be taken as our " system of reference " in this case. In other words, our measurements of the speed of a body on the earth are relative to the earth, which is itself moving. We say a car is moving at 60 miles per hour, whereas, actually, it is only moving 60 miles per hour with respect to the earth. It is actually travelling at some great speed through space in addition to the 60 miles per hour developed by the engine. The expression for velocity is very dependent, therefore, on the exact way in which it is measured. As a further example, consider raindrops falling towards the ground. If there is no wind they fall directly downwards. To a man stationary on the ground the drops are falling vertically with a definite speed. If the man runs in any direction on the ground, however, the drops no longer appear to fall either vertically or with the same speed as before. Even when no wind is blowing the drops seem to be beating into his face (i.e., coming on the slant) with a greater velocity than before. If a wind is blowing a further complication ensues, for now the drops are in a medium which is itself moving. To have some idea of the actual speed of the drops of rain in this case it is necessary to measure them with respect to a stationary observer (stationary, that is, compared with the earth), and then also to determine the movement of the air, or, what is the same thing, the velocity of the wind.

If we were in a closed carriage of a railway train which was such that the movement of the wheels could not be heard or felt, and if we had no means of measuring except in length and time, we should be able to find the velocity of a fly in the carriage, and this would be relative to the carriage itself. The train might travel with uniform velocity, or be retarded or accelerated, but, as far as our measurements go, the velocity of the fly in this limited region would be the same if it continued its motion uniformly in the carriage. Actually, the true velocity with respect to the earth would be variable, and the variation would depend on the train's movement. Regarding the earth for the moment to be at rest, the only way to measure the fly's velocity is to get outside the carriage and measure from the " stationary " earth.

Now, when it comes to the normal measurements, we have to realize that we are in precisely the same position as the observer in the closed carriage. The earth is moving as part of the solar system. Our measurements of velocities can be made with respect to this system just as those in the carriage are made with respect to the carriage.

It is clear, therefore, by analogy, that the *actual* velocity of movement of a particle in our solar system cannot be determined by measurements made within the system. We need outside, stationary reference points from which to measure and to decide whether we are moving with a uniform speed or not.

Attempts were made to reach such a method of measurement when it was assumed that the ether was the system of reference and the absolute value of a velocity was supposed to be that measured with respect to the ether. Now light is propagated in the ether, as we have seen, and, therefore, if it travels with a constant speed, the time it takes to pass from one point to another should depend on whether we travel with the light or against it —i.e., there should be a difference in the observed velocity as measured on the earth—it should apparently go quicker against the direction of movement of the earth than when moving with it.

An elaborate optical experiment was performed by Michelson and Morley to test this point, and it was found that there was no observed difference. It appears that the light travels in the ether just as though the earth were still. This experiment showed the impossibility of measuring or even detecting the velocity of the earth with respect to the ether. Other experiments have also demonstrated this failure. This indicates the uselessness of the ether as a system of reference, and a theory was developed which omits any reference to it. It does not accept or deny the existence of the ether, but merely does not refer to it. This theory is Einstein's theory of relativity.

Unfortunately, his method of procedure is far too complex to put into simple language, but by an application of a system of mathematics which appears to be very involved to the uninitiated he deduced many important consequences. He showed that if measurements of length are made there is the equivalent of a contraction of the measuring rod in the direction of motion which does not occur when the measuring rod is at right angles to the movement. The velocity of light, according to the theory, is to be taken as the maximum speed attainable, and it is regarded as constant.

Another conclusion he arrived at is quite opposed at first sight to the accepted, classical mechanics of Newton, namely, that the mass of a body is not invariant—i.e. has not always the same value. It is to be noticed that although this statement appears to be in direct contradiction to the ideas which were taken as absolutely fundamental before 1905, in reality it only becomes different from Newtonian mechanics when we are dealing with masses moving with very great speeds—in fact, with speeds approaching what is regarded as the limiting value, that of the velocity of light.

In effect, he says that if the mass of a body at rest is m_0 (and this was the invariable mass of that body in terms of Newtonian mechanics), the value of the mass, when moving with a velocity v, is m where

$$m = \frac{m_0}{\sqrt{1 - \left(\dfrac{v}{c}\right)^2}} \dotfill (i)$$

where c is the velocity of light.

The exact nature of this change of mass he showed to be equal to the gain of kinetic energy divided by c^2. When we remember that $c = 3 \times 10^{10}$—i.e. thirty thousand million centimetres per second—we see that $c^2 = 9 \times 10^{20}$, and we realise that a gain in kinetic energy, which is to be divided by this number, must be very great in order to produce an appreciable quotient. In other words, ordinary masses moving at normal speeds have no measurable change in mass.

Referring to equation (i) above, we see that if it were possible for the moving body to have a velocity c equal to that of light, the mass, m, would become

$$\frac{m_0}{\left(1 - \dfrac{c^2}{c^2}\right)^{\frac{1}{2}}} = \frac{m_0}{0}$$

Now, the quotient obtained by dividing any finite number by 0 is infinitely large. In other words, a body going with the velocity of light would acquire infinite mass.

Perhaps the student will appreciate the predictions of the theory of relativity in this respect much better by considering the values of the masses acquired for definite speeds. If a body has a mass of m_0 at rest, substitution in equation (i) shows that it will have the following values for the velocities quoted :

Velocity		Mass
0·5 c. = 1·5 × 10^{10} cm. per sec.		1·15 m_0
0·9 c. = 2·7 × 10^{10} ,, ,,		2·3 m_0
0·99 c. = 2·97 × 10^{10} ,, ,,		7·0 m_0

Now, ordinary large-scale objects never approach these tremendous speeds. The tremendous high speed records obtained in flying have not been greater than 480 miles per hour, or 704 ft. per sec., which is about 21,120 cm. per sec. If we say 25,000 cm. per second could be obtained, this is only a minute fraction of c of the order of ·0000008 c, so m would be

$$m = \frac{m_0}{\sqrt{1 - (\cdot 0000008)}} = m_0 \, (1 + 3 \cdot 2 \times 10^{-13})$$

i.e. $m = 1 \cdot 00000000000032 \times m_0$

If we imagine that we are capable of flying a machine at this high speed of 480 miles per hour and that the machine were to have a mass at rest of 50,000 kilograms (about 50 tons), the gain in mass would only be about ·0000015 gm. or ·000000005 oz.

It seems almost an obvious comment that, if this be so, there does not seem to be much wrong with the Newtonian mechanics, which does not make all this fuss and indulge in large flights of higher mathematics to show that the change in mass is of this absurdly minute amount. The Newtonian mechanics certainly is, for all practical purposes, correct when dealing with large-scale phenomena of this kind, and only breaks down when we consider such a case as the electrons in the β ray streams ejected by radioactive bodies. In this case the correction for the variation in mass of the corpuscles gives a value of e/m which agrees with experiment and emphasizes the constancy of *e*, the electronic charge.

The theory of relativity also offers an explanation of an outstanding discrepancy between theory and observed result in connexion with the planet Mercury. There was a minute yet observable difference in its path with time which had been a puzzle for some years. The slight correction which the principle introduces clears up this point.

Again, according to the principle of relativity, there should be an interaction between radiation and a strong gravitational field.

If light were a stream of particles, then we should expect that when the stream passed near a large body there would be an attraction, just as there is on a body near the earth. Now there is an equivalent effect, according to the theory of relativity, on ordinary waves such as light waves. Any radiation, in fact, has allotted to it its equivalent energy, and this allows calculations to be made of the effect of the pull of a heavenly body on a ray of light which happens to travel near it.

The expeditions which have set out to observe stars during a solar eclipse have aimed at finding out if such a pull is exerted by the " gravitational field " of the sun, for the change in direction of the rays of light should make the stars appear slightly out of place. The position stars should occupy during eclipse is calculated beforehand, and those stars which are normally invisible as the line of sight is just grazing the sun are chosen. The exact position they appear to occupy is calculated from photographs, and there is some reason to believe that the shift predicted by the theory is measurable.

Nowadays there are many interesting speculations as to the nature of radiation or waves in space, and we shall see in our next Lesson something of these modern speculations as to the nature of waves and corpuscles in the theory of Wave Mechanics.

LESSON 27

Recent Advances in Physics

(See plate 61)

IN many branches of Physics the investigation of small-scale phenomena and the effect of great speed has led the physicist and the mathematical physicist to a collaboration that has yielded results which some ten or twenty years ago would have seemed fantastic. We have seen from a consideration of the quantum theory that when there is an interaction between radiation and matter, the former always deals in energy bundles, or quanta, of size $h\,n$ where h is Planck's constant and n is the frequency of the radiation. In fact, the quantum is often regarded in much the same way as Newton regarded his corpuscles in the celebrated corpuscular theory of light, and in this respect there is a reversion to this old theory. The beam of radiation (light and any other electro-magnetic wave) is regarded as conveying its energy in *photons*, each of which carries the quantum $h\,n$.

The use of the word photon itself suggests a discrete corpuscle of the radiation, and the application of this idea has led to some recent developments.

For example, A. H. Compton made a theoretical investigation of what happens when a beam of X-rays falls on electrons. He assumed that the energy in the X-ray beam was conveyed by photons (quanta) which behaved as discrete corpuscles and hit an electron in such a way that one can make use of many of the laws of impact that are applicable when two billiard balls collide.

Fig. 1 shows his method of treatment. An incident beam of X-rays enters from left to right and hits an electron at O. It is assumed that in the impact we are dealing with a photon of energy $h n$, and an electron. After impact the photon rebounds in one direction, as shown, having a new energy value $h n'$ (i.e. as a quantum of another radiation which is less than $h n$ because some energy has been imparted to the electron), and the electron recoils, as shown, in another direction. Compton calculated the values of $h n'$ and the velocity of the electron after impact by applying the principles of conservation of momentum *and of energy*. The interesting conclusions which were arrived at lead one to expect that after such a collision the radiation has a smaller frequency n' and that recoil electrons move in the space with a predetermined value.

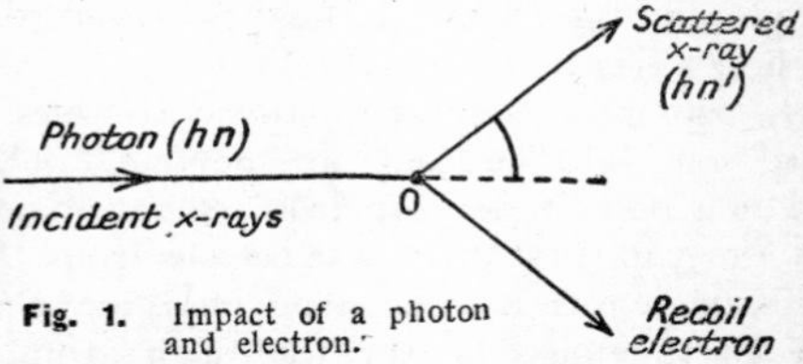

Fig. 1. Impact of a photon and electron.

It will be seen, as the frequency n' is less than n, the wave length of the " scattered " X-ray will be larger than the incident beam. Not only was a lengthening of the wave length predicted, but also the amount of wave length change was shown to depend on the actual angle at which it happened to be scattered.

All these conclusions were verified by experiment. Using an X-ray spectrometer, the wave lengths of the scattered X-rays were measured for different angles of scattering, and the wave length change was found almost exactly as the theory predicted. Also, using a cloud condensation apparatus, photographs of the tracks of electrons showed the presence of short tracks which exactly fitted the anticipated recoil electrons. In this case there

certainly seemed to be ample proof that the X-ray " waves "
behaved as corpuscles, and there was support for the use of the
term photon to describe the phenomenon. Since the same laws
are applicable in the case of all the electro-magnetic radiations,
it seemed that many phenomena could be explained in terms
of a common conception, that of a corpuscle. On the other
hand, this notion is not so useful in giving an explanation of
such things as interference, diffraction, etc. There still remains
this curious fact, that one set of properties of radiation can be
best explained in terms of a wave theory, and another set of
observed results can be better explained if we use the photon
development of the quantum theory as a theoretical background.
In almost all cases the wave theory gives the broad outline
explanation and the quantum theory developments give the
detail and account for those observed results for which the wave
theory has no explanation.

Protons. There are many corpuscles which, it would appear
at first sight at least, are beyond doubt discrete particles and
which do not develop from radiation ideas. Of these the first
we met in this Course was the electron. This particular corpuscle
was shown to be a negative charge of a mass so small, compared
with the mass of the hydrogen atom, that we say it is not
associated with matter at all.

All the *positive* charges we have so far met with in this Course
have been of a much more massive structure. The smallest
positive charge is that on the nucleus of the hydrogen atom.
This charge is associated with the mass of the hydrogen atom
and is equal in size but opposite in sign to the charge on the
electron. It will be remembered that the hydrogen atom was
considered to be a nucleus with one electron moving about it.
For the heavier atoms we have a similar simplified picture.
The heavier the atom the bigger the positive charge of the nucleus,
and correspondingly bigger is the number of electrons rotating
about that nucleus.

Now, since for the heavier atoms the nuclear charge is a whole
number of times that of the hydrogen nucleus, it seems obvious
why a theory has developed on the lines of assuming that a
tentative unit of positive electricity is that associated with the
matter forming the hydrogen nucleus. The proton, as this
unit is called, is then used in building up other atoms. For
example, the atom of sodium is supposed to be made of a nucleus

containing eleven protons and surrounded by eleven electrons. Until the end of the year 1932 positive electricity had never been isolated in a state free from matter as had the negative charge. But in the course of very intensive researches carried out in the last few years, one experiment which was described in 1933 seemed to produce clear evidence that the " positive electron " was isolated. Cloud condensation experiments were performed and the tracks of electrons and other ionizing agents, liberated by penetrating, cosmic radiation, were photographed. The action of magnetic fields causing the tracks to be bent was also investigated. In some of the photographs tracks were obtained which were bent in a direction opposite to that in which the electron tracks were bent. This showed that the track was produced by a positively charged particle. Now, from a knowledge of the magnetic field it is a fairly simple matter to estimate the magnitude of the particle if its charge is known. The estimated mass of the newly discovered particle was much less than that of a proton, so that it could not be associated with matter (unless, indeed, the hydrogen atom is not the smallest portion of matter which can be isolated). There seems to be little doubt that this experiment isolated the positive electron, although it made no *definite* measurements of the mass, etc., of it (Fig. 2, Plate 61).

The Neutron. Yet another corpuscle is known to modern Physics under the name of the *neutron*, which, as its name suggests, is neutral in charge. This uncharged corpuscle is released when certain substances are bombarded by *a* rays and swiftly-moving protons. A full account of the experiment which led Dr. Chadwick to isolate and describe this corpuscle, is, however, too long to include here.

It is thus seen that the number of different corpuscles which have been isolated has increased, and more and more phenomena receive an explanation in terms of them. However, during the past few years much important work has been carried out both on the theoretical and experimental sides, which has had an effect just the reverse of that produced by the introduction of the photon. This work is usually classified under the title of the New Quantum Theory, one aspect being Wave Mechanics.

Wave Mechanics. Schroedinger, who was a pupil of Count de Broglie, advanced a mathematical idea that was first introduced by de Broglie, in which a study of a moving corpuscle led to a mathematical form to express its movement, which was similar in general appearance to that which describes waves travelling through space. A moving electron, for example, in this treatment is expressed by an equation which looks very similar to that of a wave.

The analogy led to the suggestion that, in effect, the moving electron might be similar to waves of suitable wave length. This does not mean quite that the new wave mechanics suggests that we must change this accepted *corpuscle*—the electron—and in its place substitute a wave : but it does suggest that in the close analogy which the mathematical development has deduced there is a chance that in some respects the electron should exhibit wave-like properties.

To use an imperfect analogy, if we have a quickly-moving ship steaming over the smooth surface of the sea, and we view this from an aeroplane well above the surface, we shall be able to see a set of bow waves moving over the surface, or we shall see the ship moving over the surface. In this analogy the ship represents the electron and the waves correspond to the wave-like structure which the waves mechanics suggests.

Now, for a corpuscle moving with a velocity v, the length of the associated wave form is deduced to be equal to h/mv, where *h* is Planck's constant and *m* the electron's mass.

Experiments have been performed to try to detect any effect of the waves, and it is a surprising fact that the results in most cases have been positive. A stream of electrons, when sent at right angles to very thin sheets of metal, instead of going through with a reduced intensity or reduced speed, have been found to spread out into definite rings, in a way very similar to the X-ray waves on passing through a thin crystal (*see* diagram, Lesson 25, page 475). This may be due to the diffraction of the waves and is, in fact, in agreement with the diffraction expected with waves of wave length $\lambda = h/mv$.

For quickly-moving electrons the calculated value of λ is of the same order as X-ray wave lengths ; Professor G. P. Thomson was the first to demonstrate the effect clearly.

Now, although the diffraction was that given for waves of X-ray wave length, the absorption of the electrons still continues to obey the laws of absorption for electrons, i.e. they are still very easily absorbed in thin sheets, whereas X-rays of the same wave length are able to penetrate relatively thick slabs of the same substance.

Another set of striking experimental evidence of the wave nature to be associated with the moving particle was obtained by the production of diffraction with ruled diffraction gratings. Here, again, one experimenter found the diffractions to produce lines just as would be produced by waves of length $\lambda = h/mv$. Although this has not been confirmed, there is striking evidence that there must be some wave-like property associated with the electron. Experiments have also been made with uncharged particles—as there is no need, according to the theory, for the particle to have a charge—and confirmation is again forthcoming to support the new theory.

Cosmic Rays. Another subject of interest in modern Physics concerns the very penetrating radiation which is found to be present when all known sources of radiation, e.g. radioactive bodies, etc., are excluded. This penetrating radiation, which is sometimes referred to as cosmic radiation, is present at great height above the earth's surface, as the balloon ascents of Prof. Picard and others have shown. At the moment the origin of the radiation is quite unknown. It certainly seems to be external to the earth, but the *exact* source is unknown. Also, we are unable to say as yet whether it is photons of a very short wavelength radiation or whether it is truly corpuscular in character.

It will be seen that this very brief résumé of some of the more recent theories advanced to account for the results obtained by experiment shows clearly the interplay which is going on between the work of the theoretical and experimental physicist.

There are no definite answers to the modern questions set, but " intelligent guesses " and considered theories, followed by the critical test by experiment, constitute a very promising attempt to go a stage farther in the disentanglement of the very intertwined threads which confront us in modern Physics.

Books Recommended for Further Study. " A Text Book of Physics," Duncan and Starling ; " A World of Sound," W. H. Bragg (Bell) ; " The Mechanism of Nature," Andrade (Bell) ; " Infra Red Photography," Rawlings (Blackie). The following are more advanced : " Electrons and Ionising Radiations," J. A. Crowther (Arnold) ; " The Nature of the Physical World," Eddington (Cambridge University Press) ; " Radioactivity and Radioactive Substances," Chadwick (Pitman) ; " Monographs in Physical Subjects " (Methuen).

This Lesson concludes our Course in Physics.

LESSON 22

Protective Devices of the Body (1)

I N Lesson 6 (Volume I, page 593) we saw how the nutritive fluids of the body were maintained in the face of varying conditions in the external environment. It will be realized by the student that, in order to effect this steady constancy in what may be called the internal environment, all the various systems of the body play their part—brain, nerves, the digestive organs, the heart, lungs and kidneys all working together towards this end. Conditions vary from time to time under the influence of extraordinary factors in the external environment, but they remain relatively stable—thanks in large measure to the co-ordinating influences of the autonomic nervous system. Though the ancient physicians of older days failed to recognize this explanation of the tendency of the body to maintain itself in health, they were well aware of its existence. Modern medicine and surgery are only successful so long as they direct their methods in accordance with these restorative methods of Nature and are so directed as to promote it.

This power of accurate response to changing conditions is a product of evolution, and is represented to its fullest extent in Man. It has allowed him to develop in spite of the hostilities of Nature. His present need is to develop still further powers of adaptation to resist the hostile influences of civilization. Now this preservation of a more or less constant state in the nutritive fluids of the body may well be regarded as a protective mechanism. But there are also other special mechanisms of a protective kind called into action in response to special dangers, and of these let us first consider some protective reflex actions. The eye is an organ of great importance and is much exposed to injury. It is a photographic camera having a lens, a shutter (the iris) and a photographic plate (the retina) made up of highly specialized end-organs capable of receiving impressions from waves of light and passing them on through the optic nerves to nerve cells in a definite area of the cortex of the brain. It can be moved in all directions by muscles attached to the globe and to the bony socket, which latter affords it much protection. Its exposed surface is covered by a highly sensitive membrane, the conjunctiva, which also lines the inner surface of the eyelids—quick-acting shutters ready to protect the eye.

The circular shutter over the lens, the iris, closes in over the lens in response to a strong light and to messages sent along a nerve belonging to the cranial set of the autonomic system. This mechanism is a great protection to the delicate structures in the retina. But the damaging effects of dust particles and harmful fumes must also be insured against. Pain is caused—and here, as always, pain is seen to be a protective sensory mechanism— tears are effused and serve to wash away or dilute the offending substance, and the eyelids blink in order mechanically to assist its removal. The blood vessels of the conjunctiva dilate and bring more lymph to repair the damage. The whole process is a good example of protective reflex action.

Take now the respiratory organs with their lining of highly sensitive mucous membrane. An irritating substance or gas enters the nasal passage. A sneeze is evoked. A sensory impulse has passed to the brain, and in response a series of motor impulses are sent out. A deep inspiration takes place followed by a blast of air forcibly sent out though the nose, and this may succeed in expelling the source of irritation. The membrane secretes mucus freely in order to dilute and enwrap it. Or the offending matter may find its way into the lower air passages. The breath, which might take it into the lungs, is immediately checked. The breath is held and the vocal cords close the entry into the larynx, and with a violent expiratory effort the offending substance is coughed up. Protective coughing also follows on inflammation of the lower air passages. The products of inflammation—dead cells, microbes, etc.—must be got rid of in order to keep the airways clear.

Vomiting is another good example of a reflex action designed to expel an irritating substance that has been taken into the stomach. The act is a highly complex one. In response to the nervous messages the salivary glands pour out their secretion more freely in order that the saliva may help to dilute the stomach contents. The gastric glands which secrete mucus also secrete more freely in order further to dilute and enwrap the irritating substance. Breathing becomes more rapid, so that the breath may be held later ; the diaphragm and abdominal muscles contract powerfully so as to increase the intra-abdominal pressure.

The larynx is closed and the breath is now held so as to shut off the airway. The lower end of the oesophagus dilates, the sphincter muscle at the inlet to the stomach relaxes, and the stomach contents are forcibly expelled. A widespread motor impulse has occurred in response to a local sensory disturbance.

Repeated pressure or rubbing of the skin produces a callosity in the affected area. The outer epithelial cells, which are normally of a horny character increase and form a thick horny layer or callous area, which serves to protect the underlying soft structures. Healing is, of course, a protective mechanism. The skin, say, has been broken. Nerve irritation is set up. The blood vessels in the area dilate and bathe the parts in cleansing lymph. New capillary vessels form in the gap, connective tissue cells develop around them to form a supporting structure, and the cells in the deeper layers of the skin, whose function it is to carry on incessant renewal as the upper layers of the skin are cast off as horny scales, take on an increased rate of growth in order to cover up the damage. Finally, we remind the student of the mechanisms employed by the body to preserve its inward heat. These are either brought quickly into action to meet sudden changes, or more slowly to meet gradual alterations in temperature. The putting on by animals of extra hair as winter approaches is an example of a slow-acting protective mechanism of this kind. In humans the bronzing of the skin that develops under exposure to the ultra-violet rays of sunlight is a similar example of slow protective response. The pigment that forms in the skin prevents the penetration of the rays to the deeper parts, where they would act harmfully if in excess.

LESSON 23

Protective Devices of the Body (2)

MAN'S chief and universal enemy is the microbe. Present everywhere in Nature, many of these lowly forms of life whose activities effect profound changes in their environment have a beneficent purpose, even when that environment is the human body. Others are potent for harm, and those types that are normally helpful to their human host may become harmful under adverse circumstances, while those whose action is purely destructive may lie dormant in or on the body, only awaiting an opportunity to invade their host and take on activities which may spell death. Such are to be found nearly always on the skin and on the mucous membranes lining the mouth, nose and throat. The first line of defence, then, is the skin and mucous membrane.

If the integrity of the skin be impaired by injury, or the surface cells of the mucous membrane damaged by irritation, or their vitality impaired by faulty nutrition, an open gateway is provided for the bacteria to enter the deeper structures, or even the blood stream in the neighbouring capillaries. Having thus gained admission, they take on very rapid multiplication, increasing at the rate of many millions in a few hours. The defence offered may be confined to a purely local effort, or the whole machinery of the body may require to be brought into action—in other words, a state of acute illness is set up in the host, with fever and its accompanying symptoms.

A pustule on the skin is an example of a purely local reaction. Pus-producing bacteria, always to be found on the skin, obtain entrance to its deeper layers owing to some slight injury or to a weakening of the general resistive powers. They attack the walls of the capillaries, which dilate and allow a free outflow of plasma through their walls, the plasma clotting as it exudes, while the lymph vessels in the vicinity become closed by the clotting of their contained lymph. The combined fibrinous network and the clotted lymph serve to shut off the invaded area from the surrounding tissues. White corpuscles (leucocytes) are hurried to the spot in great numbers from the neighbouring lymphatic glands. The latter may become enlarged and swollen as the result of their increased activity.

The leucocytes envelop the bacteria by means of exuding processes of their protoplasm, and, having drawn the organisms into their substance, digest and so destroy them. This is the process known as phagocytosis. Leucocytes and lymphatic glands thus constitute the second line of defence. If the invasion is severe or the resistive powers of the individual be impaired, the glands may become infected and their substance broken down into pus. Or this line of defence may fail to check the infection, which then invades the general blood stream—the condition known as septicaemia. To complete the story of the pustule or boil, pus forms and consists of dead and living bacteria, leucocytes, and broken down tissue material. This débris, as recovery takes place, is discharged from the centre of the inflamed area.

Despite the occurrence of a local reaction on the part of the host, some types of bacteria when conditions are favourable, produce, as the result of their life processes, highly poisonous substances, which, being absorbed into the blood stream, may produce serious disturbance.

Diphtheria is a well-known instance. There is severe local reaction in the mucous membrane of the throat and mouth, the common site of attack by the organisms of this disease. The further encroachment of the enemy is prevented, but there is nevertheless absorption of much poisonous material produced by the rapid growth and death of the bacteria. This tends to poison the nerves, especially some of the cranial nerves and the nerves which control the heart and lungs ; paralysis ensues and may prove fatal. The defence lies in the production by the infected body of an antitoxin able to counteract the action of the toxin. This substance can be obtained, as it were, artificially, by giving an animal repeated and increasing though harmless doses of the toxin, the latter being obtained by allowing the bacteria to grow in a broth.

The animal being thus inoculated, the anti-toxin is found in the serum and is available for providing a reinforcement of the protective powers of the blood of the infected person. But the bacteria of some types may find their way into the general blood stream, and then a further protective process is called into action. It is obvious that the danger of such an invasion is a very grave one, since the organisms may be carried to any vital organ, there to carry on their destructive work. The serum of the blood produces specific immunizing substances or anti-bodies. These have the power of making the bacteria clump together into masses, the process being spoken of as agglutination. These substances cannot so act unless another substance is present in the serum, which substance serves, as it were, to complete the work of the antibody. This other substance is known as the complement to the agglutinating substance. Together they bring about the dissolution of the bacteria.

The antibody is of a specific kind in relation to the type of invading organism, and since by experimental inoculation of animals it can be produced in the animal's blood, it can be used in medical treatment to effect immunity to possible infection or to cure an existing one. The presence of the antibody renders the leucocytes more effective in their work, since it is easier for them to attack the bacteria in their clumped-together condition. It also renders the bacteria more susceptible to attack.

These natural defences are in many cases dependent for their efficiency on the general health, i.e., on the stability of the physico-chemical processes in the face of hostile factors in the environment. Failure to maintain the temperature of the body under sudden changes of the external temperature gives the opportunity for bacterial invasion. Pneumonia and influenza, following on chills, are familiar examples. Faulty nutrition impairs the resistance of the mucous membranes. Fatigue, worry, and mental depression weaken the activity of the autonomic system and its regulating functions, on which so much depends. Chronic poisoning from defective internal cleanliness lowers the powers of reaction to further and more acute infection. It is thus that the efficiency of the defensive forces against infection depends largely on personal habits of living.

LESSON 24

Sex Organs of the Human Body

THE individual organism is a link in a long chain of lives, and physiological life may be regarded as a circle in which a series of events is repeated over and over again. Egg cell, foetus, the newly born child, the adult, and again the reproductive cell complete the unending cycle. Thus the sex organs occupy a vastly important position in the scheme of physiology. Nor is their importance limited to the reproduction of the species. They play a very large part in the development of the special sex characteristics and in the upkeep and repair of the body. It has been pointed out in Lesson 17 (Volume 4, page 567) how closely the internal secretions of the sex glands are linked up with all the other hormones produced by the various internal secreting glands. Our special interest now is with their functions as directly concerned with reproduction.

In the male the reproductive organs consist of two testes and the ducts which lead from them. The testis is a glandular organ which shortly before birth descends from the peritoneal cavity of the abdomen into the scrotal sac, enclosed in a process of the peritoneal membrane. The cavity in which it lies then becomes cut off from the general peritoneal sac and the testis remains enclosed in its own serous sac. The gland is divided into lobules, each of which consists of several convoluted tubes. These tubes end in ducts, which unite to form a single much convoluted

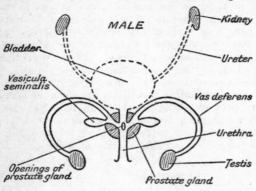

tube, the folds of which form a small mass attached to the testis and known as the epididymis. In its turn this tube is prolonged into a larger thick-walled tube, the *vas deferens*. This opens into the urethra behind the base of the penis, and provides the channel whereby the spermatozoa, having their origin in the cellular tubules of the testis, enter the urethra in the sexual act

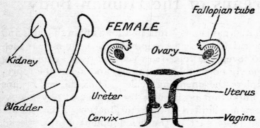

HUMAN SEX ORGANS. Male and female reproductive system.
From " An Outline for Boys and Girls and their Parents," by courtesy of Mrs. Naomi Mitchison and Victor Gollancz, Ltd.

and are discharged. The process is assisted by the added secretions of two glandular bodies, the *vesiculae seminales*, which are outgrowths of the vas deferens and pour their secretion into it, and by the secretion of the prostate gland.

These secretions together make up the semen, which consists of vast numbers of spermatozoa suspended in a richly albuminous fluid. The spermatozoon is derived by developmental stages from the epithelium which lines the tubules of the testis. It consists of a head, a short neck, a body, and a long highly motile tail, by the lashing movements of which the sperm cell makes its way through the genital passages of the female to reach and fertilize the ovum. The head is flattened and oval, has a sharp cutting edge, and contains a well-marked nucleus. Spermatozoa are being continually formed in very large numbers during the sexual life, and are temporarily stored in the vesiculae seminales, whence they are discharged from time to time, either during the sexual act or by involuntary emissions.

There are also to be found in the testis strands of epithelial cells lying amongst the connective tissue and accompanying the blood vessels. They contain crystalloid bodies and are known as interstitial cells. They produce the hormone substance which, in conjunction with other glands, brings about the male sex characteristics.

The female sex organs consist of (1) the right and left ovaries, the functions of which are to produce the germ cells or ova; (2) a fallopian tube on each side, through which the ova pass to the uterus or womb, the organ in which the ovum develops into the foetus; and (3) the vagina, the passage through which insemination occurs and through which the young animal is born. The ovary is a gland having the size of a large walnut. It consists of a fibrous stroma covered with a layer of cubical cells, the germinal epithelium, which extend here and there deeply into the stroma. The substance of the ovary is crowded with large numbers of tiny rounded cells, the oocytes or primitive germ cells. In the stroma are also a number of large epithelial cells, the interstitial cells, whose function it is to produce the female sex hormone.

Some of the germ cells during the sexual life undergo a process of ripening. As the cell ripens it becomes enclosed in a vesicle known as a " Graafian follicle," consisting of a cellular wall enclosing a fluid in which lies the germ cell. These follicles can be seen projecting from the surface. The vesicle, as it increases in size owing to increase in its fluid contents, reaches the surface of the ovary and finally bursts, and in doing so releases the ovum. The egg cell then enters the fallopian tube, a hollow tubular structure about 4 inches long. The inner opening of this tube communicates with the upper part of the interior of the womb, while its outer end opens freely into the general peritoneal cavity by an opening surrounded by delicate fringe-like processes, one of which is in close contact with the ovary of its own side. In this way the ovum is directed into the tubes. The inner surface of the tube is lined with a ciliated epithelium. The waving action of the cilia propels the ovum towards the uterus. It is while the ovum is in the outer third of the length of the fallopian tube that fertilization is usually effected.

The process of ripening of an ovum is called ovulation, and in the human species it occurs once in about every four weeks—the function known as menstruation. After the follicle ruptures it becomes filled up with a substance derived from the cellular wall of the follicle, together with a mass of jelly-like connective tissue and blood clot. This structure, the *corpus luteum*, disappears after a time unless pregnancy supervenes on ovulation, when it persists during pregnancy and increases in size.

The ovum is a spheroidal cell surrounded by a transparent membrane. Its protoplasm is rich in fatty and albuminous granules, and it shows a well-marked nucleus. It is derived from the primitive germ cells which at first lie interspersed among the cells of the germinal epithelium, covering and dipping into the ovarian substance.

At birth there are about 70,000 immature oocytes, only a very small fraction of which reach maturity—perhaps 400 during the sexual life. Comparatively few of these, of course, become fertilized. Spermatozoa are produced by Nature on a still more lavish scale. In one sexual act it is calculated that more than 200,000,000 spermatozoa are discharged, and only one of these effects fertilization.

LESSON 25

Process of Human Reproduction

WE continue our study of the female reproductive organs. The womb is a pear-shaped organ lying in the pelvic cavity between the rectum and bladder. It is about three inches in length, the upper portion about two inches wide. The lower end forms the neck or cervix of the organ, and the lower end of the neck projects into the cavity of the vagina. The uterine walls are composed of layers of muscle, and though the womb is a hollow organ, its walls are, normally, almost in contact. The cavity of the body of the womb is about an inch wide by an inch and a half long, and has three openings into it, one from the vagina through the cervix and one on each side into the Fallopian tubes. It is lined by a mucous membrane known as the endo-metrium, consisting largely of tubular glands dipping into its substance from the epithelium which forms its inner surface. The function of the womb is entirely confined to the reception of the fertilized ovum and the lodgement of the growing foetus until it is sufficiently developed to be born. The endometrium is always in a state of constant change during the sexual life. Much of it is shed every four weeks during menstruation.

In the pregnant womb the lining membrane becomes highly specialized in order to embed and nourish the growing ovum, and the greater part of it is cast off after the child is born. The capacity of the womb to accommodate a full-term child, entailing its increase in size to about four times its normal length, and twenty to thirty times its normal weight, and the subsequent return of the organ to its normal size, is a truly remarkable instance of the adaptive powers of the human body.

The vagina is the passage between the womb and the external opening between the lips or vulvae. It has a front and back wall, the former about three inches long and the latter about an inch longer. The external opening is partly closed in the virgin by a special fold of mucous membrane, the hymen, and at the upper end the mouth of the womb projects from half to one inch into the vaginal cavity. The cavity is lined with a tough epithelium that has no glands in it, lubrication of its surface being effected by special glands near the vulva. The rest of the wall is com-posed of fibrous and muscular tissue which permits of contraction and expansion in sexual intercourse and parturition.

The function known as menstruation is closely connected with that of ovulation. Every four weeks the womb becomes con-gested and its mucous membrane thickened. The more superficial layers of this membrane are then cast off, with blood from the ruptured blood vessels of the membrane. When the menstrual flow ceases the membrane repairs itself, and then prepares for a similar happening. This function begins at puberty, i.e. when the ova first take on the process of ripening, and its object is to prepare the uterine lining for the reception of a fertilized ovum. It provides a raw surface on which the ovum can easily become grafted, and so retained for nourishment from the maternal blood stream and subsequent growth. This is first of all effected by the special changes that take place in the lining membrane around the ovum, and later by the development of a special arrangement of blood vessels belonging partly to the foetus and partly to the uterus, called the placenta. Large blood vessels pass to and from the foetus to the placenta by means of the umbilical cord.

The functions of ovulation and menstruation are governed by the action of various hormones. The action and interaction of these hormones has been the object of much recent research, and is not as yet fully understood. The various changes that take place in the epithelium of the uterus during the sexual cycle are probably dependent on a mutual cooperation between a hormone secreted by the ovarian follicle and another secreted by the corpus luteum. There is definite evidence also that the ovarian function, as regards ovulation, is under the influence of the anterior portion of the pituitary gland. The cessation of menstruation during pregnancy is due to the inhibitory action of the hormone secreted by the corpus luteum, which, as we have noted, increases in size and activity at this time.

Fertilization is effected by the union of the male and female germ cells. During coitus the spermatozoa are deposited at the entrance to the cervix, or in some portion of the vagina. They make their way by the flagellation of their tails into the cervix, through the uterine cavity and into the Fallopian tubes. Here one sperm cell meets a mature ovum and, by means of its sharp head, penetrates its wall. The head and neck of the spermatozoon enter its substance and become converted into the male pronucleus. It contains the same number of chromosomes as the nucleus of the female cell, so that when the two pronuclei unite, as they now proceed to do, the nucleus resulting from the fusion contains an equal number of chromosomes derived from the two parent cells.

The fertilized ovum then divides into two parts : each of these again divides into two, subdivision occurring until a mulberry-shaped mass, the morula, is formed. A cavity appears in its midst, converting it into a hollow blastula. At first the wall is composed of a single layer of cells, except at one part, where some cells are bunched together as an inner cell mass. Later this inner cell mass grows round the interior of the wall, which then comes to consist of two layers, the epiblast and hypoblast.

Later still, a third layer forms between these, and is called the mesoblast. The subsequent development of these layers of cells by multiplication and specialization into the various organs and tissues is the subject of a special branch of physiology with which we cannot now deal.

It is important that the student should realize from this brief account of the reproductive function how intimately it is connected with the well-being of the body as a whole. The influence is mutual. On the one hand, the health of the germ cell is dependent on the health of the maternal blood stream, as determined by the presence of suitable nutritive material and the absence of toxic agents. On the other, the whole system of governance of the functions of the body, its growth and maintenance, is dependent on the healthy activity of the sex glands.

LESSON 26

The Human Machine in Action

IN bringing these Lessons to a close, let us take a final, if brief, look at the human body in its make-up and action as a machine with powers of motion and locomotion. We may regard it from this point of view as a highly complicated system of muscular engines exerting their power on a system of levers or, in engineering parlance, crank-pins. Though the whole equipment of muscle engines and levers is present in the new-born child, their use has to be learned. From the earliest efforts to grasp an object, to balance the body on its two legs, to take the first few faltering footsteps, to utter the first words, dozens of muscles have to be set in motion at the right instant and in the right order, and with the right amount of strength. Later we acquire the ability to run and jump and to use the fingers for finely adjusted movements ; we achieve proficiency in sport and games calling for the very accurately co-ordinated action of scores of muscle engines timed to function to the fraction of a second, and by constant practice we develop a high degree of skill in the pursuit of some handicraft.

Such perfect adjustment in timing and strength can only be effected by sets of muscles acting reciprocally, each set having to give and take as the other takes and gives. Thus, to take a simple example, when we bend the elbow the biceps muscle attached to the front of the forearm contracts, and the triceps muscle, extending along the back of the arm and attached to the back of the elbow, relaxes. When we again straighten the elbow the mechanism is reversed. The resultant movement is, therefore, steady and smooth. To enable one set of muscles to feel exactly what its opposing set is doing all the time, Nature provides them with special end-organs set among the muscle cylinders and in the tendons or fibrous attachments of the muscles. From these receptors nerve fibres convey messages to nerve exchanges in the central nervous system, from which messages pass to the opposing muscles. Every set of muscles is thus kept constantly informed of the conditions obtaining in every other set.

The highly complex character of this system of intercommunication is one of the greatest marvels of Nature. To take a single step, three hundred separate muscles have to be set going, and from each of these messages are being sent to the brain and a similar number from automatic control centres. Constant functioning causes the controls to become automatic. If we, then, bring conscious interference to bear, the movements are less smooth and become clumsy.

As has been pointed out in Lesson 4 (Volume 1, page 586), the muscle engines of the body are capable of putting about 25 per cent of the actual energy supplied in the food to effective use in the form of work done. The rest appears as heat, or is wasted in friction. The actual work done by a muscle or set of muscles is greatly enhanced by the fact that the bones on which they exert their pull form a system of levers. Examples of the three orders of levers are

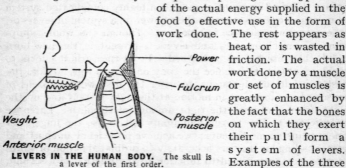

LEVERS IN THE HUMAN BODY. The skull is a lever of the first order.

Sir A. Keith's "Engines of the Human Body"

found in different parts of the body. In the first order we have one end of the lever applied to the point of resistance or weight; at the other end the force is applied, and the fulcrum is between the two. The nearer the fulcrum to the resistance, and the longer the power arm, the greater will be the force exerted by a given effort. At the same time the movement effected is at a slower speed than when the fulcrum is nearer the point of application of the power, in which case there is less power but greater speed.

Nodding movements of the head on the spinal column illustrate the point. The greater part of the weight of the skull lies in front of the articulation of the skull on the spine. The pull of the powerful muscles at the back of the neck acts on the skull well behind this point, while the opposing muscles in the front of the neck are not only weaker, but are attached to the skull immediately in front of the fulcral point. As a result of the far greater power exerted by the back-of-the-neck muscles, the neck can be readily broken by force applied upwards to the chin. Nodding and side-to-side movements call for less muscular force, but greater speed.

As an example of the second order of levers, the foot may be chosen. The bones of the foot form an arched or bent lever, and the weight of the body rests on the summit of the arch. The pad under the toes acts as the fulcrum, and the distance between the fulcrum and the point at which the weight is applied is greater than the distance between the fulcrum and the tip of the posterior arch of the lever, where the power is exercised by the powerful muscle

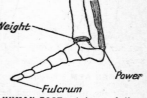

HUMAN FOOT. A lever of the second order.

forming the calf of the leg, and attached to the heel by the tendon Achilles. The anterior pillar varies in length in individuals. Where it is shorter than usual it is designed for greater power and less speed, and vice versa. Thus we usually find a sprinter has a long foot, and a heavy man a short one. Power can, of course, be increased by constant exercise, as in hill-climbing. Flattening of the arched lever does not necessarily decrease either speed or power. So-called flat-foot trouble is due to lack of mobility in the small bones which make up the arch, the result of lack of proper exercise and muscular weakness. There are no less than seventeen small muscles in the foot needing constant use.

As an example of a human lever of the third order, we may take the forearm and hand. Here the fulcrum is the elbow, the weight is applied at the hand end, and the power is applied between the weight and the fulcrum by the brachial muscle attached to the front of the arm bone and pulling on the upper end of the forearm. Here the power is applied at a point so close to the fulcrum that it works at a great disadvantage as regards strength ; but what is lost in power is gained in speed—a speed of movement which is of enormous value. In the act of climbing the lever action is reversed. The weight now acts at

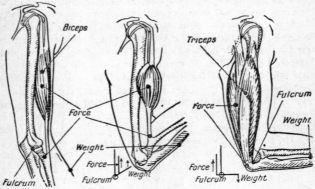

HUMAN ARM. Forearm and hand constitute a lever of the third order, in which the fulcrum is the elbow, the weight is applied by way of the hand, and the power is applied between the weight and the fulcrum by the brachial muscle pulling on the upper end of the forearm.

the top of the arm bone, the forearm is fixed, the fulcrum is at the elbow, and the biceps muscle acts at slower speed, but to a greater advantage in strength. The longer forearm of the ape is adapted for climbing, but moves clumsily and slowly compared to the shorter forearm of Man, which is adapted for speed and accuracy of movement, rather than strength and reach.

Bibliography. " The Human Body," by Sir Arthur Keith (Home University Library) ; " Engines of the Human Body," by Keith (2nd ed., 1925) ; " Handbook of Physiology," by Prof. R. J. S. McDowell ; " Sex," by Prof. Patrick Geddes and Sir J. Arthur Thomson (Home University Library) ; " Concise Home Doctor " (Amalgamated Press).

This Lesson concludes our Course in Physiology.

LESSON 7

Use of Final Hooks

BEFORE proceeding further with the study, the student should compare his work on Exercises 22 and 23, which were set in Lesson 6, Volume 5, page 570, with the keys below. At this stage it will be interesting for him to have these exercises dictated several times each so that he may gradually accustom himself to writing from the spoken word.

KEY TO EXERCISE 22

1. With your approval, I shall speak to the traveller myself and make every endeavour to influence him in favour of the proposal.
2. The place of the gathering on Friday next is very near to the Waverley Hotel.
3. We think we shall be able to recover the missing valuables. The initial delay, however, is in favour of the thieves.

KEY TO EXERCISE 23

In the previous Lesson we discussed the use of initial hooks. We will now consider how hooks may be employed at the end of strokes to represent *f* or *v*, *n*, and *shun*.

A small final hook, written on the same side as circle *s* to straight strokes, adds *f* or *v*, thus, ⟍ pave, ⟍ above, ⌐ tough, ⌐ dove, ⌐ chafe, ⌐ Jove, ⌐ drive, ⌐ drives, ⟋ rough, ⟋ wave, ⟋ waves, ⟋ serve, ⟋ serves. Note how *s* is added by writing circle inside the hook.

A small final hook written on the opposite side to the *f/v* hook adds *n* to straight strokes, thus, ⟍ pain, ⟍ bone, ⌐ tone, ⌐ chain, ⌐ Jane, ⎯ cane, ⟍ broken, ⟋ run, ⟋ won.

In order to express the addition of a final circle or hook to straight strokes hooked for *n* we simply write the circle or hook on the *n*-hook side of the stroke, thus, ⟍ pine, ⟍ pines, ⟍ ban, ⟍ bans, ⌐ dine, ⌐ dines, ⟋ retain, ⟋ retains, ⌐ John, ⌐ John's, ⎯ gain, ⎯ gains, ⎯ against, ⎯ expense, ⎯ expenses, ⌐ Dan, ⌐ dance, ⌐ danced, ⌐ dances.

In the case of curved strokes, a small final hook represents *n*, circle *s* being added by writing the circle inside the hook, thus, ⌒ mine, ⌒ mines, ⌒ line, ⌒ lines, ⟩ earn, ⟩ earns. There is no *f/v* hook to curves.

These hooks may be used in the middle of outlines when they join easily to the following stroke, thus, ⌐ defence, ⌐ define, ⟍ provide, ⟋ refer, ⟋ referring, ⟋ reference, ⌐ training, ⌐ telephone, ⎯ evening, ⟩ arrange. Note ⎯ meantime, ⎯ minute, ⎯ window, ⎯ lounge, ⎯ county, where the medial stroke *n* is preferable.

For the syllable *-ner* the sign ⌣ is preferred, except after a straight upstroke, thus, ⎯⌣ keener, ⎯ banner, ⌒ liner, but ⌒ runner, ⟋ winner.

After a curved stroke the light sound of *-nce* is represented by stroke *n* with the circle added, thus, ⟍ fence, ⌒ lance, ⌒ allowance.

USE OF FINAL HOOKS

When a vowel follows *f*, *v*, or *n* at the end of a word it is necessary, in order to place the vowel-sign, to use the stroke *f*, *v*, or *n*, as in ⌒ coffee, ⌒ cough, ⌐ Duffy, ⌐ Duff, ⌐ funny, ⌐ fun.

ABBREVIATIONS

╲ been, ╱ general-ly, ╲ behalf, └ advantage, ┬ difficult, ┬ difficulty, ⸜ within, (southern, ⌒ northern, ⌒ opinion, ⸝ balance, ♪ circumstance, ⌒ significance, ⌒ signify-ied-icant.

SOME USEFUL PHRASES

⟩ they are, ╲ I have been, ⋀ we have been, ⌐ had been, ⟩ their own, ⸍ our own, ╲ better than, ⌒ more than, ⟋ which have, ┬ out of.

EXERCISE 24

COPY AND TRANSCRIBE

(Unimportant vowels are omitted)

A large final hook adds the sound of -*shun* or -*zhun*. This hook is written inside curves, thus, ⟋ fashion, ⟍ vision, ⎰ division, ⟍ provision, ⟋ session, ⟋ motion, ⟍ promotion, ⟋ commotion, ⟋ mission, ⟍ permission, ⟋ nation, ⟋ national, ⟋ examination, ⟋ lotion, ⟋ relations.

There are several slight restrictions in the placing of the -*shun* hook to straight strokes, and the following points should be carefully noted:

When a straight stroke begins with a hook, circle, or loop, the -*shun* hook is written on the *opposite* side in order to balance the outline, thus, ⟋ Grecian, ⟋ aggression, ⟋ section, ⟋ station, ⟍ expression.

After ⟍ ⟍ and ⟋ the -*shun* hook is written away from the curve, the reason again being a matter of balance, thus, ⟋ fiction, ⟋ vacation, ⟋ location, ⟋ selection.

The -*shun* hook is always written on the right-hand side of simple *t*, *d*, and *j*, thus, ⟋ addition, ⟋ edition, ⟋ invitation, ⟋ magician.

When added to the other simple straight strokes, it is written on the side opposite to the last vowel, thus, ⟋ caution, ⟋ occasion, ⟋ actions, ⟍ operation, ⟋ ration, ⟋ rational.

EXERCISE 25
READ AND WRITE

notion   notions   tension   extensions   ammunition   mansions

explanation   formation   missionary   manipulation   oppression

depression   hesitation   illustration   suction   navigation   dislocation legation   occupation   application   auction   auctioneer   erection

petition   reputation   presentation.

When *-shun* follows the circle *s* or *ns*, it is represented by continuing the circle to the other side of the stroke, thus,   decision,   position,   proposition,   possession,   possessions,   taxation,   transition.   A third-place vowel between the *s* and *-shun* is placed as shown. Other vowels between *s* and *-shun* may safely be omitted.

In words ending in *-uation*, or *-uition*, the stroke *sh* and hook *n* are generally used, thus,   tuition,   situation.   In several such words, however, where there is no danger of confusion, the *-shun* may be used, thus,   superannuation,   fluctuation.

EXERCISE 26

WRITE IN SHORTHAND

1. Fusion, infusion, evasion, revision, admission, admonition, elevation.
2. Celebration, discussion, infection, impression, transaction, Russian, Prussian, deputation.
3. Sensation, supposition, indecision, physicians, education, commissioner, obligation.

(Keys to the above Exercises are given in Lesson 8.)

LESSON 8

Another Step in Theory

BEFORE proceeding further with the study of the theory the reader would be well advised to check his attempts at Exercises 24 and 26 from the following keys. He can then turn to the consideration of the upward and downward *L* and the upward and downward *R*.

KEY TO EXERCISE 24

1. Referring to our talk with John Dunn at the Northern Hotel last evening, I have discussed all the circumstances with Mr. Henry Bannerman and he promised to arrange to have the books gone through again. In his opinion the balance should have been more than twice the figure now given.

2. On behalf of the members of the Southern branch of the society Mr. John Lane expressed thanks for the able assistance given by those of the Northern branch. All possible difficulties had been got out of the way, and their stay in Rushton had been very happy.

KEY TO EXERCISE 26

Upward and Downward L. There are one or two points in regard to the writing of stroke *l* to which attention is now drawn. In the first place it should be noted that *l* is usually written upward. In the following cases, however, it is written downward:—

SIMON BOLIVAR
(1783–1830). Born at
Caracas, he led the
Venezuelan revolt
against Spain and
became dictator of
Colombia and Peru.
MODERN HISTORY 27

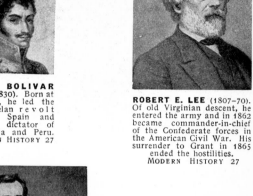

ROBERT E. LEE (1807–70).
Of old Virginian descent, he
entered the army and in 1862
became commander-in-chief
of the Confederate forces in
the American Civil War. His
surrender to Grant in 1865
ended the hostilities.
MODERN HISTORY 27

LEON GAMBETTA
(1838–82). French
patriot, who after
Sedan proclaimed
the Republic and
organized the na-
tional defence.
MODERN HISTORY 28

ABRAHAM LINCOLN (1809–65), son of
a Kentucky farmer, became a lawyer
and Republican politician, and in 1860
was elected president of the U.S.A. He
emancipated the slaves in 1863, was
re-elected president in 1864, and successfully concluded the Civil War.
He was shot by a madman while with
his family in the theatre at Washington,
April 14, 1865, and died the next day.
MODERN HISTORY 27

AFTER SEDAN. On September 1, 1870, the French army under Macmahon, marching to the support of Marshal Bazaine, shut up in Metz, was surrounded by the Germans under Moltke, and after fighting a hopeless battle all day, was compelled to capitulate. More than 100,000 French were taken prisoner, including the Emperor. This picture shows Napoleon III and Bismarck discussing the position on the following morning.

MODERN HISTORY 28

After W. Camphausen

HALL OF MIRRORS, VERSAILLES. In this ornate chamber in Louis XIV's magnificent palace, William I was proclaimed first German emperor on Jan 18, 1871, and, by the irony of circumstance, the German delegates signed the dictated Treaty of Versailles on June 28, 1919. This picture shows the Hall in use as a German war hospital during the siege of Paris in 1871. MODERN HISTORY 28

Plate 56   *Volume VI*

ANOTHER STEP IN THEORY

(a) At the beginning of a word when a vowel comes before *l* and the *l* is followed by a simple horizontal stroke, thus, ⌒ alone, ⌒ along, ⌒ Allen, ⌒ Alec. Note ⌒ loan, ⌒ long, ⌒ luck, where no vowel precedes the *l*.

(b) When *l* follows ╲ ╲ ◡ or a straight upstroke and the *l* is the last sound in the word, thus, ⌇ fall, ⌇ fill, ⌇ feel, ⌇ full, ⌇ vale, ⌇ veal, ⌿ reveal, ⌐ scale, ⌇ skill, ⌇ rule, ⌇ rail, ⌣ barrel. Note the following words in which a vowel follows *l*: ⌣ folly, ⌣ fellow, ⌣ fellows, ⌢ lovely, ⌒ relay, ⌣ sickly.

(c) After *n* or *ng*, thus, ⌇ only, ⌇ unless, ⌐ canal, ⌐ wrongly.

When *l* immediately precedes or follows a circle which is attached to a curve, it follows the direction of the circle, thus, ⌐ listen, ⌇ vessel, ⌐ Lawson, ⌐ Kingsley, ⌐ muscle.

Upward and Downward R. The two forms of *r* have already been discussed in Lessons 2 and 5 (Volume 5, pages 550 and 565), to which reference should be made, if necessary. The following additional points should now be noted.

(a) Upward *r* is written after a curve and circle in such words as ⌐ officer, ⌐ officers, ⌐ answer, ⌐ sincere, ⌐ necessary, where the downward form would be somewhat awkward.

(b) When the *r* is hooked and follows another stroke it is generally written upward, thus, ⌐ burn, ⌐ fern, ⌐ adjourn, ⌐ portion.

(c) After two downstrokes the upward *r* is preferable, thus, ⌐ prepare, ⌐ Shakespeare, in order to avoid three descending strokes. After *f* or *v*, however, the downward *r* is preferred because of the more flowing form, thus, ⌐ pinafore.

Medially the upward *r* is usually preferred, as in 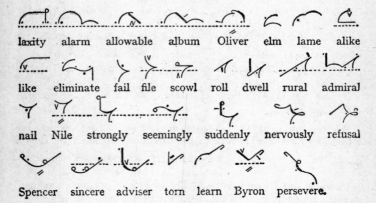 park, mark, durable. In some derivative words, such as powerful, barely, the downward *r* is retained.

EXERCISE 27

READ AND WRITE

laxity   alarm   allowable   album   Oliver   elm   lame   alike

like   eliminate   fail   file   scowl   roll   dwell   rural   admiral

nail   Nile   strongly   seemingly   suddenly   nervously   refusal

Spencer   sincere   adviser   torn   learn   Byron   persevere.

EXERCISE 28

WRITE IN SHORTHAND

1. *The* damage *to-the* car *was* heavy, *as-the* speed *of-the* lorry at-*the*-time *of-the* collision *was* said *to-be* forty miles *an hour* at-least.

2. *We* hope *you*-will receive-*the* rest *of-the* rugs *from* Lawson *and* Barrie *in two* or three days.

3. *In*-answer *to-your* application, *we-are* enclosing full details *of-the* Burns alarm bell. If-*you* so desire *we-shall* ask *our* traveller *to-call and* see *you*.

Compound Consonants. In addition to the double consonants formed by the initial hooks *r* and *l*, we have what are termed compound consonants, as set out in the next page.

Sign		Name	Letters	As in	
⌒		Kwā	QU	*qu*ick,	re*qu*est
⌒		gwā	GW, GU	*Gw*ynn,	lin*gu*ist
ʃ	(up)	wel	WL	*w*ai*l*,	*wil*d
ʃ	(up)	hwel	WHL	*wh*i*l*e,	*whl*eel
⌐	(down)	ler	LR	fee*ler*,	scho*lar*
⌐	(down)	rer	RR	fai*rer*,	poo*rer*
⌒		emp	MP, MB	da*mp*,	e*mb*alm
ʋ		hwā	WH	*wh*ere,	*wh*ip

The illustrations in Exercise 29 show clearly the exact value of these signs.

EXERCISE 29
READ AND WRITE

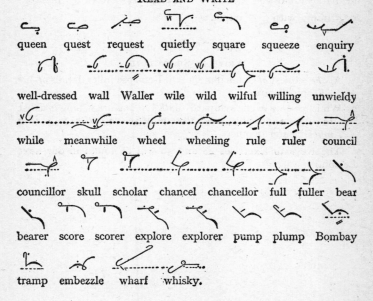

queen quest request quietly square squeeze enquiry

well-dressed wall Waller wile wild wilful willing unwieldy

while meanwhile wheel wheeling rule ruler council

councillor skull scholar chancel chancellor full fuller bear

bearer score scorer explore explorer pump plump Bombay

tramp embezzle wharf whisky.

The initial hooks in *wl* and *whl* are read first, so that if a vowel precedes the sound of *w* the stroke form of *w* or *wh* must be used, thus, ⟋ while, but ⟋ awhile. The form of *l* or *r* which is used in the root word is retained in the derivative, thus, ⎰ toil, ⎰ toiler; ⎰ jail, ⎰ jailer; ⎰ fill, ⎰ filler; ⎰ score, ⎰ scorer; ⎰ fair, ⎰ fairer. The use of the form ⟍ *rer* is confined to derivatives of words taking the downward *r*.

These thickened forms ⟨ *lr*, ⟩ *rr* are not used finally if a vowel follows the *r*, as ⎰ fuller, but ⎰ foolery.

The heavy sign ⌢ may be hooked, thus, ⎓ scamper, ⎙ lumber, ⎦ dampen, ⎘ ambition. The sign ⌢, however, is not used when one of the four double consonants *pr*, *br*, *pl*, or *bl* immediately follows *m*. Compare ⎘ empress with ⎙ emperor; ⎙ imply with ⎙ impel.

EXERCISE 30
Write in Shorthand

1. At-*the* request *of* Councillor Quinn, I-enclose fuller details *of-our* "Empire" cars.
2. While *we-have* every sympathy *with you and are* willing *to* assist *in-any*-way possible, *we-shall* require *you to put-the* facts *in a much* clearer manner.

(The Keys to Exercises 28 and 30 will be found in our next Lesson.)

LESSON 9

The Aspirate and Halving Principle

BELOW are given the keys to Exercises 28 and 30. After any mistakes have been noted it is suggested that the exercises be taken down from dictation several times at increasing rates of speed. This Lesson deals with the aspirate and the halving principle, as it is called, on which there are exercises for the student to copy and transcribe.

KEY TO EXERCISE 28

KEY TO EXERCISE 30

Aspirate. It will be remembered that in Lesson 2 (Volume 5, page 550) the use of the two stroke forms of *h* was discussed. The rule then explained was to the effect that before *k* or *g*, or when standing alone, *h* was written downwards, thus, 〰 Hogg, 〰 Haig, 〰 he, 〰 high, and that generally the upward form was most convenient for joining to other consonants, thus, 〰 hope, 〰 head, 〰 hedge, 〰 heavy, 〰 history, 〰 hotel, 〰 half, 〰 hence, 〰 houses.

Note specially the following examples of stroke *h* being used medially : 〰 behave, 〰 adhere, 〰 overhaul, 〰 mahogany. Before the strokes 〰 〰 〰, however, the downward *h* is reduced to a tick, thus, 〰 home, 〰 whom, 〰 Hamilton, 〰 hail, 〰 health, 〰 help, 〰 holding, 〰 holiday, 〰 hair, 〰 here, 〰 herself, 〰 horse.

In some cases the use of the stroke *h* medially would give an awkward or lengthy outline, and here the *h* is represented by a light dot placed before the vowel, thus, 〰 manhood, 〰 neighbourhood, 〰 likelihood, 〰 leasehold, 〰 perhaps.

Halving Principle. We come now to a most important principle, a knowledge of which will enable the learner greatly to increase his vocabulary. The following rules should be noted most carefully :—

In one-syllable words, a *light* stroke is halved to indicate, without actually writing, a following *t*, thus, 〰 fay, 〰 fate, 〰 lay, 〰 late, 〰 fie, 〰 fight, 〰 lie, 〰 light, 〰 may, 〰 mate, 〰 knee, 〰 neat, 〰 no, 〰 note, 〰 notes. In the word *notes* it will be seen that the circle *s* is, as usual, read last at the end of the word.

Similarly, in one-syllable words a *heavy* stroke is halved for the addition of *d*, thus, 〰 die, 〰 died, 〰 guy, 〰 guide, 〰 love, 〰 loved, 〰 move, 〰 moved, 〰 charge, 〰 charged.

In words of two or more syllables, however, a stroke is halved to indicate the addition of either *t* or *d*, thus, ⌐ credit, ⎰ debit, ⌂ rabbit, ⌐ applied, ⌐ little, ⌐ noted, ⌐ visited.

Note ⌐ bit, ⌐ plied, one-syllable words where the strokes must be written in full. Compare them with ⎰ debit and ⌐ applied, two-syllable words.

ABBREVIATIONS

⌐ information, ⌐ satisfaction, ⌐ justification, ⌐ generalization, ⌐ whether, ⌐ importance-ant, ⌐ improve-d-ment, ⌐ impossible.

EXERCISE 31
WRITE IN SHORTHAND

1. Acting *on information* received, *two* officers visited *the* Hamilton Hotel *in* Haddow Road, *and* took many notes.
2. *It-is impossible to* say yet *whether* or not *the* change will-*be an* improvement.

EXERCISE 32
COPY AND TRANSCRIBE

1. [shorthand outlines]

2. [shorthand outlines]

We will now consider the further application of this very useful principle. When a stroke has a finally-joined diphthong, or a final hook, it may be halved for *t* or *d*, thus, ⌐ bout *or* bowed, ⌐ about, ⌐ doubt, ⌐ proud; ⌐ issued, ⌐ mute, ⌐ feud; ⌐ paint *or* pained; ⌐ bent *or* bend; ⌐ tent *or* tend; ⌐ repent, ⌐ ripened; ⌐ meant *or* mend, ⌐ amounts, ⌐ amends; ⌐ rent *or* rend, ⌐ rents *or* rends.

Half-length *h*, when not joined to another stroke, is always written upwards, thus, ⟋ height, ⟍ heights, ⌒ hound, ⌒ hounds.

Where the half-length upward *r* would stand alone, or with only a final *s* added, it is preferable to write the *r* and the *t* in full, as in ⟋ right, ⟋ rights. Half-length *r* ⟋ might be misread for *and* or *should*.

The strokes *m* and *n* are halved and thickened to indicate a following *d*, thus, ⌒ made, ⌒ mud, ⟍ ashamed, ⌒ modern, ⌒ middle; ⌣ end, ⌣ need, ⌣ sound, ⌣ intends, ⟍ undoubtedly.

Downward *l* and downward *r* are halved and thickened to indicate a following *d*, thus, ⟊ old, ⟍ bowled, ⟍ filled, ⟊ world; ⟍ bored, ⟍ heard, ⟍ hardly, ⟍ wired, ⟍ standard.

When a vowel comes between *l-d* or *r-d*, the full strokes are written, thus, ⌒ card, but ⌒ carried; ⌒ marred, but ⌒ married.

Final *lt* is expressed by ⌒ , and final *rt* is usually expressed by ⟋ , thus, ⟍ belt, ⟍ start.

Unless the junction is quite clear, strokes of unequal length should not be joined. For instance, in the outline for *effect* half-length *k* would not be clear: the outline ⟍ must therefore be used. To show the difference in size, disjoin half-length *t* or *d* when they follow strokes *t* or *d*, thus, ⟍ credited, ⟍ treated, ⟍ dictated.

ABBREVIATIONS

⌒ quite, — could; ⌒ accord-ing (to), ⌣ cared; ⌒ guard, ⌣ great; ⌒ called, ⌣ equalled, cold; ⌣ gold; ⟨ that, ⟨ without; ⟋ wished.

EXERCISE 33

COPY AND TRANSCRIBE

1. [shorthand symbols]

[shorthand symbols]

2. [shorthand symbols]

[shorthand symbols]

3. [shorthand symbols]

(The Keys to the Exercises in this Lesson are given in Lesson 10.)

LESSON 10

Doubling Principle and the Prefixes

HAVING checked his attempts at the exercises given in Lesson 9 with the following keys, and restudied any of the rules which errors may show have not been sufficiently grasped, the student may now proceed to the consideration of what is known as the Doubling Principle.

KEY TO EXERCISE 31

1. [shorthand symbols]

[shorthand symbols]

2. [shorthand symbols]

KEY TO EXERCISE 32

1. There is no justification for the action of Mr. Hawkins, whose charges are founded on mere generalization.
2. The importance of the occasion is not lost sight of by the shop-keepers in the neighbourhood.

KEY TO EXERCISE 33

1. According to the evidence of the guard of the train, the packets were intact when handed over at the end of the trip.
2. As indicated in the report, there is great need for vigilance on the part of the staff in the Accounts Department.
3. It has been stated that the cost of the machine, over a thousand pounds, was hardly justified by the results.

Doubling Principle. Curved strokes may be doubled in length to indicate the addition of the syllable *tr*, *dr*, *THr*, and in common words—*ture*; thus, ⌣ knee, ⌣ neater, ⌣ enter; ⌣ fie, ⌣ fighter, ⌣ father, ⌣ fodder, ⌣ feature; ⌣ nigh, ⌣ nitre, neither; ⌣ nature, ⌣ natural, ⌣ central; ⌣ folder.

Note that stroke *l*, standing alone, is doubled for *tr* only; thus, ⌣ letter, ⌣ letters, ⌣ alter; but ⌣ leader, ⌣ leaders, ⌣ leather.

A straight stroke may be doubled in length if it follows another consonant, or circle *s*, or has a final hook or joined diphthong; thus, ⌣ cater, but ⌣ skater, ⌣ educator; ⌣ potter, but ⌣ captor, ⌣ spider; ⌣ water, but ⌣ wonder, ⌣ operator; ⌣ daughter, but ⌣ tutor, ⌣ doubter, ⌣ imitator.

⌣ *mp*, *mb* may be doubled for the addition of *-er*, and ⌣ *ng* for *-kr*, *-gr*; thus, ⌣ jump, ⌣ jumper, ⌣ tamper; ⌣ long, ⌣ longer, ⌣ Ingersoll.

The hooked form ⌒ is used for *mpr*, *mbr*, when immediately following an upstroke or *k*; in all other cases the double-length form is used; thus, ⌒ lumber, ⌒ hamper, ⌒ cumbersome, but ⌐ damper.

The double-length form ⌣ is used for *ng-kr*, *ng-gr* initially and when following a circle or an upstroke; in all other cases the hooked form is written; thus, ⌣ anger, anchor, ⌐ anchorage, ⌣ sinker, ⌒ rancour, ⌒ linger, but ⌐ bunker. ⌐ drinker, ⌣ canker.

<h2 style="text-align:center">EXERCISE 34</h2>

COPY AND TRANSCRIBE

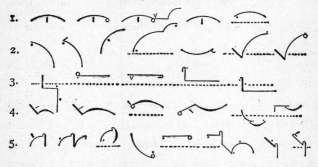

When the present tense of a verb is written with either a double-length character or a hooked form, the past tense is written with the halving principle; thus, ⟍ ponder, ⟍ pondered; ⟍ counter, ⟍ countered; ⟋ hinder, ⟋ hindered; ⌒ matter, ⌒ mattered; ⌒ linger, ⌒ lingered; ⌒ slumber, ⌒ slumbered.

The light sound of *thr* is represented by the hooked form; thus, ⟍ Arthur, ⟍ panther.

The doubling principle is not employed when a vowel follows final *tr*, *dr*, etc.; thus, ⊂ flatter, but ⊂ flattery; ⌐ anger, but ⌐ angry; ⟋ winter, but ⟋ wintry.

All double-length downstrokes are written through the line. Double-length horizontals are written above the line for the first position, and on the line for the second and third positions. Double-length upstrokes are written in accordance with the usual rules of position writing—above, on, or through the line.

The doubling principle can be usefully employed in phraseography for the indication of the words *their*, *there*, *other*, and *dear*, as follows:—

⌐ in their opinion, ⌐ in other cases, ⌐ I know there is, ⌐ for some other reason, ＼ upon their, ⌐ my dear madam, (I think there is, ⌐ my dear sir.

Note the phrases: ⌐ had not, do not; ⌐ did not.

ABBREVIATIONS

⌐ cannot; ⌐ gentleman, ⌐ gentlemen; ⌐ particular, ＼ opportunity; ⌐ child; ⌐ build-ing; ⌐ told; ⌐ tried, ⌐ trade, toward, ⌐ towards; ⌐ hand, ⌐ under; ⌐ chaired, ⌐ cheered; ⌐ sent; ⌐ third, ⌐ short; ⌐ spirit; ⌐ yard, ⌐ word; ⟋ rather, writer; ⟋ wonderful-ly;) therefore; ⌐ school, ⌐ schooled.

EXERCISE 35

WRITE IN SHORTHAND

1. I-*think-there-is* a *great*-deal *of-truth* *in-the* statement made, *and-we* should, *therefore*, look *very-care*fully into-*the* matter, *and* see *whether* *it-is* possible *to* remedy-*the* present state-*of* affairs.

2. I-know-*there-is a* list *of* figures *on hand, but* I-*do*-not-*think that-we-can* rely upon-*their* accuracy.

3. *The* crowd *in-the school yard cheered with spirit, and* gave-*the writer a wonderful* reception.

Prefixes. We will now discuss the manner in which several frequently-occurring prefixes may be rapidly and legibly expressed in Pitman's Shorthand.

Initial *con-, com-,* is represented by a light dot; thus, ∨ compel, ↘ compelled, ◡ commend, ◡ commence, ↗ control, ⌐ controlled, ⌐ connect, ⌐ connexion.

You will see that in words like *commend, commence,* the stroke *m* is not written, because the *m* is actually contained in the prefix *com* and there is no need to repeat it. In the same way the stroke *n* is not written in such words as *connect, connexion.*

Note ⌐ commission, ⌐ commissioner, where the use of the fuller form gives a more facile outline.

Medial *con-, com-, cog-,* in a word or in a phrase may be represented by disjoining the form immediately following the *con-,* etc.; thus, ↘ I am compelled, ↘ in compliance; ↘ becoming, ⌐ incompetent, ↗ recognize, ↗ circumference.

Accom- is represented by *k,* joined or disjoined; thus, ⌐ accommodation, ⌐ accomplish.

Intro- is expressed by the double-length ◡ *ntr*; thus, ⌐ introduce, ⌐ introducing.

Magna-, etc., is expressed by disjoined *m,* as in ⌐ magnify, ⌐ magnitude, ⌐ magnanimous.

Trans- may be contracted by omitting the *n*; thus, ⌐ transfer, ⌐ transmit, ⌐ transgression; but sometimes the full outline **is** preferable, as in ⌐ transit, ⌐ transaction.

Self- may be represented by a disjoined circle *s*, written in the second vowel-place; thus, 🖉 self-reliance.

Self-con- is expressed by a disjoined circle *s*, written in the place of the *con-* dot; thus, 🖉 self-control.

In- before ⎮ *str*, ⌐ *skr*, ⌐ *h* is expressed by a small hook written in the same direction as the circle; thus, 🖉 instrument, 🖉 inscriber, 🖉 inhabit. This small hook is, however, never used in negative words. Note 🖉 hospitable, 🖉 inhospitable.

The prefixes *il-*, *im-*, *in-*, *un-*, *ir-*, are represented generally by repeating the *l*, *m*, *n*, or *r*, as in ⌐ legal, ⌐ illegal, 🖉 mortal, ⌐ immortal; ⌐ necessary, ⌐ unnecessary; ⌐ redeemable, ⌐ irredeemable.

The prefixes *il-* and *ir-* may, however, be represented by writing the initial *r* or *l* downwards, where the rules permit of this being done; thus, ⌐ resolute, ⌐ irresolute, ⌐ limitable, ⌐ illimitable.

EXERCISE 36
Copy and Transcribe

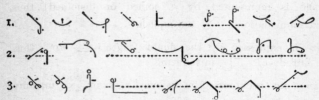

(The Keys to the Exercises in this Lesson are given in our next Lesson.)

LESSON 11

Word-endings and Diphones

BELOW will be found the Keys to Exercises 34, 35, and 36. Before proceeding with the study we suggest that Exercise 35 should be dictated a number of times, until it can be written at a speed of at least 60 words a minute with ease and accuracy. The student is reminded not to grasp the pen too tightly or to press too heavily on the paper.

KEY TO EXERCISE 34

1. motor, motors, motor-cycle, mutter (mother), matter.
2. ardour, harder, later, latterly, neuter, builder, builders.
3. dictator, scatter, kinder, tractor, director.
4. bump, bumper, sombre, hunger, finger conquer.
5. older, elderly, lather, features, canters, caterpillar, better, plotter.

KEY TO EXERCISE 35

Key to Exercise 36

1. competent, common, compensate, compensation, conductor, constant, constable, incomplete, recognized.
2. reconsider, commissioner, accomplice, introducing, magnificence, translated, transmission.
3. self-possession, self-possessed, self-controlled, instructor, inhale, inhabitants, inhabited, inherent.

Suffixes and Word-Endings. The stroke ⌣ *ng* is usually employed for the termination *-ing*; but in cases where the stroke would be awkward to write the sound *-ing* may be represented by a light dot, thus, ⟋ requesting, ⌐ meeting, ⌐ covering, ⟋ serving, ⌐ coughing, ⟋ winning, ⌐ getting, ⟨ assuring, ⌐ teaching, ⟍ breeding, ⌐ muttering. Usually, the dot *-ing* is used after a light downstroke.

Where *-ing* is represented by a dot the plural *-ings* is represented by a light dash, thus, ⌐ meeting, ⌐ meetings; ⟋ morning, ⟋ mornings.

The suffix *-mental-ly-ity* is expressed by a disjoined ⌐ *mnt*, thus, ⟋ experimental, ⟋ sentimental-ly-ity.

The endings *-fulness*, *-lessness*, are expressed by a disjoined ⟍ *fs* and ⌐ *ls* respectively, thus, ⟍ thoughtfulness, ⟍ thoughtlessness.

The suffix *-ship* is represented by ⟋ *sh*, joined or disjoined, as convenient, thus, ⟋ friendship, ⌐ citizenship, ⟍ hardship.

The endings *-ality*, *-ility*, *-arity*, *-ority*, are expressed by disjoining the stroke which comes before the ending, thus, ⟍ for(m)ality, ⟍ lia(b)ility, ⟋ regu(l)arity, ⟋ ma(j)ority, ⟍ mi(n)ority.

The endings *-logical-ly* are expressed by a disjoined / *j*, thus, ⟋ psychological-ly.

WORD-ENDINGS AND DIPHONES

The suffix -ly is expressed by a joined or disjoined l, and in some cases by the hooked form, thus, ⌣ fairly, ⌣ instantly, ⌐ deeply, ⌐ actively, ⌐ sensitively.

The endings -ward, -wart; -yard are expressed by a half-sized w and y respectively, thus, ⌐ backward, ⌐ forward, ⌐ stalwart; ⌐ backyard, ⌐ brickyard.

EXERCISE 37
COPY AND TRANSCRIBE

1.

2.

3.

4.

EXERCISE 38
WRITE IN SHORTHAND

1. paying, hiring, pouncing, folding, promoting, searching.
2. casting, castings, brutality, suitability, legibility, possibility.
3. consignment, resentment, horsemanship, lawfulness, lawlessness.

Diphones. In some words we have two consecutive vowels, pronounced separately. For example, in the word *idea* it will be noted that the ē and the ă are both clearly sounded. Such vowels are represented by the angular signs ᴠ and ᴧ, which are termed *Diphones*.

The first sign ↗ represents a dot vowel immediately followed by another vowel—long or short, and the second ↱ represents a dash vowel similarly followed by another vowel. The signs are written in the place of the *first* vowel of the combination. Study the following words.

EXERCISE 39

sahib   payable   saying   surveyor   gaiety   player   theory   ideal

theatre   carrying   piano   previous   experience   serious   seriously

various   senior   drawing   co-operation   growing   lowest   lower

brewer   brewery   cruelty   jewels   ruinous   Lewis.

The consecutive vowels in some words like *question*, although not sounded separately, are, for convenience, represented by the sign ↗ , thus, question, union, suggestion, million.

The art of phrasing, which plays an important part in speed writing, will be dealt with fully in a future Lesson, but in the meantime the reader should make himself thoroughly conversant with the following frequently occurring phrases.

dear sir   I believe   at all costs

yours truly   I will tell you   in our

yours faithfully   I am surprised   in our opinion

yours obediently   by all means   in my opinion

ABBREVIATIONS

⌐ anything, ⌣ nothing, ⌢ something, ⌐ everything, ⌐ selfish-ness, ⌐ inscribe-d, ⌐ inscription, ⌐ instruction.

⌐ instructive.

EXERCISE 40

COPY AND TRANSCRIBE

1. [shorthand outlines]

2. [shorthand outlines]

3. [shorthand outlines]

EXERCISE 41

WRITE IN SHORTHAND

1. If-*you-are* agreeable I-*shall call* at-*your* office *on*-Friday at four if-*that-is* convenient.

2. *The* theory advanced by-*the* Italian historian *is very* ingenious.

3. *On-the instructions of-the* commissioner *the inscription on-the* wall *was* removed, *as-it-was* considered unsuitable.

(The Keys to the Exercises contained in this Lesson are given in Lesson 12.)

LESSON 12

Advanced Phrasing and Figures

BELOW will be found the Keys to the Exercises set in the preceding Lesson. As has been suggested the Exercises should be dictated several times in order to increase facility in pen manipulation. The explanation of the actual theory of the subject is completed in the course of this Lesson, while, in addition to this, the student will note that advanced methods of Phrasing are also introduced.

KEY TO EXERCISE 37

1. Only the skill of the driver in instantly applying his brakes prevented what might have been a fatality.

2. Mr. Jones regretted his inability to be present at the regimental dinner on Monday.

3. The hopelessness of the position was fully recognized by the majority of those present at the meeting, which was under the chairmanship of Colonel Johnson.

4. The scaffolding fell on to the pavement, and several men who happened to be passing narrowly escaped injury.

KEY TO EXERCISE 38

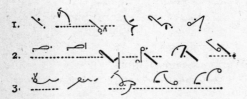

KEY TO EXERCISE 40

1. The man answered the various questions of Mr. Lewis without any hesitation.

2. You should by all means visit the British Museum when you are in London next month.

3. We visited the Gaiety Theatre last evening, and spent an agreeable hour or two.

KEY TO EXERCISE 41

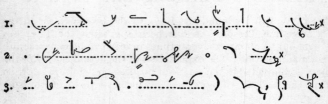

ADVANCED PHRASING AND FIGURES

Abbreviated W. It will be remembered that an initial semicircle attached to ⎯ ⎯ ⌢ ⟍ ⟋ represents *w*, as in ⎯ walk, ⎯ wag, ⤳ womanly, ⟋ war, ⤳ worry. In a small group of words *medial w* may also be represented by a small semicircle, the left half of a circle representing *w* followed by a dot vowel, and the right half of a circle representing *w* followed by a dash vowel. The study of the following examples will make this clear : ⤳ memoir, ⤳ reservoir, ⟍ twelve, ⟍ twenty, ⤳ frequent, ⤳ subsequent, ⤳ herewith, ⤳ sandwich, ⤳ Brunswick, ⤳ Cornwall, ⤳ breakwater, ⤳ misquoted, ⤳ guesswork, ⤳ gasworks, ⟍ driftwood. It will be seen that the semicircle is written in the position of the vowel following the *w*. Note the following special forms :— ⤳ quality, ⤳ qualify, ⤳ qualification, ⤳ somewhat.

Negative Words. It is very important that positive and negative words should be clearly distinguished. In some cases this is easily done simply by applying the ordinary rules for the writing of *r* or *l*. Thus we have ⤳ resolute but ⤳ irresolute, ⤳ relevant, but ⤳ irrelevant. In cases where the distinction cannot be made in this way the initial consonant is repeated, thus, ⤳ legal, ⤳ illegal; ⤳ necessary, ⤳ unnecessary; ⤳ moderate, ⤳ immoderate; ⤳ noticed, ⤳ unnoticed; ⤳ known, ⤳ unknown; ⤳ material, ⤳ immaterial.

ABBREVIATIONS

⟍ probable-ly-ility, ⤳ expect-ed, ⟩ suspect-ed, ⤳ inspect-ed-ion, ⎯ together, ⎯ altogether, ⤳ yesterday, ⤳ investigation, ⤳ January, ⤳ February, ⤳ knowledge, ⤳ acknowledge.

EXERCISE 42

COPY AND TRANSCRIBE

1. [shorthand outlines]

2. [shorthand outlines]

3. [shorthand outlines]

EXERCISE 43

WRITE IN SHORTHAND

1. *Whether-the* action *of-the* committee *was* legal or illegal *is expected to-be* fully discussed at-*the investigation in January.*
2. *It-is*-unnecessary *for* us *to* state *that-the* material, *which-was* made by Cornwallis *and* Hardwick, *is of-the* best quality.

Figures. The figures *one* to *seven*, and the figure *nine* are written in shorthand; thus, [shorthand outlines] ×
All other numbers, except round numbers, are usually represented by the ordinary Arabic numerals. *Hundred* is represented by ⌣ , *thousand* by (or (and *million* by ⌢ , and thus we have ⌣ for 400, 4(for 4,000, ⌣ for 400,000; 5 for £500, 5 for £500,000.

Advanced Phrasing. The reader is already acquainted with the general principles of phrasing, by which the outlines for certain groups of words may be joined, thus saving time and increasing the speed of writing. In more advanced writing this principle is considerably extended, and in this Lesson we will consider its further development. We will first of all deal with the manner in which Circles, Loops, and Hooks play a part in phrasing.

1. The small circle, besides being used for *as, has, is, his,* in the ordinary way, may be used to represent *us,* as in ⌣ of us, ⌣ to us, ⌣ from us, ⌣ let us. (Note ⌣ please let us know.)

2. The initial large circle may be used to represent :—

(*a*) *as we,* as in ⌣ as we have, ⌣ as we have said, ⌣ as we think.

(*b*) *as* and *w,* as in ⌣ as well as, ⌣ as well as our, ⌣ as well as your, ⌣ as will be seen.

(*c*) *as* and *s,* as in ⌣ as soon as, ⌣ as soon as they were, ⌣ as soon as we have. (Note also ⌣ as soon as convenient, ⌣ as soon as possible.)

3. The medial and final large circle may be used to represent the following :—

(*a*) *is* and *s,* as in ⌣ it is said, ⌣ it is suggested, ⌣ it is certain.

(*b*) *his* and *s,* as in ⌣ for his sake, ⌣ at his side.

(*c*) *s* and *s,* as in ⌣ in this city.

(*d*) *s* and *has,* as in ⌣ this has been.

The above lists are, of course, not exhaustive, and other phrases may be constructed on the lines suggested. Such phrases should be practised many times until they can be written with ease and rapidity.

EXERCISE 44
COPY AND TRANSCRIBE

1.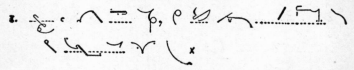

2. [shorthand symbols]

3. [shorthand symbols]

(The Keys to the Exercises contained in this Lesson are given in our next and final Lesson.)

LESSON 13

Final Lesson

AFTER comparing his attempts with the Keys to Exercises 42, 43, and 44 given below, the student should carefully study the further instruction given in the art of phrasing. He will no doubt have realized the speed-producing possibilities of its application, and will seek to extend his knowledge in every possible way.

KEY TO EXERCISE 42

1. It is expected that the fund which was opened yesterday will reach a hundred pounds, probably more, by the end of January.

2. I shall probably be in town on the second of February, by which time I have no doubt your investigation will be completed. I leave Cornwall at the beginning of the last week in January.

3. I have to acknowledge that I am somewhat puzzled by the Brunswick case. Have you any definite knowledge of the movements of the suspected men who were seen together shortly after the crime was discovered?

KEY TO EXERCISE 43

1. [shorthand symbols]

[shorthand symbols]

2. [shorthand outlines]

[shorthand outlines] x

KEY TO EXERCISE 44

1. Please let us know when you will be again in this city, as we think that we shall require a large quantity of your special fabric in the early future.
2. It is said that the men left the premises by the skylight. It is certain that they did not leave by the door.
3. It is suggested to us that this is a suitable time to launch such a scheme, and we shall do so as soon as convenient.

Advanced Phrasing. In Lesson 12 (page 531) it was shown how the circles are employed in phrasing. We will now consider how the loops and hooks may also be used to advantage in phrasing.

The loop *st*, for instance, is used for *first*, as in [shorthand] at first, [shorthand] for the first time, [shorthand] in the first place. The *nst* loop is used for *next*, as in [shorthand] Monday next, [shorthand] Wednesday next.

The *r* and *l* hooks are employed to represent a few miscellaneous words, as, for example, in [shorthand] in our, [shorthand] in our opinion, [shorthand] it appears, [shorthand] it appears that, [shorthand] at all, [shorthand] by all, [shorthand] by all means, [shorthand] it is only necessary, [shorthand] it can only be, [shorthand] it may only be.

The *n* hook may be used for *than*, *own*, *been*, as in

(*a*) [shorthand] better than, [shorthand] older than, [shorthand] more than, [shorthand] rather than, [shorthand] smaller than.

(*b*) [shorthand] your own, [shorthand] our own, [shorthand] their own.

(*c*) [shorthand] I have been, [shorthand] we have been, [shorthand] I had been, [shorthand] we had been, [shorthand] they had been.

(537)

The *v* hook may similarly be used for a number of miscellaneous words. Note how it is employed in the following phrases:—

⌐ ought to have been, ⌐ who have, ⌐ who have been, ⌐ which have, ⌐ which have been (note, however, ⌐ we have, ⌐ can have); ⌐ out of, ⌐ rate of, ⌐ state of affairs, ⌐ state of things, ⌐ get rid of; ⌐ ⌐ Monday afternoon, ⌐ Monday evening; ⌐ at all events, ⌐ into effect.

The Halving Principle can be adapted to indicate several words. Bearing in mind the rule that by halving a stroke we add *t* or *d*, there will be little or no difficulty in comprehending the following phrases.

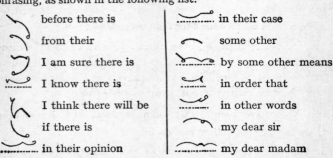

if it		you were not	
if it would be		you are not	
if it is not		I would be	
able to make		we would be	
you will be able to		few words	
you will not		at some time	
you cannot		at the same time	

The Doubling Principle may also be usefully employed in phrasing, as shown in the following list.

before there is	in their case	
from their	some other	
I am sure there is	by some other means	
I know there is	in order that	
I think there will be	in other words	
if there is	my dear sir	
in their opinion	my dear madam	

FINAL LESSON

Other phrases may be formed by the omission of certain consonants, syllables, or words. The examples which follow should be carefully studied and practised.

Outline	Phrase	Outline	Phrase
⌁	I have received	⌁	I hope
⌁	we have received	⌁	we have concluded
⌁	in reply	⌁	in conclusion
⌁	last week	⌁	into consideration
⌁	next week	⌁	shall be taken into consideration
⌁	last month	⌁	as a rule
⌁	next month	⌁	in a few days
⌁	you must be	⌁	about the matter
⌁	as far as possible	⌁	in reference to
⌁	as soon as possible	⌁	with reference to

In the space at our disposal it has been possible to touch only very lightly on advanced phrasing, but the foregoing examples will show how the judicious use of phrasing must, as a matter of course, increase speed in writing. The student should seek to extend his knowledge of this aspect of the system, but he should remember that phrasing, like most other things, can be overdone. It should be borne in mind that unless a phrase is speedy, easily written, and easily read, it had better be avoided. A "classic" example of a phrase which does not fulfil all these conditions is

⌁ × It is certainly speedy and easily written, but would scarcely convey the assertion *I can cook cake.*

It is suggested that a good method of practising these phrases is to take them in groups of five or six, copying them carefully on the top line of the notebook. On the next line write them again, slightly faster if possible, and so on until each of them can be written smoothly and rapidly. A light touch in writing should be cultivated. The *Phrase Drill Notebook* is very convenient for practice of this nature.

This Lesson concludes our Course in Pitman's Shorthand

LESSON 18

Vowel Changes in Verbs (1)

A CONSIDERABLE number of verbs alter the vowel of their stem whenever the stem bears the stress—that is, in the third person plural, and all the singular persons of the imperative, present indicative, and present subjunctive. The terminations as well as the stem of all other tenses are, as a rule, perfectly regular. All verbs the stem vowels of which undergo changes may be grouped as follows :

Verbs of the first and second conjugations with *e* in their stem expand this vowel into *ie* in the persons and tenses above-mentioned, e.g. *sembrar*, to sow ; *defender*, to defend.

PRESENT INDICATIVE.

siembro	*sembramos*	*defiendo*	*defendemos*
siembras	*sembráis*	*defiendes*	*defendéis*
siembra	*siembran*	*defiende*	*defienden*

IMPERATIVE.

siembra	*sembremos*	*defiende*	*defendamos*
siembre Vd.	*sembrad*	*defienda Vd.*	*defended*
siembre	*siembren*	*defienda*	*defiendan*

PRESENT SUBJUNCTIVE.

siembre	*sembremos*	*defienda*	*defendamos*
siembres	*sembréis*	*defiendas*	*defendáis*
siembre	*siembren*	*defienda*	*defiendan*

Verbs conjugated like *sembrar* and *defender* :

to guess	*acertar*	to ascend	*ascender*
to augment	*acrecentar*	to listen	*atender*
to encourage	*alentar*	to descend	*descender*
to press	*apretar*	to light	*encender*
to rent	*arrendar*	to understand	*entender*
to traverse	*atravesar*	to extend	*extenderse*
to warm	*calentar*	to stink	*heder*
to shut	*cerrar*	to split	*hender*

to begin	*comenzar*	to lose	*perder*
to recommend	*recomendar*	to transcend	*transcender*
to awake	*despertar*	to pour	*verter*
to correct	*enmendar*	to snow	*nevar*
to begin	*empezar*	to think	*pensar*
to bury	*enterrar*	to break	*quebrar*
to govern	*gobernar*	to confess	*confesar*
to freeze	*helar*	to water	*regar*
to manifest	*manifestar*	to sit down	*sentarse*
to deny	*negar*	to tremble	*temblar*

VOCABULARY.

the mass	*la misa*	a lamp	*una lámpara*
a plantation	*una plantación*	simple	*sencillo*
a country	*un país*	the north	*el norte*
the mountain range	*la sierra*	a valley	*un valle*
		a river	*un río*
to come near	*acercarse*	absolutely	*en absoluto*
at such a	*a tan*	such a thing	*semejante cosa*

Exercise I.

TRANSLATE INTO SPANISH : 1. Guess who is there. 2. Sit down on that armchair. 3. Do you want us to shut that door ? 4. At what time does the Mass begin ? 5. At ten o'clock sharp. 6. Let us warm ourselves. 7. They deny (their) having sold it at such a low price. 8. Perhaps it will freeze tomorrow. 9. How do they water their plantations ? 10. Allow me to sit down. I am very tired. 11. Come near the fire and warm yourself. 12. I confess I do not understand it. 13. It is very simple. The branches of the company extend all over (trs. *por todo*) the country. 14. Why do they not light the lamps ? 15. I do not know. they always light them at seven o'clock. 16. The railway traverses the mountain range, and descends into the (*al*) valley. 17. Awake me at six o'clock sharp. 18. I recommend you not to forget it. 19. Correct that letter. 20. Does it often snow in the north of Spain ? 21. I am sure that if he loses he will not pay. 22. Do not break it. 23. Pour the water slowly. 24. Let us sit down near the river. 25. I thought he would go.

Verbs of the first and second conjugations with *o* in their stem change that vowel into *ue* in the persons and tenses already mentioned, e.g. *encontrar*, to find ; *volver*, to return.

Present Indicative.

encuentro	encontramos	vuelvo	volvemos
encuentras	encontráis	vuelves	volvéis
encuentra	encuentran	vuelve	vuelven

Imperative.

encuentra	encontremos	vuelve	volvamos
encuentre Vd.	encontrad	vuelva Vd.	volved
encuentre	encuentren	vuelva	vuelvan

Present Subjunctive.

encuentre	encontremos	vuelva	volvamos
encuentres	encontréis	vuelvas	volváis
encuentre	encuentren	vuelva	vuelvan

Verbs conjugated like *encontrar* and *volver* include :

to agree	acordar	to renew	renovar
to remember	acordarse	to beg	rogar
to go to bed	acostarse	to loose	soltar
to breakfast	almorzar	to sound	sonar
to sharpen	amolar	to dream	soñar
to bet	apostar	to thunder	tronar
to approve	aprobar	to fly	volar
to be ashamed	avergonzarse	to cook	cocer
to hang up	colgar	to give back	devolver
to check	comprobar	to ache	doler
to console	consolar	to envelope	envolver
to count	contar	to rain	llover
to cost	costar	to grind	moler
to discount	descontar	to bite	morder
to exert oneself	esforzarse	to move	mover
to play	jugar	to smell	oler
to show	mostrar	to promote	promover
to populate	poblar	to resolve	resolver
to prove	probar	to be in the habit of	soler
to remember	recordar	to absolve	absolver

Note.—*Oler* takes an *h* whenever the *o* is expanded into *ue*.— *huelen,* they smell.

Vocabulary.

a bag	una maleta	the ally	el aliado
the head	la cabeza	a dollar	un duro
a wise man	un sabio	a fool	un tonto

VOWEL CHANGES IN VERBS (1)

to trot	*trotar*	to gallop	*galopar*
to confirm	*confirmar*	a dog	*un perro*
any more	*ya no*	the plain	*la llanura*
tennis	*tennis*	to run	*correr*

EXERCISE II.

TRANSLATE INTO SPANISH : 1. Do you remember his address ?
2. No ; I have forgotten it. 3. Do you (plural) generally go to
bed very early ? 4. We go to bed between 11 and 12 o'clock.
5. At what time do you have your breakfast ? 6. As soon as
we get up. 7. Do you (pl.) approve (of) his conduct ? 8. We
have not had any news from them yet. 9. How much does that
bag cost you ? 10. It only cost me 20 pesetas. 11. Does she
play (trs. *al*) tennis ? 12. Yes ; I think she plays very well.
13. How much do they discount ? 14. They discount 3 pesetas
in every 5 dollars. 15. Why do you not renew your ticket ?
16. It is not necessary. I shall be very busy next month. 17.
It does not thunder any more. Is it still raining ? 18. No ;
it does not rain now. 19. I beg you to wire to him the result at
once. 20. Do not come back without confirming the news.
21. Show them the receipts. 22. Fools dream what they want,
and wise men what they can (*pueden*). 23. I bet anything
(*cualquier cosa*) that (*a que*) I guess what he is doing now. 24.
They are in the habit of calling on us every Sunday.

KEY TO EXERCISE IN LESSON 17.

1. ¿ Sabe Vd. su nombre ? 2. Lo marqué en la lista. 3. No
toque Vd. ninguno de esos cuadros. 4. Que busquen sus papeles.
5. Se lo expliqué dos veces. 6. No creo que las tropas venzan
a los rebeldes tan fácilmente como el gobierno espera. 7. Lo ha
hecho sencillamente para que yo se lo agradezca. 8. Obedezca Vd.
y traduzca esos documentos. 9. No reconozco su autoridad y, por
consiguiente, no obedezco sus órdenes. Castígueme Vd. si cree
que lo merezco. 10. No ; no tengo ningún derecho a juzgar su
conducta. Júzguela Vd. mismo. 11. Es muy probable que el
incendio se extinga antes de la media noche. 12. Tome Vd. un
tranvía y coja el tren expreso. 13. Protejámosla. 14. Estoy
seguro de que no corregirá sus ejercicios. 15. Exija Vd. que le
paguen un mes por adelantado. 16. No le autoricé a cancelar el
contrato. 17. Solemnicemos su cumpleaños. 18. No nos dis-
frazamos. 19. Atestigué su honradez. 20. Que averigüe su para-
dero. 21. Se escabulleron de las manos de la policía.

LESSON 19

Vowel Changes in Verbs (2)

VERBS of the third conjugation with *e* or *o* in the stem, besides expanding these vowels into *ie* or *ue* when the stress falls upon them, also change them into *i* or *u* in the first person plural of the imperative, first and second persons plural of the present subjunctive, and, in general, in all those persons in which the termination includes the diphthongs *ie* or *io*. Examples of this class of verb are : *dormir*, to sleep ; *sentir*, to feel, or to be sorry ; and below are set out the various tenses, singular and plural, of these two verbs.

PRESENT INDICATIVE.

siento	*sentimos*	*duermo*	*dormimos*
sientes	*sentís*	*duermes*	*dormís*
siente	*sienten*	*duerme*	*duermen*

IMPERFECT.

sentía	*sentíamos*	*dormía*	*dormíamos*
sentías	*sentíais*	*dormías*	*dormíais*
sentía	*sentían*	*dormía*	*dormían*

PAST DEFINITE.

sentí	*sentimos*	*dormí*	*dormimos*
sentiste	*sentisteis*	*dormiste*	*dormisteis*
sintió	*sintieron*	*durmió*	*durmieron*

FUTURE.

sentiré	*sentiremos*	*dormiré*	*dormiremos*
sentirás	*sentiréis*	*dormirás*	*dormiréis*
sentirá	*sentirán*	*dormirá*	*dormirán*

CONDITIONAL.

sentiría	*sentiríamos*	*dormiría*	*dormiríamos*
sentirías	*sentiríais*	*dormirías*	*dormiríais*
sentiría	*sentirían*	*dormiría*	*dormirían*

DOWAGER EMPRESS OF CHINA. Tzu - Hsi (1835–1908) entered the seraglio of the emperor Hsien Feng at the age of fifteen. On his death in 1861 her son came to the throne, but she seized the reins of government and henceforth until her death ruled China with conspicuous ability.

MODERN HISTORY 30

E V. A.

ALEXANDER I (1857–93). Son of Prince Alexander of Hesse, he was elected prince of Bulgaria in 1879, but was compelled to abdicate in 1886, and retired to Austria.

MODERN HISTORY 29

ABDUL HAMID II (1842–1918). He became sultan in 1876 on the deposition of his brother : his long reign was marked by territorial losses and pronounced misgovernment. In 1909 he was deposed by the Young Turks.

MODERN HISTORY 29

PRELUDE TO TRAGEDY. Accompanied by his wife, the Archduke Francis Ferdinand, heir to the imperial throne of Austria-Hungary, paid a visit to Serajevo, the chief town of Bosnia, on June 28, 1914. This photo shows the royal pair leaving the Town Hall to re-enter their carriage. Two or three minutes later, a Bosnian high-school student fired two shots, instantly killing both the archduke and his wife. MODERN HISTORY 31

Photo, Walter Tausch

A GERMAN ASSAULT. This German photograph shows steel-helmeted " field-greys "—or " Jerries," as the British " Tommy " called them— advancing across " No Man's Land " through tangled wire and beneath a rain of shells. MODERN HISTORY 32

Photo, Imperial War Museum

Plate 58   Volume VI

VOWEL CHANGES IN VERBS (2)

IMPERATIVE.

siente	sintamos	duerme	durmamos
sienta Vd	sentid	duerma Vd	dormid
sienta	sientan	duerma	duerman

PRESENT SUBJUNCTIVE.

sienta	sintamos	duerma	durmamos
sientas	sintáis	duermas	durmáis
sienta	sientan	duerma	duerman

IMPERFECT SUBJUNCTIVE.

sint-iera, -iese	durm-iera, -iese
sint-ieras, -ieses	durm-ieras, -ieses
sint-iera, -iese	durm-iera, -iese
sint-iéramos, -iésemos	durm-iéramos, -iésemos
sint-ierais, -ieseis	durm-ierais, -ieseis
sint-ieran, -iesen	durm-ieran, -iesen

PRESENT PARTICIPLE.

sintiendo	durmiendo

The more important verbs belonging to this class are as follow :

to adhere	adherirse	to wound	herir
to advise	advertir	to boil	hervir
to repent	arrepentirse	to infer	inferir
to concern	concernir	to invest	invertir
to lie	mentir	to convert	convertir
to die	morir	to become	convertirse
to prefer	preferir	to digest	digerir
to discern	discernir	to suggest	sugerir

to confer, to grant	conferir	to enjoy oneself	divertirse
to proffer, to utter	proferir	to go to sleep	dormirse
to refer, to allude	referirse	to scold, to censure	zaherir

VOCABULARY.

to kill	matar	to shoot	fusilar
to save	salvar	to remain	quedarse
to stay	permanecer	to preserve	conservar
to last	durar	the invasion	la invasión

bad luck	*mala suerte*	an invader	*un invasor*
the peasant	*el labriego*	a mayor	*un alcalde*
a brave man	*un valiente*	the honour	*el honor*
the sands	*la playa*	a draught	*una corriente*
the fame	*la fama*	the field	*el campo*
waste lands	*eriales*	a church	*una iglesia*
the barrack	*el cuartel*	the hospital	*el hospital*
national	*nacional*	by order of	*por orden de*
along	*por*	to close	*cerrar*

to become dark	*obscurecer*	the companion	*el compañero*
to transform	*transformarse*	really, truly	*verdaderamente*
a citizen	*un ciudadano*	with regard to	*respecto a*
a fellow-citizen	*un conciudadano*	I do not mind	*me es igual*
an enterprise	*una empresa*	bitterly	*ásperamente*
the movement	*el movimiento*	the negligence	*la negligencia*
the embankment	*el malecón*	to take a walk	*dar un paseo*
the conversation	*la conversación*		

EXERCISE I.

TRANSLATE INTO SPANISH : 1. That does not concern me. 2. They repented as soon as they read the consequences of their negligence. 3. Every citizen would become a soldier in case of an invasion. 4. Did you enjoy yourselves that evening ? 5. No ; we really had very bad luck. Hardly had we arrived at the gardens when it began to rain. 6. Is the water boiling ? 7. No ; it has not begun to boil yet. 8. The invaders killed or wounded many peasants who refused to give information with regard to the movements of the national army. 9. The mayor of the town was shot by order of the general. He died as a brave man. 10. The prisoner lied in order to save the life of his fellow-citizens. 11. The king granted him great honours. 12. They were sleeping when the news arrived. 13. Do you prefer to remain here, or to take a walk along the embankment ? 14. I do not mind. Just as you like (trs., whatever you prefer).

Some third conjugation verbs with an *e* in the stem do not expand that vowel into *ie*, but simply change it into *i* in certain tenses and persons. An example of such a verb is *pedir*, to ask for ; the conjugation of which will now be given

VOWEL CHANGES IN VERBS (2)

INDICATIVE MOOD.

Present		Imperfect	
pido	*pedimos*	*pedía*	*pedíamos*
pides	*pedís*	*pedías*	*pedíais*
pide	*piden*	*pedía*	*pedían*

Past Definite		Future	
pedí	*pedimos*	*pediré*	*pediremos*
pediste	*pedisteis*	*pedirás*	*pediréis*
pidió	*pidieron*	*pedirá*	*pedirán*

SUBJUNCTIVE MOOD.

Present		Imperfect		
pida		*pidiera*	or	*pidiese*
pidas		*pidieras*	,,	*pidieses*
pida		*pidiera*	,,	*pidiese*
pidamos		*pidiéramos*	,,	*pidiésemos*
pidáis		*pidierais*	,,	*pidieseis*
pidan		*pidieran*	,,	*pidiesen*

PRESENT PARTICIPLE : *pidiendo*.
PAST PARTICIPLE : *pedido*.

Conjugated like *pedir* are :

to gird	*ceñir*	to compete	*competir*
to conceive	*concebir*	to correct	*corregir*
to melt	*derretir*	to dismiss	*despedir*
to select	*elegir*	to forward	*expedir*
to fry	*freir*	to groan	*gemir*
to prevent	*impedir*	to measure	*medir*
to persecute	*perseguir*	to continue	*proseguir*
to rule	*regir*	to laugh	*reirse*
to surrender	*rendirse*	to quarrel	*reñir*
to repeat	*repetir*	to follow	*seguir*
to smile	*sonreirse*	to dye	*teñir*
	to bid farewell	*despedirse*	
	to be of use, to serve	*servir*	
	to dress oneself	*vestirse*	

Verbs in the above classes may also be subjected to the euphonic or customary changes. Thus, for instance, the present tense of *regir*, to rule, is *rijo*, and not *rigo*; and the present participle of *ceñir*, to gird, is *ciñendo*, instead of *ciñiendo*. This last peculiarity of omitting the vowel *i*, into which the original *e* of the stem is changed, whenever it occurs in front of the diphthongs *ie, io*, is also followed by the verb *reir*, to laugh, and its derivative *sonreir*, to smile; *riendo, sonriendo, rieron, sonrieron*, must therefore be used instead of *riiendo, sonriiendo, riió, sonriió*.

Some verbs ending in *quirir*, as *adquirir*, to acquire, and *inquirir*, to inquire, expand the radical vowel *i* into *ie* when the accent falls upon it, but are otherwise regular : *adquiero*, I acquire; *inquiera Vd.*, inquire.

Vocabulary.

to cut	*cortar*	the surname	*el apellido*
to break out	*estallar*	a teacher	*un profesor*
to relate	*contar*	the fortress	*la fortaleza*
the hair	*el cabello*	a trifle	*una bagatela*

hot, *caliente* ; the log, *el tronco* ; the siege, *el sitio*

Exercise II.

Translate into Spanish : 1. The contractors dismissed all their workmen as soon as the war broke out. 2. They laughed when I related it to them. 3. I wash and dress myself in less than half an hour. 4. Ask for some more hot water. 5. They quarrelled for a trifle. 6. Do not let us forward the parcels until next week. 7. The fortresses surrendered after a siege which lasted nearly a year. 8. His wife used to dye her (trs., *el*) hair. 9. Who corrects her exercises ? 10. I correct hers and my teacher corrects mine. 11. Let us select one. 12. I bade farewell to all my friends. 13. We do not wish to compete with them in (the) South American markets. 14. Do they compete with you in Spain ? 15. It is impossible to prevent them from competing with us. 16. Follow them. 17. Repeat your surname.

Key to Exercises in Lesson 18.

(I) 1. Acierte Vd. quien está allí. 2. Siéntese Vd. en ese sillón. 3. ¿ Desea Vd. que cerremos aquella puerta ? 4. ¿ A qué hora comienza la misa ? 5. A las diez en punto. 6. Calenté-monos. 7. Niegan haberlo vendido a tan bajo precio. 8. Tal vez hiele mañana. 9. ¿ Cómo riegan sus plantaciones ? 10. Permítame Vd. que me siente. Estoy muy cansado. 11. Acérquese

Vd. al fuego y caliéntese. 12. Confieso que no lo entiendo. 13. Es muy sencillo. Las sucursales de la compañía se extienden por todo el país. 14. ¿ Por qué no encienden las lámparas ? 15. No lo sé ; siempre las encienden a las siete. 16. El ferrocarril atraviesa la sierra y desciende al valle. 17. Despiérteme Vd. a las seis en punto. 18. Le recomiendo que no lo olvide. 19. Corrija Vd. esa carta. 20. ¿ Nieva a menudo en el norte de España ? 21. Estoy seguro de que si pierde no pagará. 22. No lo rompa Vd. 23. Vierta Vd. el agua despacio. 24. Sentémonos cerca del río. 25. Creí que iría.

(II) 1. ¿ Se acuerda Vd. de sus señas ? 2. No : las he olvidado. 3. ¿ Se acuestan Vds. generalmente muy temprano ? 4. Nos acostamos entre las once y las doce. 5. ¿ A qué hora almuerzan Vds. ? 6. Tan pronto como nos levantamos. 7. ¿ Aprueban su conducta ? 8. No hemos tenido noticias suyas todavía. 9. ¿ Cuánto le cuesta a Vd. esa maleta ? 10. Sólo me cuesta veinte pesetas. 11. ¿ Juega al tenis ? 12. Si ; creo que juega muy bien. 13. ¿ Cuánto descuentan ? 14. Descuentan tres pesetas en cada cinco duros. 15. ¿ Por qué no renueva Vd. su billete ? 16. No es necesario. Estaré muy ocupado el mes que viene. 17. Ya no truena. ¿ Está lloviendo todavía ? 18. No ; ahora no llueve. 19. Le ruego a Vd. que le telegrafie el resultado enseguida. 20. No vuelva Vd. sin confirmar la noticia. 21. Muéstreles Vd. los recibos. 22. Los tontos sueñan lo que desean y los sabios lo que pueden. 23. Apuesto cualquier cosa a que acierto lo que está haciendo ahora. 24. Suelen visitarnos todos los domingos.

LESSON 20

Verbs in-*Ucir*

ALL verbs ending in *ucir*, except *lucir*, to shine, and its derivatives, besides taking a *z* in front of the radical *c* when this letter is followed by the vowels *a* or *o*, form their past definite by changing the last *c* of the stem into *j* and adding the terminations *e, iste, o, imos, isteis, eron*. The imperfect and future subjunctive of verbs of this kind are obtained as usual by dropping the final syllable *ron* from the third person plural of the past definite and affixing the terminations *ra, ras, ra, se, ses, se, re, res, re,* etc. It follows, therefore, that these tenses present the same anomaly in introducing a *j* in the stem instead of the original *c*. For example, the verb *traducir*, to translate :

INDICATIVE MOOD.

Present Part. : *traduciendo.* Past Part. : *traducido.* Present : *traduzco, traduces, traduce, traducimos, traducís, traducen.* Imperfect : *traducía, traducías, traducía,* etc. Past Definite : *traduje, tradujiste, tradujo, tradujimes, tradujisteis, tradujeron.* Future : *traduciré, traducirás, traducirá,* etc. Conditional : *traduciría, traducirías, traduciría.* Imperative : *traduce, traduzca Vd., traduzcamos, traducid, traduzcan.*

SUBJUNCTIVE MOOD.

Present : *traduzca, traduzcas, traduzca, traduzcamos, traduzcáis, traduzcan.* Imperfect : *tradujera, tradujeras, tradujera, tradujéramos, tradujerais, tradujeran ; tradujese, tradujeses, tradujese, tradujésemos, tradujeseis, tradujesen.* Future : *tradujere, tradujeres, tradujere, tradujéremos, tradujereis, tradujeren.*

Other verbs conjugated like *traducir* are :

conducir	to lead	*producir*	to produce
deducir	to deduct	*reducir*	to reduce
inducir	to induce	*seducir*	to seduce

KEYS TO EXERCISES IN LESSON 19.

(I). 1. Eso no me concierne. 2. Se arrepintieron tan pronto como leyeron las consecuencias de su negligencia. 3. Cada ciudadano se convertiria en soldado en caso de una invasión. 4. ¿ Se divirtieron Vds. aquella noche ? 5. No ; verdaderamente tuvimos muy mala suerte. Apenas habiamos llegado a los jardines cuando comenzó a llover. 6. ¿ Está hirviendo el agua ? 7. No ; no ha empezado a hervir todavia. 8. Los invasores mataron o hirieron a muchos labriegos que se negaron a dar informes respecto a los movimientos del ejército nacional. 9. El alcalde de la ciudad fué fusilado por orden del general. Murió como un valiente. 10. El prisionero mintió para salvar la vida de sus conciudadanos. 11. El rey le concedió grandes honores. 12. Estaban durmiendo cuando llegó la noticia. 13. ¿ Prefiere Vd. quedarse aqui, o dar un paseo por el malecón ? 14. Me es igual. Lo que Vd. prefiera.

(II). 1. Los contratistas despidieron a todos sus obreros tan pronto como estalló la guerra. 2. Se rieron cuando se lo conté. 3. Me lavo y me visto en menos de media hora. 4. Pida Vd. más agua caliente. 5. Riñeron por una bagatela. 6. No expidamos los paquetes hasta la semana que viene. 7. Las fortalezas se rindieron después de un sitio que duró cerca de un año. 8. Su mujer se teñía el cabello. 9. ¿ Quién corrige sus ejercicios ? 10. Yo corrijo los suyos y mi profesor corrige los míos. 11. Elijamos uno. 12. Me despedí de todos mis amigos. 13. No deseamos competir con ellos en los mercados sud-americanos. 14. ¿ Compiten ellos con Vds. en España ? 15. Es imposible impedirles que compitan con nosotros. 16. Sígalos Vd. 17. Repita Vd. su apellido.

LESSON 21

A Dozen Irregular Verbs

Besides the partially irregular verbs already given, there are a few other Spanish verbs the irregularities of which are of such a peculiar nature that they do not allow of any classification in groups, and must therefore be learnt by heart in each particular instance. As most of these verbs are very important and their number is not large, we now proceed to give their full conjugations in alphabetical order.

INDICATIVE MOOD of *Andar*, to walk.

Present Part. : *andando*. Past Part. : *andado*. Present : *ando, andas, anda*, etc. Imperfect : *andaba, andabas, andaba*, etc. Past Definite : *anduve, anduviste, anduvo, anduvimos, anduvisteis, anduvieron*. Future : *andaré, andarás, andará*. etc. Conditional : *andaría, andarías, andaría*, etc. Imperative : *anda, ande Vd., andemos, andad, anden Vds*.

SUBJUNCTIVE MOOD.

Present : *ande, andes, ande*, etc. Imperfect : *anduviera, anduvieras, anduviera, anduviéramos, anduvierais, anduvieran ; anduviese, anduvieses, anduviese, anduviésemos, anduvieseis, anduviesen*. Future : *anduviere, anduvieres anduviere, anduviéremos, anduviéreis, anduvieren*.

INDICATIVE MOOD of *Caber*, to be able, to be contained.
Present Part.: *cabiendo*. Past Part.: *cabido*. Present: *quepo,
cabes, cabe, cabemos, cabéis, caben*. Imperfect: *cabía, cabías,
cabía*, etc. Past Definite: *cupe, cupiste, cupo, cupimos, cupisteis,
cupieron*. Future: *cabré, cabrás, cabrá*, etc. Conditional:
cabría, cabrías, cabría, etc. Imperative: *cabe, quepa, quepamos,
cabed, quepan*.

SUBJUNCTIVE MOOD.

Present: *quepa, quepas, quepa, quepamos, quepáis, quepan.*
Imperfect: *cupiera, cupieras, cupiera, cupiéramos, cupierais,
cupieran; cupiese, cupieses, cupiese, cupiésemos, cupieseis,
cupiesen*. Future: *cupiere, cupieres, cupiere, cupiéremos,
cupiereis, cupieren.*

INDICATIVE MOOD of *Caerse*, to fall.

Present Part.: *cayendo*. Past Part.: *caído*. Present: *caigo,
caes, cae, caemos, caéis, caen*. Imperfect: *caía, caías, caía*,
etc. Past Definite: *caí, caíste, cayó, caímos, caísteis, cayeron.*
Future: *caeré, caerás, caerá*, etc. Conditional: *caería, caerías,
caería*, etc. Imperative: *cae, caiga, caigamos, caed, caigan.*

SUBJUNCTIVE MOOD.

Present: *caiga, caigas, caiga, caigamos, caigáis, caigan.* Imperfect: *cayera, cayeras, cayera, cayéramos, cayerais, cayeran;
cayese, cayeses, cayese, cayésemos, cayeseis, cayesen*. Future:
cayere, cayeres, cayere, cayéremos, cayereis, cayeren.

INDICATIVE MOOD of *Dar*, to give.

Present Part.: *dando*. Past Part.: *dado*. Present: *doy, das,
da, damos, dais, dan*. Imperfect: *daba, dabas, daba*, etc. Past
Definite: *di, diste, dió, dimos, disteis, dieron*. Future: *daré,
darás, dará*, etc. Conditional: *daría, darías, daría*, etc. Imperative: *da, dé, demos, dad, den.*

SUBJUNCTIVE MOOD.

Present: *dé, des, dé, demos, deis, den*. Imperfect: *diera,
dieras, diera, diéramos, dierais, dieran; diese, dieses, diese,
diésemos, dieseis, diesen*. Future: *diere, dieres, diere, diéremos,
diereis, dieren.*

INDICATIVE MOOD of *Decir*, to say, to tell.

Present Part.: *diciendo*. Past Part: *dicho*. Present: *digo,
dices, dice, decimos, decís, dicen*. Imperfect: *decía, decías, decía,*

A DOZEN IRREGULAR VERBS

etc. Past Definite : *dije, dijiste, dijo, dijimos, dijisteis, dijeron.*
Future : *diré, dirás, dirá, diremos, diréis, dirán.* Conditional :
diría, dirías, diría, etc. Imperative : *di, diga, digamos, decid,
digan.*

SUBJUNCTIVE MOOD.

Present : *diga, digas, diga, digamos, digáis, digan.* Imperfect :
*dijera, dijeras, dijera, dijéramos, dijerais, dijeran ; dijese, dijeses,
dijese, dijésemos, dijeseis, dijesen.* Future : *dijere, dijeres, dijere,
dijéremos, dijereis, dijeren.*

NOTE. All the compounds of *decir*, such as *contradecir*, to
contradict, *maldecir*, to curse, *bendecir*, to bless, *predecir*, to predict,
etc., follow the irregularities of the original verb except in the
future and conditional indicative, which are perfectly regular in
their formation, and in the second persons of the imperative,
which are *contradice, maldice,* etc.

Bendecir and *maldecir* have both two past participles, one of
them being regular and the other irregular : *las bendecirá*, he
will bless them ; *la contradeciría*, I would contradict her ; *maldijo
su mala suerte*, she cursed her bad luck ; *Dios lo bendiga*, may
God bless him ! *el obispo ha bendecido las tropas*, the bishop has
blessed the troops ; *maldito sea el criminal !* may the murderer
be cursed !

INDICATIVE MOOD of *Hacer*, to do, to make.
Present Part. : *haciendo.* Past Part. : *hecho.* Present : *hago,
haces, hace, hacemos, hacéis, hacen.* Imperfect : *hacía, hacías,
hacía,* etc. Past Definite : *hice, hiciste, hizo, hicimos, hicisteis
hicieron.* Future : *haré, harás, hará, haremos, haréis, harán.*
Conditional : *haría, harías, haría,* etc. Imperative : *haz, haga,
hagamos, haced, hagan.*

SUBJUNCTIVE MOOD.

Present : *haga, hagas, haga, hagamos, hagáis, hagan.* Imperfect : *hiciera, hicieras, hiciera, hiciéramos, hicierais, hicieran ;
hiciese, hicieses, hiciese, hiciésemos, hicieseis, hiciesen.* Future :
hiciere, hicieres, hiciere, hiciéremos, hiciereis, hicieren.

INDICATIVE MOOD of *Ir*, to go.
Present Part. : *yendo.* Past Part. : *ido.* Present : *voy, vas,
va, vamos, vais, van.* Imperfect : *iba, ibas, iba, íbamos, ibais,
iban.* Past Definite : *fui, fuiste, fué, fuimos, fuisteis, fueron.*
Future : *iré, irás, irá,* etc. Conditional : *iría, irías, iría, etc.*
Imperative : *ve, vaya, vayamos, id, vayan.*

SPANISH 21

SUBJUNCTIVE MOOD.

Present : *vaya, vayas, vaya, vayamos, vayáis, vayan.* Imperfect : *fuera, fueras, fuera, fuéramos, fuerais, fueran ; fuese, fueses, fuese, fuésemos, fueseis, fuesen.* Future : *fuere, fueres, fuere, fuéremos, fuereis, fueren.*

INDICATIVE MOOD of *Oir*, to hear.

Present Part. : *oyendo.* Past Part. : *oído.* Present : *oigo, oyes, oye, oímos. oís, oyen* Imperfect : *oía, oías, oía,* etc. Past Definite : *oí, oiste, oyó oimos, oisteis, oyeron.* Future : *oiré, oirás, oirá* etc. Conditional : *oiría, oirías, oiría,* etc. Imperative : *oye, oiga, oigamos, oíd. oigan.*

SUBJUNCTIVE MOOD.

Present : *oiga, oigas. oiga oigamos, oigáis, oigan.* Imperfect : *oyera, oyeras oyera, oyéramos, oyerais, oyeran ; oyese, oyeses, oyese, oyésemos, oyeseis, oyesen.* Future : *oyere, oyeres, oyere, oyéremos, oyereis, oyeren.*

INDICATIVE MOOD of *Poder*, to be able.

Present Part. : *pudiendo.* Past Part. : *podido.* Present : *puedo, puedes, puede, podemos, podéis, pueden.* Imperfect : *podía, podías, podía.* etc. Past Definite : *pude, pudiste, pudo, pudimos, pudisteis, pudieron.* Future : *podré. podrás, podrá* etc. Conditional : *podría podrías, podría.* etc. Imperative : Lacking.

SUBJUNCTIVE MOOD.

Present : *pueda, puedas pueda, podamos, podáis, puedan.* Imperfect : *pudiera, pudieras, pudiera, pudiéramos, pudierais, pudieran ; pudiese, pudieses, pudiese, pudiésemos, pudieseis, pudiesen.* Future : *pudiere, pudieres, pudiere, pudiéremos, pudiereis, pudieren.*

INDICATIVE MOOD of *Poner*, to put.

Present Part. : *poniendo.* Past Part. : *puesto.* Present : *pongo, pones, pone, ponemos ponéis, ponen.* Imperfect : *ponía, ponías, ponía,* etc. Past Definite : *puse, pusiste puso, pusimos, pusisteis pusieron.* Future : *pondré pondrás, pondrá, pondremos, pondréis, pondrán.* Conditional : *pondría, pondrías, pondría, pondríamos, pondríais. pondrían.* Imperative : *pon, ponga, pongamos, poned, pongan.*

(554)

A DOZEN IRREGULAR VERBS

SUBJUNCTIVE MOOD.

Present : *ponga, pongas, ponga, pongamos, pongáis, pongan.*
Imperfect : *pusiera, pusieras, pusiera, pusiéramos, pusierais, pusieran ; pusiese, pusieses, pusiese, pusiésemos, pusieseis, pusiesen.* Future : *pusiere, pusieres, pusiere, pusiéremos, pusiereis, pusieren.*

INDICATIVE MOOD of *Querer*, to wish, be willing, want, like.

Present Part. : *queriendo.* Past Part. : *querido.* Present : *quiero, quieres, quiere, queremos, queréis, quieren.* Imperfect : *quería, querías, quería,* etc. Past Definite : *quise, quisiste, quiso, quisimos, quisisteis, quisieron.* Future : *querré, querrás, querrá,* etc. Conditional : *querría, querrías, querría, etc.* Imperative : *quiere, quiera, queramos, quered, quieran.*

SUBJUNCTIVE MOOD.

Present : *quiera, quieras, quiera, queramos, queráis, quieran.* Imperfect : *quisiera, quisieras, quisiera, quisiéramos, quisierais, quisieran ; quisiese, quisieses, quisiese, quisiésemos, quisieseis, quisiesen.* Future : *quisiere, quisieres, quisiere, quisiéremos, quisiereis, quisieren.*

INDICATIVE MOOD of *Saber,* to know.

Present Part. : *sabiendo.* Past Part. : *sabido.* Present : *sé, sabes, sabe, sabemos, sabéis, saben.* Imperfect : *sabía, sabías, sabía,* etc. Past Definite : *supe, supiste, supo, supimos, supisteis, supieron.* Future : *sabré, sabrás, sabrá,* etc. Conditional : *sabría, sabrías, sabría,* etc. Imperative : *sabe, sepa, sepamos, sabed, sepan.*

SUBJUNCTIVE MOOD.

Present : *sepa, sepas, sepa, sepamos, sepáis, sepan.* Imperfect : *supiera, supieras, supiera, supiéramos, supierais, supieran ; supiese, supieses, supiese, supiésemos, supieseis, supiesen.* Future : *supiere, supieres, supiere, supiéremos, supiereis, supieren.*

VOCABULARY.

to stop	*parar*	a bottle	*una botella*
to be careful	*tener cuidado*	the saloon	*el salón*
to take a seat	*sentarse*	a litre	*un litro*
the victory	*la victoria*	to stay	*quedarse*
the intention	*la intención*	the truth	*la verdad*

a tip	*una propina*	a workshop	*un talle.*
the pocket	*el bolsillo*	regards	*recuerdos*
the estate	*la hacienda*	the ruin	*la ruina*
wine	*vino*	the stairs	*la escalera*

to be back, *estar de vuelta ;* the town-hall, *el ayuntamiento ;* a cup of chocolate, *una taza de chocolate ;* at that time, *en aquella época.*

LESSON 22

Prepositions and Some More Irregular Verbs

PREPOSITIONS in Spanish may be either separable or inseparable. Separable prepositions consist of one word, which is always placed in front of a noun, a pronoun, a verb, or an adverb : *con leche*, with milk ; *contra mí*, against me ; *sin payar*, without paying ; *hasta entonces*, until then. Inseparable prepositions are only used in composition with other words : *pro* in *pronombre*, pronoun, and *procónsul*, proconsul ; *sus* in *suspender*, to suspend ; *trans* in *transformar*, to transform.

The separable prepositions are as follow : *a*, to, at ; *ante*, before ; *bajo*, under ; *cabe*, close to ; *con*, with ; *contra*, against ; *de*, of, from ; *desde*, from, since ; *en*, in, at, on ; *entre*, between, among ; *hacia*, towards ; *hasta*, till, until, as far as ; *para*, for, in order to ; *por*, for, by ; *según*, according to ; *sin*, without ; *so*, under ; *sobre*, upon about, on ; *tras*, after.

According to the Spanish Academy, the inseparable prepositions are : *ab, abs, ad, ana, anfi, anti, apo, cata, cis, des, di, dia, dis, en, epi, es, ex, extra, hiper, hipo, in, inter, meta, o, ob, para, per, peri, pos, pre, preter, pro, re, res, sin, sub, so, son, sor, sos, su, sus, super, trans, ultra*. These prepositions, which cannot be used by themselves, have generally the same meaning as in English. Thus : *abjurar*, to abjure ; *admirar*, to admire ; *anatema*, anathema ; *anfiteatro*, amphitheatre ; *antípodas*, antipodes ; *apostatar*, to apostatize ; *disentir*, to dissent ; *diámetro*, diameter ; *epígrafe*, epigraph ; *incapaz*, incapable ; *irregular*, irregular ; *reelegir*, to re-elect ; *suspender*, to suspend ; *subdivisión*, subdivision ; *superintendente*, superintendent ;

transparente, transparent ; *transportar*, to transport ; *ultramarino*, ultramarine.

Irregular Verbs. We now continue in alphabetical order the conjugations of the unclassifiable irregular verbs.

INDICATIVE MOOD of *Salir*, to go out.

Present Part. : *saliendo*. Past Part. : *salido*. Present : *salgo, sales, sale, salimos, salís, salen.* Imperfect : *salía, salías, salía,* etc. Past Definite : *salí, saliste, salió, salimos, salisteis, salieron.* Future : *saldré, saldrás, saldrá,* etc. Conditional : *saldría, saldrías, saldría,* etc. Imperative : *sal, salga, salgamos, salid, salgan.*

SUBJUNCTIVE MOOD.

Present : *salga, salgas, salga,* etc. Imperfect : *saliera, salieras, saliera, saliéramos, salierais, salieran ; saliese, salieses, saliese, saliésemos, salieseis, saliesen.* Future : *saliere, salieres, saliere, saliéremos, saliereis, salieren.*

INDICATIVE MOOD of *Traer*, to bring.

Present Part. : *trayendo*. Past Part. : *traído*. Present : *traigo, traes, trae, traemos, traéis, traen.* Past Definite : *traje, trajiste, trajo, trajimos, trajisteis, trajeron.* Imperative : *trae, traiga, traigamos, traed, traigan.*

INDICATIVE MOOD of *Valer*, to be worth.

Present Part. : *valiendo*. Past Part. : *valido*. Present : *valgo, vales, vale, valemos, valéis, valen.* Imperfect : *valía, valías, valía,* etc. Past Definite : *valí, valiste, valió, valimos, valisteis, valieron.* Future : *valdré, valdrás, valdrá, valdremos, valdréis, valdrán.* Conditional : *valdría, valdrías, valdría,* etc. Imperative : *vale, valga, valgamos, valed, valgan.*

SUBJUNCTIVE MOOD.

Present : *valga, valgas, valga,* etc. Imperfect : *valiera, valieras, valiera, valiéramos, valierais, valieran ; valiese ; valieses valiese, valiésemos, valieseis, valiesen.* Future : *valiere, valieres, valiere, valiéremos, valiereis, valieren.*

INDICATIVE MOOD of *Venir*, to come.

Present Part. : *viniendo*. Past Part. : *venido*. Present : *vengo, vienes, viene, venimos, venís, vienen.* Imperfect : *venía, venías, venía,* etc. Past Definite : *vine, viniste, vino, vinimos, vinisteis, vinieron.* Future : *vendré, vendrás, vendrá, vendremos, vendréis, vendrán.* Conditional : *vendría, vendrías, vendría,* etc. Imperative : *ven, venga, vengamos, venid, vengan.*

SUBJUNCTIVE MOOD.

Present : *venga, vengas, venga*, etc. Imperfect : *viniera, vinieras, viniera, viniéramos, vinierais, vinieran : viniese, vinieses, viniese, viniésemos, vinieseis, viniesen.* Future : *viniere, vinieres, viniere, viniéremos, viniereis, vinieren.*

INDICATIVE MOOD of *Ver*, to see.

Pres. Part. : *viendo.* Past Part. : *visto.* Present : *veo, ves, ve, vemos, veis, ven.* Imperfect : *veía, veías, veía*, etc. Past Definite : *vi, viste, vió, vimos, visteis, vieron.* Future : *veré, verás, verá*, etc. Conditional : *vería, verías, vería*, etc. Imperative : *ve, vea, veamos, ved, vean.*

SUBJUNCTIVE MOOD.

Present : *vea, veas, vea, veamos, veáis, vean.* Imperfect : *viera, vieras, viera, viéramos, vierais, vieran ; viese, vieses, viese, viésemos, vieseis, viesen.* Future : *viere, vieres, viere, viéremos, viereis, vieren.*

INDICATIVE MOOD of *Yacer*, to lie.

NOTE. *Yacer* also means " to be deposited," and in this sense is especially used in inscriptions on tombstones : *Aquí yace,* here lies, etc.

Present Part. : *yaciendo.* Past Part. : *yacido.* Present : *yazco, yaces, yace, yacemos.* etc. Imperfect : *yacía, yacías, yacía*, etc. Past Definite : *yací, yaciste, yació, yacimos, yacisteis, yacieron.* Future : *yaceré, yacerás, yacerá, yaceremos, yaceréis, yacerán.* Conditional : *yacería, yacerías, yacería*, etc. Imperative : *yace* or *yaz, yazca, yazcamos, yaced, yazcan.*

SUBJUNCTIVE MOOD.

Present : *yazca, yazcas, yazca*, etc. Imperfect : *yaciera, yacieras, yaciera, yaciéramos, yacierais, yacieran ; yaciese, yacieses, yaciese, yaciésemos, yacieseis, yaciesen.* Future : *yaciere, yacieres, yaciere, yaciéremos, yaciereis, yacieren.*

VOCABULARY.

a collar	*un cuello*	the tie	*la corbata*
the socks	*los calcetines*	the world	*el mundo*
a shirt	*una camisa*	a secret	*un secreto*
a shop	*una tienda*	so (adv.)	*de modo que*
a mastiff	*un mastín*	the height	*la altura*
the corner	*la esquina*	vigilant	*vigilante*
what can I do for you ?		*¿ en qué puedo servirle ?*	

the whispering	*el murmullo*
the barking	*los ladridos*
the rushes	*los cañaverales*
to make haste	*darse prisa*
at leisure	*con calma*, or *despacio*
a bunch of flowers	*un ramo de flores*
the hothouse	*el invernadero*
the British Consul	*el cónsul británico*, or *inglés*
to ring the bell	*tocar el timbre*
to be worth while	*valer*, or *merecer la pena*
it is very kind of you	*es Vd. muy amable*
a letter of introduction	*una carta de recomendación*

EXERCISE.

TRANSLATE INTO SPANISH : 1. Did you (pl.) hear the noise ? 2. No ; we were too far away. 3. I never go out in the evening, so you may telephone any time after six o'clock. 4. Do you want me to bring the documents ? 5. I think it would be better if you sent them by post. I should like to read them again at leisure before making up my mind. 6. Just as you like. 7. What would you like to do this afternoon ? 8. I should like to buy some collars and ties. 9. Then I will accompany you. I also must buy some socks and shirts. 10. At what time do the shops close ? 11. Many of them close at five o'clock, but others remain open until six o'clock. 12. We must make haste if we want to get (arrive) there in time. 13. How much is that bunch of flowers worth ? 14. I do not think it is worth more than one shilling. 15. Do you want me to buy it ? 16. I do not think it is worth while. 17. When are you going (trs. *cuándo va Vd.*) to show me your hot-house ? 18. Any time (trs., *cuando*) you like.

LESSON 23

Principal Prepositions in Use

PREPOSITIONS or adverbial prepositions in English are not always rendered in Spanish by the same words. For instance, " about " is translated variously by *en ; por ; sobre ; acerca de ; a punto de ; para ; unos ; poco más o menos* and *de*. We therefore give a list of these English prepositions with their corresponding translations according to the specific meaning required in the selected sentence.

ABOUT, meaning " within," is rendered by *en*. They are about the theatre, *están en el teatro*.

ABOUT, meaning " through," is translated by *por*. He used to go about the roads begging for alms, *iba por los caminos pidiendo limosna*.

ABOUT, meaning " on," is translated by *sobre* or *acerca de*. She has not told me anything about that aspect of the business, *no me ha dicho nada sobre* (or *acerca de*) *ese aspecto del negocio*.

ABOUT, meaning " on the point of," is translated by *a punto de* or *para*. He was about to send a telegram when we arrived, *estaba a punto de* (or *para*) *telegrafiar cuando nosotros llegamos*.

ABOUT, meaning " more or less," is rendered by *sobre*, *unos*, *unas*, or *poco más o menos*. The picture must have cost about 40 dollars, *el cuadro debe costar sobre* (or *unos* or *poco más o menos*) *cuarenta pesos*.

ABOUT is sometimes translated by *de*. We were speaking about him, *estábamos hablando de él*.

AFTER, referring to time or position (adverb), is rendered by *después de* or *tras*. After 4 p.m., *después de las cuatro de la tarde* ; after the spring comes the summer, *tras la primavera viene el verano*.

AFTER, meaning " according to," is rendered by *a*, *según*, *con arreglo a*, *a la manera de*. After the French fashion, *a la (moda) francesca* ; they will act according to circumstances, *obrarán según* (*con arreglo a*) *las circunstancias* ; after Velazquez, *a la manera de Velazquez*.

AGAINST is rendered by *contra*. The troops advanced against the town, *las tropas avanzaron contra la ciudad*.

AT is generally translated by *a*. At the door of the house, *a la puerta de la casa* ; at 30 years of age, *a los trienta años de edad* ; at less than two shillings a dozen, *a menos de dos chelines la docena*.

AT, meaning " in," is translated by *en*. At Madrid, *en Madrid* ; at home, *en casa*.

BEFORE, as opposite to " after," is rendered by *antes de* before a noun, adjective, or infinitive, and by *antes que* before a pronoun or any tense of a verb. Before speaking to him, *antes de hablar con él ;* before next week, *antes de la semana que viene ;* before he speaks, *antes que hable.*

BEFORE, as opposite to " behind," must be translated by *delante de.* We wrote the letter before her, *escribimos la carta delante de ella ;* he was before me, *estaba delante de mí.*

BEFORE, meaning " in the presence of," is rendered by *ante.* He appeared before the judge, *compareció ante el juez.*

BETWEEN and AMONG are always translated by *entre.* Between 3 and 4 o'clock, *entre las tres y las cuatro ;* among the Japanese, *entre los japoneses.*

BY is generally translated *por.* The world was made by God, *el mundo fué hecho por Dios.*

BY, meaning " in," is translated by *de.* By day, *de día ;* by night, *de noche.*

BY, meaning " close to," is rendered by *junto a, cabe,* or *cerca de.* It was by the table, *estaba junto a (cabe,* or *cerca de) la mesa.*

BY is translated by *a* in sentences such as the following : Little by little, *poco a poco ;* one by one, *uno a uno.*

FOR, implying relation, must be rendered by *para.* He knows much for his age, *sabe mucho para su edad ;* it is very large for him, *es muy grande para él.*

FOR, implying duration in the future, is often rendered by *para.* It will last for ever, *durará para siempre.*

FOR, implying destination, is always translated by *para.* This bunch of flowers is for her, *este ramo de flores es para ella ;* is that the train for Carthagena ? *¿ es ése el tren para Cartagena ?*

FOR, meaning " for the sake of," is rendered by *por.* He died for his country, *murió por su patria ;* I did it for you, *lo hice por Vd.*

FOR, meaning " on behalf of," must also be translated by *por.* He always signs it for me, *siempre lo firma por mí ;* let us vote for him, *votemos por él.*

FOR, meaning " on account of," is translated by *por.* They granted it to him for his gallantry, *se lo concedieron por su valor.*

FOR, meaning " during," is *durante* or *por.* We lived there for five months, *vivimos allí durante cinco meses.*

FOR, meaning " in exchange," is *por.* I would sell it for three pounds, *lo vendería por tres libras.*

FOR, " instead of," is *por.* She took me for my friend, *me tomó por mi amigo.*

FOR, meaning " to fetch," is translated by *por*. I went for stamps, *fui por sellos ;* he came for me, *vino por mí*.

FROM, implying origin, is *de*. All those oranges come from Spain, *todas esas naranjas vienen de España*.

FROM, referring to distance or time, is *desde*. From Genoa to Geneva, *desde Genova a Ginebra ;* from May 15, 1892 *desde el quince de Mayo de mil ochocientos noventa y dos*.

IN after superlatives, should be translated by *de*. Antwerp was the most formidable fortress in Belgium, *Amberes era la fortaleza más formidable de Belgica ;* London is the largest city in the world, *Londres es la ciudad más grande del mundo*.

IN is always rendered by *en*, but in front of the words " morning," " afternoon," " evening," and " night " should be translated by *por*. In the summer, *en el verano ;* in the shop, *en la tienda ,* in the evenings, *por las noches*.

INTO is translated by *en*. Into the pocket, *en el bolsillo*.

INTO, after a verb of motion, is translated by *a*. He went into the dining-room, *entra al comedor*.

OF is nearly always translated by *de*. The market of the town, *el mercado de la ciudad*.

ON, meaning " upon," is rendered by *sobre* or *en*. It was on her dressing-table ; *estaba sobre* (or *en*) *su tocador*.

ON, before the days of the week or of the months, is never translated. He left on September the 16th, *salió el dieciseis de Septiembre ;* shall I see you on Thursday ? *¿ veré a Vd. el jueves ?*

THROUGH is rendered by *por*. The train passes through Paris, *el tren pasa por París*.

TILL or UNTIL is translated by *hasta*. I shall not see you until next Christmas, *no los veré a Vds. hasta la próxima Pascua*.

To is generally rendered by *a*. I wrote to him, not to her, *le escribí a él, no a ella*.

To in front of a verb is translated either by *a* or *para*. He has come to see me, *ha venido a verme ;* we want more money to buy them, *necesitamos más dinero para comprarlos ;* would you like to speak to him ? *¿ quisiera Vd. hablarle ? Para* also means " in order to."

To must be rendered by *en* in sentences like the following : From town to town *de ciudad en ciudad ,* from time to time, *de vez en cuando*.

TOWARDS is translated by *hacia*. Towards the north-east,

PRINCIPAL PREPOSITIONS IN USE

hacia el nordeste. When "towards" is used in a sentence referring to personal conduct, it must be rendered by *para con*. His behaviour towards his son leaves much to be desired, *su conducta para con su hijo deja mucho que desear*.

UNDER is translated either by *debajo de* or *bajo*. Under the counter, *debajo del mostrador*, or *bajo el mostrador*.

WITH must always be rendered by *con*. With care, *con cuidado* ; with great interest, *con gran interés*.

WITHOUT is always translated by *sin*. It is impossible to learn without studying, *es imposible aprender sin estudiar*.

VOCABULARY.

to knock	*llamar*	the bill	*la cuenta*
to embrace	*abrazar*	a key	*una llave*
to go over	*pasarse*	the will	*la voluntad*
to kiss	*besar*	a wrapper	*una faja*
to please	*agradar*	the woman	*la mujer*
to complain	*quejarse*	a lady	*una señora*
to get lost	*perderse*	a gentleman	*un caballero*
to register	*certificar*	the plate	*el plato*
an actor	*un actor*	even (adv.)	*hasta*
to roast	*asar*	veal	*ternera*
mutton	*carnero*	a cutlet	*una costilla*

to burn oneself *quemarse*
to shake hands *darse la mano*
to take shelter *refugiarse, cobijarse*

EXERCISE.

TRANSLATE INTO SPANISH : 1. Where did you go this morning ? 2. We went as far as the post office. 3. Did you buy the stamps I told you ? 4. We bought five penny stamps, three postcards, and two wrappers for the newspapers, but we could not register the parcel you gave us ; it was too late. 5. What have you done with the parcel ? 6. We posted it without registering it. 7. I am afraid it will get lost. 8. We have no news from them since last month. 9. We were about to leave London when she fell ill. 10. Go towards the hotel while I cash this cheque. Have you got the key ? 11. I have forgotten it. Will you lend me yours ? 12. Here, you have it. Put it where I can see it when I come. 13. I will not go to bed until you come. Knock at the window, and I will give it to you. 14. What a beautiful night !

Do not go home so early. Come with me. 15. No ; it is rather late, and I want to write some letters before going (*trs.*, to go) to bed. 16. I shall be back in (within) a few minutes.

KEY TO EXERCISE IN LESSON 22.

1. ¿ Oyeron Vds. el ruido ? 2. No ; estábamos demasiado lejos. 3. Nunca salgo por las noches, de modo que puede Vd. telefonear a cualquier hora después de las seis. 4. ¿ Quiere Vd. que traiga los documentos ? 5. Creo que sería mejor si los mandase Vd. por correo. Quisiera leerlos otra vez despacio antes de decidirme. 6. Como Vd. quiera. 7. ¿ Qué quisiera Vd. hacer esta tarde ? 8. Quisiera comprar algunos cuellos y corbatas. 9. Entonces le acompañaré a Vd. Yo también tengo que comprar algunos calcetines y camisas. 10. ¿ A qué hora se cierran las tiendas ? 11. Muchas de ellas se cierran a las cinco, pero otras permanecen abiertas hasta las seis. 12. Tenemos que darnos prisa si queremos llegar a tiempo. 13. ¿ Cuánto vale ese ramo de flores ? 14. No creo que valga más de un chelín. 15 ¿ Quiere Vd. que lo compre ? 16. No creo que merezca la pena. 17. ¿ Cuándo va Vd. a enseñarme su invernadero ? 18. Cuando Vd. quiera.

LESSON 24

Rules on the Conjunctions

CONJUNCTIONS are invariable, and may be either simple or compound. Simple conjunctions consist of only one word, as *si*, if ; *pero*, but ; and compound conjunctions are those formed by two or more words, as *con tal que*, provided that ; *a fin de que*, in order that. Spanish conjunctions are divided into nine classes, namely : copulative, disjunctive, adversative, conditional, causal, continuative, comparative, conclusive, and illative.

Copulative conjunctions are those which merely connect words, clauses, or sentences. Such are : *y* or *e*, and *ni*, neither, nor ; *que*, that. *Vd. y yo*, you and I ; *Inglaterra e Irlanda*, England and Ireland ; *ni lo vi, ni lo oí*, I neither saw nor heard him ; *me dijo que no le quedaba más dinero*, she told me that she had no more money left. The substitution of *e* for *y* in front of a word beginning with *hi* is not made when an *e* follows the *i*. *Tuvieron que alimentarse de moluscos y hierbas*, they had to feed on shellfish and herbs. Chileans use an *i* instead of the Spanish *y* whenever this letter stands for a vowel. Thus they write *rei*, king ; *mui*, very ; *aeroplanos i globos*, aeroplanes and balloons.

Disjunctive conjunctions express difference, separation, or alternative between two or more objects, ideas, or persons. To this group belong *o, u,* or *ora*, now ; and the adverbs *ahora, ya, bien*, whenever they are repeated. *Vencer o morir*, to conquer or to die ; *patronos u obreros*, masters or workmen ; *ora en francés, ora en inglés*, now in French, now in English ; *cruzando ahora un río, ahora un lago*, crossing now a river, now a lake ; *ya triste, ya alegre*, now sad, now joyful ; *bien en oro o bien en plata tiene que pagarme hoy*, either in gold or in silver he must pay me today.

Adversative conjunctions suggest opposition or inconsistency between what has been said and what is going to be said. The principal among these are : *pero,* but ; *aun cuando, aunque*, although, though, even if ; *antes, antes bien, más bien*, rather ; *bien que*, although ; *por más que, por mucho que, no obstante, sin embargo*, however, however much, nevertheless ; *a pesar de, con todo eso*, in spite of ; *sino,* but ; *siquiera*, even if. *Quisiera ir pero no tengo tiempo*, I should like to go, but I have no time ; *no aceptará aunque se lo ofrezcan a mitad de precio*, he will not accept, even if they offer it to him at half price ; *el conquistador, aunque cruel, fué bravo*, the conqueror, though cruel, was brave ; *no necesita consejo sino ayuda*, she does not need advice, but help ; *hágale Vd. ese favor siquiera sea por lástima*, do him that favour, even if it be only out of pity ; *por mucho que trabaje, no creo que lo acabe en una semana*, however much he may work, I do not think he will finish it in a week ; *no sabían sin embargo, que su padre estaba parando en la misma fonda*, they did not know, however, that their father was staying at the same hotel ; *todavía está muy fuerte a pesar de sus años*, he is still very strong, in spite of his years.

Conditional conjunctions point out the condition for a certain circumstance to take place. Such are : *si, como*, if ; *con tal que, siempre que, dado que*, provided that, as long as ; *ya que*, since. *Lo haré si puedo*, I shall do it if I can ; *como no telegrafíe a tiempo, perderemos el contrato*, if he does not telegraph in time we shall lose the contract ; *con tal que me avisen, estaré listo*, provided they let me know, I shall be ready ; *que se divierta con tal que cumpla su deber*, let him enjoy himself as long as he does his duty ; *ya que él no escribe, lo escribiré yo*, since he does not write, I will write it myself.

The conjunction *si* is sometimes used to express doubt, or to emphasize the meaning of a sentence : *¿ Si será verdad que el Banco de Cuenca ha quebrado ?* I wonder if it is true that the Bank of Cuenca is bankrupt ? *¡ Si estábamos con él !* Were we with him !

Causal conjunctions are those which precede a sentence in which the reason or cause of something is given. These are : *porque*, because ; *pues, pues que, puesto que, supuesto que*, as, since, for. *No se lo diji porque no lo sabía*, I did not tell him, because I did not know it ; *no pudieron entrar pues la casa estaba cerrada*, they could not get in, as the house was closed ; *debemos hacerlo puesto que lo hemos prometido*, we must do it, for we have promised it ; *no me preocuparé puesto que a él no importa*, I will not worry (about it) since he does not care.

Continuative conjunctions are those which continue or support a sentence, as *pues*, then ; *así pues, así que*, so. *Digo, pues, que salió de aquel peligro*, I say, then, that he came out of that danger ; *así que no tuvo más remedio que confesar el crimen*, so he could not help but to confess his crime.

Comparative conjunctions express comparison between things or sentences. Such are ; *como*, as, like ; *así*, thus, so ; *así como*, as, just as. *Como a Vd. le gusta*, as you like it ; *así me lo explicó*, so he explained it to me ; *así pereció uno de los descubridores españoles más ilustres*, thus perished one of the most illustrious of Spanish discoverers ; *así como la tierra gira alrededor del sol, así gira la luna alrededor de la tierra*, just as the earth turns round the sun, so the moon turns round the earth.

Conclusive conjunctions are those used in front of a sentence in which the aim or object of a previous phrase is explained. Among these the principal are : *para que, a fin de que*, in order that, that, so that. *Envíeme Vd. las señas para que les escriba*, send me their address, so that I may write to them ; *se los di a fin de que los comprobara*, I gave them to him that he might check them ; *telegrafíele Vd. enseguida para que sepa el resultado mañana por la mañana*, wire to him at once, in order that he may know the result tomorrow morning.

RULES ON THE CONJUNCTIONS

Illative conjunctions express a consequence of, or deduction from, what has just been said in the preceding sentence. The principal among these are : *conque, luego, por consiguiente, por lo tanto,* so, therefore ; *pues, entonces,* then. *Le ha dado dinero y lo ha recomendado a sus amigos, conque no puede quejarse,* he has given him some money and has recommended him to his friends, **so** he cannot complain ; *mi socio no está ahora en Londres, y, por consiguiente, no puedo dar una respuesta definitiva a su pregunta,* my partner is not in London now, and therefore I cannot give a definite answer to your question ; *¿ si no ha querido decir eso, entonces, qué es lo que ha querido decir ?* if he did not mean that, then what did he mean ?

Interjections. Among the principal interjections are the following : *ah, ay, bah, ca, ea, eh, hola, huy, oh, ojalá, puf, quiá, uf,* and so on. *Ah* and *oh* express admiration ; *ay* and *huy* pain or grief ; *bah* disappointment . *ca* and *quiá* doubt ; *ea* encouragement and hurry ; *hola* stands for halloo, hullo ; *ojalá* implies a wish ; *puf* and *uf* disgust or fatigue.

VOCABULARY.

to climb	*trepar*	martial law	*ley marcial*
to charge	*cobrar*	warfare	*guerra*
to imagine	*imaginar*	belligerent	*beligerante*
to earn	*ganar*	compulsory	*obligatorio*
to kill	*matar*	naval	*naval*
to use	*usar*	invulnerable	*invulnerable*
to warn	*advertir*	invincible	*invencible*
to exercise	*ejercer*	successful	*con éxito*
to get ruined	*arruinarse*	the attack	*el ataque*
to lack	*carecer de*	the usages	*los usos*
copper	*cobre*	the power	*el poder*
iron	*hierro*	the abuse	*el abuso*
due	*debido*	belonging	*perteneciente*
risky	*arriesgado*	far less	*mucho menos*
the eye	*el ojo*	hostile	*hostil*
a lot	*muchísimo*	present	*presente*
the castle	*el castillo*	alarm	*alarma*
that is	*es decir*	unnecessary	*innecesario*
the means	*los medios*	on foot	*a pie*
happy	*feliz*	to exaggerate	*exagerar*
at discretion	*a discreción*	a submarine	*un submarino*
		an individual	*un individuo*

to be photographed	*retratarse*	to take a photograph	*sacar una fotografía*
proportionately	*en proporción*	the oppression	*la opresión*
a large sum	*una gran cantidad*	exclusively	*exclusivamente*
up to now, as yet	*hasta ahora*	there is no occasion	*no hay motivo*
according to, in accordance with	*con arreglo a*	the temperature	*la temperatura*

Exercise.

TRANSLATE INTO SPANISH : 1. Rivers and valleys ; copper and iron. 2. It was neither cold nor hot ; the temperature was very pleasant. 3. We climbed to the top of the highest mountain. 4. We were not allowed (trs. they did not allow us) to take a photograph of the castle. 5. Would you like (use *querer*) to have your photo taken ? 6. How much do you charge for a dozen ? 7. Do you prefer this or that one ? 8. I do not like (*gustar*) either of them. 9. Now on foot, now on horseback. 10. I would not believe it, even if I saw it with my own eyes. 11. However much she may study, she will never play the piano like him. 12. In spite of everything he said, I cannot believe him. 13. Write to him today, even if it is only a couple of words. 14. Better (trs., *más vale*) late than never, but better early (trs., *pronto*) than late. 15. Although I warned him that the enterprise was risky he invested (in it) a large sum of money. 16. He spends more than he earns ; so he will soon be ruined. 17. It will be exclusively his fault, since we warned him in time. 18. We did not go, because it was raining.

Key to Exercise in Lesson 23.

1. ¿ A dónde fueron Vds. esta mañana ? 2. Fuimos hasta el correo. 3. ¿ Compraron Vds. los sellos que les dije ? 4. Compramos cinco sellos de penique, tres tarjetas postales y dos fajas para los periódicos, pero no pudimos certificar el paquete que nos dió Vd. : era demasiado tarde. 5. ¿ Qué han hecho Vds. con (*or* del) paquete ? 6. Lo echamos al correo sin certificarlo. 7. Temo que se pierda. 8. No tenemos noticias suyas desde el mes pasado. 9. Estábamos para salir de Londres cuando cayó enferma. 10. Vaya Vd. hacia el hotel mientras yo cobro este cheque. ¿ Tiene Vd. la llave ? 11. La he (*or* se me ha) olvidado ; ¿ quiere Vd. prestarme la suya ? 12. Aquí la tiene Vd. Póngala

donde pueda verla cuando venga. 13. No me acostaré hasta que venga Vd. Llame Vd. a la ventana y se la daré. 14. ¡ Que noche más hermosa ! No vaya Vd. a casa tan temprano. Venga Vd. conmigo. 15. No ; es bastante tarde, y quiero escribir algunas cartas antes de acostarme. 16. Estaré de vuelta dentro de unos minutos.

LESSON 25

Writing Letters

IN addressing a person by the Christian name, the words *Don* (Mr.), *Doña* (Mrs. and Miss) should be placed in front of the name ; but if by the surname alone, *Señor* (Mr.), *Señora* (Mrs.), *Señorita* (Miss) should be used—*Don Juan, Don Guillermo, Doña Ana, Doña Isabel ; Señor Gomez, Señor Gonzalez, Señora Pérez, Señorita Rodriguez.* In formal address, in writing, both prefixes are generally used in front of the full name—*Señor Don Juan Gomez, Señor Don Guillermo Gonzalez, Señora Doña Ana Pérez, Señorita Doña Isabel Rodriguez. Señor, Señora, Señorita, Don, Doña* are very frequently contracted to *Sr., Sra., Srta., Dn.,* or simply *D.* and *Dña : Sr. D. Luis Solé ; Sra. Dña. María Morata.*

In speaking about or in introducing a person or persons, the corresponding articles must be placed in front of the words *Señor, Señores, Señora, Señoras, Señorita, Señoritas : Tengo el gusto de presentar a Vd. a la Señorita Gomariz,* I have the pleasure of introucing Miss Gomariz to you ; *hemos escrito esta mañana a los Srs. Valdivia y Compañia,* we have written this morning to Messrs. Valdivia and Co.

Señorito stands for master ; *Señorito Pedro,* Master Peter.

A peculiar Spanish custom is that a woman does not lose her maiden name after marriage ; she simply adds her husband's surname to her own by means of the preposition *de.* Thus, for instance, if *Señorita Isabel Rodriguez* married *Don Luis Solé,* her full formal name after marriage would become *Sra. Doña Isabel Rodriguez de Solé.* The children of this couple would use both their father's and mother's surnames, and sign themselves, for instance, *Alfonso Solé Rodriguez,* and *Carmen Solé Rodriguez.* For this reason Spanish names often appear long and confusing to foreigners.

When addressing a person in the course of a conversation, only the first—that is, the father's surname—should be used. Thus *Don Gonzalo Martinez Gutierrez* may be addressed either as *Don Gonzalo* or as *Señor Martinez*, but never as *Señor Guitierrez* or *Don Martinez*.

In ordinary private correspondence, "Dear" or "My dear," by which a letter is generally started, is translated by *Querido*, *Querida*, *Queridos*, *Queridas*, or *Mi querido*, *Mi querida*, etc., according to the gender and number of the persons addressed. My dear friend, *Mi querido amigo* or *Mi querida amiga*; Dear parents, *Queridos padres*.

In commercial or formal correspondence, "Dear Sir," "Dear Madam," "Dear Sirs," "Dear Mesdames" should be rendered in the following manner : if a person is addressing another single person, by *Muy Señor mío* or *Muy Señora mía*; if a person is writing to several, by *Muy Señores míos* or *Muy Señoras mías*; if several persons are supposed to be addressing one, by *Muy Señor nuestro* or *Muy Señora nuestra*; and, finally, if several are addressing more than one, by *Muy Señores nuestros* or *Muy Señoras nuestras*.

A private letter is usually closed with the words *Suyo afectísimo* (*amigo*) or *Suya afectísima* (*amiga*), "Yours sincerely" or "Yours affectionately," which are generally abbreviated to *Suyo affmo* or *Suya affma*.

The old-fashioned formal endings *Suyo affmo amigo que sus pies besa* (who kisses your feet) and *Suyo affmo amigo que su mano besa* (who kisses your hand) are no longer used in Latin America but confined to Spain. Even in that country the form used today is *q.e.s.m.*, meaning "*que estrecha su mano*," who presses your hand, i.e. shakes your hand. In Latin America, We are, Dear Sirs, Yours faithfully, would be rendered by *Quedamos de Vds. muy atentos y S.S.* (We remain your attentive and sure servitors) ; *Somos* or *quedamos de Vd.* (or *de Vds.*) *seguros servidores ;* or *Su seguro servidor*, or *Suyo seguro servidor que su mano besa*, or *Sus atentos y seguros servidores que su mano besan* (Your obedient servant). As these closing sentences of elaborate politeness have now become a mere matter of form, they are almost invariably abbreviated to the initial letters of each word. *Suyo affmo S. S. Q. S. M. B.*, or *Suyo affmo s. s. q. s. m. b.*

The following model letters show practically the manner in which these formal phrases are generally used.

WRITING LETTERS

Private and Commercial Correspondence.

Mi querida amiga, (fem. form)
  Acabo de recibir su invitación para el 8 de Marzo y siento
decirle que no podré estar en Londres para esa fecha. Le doy,
sin embargo, las gracias por su amabilidad.

Suya affma amiga,

My dear Friend,
  I have just received your invitation for the 8th of March, and
I am sorry to say that I shall not be able to be in London by
that date. I, nevertheless, thank you for your kindness.

Yours sincerely,

Muy señores míos,
  Me tomo la libertad de ofrecerles mis servicios por si aun no
tienen Vds. representante en esta ciudad. En cuanto a informes
pueden Vds. dirigirse al Sr. Don Felipe Fernández, establecido
en Madrid, en la calle de Alcalá numero 35.
  En espera de su amable respuesta quedo de Vds.,

s. s. q. s. m. b.

Dear Sirs,
  I take the liberty of offering you my services in case you
are not yet represented in this town. For references you can
apply to Mr. Felipe Fernández, whose office is at 35, Alcalá
Street, Madrid.
  Trusting to be favoured with a reply, I beg to remain,

Dear Sirs, Your obedient servant,

Muy señor nuestro,
  A su debido tiempo recibimos su carta del 17 del mes pasado,
en que nos avisaba Vd. las condiciones de embarque e incluía
copias de los conocimientos y pólizas de seguros. Tenemos el
gusto de remitirle la adjunta letra sobre Valparaíso, pagadera
a la vista.

Nos repetimos suyos S. S.

Dear Sir,
  We have duly received your letter of the 17th ult. informing
us of the conditions of shipment and enclosing copies of bills of

lading and insurance policies. We have now pleasure in forwarding you the enclosed draft on Valparaiso, payable at sight.

Yours truly,

VOCABULARY.

to draw on	*girar*	the draft	*la letra, el giro*
to divide	*dividir*	per cent	*por ciento*
the assets	*el activo*	sellers	*vendedores*
a security	*una garantía*	net weight	*peso neto*
a dividend	*un dividendo*	reserved	*reservado*
carriage paid	*porte pagado*	the space	*el espacio*
a quarter	*un trimestre*	the advice	*el aviso*
buyers	*compradores*	to endorse	*endosar*
money order	*giro mutuo*	the gauge	*la trocha*
a sample	*una muestra*	a signature	*una firma*
to meet	*reunirse*	to fill up	*llenar*
the liabilities	*el pasivo*	the discount	*el descuento*
to transact business	*negociar*	the voucher	*el comprobante*
dry goods	*tejidos, paños*	paper currency	*papel moneda*
gross weight	*peso bruto*	wholesale prices	*precios al por mayor*
a power of attorney	*un poder*	an instalment	*un plazo, una cuota*
to acknowledge receipt	*acusar recibo*	according to	*con arreglo a*
a kilogramme	*un kilógramo* or *kilo.*	the rolling stock	*el material rodante*
a limited liability company	*una sociedad anónima*	a joint-stock company	*una sociedad por acciones*
a bill of lading	*un conocimiento de embarque*	the board of directors	*el consejo de administración*
an insurance policy	*una póliza de seguros*	the style	*la razón social*
kindly	*sírvase Vd.* or *haga Vd. el favor de*	a certificate of origin	*un certificado de origen*
the—as well as the	*tanto los—como los*	on account of non-payment	*por falta de pago*
an estimate	*un presupuesto, un cálculo*	the Customs tariff	*el arancel de aduanas*
		a chartered accountant	*un perito mercantil*

the sinking	el fondo de amor-	the Bank	
fund	tización	rate	la tasa del Banco
to credit	abonar en cuenta	retail prices	precios al por
to operate	operar, negociar		menor

EXERCISE.

TRANSLATE INTO SPANISH : 1. That firm only sells dry goods.
2. He did not endorse the draft. 3. They did not want to allow
us a discount of more than 2 per cent. 4. The estimate amounted
to £2,000. 5. We do not draw on (trs., *contra*) that town.
6. The Bank rate was less than 4 per cent. 7. The present sinking
fund is smaller than it used to be five years ago. 8. The assets
of the Bank amount to £3,000,000, and the liabilites to £1,000,000.
9. Do you know any English chartered accountant established
in Caracas ? 10. The buyers, as well as the sellers, complain of
the Customs tariff. 11. They always draw at sight ; it would
be more convenient for us if they drew at thirty days. 12. Its
gross weight is five kilogrammes, but its net weight is only two
kilogrammes. 13. The gauge of the new railway line will be
less than a metre. 14. They formed a joint-stock company.
15. How do you advise me to send the money ? 16. Send it by
money order. 17. Did you buy the goods at retail or wholesale
prices ? 18. The firm changed its style two years ago.

KEY TO EXERCISE IN LESSON 24.

1. Ríos y valles ; cobre y hierro. 2. No hacía ni frío ni
calor ; la temperatura era muy agradable. 3. Trepamos a la
cumbre de la montaña más alta. 4. No nos permitieron que
sacáramos una fotografía del castillo. 5. ¿ Quisiera Vd. retratarse?
6. ¿ Cuánto cobra Vd. por una docena ? 7. ¿ Prefiere Vd. ésta o
aquella ? 8. No me gusta ninguna de las dos. 9 Ora a pie,
ora a caballo. 10. No lo creería aunque lo viera con mis propios
ojos. 11. Por mucho que estudie nunca tocará el piano como
él. 12. A pesar de todo lo que dijo no puedo creerlo. 13. Es-
críbale Vd. hoy aunque sólo sea un par de palabras. 14. Más vale
tarde que nunca, pero más vale pronto que tarde. 15. Aunque
le advertí que la empresa era arriesgada invirtió en ella una gran
cantidad de dinero. 16. Gasta más de lo que gana, de modo que
pronto se arruinará. 17. Será culpa suya exclusivamente,
puesto que se lo advertimos a tiempo. 18. No fuimos porque
estaba lloviendo.

LESSON 26

Rules on Accentuation

THOUGH the vowel of a word upon which the stress should be placed is sometimes distinguished by the graphic accent ('), called acute, this is far from being always the case; the student must not only know which is the stressed syllable of every word, but also all those words which require this syllable to be designated by that written mark. In order properly to apply both these orthographical and prosodical accents, the following rules should be borne in mind:

No consonant is ever accented. Vowels only are susceptible of this distinction: *púlpito*, pulpit; *católico*, catholic; *débil*, weak.

Monosyllables should not be graphically accented unless they have two different meanings. In this case, one of the exceptions is always accented: *en*, in; *al*, to the; *un*, one; *cal*, lime; but *él dé*, he may give; *de él*, from him; *mas*, but; *más*, more; *mi casa para mí*, my house for myself. The accents on the preposition *a* and on the conjunctions *e, o, u* have been omitted in accordance with the ruling of the Spanish Academy made just before the Great War.

Most words of two or more syllables ending in *a, e, o* bear the stress on the syllables before the last, and require no accent; *almirantazgo*, admiralty; *vinagre*, vinegar; *caballeriza*, stable. The same rule applies to most words ending in the diphthongs *ia, ie, io, ua, uo*; *gloria*, glory; *superficie*, surface; *armario*, wardrobe; *antigua*, old; *ambiguo*, ambiguous. There are, however, some words which deviate from this rule, and must therefore be accented on the proper syllable. Prominent among these exceptions are the various tenses of the verbs which follow the accentuation given in the model conjugations: *comería*, I would eat; *hablará*, he will speak; *decía*, he used to say; *entré*, I entered; *corrió*, she ran; *véndalo Vd.*, sell it. Examples of other exceptions are: *alegría*, joy; *desafío*, duel; *héroe*, hero; *ganzúa*, latchkey; *exceptúo*, I except; *música*, music; *café*, coffee; *bajá*, pasha; *quizá*, perhaps; *máquina*, engine; *empréstito*, loan.

ACCENTUATION

Most words ending in *i* or *u* bear the graphic accent on these vowels : *baladí*, worthless ; *jabalí*, wild boar ; *Perú* : *tribú*, tribe, etc. Exceptions to this rule are : *álcali*, alkali ; *metrópoli*, metropolis ; *espíritu*, spirit, and a few other words.

Words ending in the consonants *b, c, d, j, l, t*, or *z* bear the stress on the last vowel, and do not require an accent : *nabab*, nabob ; *abad*, abbot ; *pared*, wall ; *corcel*, charger ; *vivac*, bivouac ; *reloj*, watch ; *zarzal*, thicket ; *azul*, blue ; *cenit*, zenith ; *carcaj*, quiver ; *audaz*, audacious ; *velocidad*, speed ; *salud*, health. The most important exceptions to this rule are : *ataúd*, coffin ; *raíz*, root ; *cárcel*, prison ; *baúl*, trunk ; *lápiz*, pencil ; *mármol*, marble ; *árbol*, tree ; *huésped*, guest ; *difícil*, difficult ; *fácil*, easy ; *cáliz*, chalice ; *fósil*, fossil ; *áspid*, aspic : *césped*, grass ; *fértil*, fertile ; *mástil*, mast.

With the exception of the third person plural of the future, all those parts of a verb ending in *an, en, on* do not carry an accent on these syllables : *vengan, comen, hablan, dijeron, temieran, hallasen, venden, corrían, estaban, comprarían*, etc., but *vendrán, comerán, hablarán*, etc. Other exceptions to the rule are the third person plural of the indicative and subjunctive present of *estar* : *están, estén*. Most other words ending in *n* carry an accent on the vowel preceding that letter : *alquitrán*, tar ; *también*, also ; *motín*, riot ; *almidón*, starch ; *constitución*, constitution ; *según*, according to, etc. Important exceptions are the following words, which bear the stress on the syllable before the last : *alguien*, somebody ; *germen*, germ ; *imagen*, image ; *joven*, young ; *margen*, margin ; *orden*, order ; *origen*, origin ; *resumen*, recapitulation ; *virgen*, virgin ; and a few others. The plural of all these words takes a graphic accent on that syllable which in the singular bears the stress : *imágenes*, images ; *órdenes*, orders ; *vírgenes*, virgins, and so on.

As a rule, words ending in *r* are emphasized on the last syllable : *altar*, altar ; *hogar*, home ; *soplar*, to blow ; *mujer*, woman ; *arder*, to burn ; *encubrir*, to conceal ; *amor*, love ; *conquistador*, conqueror ; *tahur*, gamester. Among the exceptions the principal are : *alcázar*, palace ; *ámbar*, amber ; *nácar*, mother-of-pearl ; *néctar*, nectar ; *azúcar*, sugar ; *cadáver*, corpse ; *cráter*, crater ; *éter*, ether ; *prócer*, prominent man ; *mártir*, martyr. All these words retain the accent in their plural : *azúcares, próceres, mártires*. The only exception to this last rule is the word *carácter*, the plural of which, *caracteres*, bears the stress on the penultimate syllable.

Most words ending in the consonant *s* are emphasized on the last syllable but one : *paraguas*, umbrella ; *martes*, Tuesday ; *enaguas*, petticoat ; *sillas*, chairs ; *fusiles*, rifles ; *acorazados*, battleships. Notable exceptions to this rule are some parts of the verbs, such, for example, as *correrás*, thou wilt run ; *hablaréis*, you will speak ; *comprábamos*, we used to buy ; *si dijéramos*, if we should say ; etc.

The following words are also important exceptions : *además*, besides ; *compás*, compass ; *jamás*, never ; *ciprés*, cypress ; *obús*, howitzer ; *francés*, French ; *portugués*, Portuguese ; *inglés*, English ; *irlandés*, Irish ; *escocés*, Scotch ; *galés*, Welsh ; *danés*, Danish ; *miércoles*, Wednesday ; *análisis*, analysis ; *hipótesis*, hypothesis ; *paréntisis*, parenthesis.

The plural and feminine forms of words ending in an emphasized syllable retain the stress (not the accent) on the same vowel : *labrador* (farmer) ; *labradora, labradores, labradoras* ; *holgazán* (idle) ; *holgazana, holgazanes, holgazanas* ; *naranjal* (orange grove), *naranjales* ; *inglés, inglesa, ingleses, inglesas* ; *español, española, españoles, españolas*. Words ending in an accented *i* retain the graphic mark in their plural : *rubí* (ruby), *rubíes* ; *alhelí* (wallflower), *alhelíes* ; *carmesí* (crimson), *carmesíes*.

When at the end of a line a word has to be divided for lack of space, the student should remember the following remarks :

Words must be divided by complete syllables : *li-bro, plu-ma, gra-má-ti-ca, car-pin-te-ro*.

As diphthongs and triphthongs form only one syllable, the vowels of which they are composed cannot be separated : *jui-cio-so, ciu-dad, es-toi-co, ha-bla-ríais, cal-cu-la-ríais*.

When the first or last syllable of a word consists of only one vowel, the writing of this vowel by itself at the end or the beginning of a line should be avoided.

The *s* which sometimes follows a preposition, in compound words, must be added to that preposition when the *s* precedes another consonant : *ins-pi-rar, obs-ti-na-do*.

The letters *ch*, *ll*, and *rr*, although double in appearance, are single in pronunciation, and therefore should never be divided : *ca-rri-co-che, ca-ba-lle-ro, ca-cha-rre-ría, cas-te-lla-no*.

FRANCE'S COMMANDERS IN THE FIELD. Marshal Césaire Joseph Jacques Joffre (centre ; 1852–1931) led the French armies from 1914 until after Verdun, at the end of 1916. Henri Philippe Pétain (right ; b. 1856) was responsible for the defence of Verdun, and in 1918 became commander-in-chief under Ferdinand Foch (left ; 1851–1929), who after service as a corps and army commander had been appointed in March generalissimo of all the Allied forces (then sorely tried by the last German offensive) on the Western front. MODERN HISTORY 32

GERMANY'S WAR LORDS. Left, Kaiser Wilhelm II (b. 1859), a grandson of Queen Victoria, succeeded his father, Frederick I, as emperor of Germany and king of Prussia in 1888, and reigned until his abdication in 1918. Since the German defeat he has lived in Holland. Centre, Field-Marshal Paul von Hindenburg (1847–1934), served in the wars of 1866, 1870–1 and 1914–18. From 1916 to the Armistice he was German generalissimo, and in 1925 and again in 1932 he was elected president of the German republic. Right, Field-Marshal Erich von Ludendorff (1865–1937), conquered Rumania in 1916 and planned the German offensives of 1918. Resigning on their failure, he fled to Sweden, but later returned to play some part in the reactionary movement. MODERN HISTORY 32

JOSEPH STALIN. Born in Georgia in 1879, he was an original member of the inner circle of the Bolshevik party, and since 1927 has been the virtual dictator of the Soviets. His actual position is that of Secretary-General of the Communist Party.

FRANKLIN DELANO ROOSEVELT (b. 1882). Became President of the U.S.A. in 1933 and was re-elected in 1936 by the greatest majority in American History. His "New Deal" policy has been responsible for vast changes in the country's economic and social life.

THE MEN OF MUNICH. At the Munich Conference, held on September 29, 1938, war was averted from Europe for the time being at the expense of Czechoslovakia, which was compelled to give up to Germany the Sudeten territories. This photograph shows the four chief figures at the Conference : left to right, Rt. Hon. Neville Chamberlain, Prime Minister of Great Britain ; Edouard Daladier, Premier of France ; Adolf Hitler, Fuehrer of the German Reich ; and Benito Mussolini, Italy's Duce.

Plate 60

Volume VI

Key to Exercise in Lesson 25.

1. Esa casa sólo vende tejidos. 2. No endosó el giro. 3. No quisieron concedernos un descuento de más del dos por ciento. 4. El presupuesto ascendió a dos mil libras esterlinas. 5. No giramos contra esa ciudad. 6. La tasa del Banco era menos del cuatro por ciento. 7. El actual fondo de amortización es menor de lo que era hace cinco años. 8. El activo del Banco asciende a tres millones de libras esterlinas y el pasivo a un millón. 9. ¿Conoce Vd. a algún perito mercantil inglés establecido en Caracas? 10. Tanto los vendedores como los compradores se quejan del arancel de aduanas. 11. Siempre giran a la vista; sería más conveniente para nosotros si girasen a trienta días vista. 12. Su peso bruto es de cinco kilos pero su peso neto es solamente dos kilos. 13. La trocha de la nueva línea férrea medirá menos de un metro. 14. Formaron una sociedad por acciones. 15. ¿Cómo me aconseja Vd. que envie el dinero? 16. Envielo Vd. por el giro mutuo. 17. ¿Compró Vd. los géneros al por menor o al por mayor? 18. La casa cambió su razón social dos años.

This Lesson concludes our Course, in Spanish.

T6

LESSON 27

Reptiles, Ancient and Modern

REPTILES, birds and mammals possess certain common characters which mark them off from the lower vertebrates. The most important constant feature of all three classes is the development in connexion with the embryo of two structures, known as foetal membranes. These are the *amnion*, which is wrapped round the embryo and serves to protect it, and the *allantois*, which is an embryonic respiratory organ. These two characters, about which we shall say more later, justify the use of the term *Amniota* to denote birds, reptiles and mammals as distinct from fishes and amphibians, to which the term *Anamnia* is applied. Reptiles are more closely related to birds than either of these classes is related to mammals, and the two former classes are often known by a common name, the *Sauropsida*.

The close relationship between sauropsidan types is shown by certain characters they possess in common. The skin gives rise to distinctive structures of an exoskeletal nature in the form of feathers or scales. The skull is joined to the vertebral column, and moves on the first vertebra about a single bony projection or occipital condyle. The skeleton of the lower jaw is built up of five or six separate bones, and this jaw is articulated with the quadrate bone of the skull. The ankle joint is formed between the two rows of tarsal bones of the pentadactyl limb. The heart consists of two auricles and a single ventricle, which is usually partially, sometimes completely, divided into halves by a septum, so that two more or less complete ventricles are formed. Functional gills are never developed at any stage, though vestigial gills, or visceral clefts, occur during development. As in amphibia, however, the terminal part of the alimentary canal and the ducts of the reproductive organs open into a common chamber or *cloaca*, through which eggs and sperms as well as faecal matter must pass in order to reach the exterior.

Reptiles, unlike birds and mammals, have a blood temperature approximating to that of the animal's surroundings. Like amphibians and fishes, they are " cold-blooded," as we say. The limbs, in those types which possess them fully developed, do not raise the body far off the ground, for the elbows are turned outwards, while the digits, of which there are five to each limb, are turned inwards. The body is covered with horny scales, and there may be bony plates in the skin. All reptiles develop from eggs with tough, leathery shells, which in a few cases hatch within the body of the mother, but more commonly are laid in some warm spot. The young appear as miniature editions of the adult, and have to shift for themselves from the start.

Prehistoric Reptiles. During the Secondary epoch reptiles formed the dominant group of backboned animals living on land. Some, however, were adapted to an aquatic life, while others modified the fore limbs into wings. By the beginning of the Tertiary epoch most of the reptilian orders had become extinct, being apparently unable to compete with mammals and birds, their own more highly evolved relatives. To the several extinct orders of reptiles we may devote a few words.

Dinosaurs flourished during Jurassic and Cretaceous times, when they were dominant animals. The very large order to which they belong (*Dinosauria*, meaning " terrible reptiles ") included a great variety of forms, some quite small but others surpassing all existing land animals in size. Some were vegetarians and walked on all fours, like *Diplodocus*, which reached the great length of ninety feet. Others were actively predaceous carnivores with formidable teeth, like *Tyrannosaurus*, which reared its fifty-foot body aloft on its hind legs. Some lived on dry land ; others preferred swamps, fresh waters, or even the zone between tide marks ; and while most were quadrupeds, some developed powerful hind limbs of disproportionate length, on which they walked or hopped about. This adaptation to progression on two legs brought about certain structural resemblances to birds which do not necessarily indicate close relationship.

Among the extinct marine reptiles the *Ichthyosaurs* or " fish-lizards " were large animals with fish-like bodies, paddle-shaped limbs and long jaws furnished with abundant strong conical teeth. They reached a length of fifty feet, and the large size of their eyes probably indicates a nocturnal habit.

Even more interesting than the dinosaurs were the related *Pterosaurs* or " winged reptiles," which hunted for food in the air. The skin was drawn out into a flying membrane much like that of the bat. But while in the bat all four fingers are greatly elongated into slender supports for this membrane, only the little finger was thus modified in the pterosaur, and formed a stout jointed rod to strengthen the outer edge of the wing. The pterosaur, *Pteranodon*, which lived in Cretaceous times, had a wing spread of 25 feet, but smaller creatures belonging to this order existed.

SOME EXTINCT REPTILES. **1.** Tyrannosaurus, length about 50 feet. **2.** Horned dinosaur, Triceratops, length 20-25 feet. **3.** Diplodocus, length about 90 feet. **4.** Pteranodon, or flying dragon. **5.** Iguanodon, about 34 feet long, remains of which have been found in Belgium and in the Isle of Wight. **6.** Ichthyosaur, or fish-lizard.

The *Theromorphs* formed a very important order of rather small reptiles living in Permian times and preserving many primitive characters, such as paired occipital condyles. The most highly developed forms, *Theriodonts*, believed to be the ancestors of mammals, had teeth modified into incisors, canines, premolars and molars, and possessed a "false palate" like the living mammal. The lower jaw was beginning to show the articulation with the squamosal bone of the skull characteristic of higher *Amniota*.

Reptiles of Today. Though so many groups of reptiles have died out, the class is still abundantly represented among existing backboned animals. Recent members of the *Reptilia* may be arranged in five orders, each with well-defined characters, as follow : (1) *Chelonia*, including tortoises and turtles ; (2) *Lacertilia*, comprising lizards, geckos, iguanas and chameleons ; (3) *Ophidia*, with its variety of snakes, vipers, pythons and boas ; (4) *Crocodilia*, or crocodiles, gavials and alligators : and (5) *Rhynchocephalia*. This last-mentioned order was abundantly represented in the earlier part of the Secondary epoch, and corresponds in many ways to the stock from which reptiles in general have taken their origin. It included a number of lizard-like forms, presenting many primitive characters, and now almost entirely extinct, being represented only by the tuatara, *Sphenodon*, which lives on small islands in the Bay of Plenty, New Zealand. It has been saved from extinction by the fact that New Zealand became isolated at an early date, so that better equipped forms have been largely kept out of these islands.

Crocodiles and alligators inhabit rivers and estuaries of tropical regions and have a lizard-like appearance, but in many ways are much more specialized. The snout is armed with powerful interlocking teeth, which constitute a deadly trap. The valvular nostrils are set on the top of the snout, so that the animal can move with most of its body submerged and at the same time breathe readily. Should it perceive an unfortunate mammal drinking or browsing on the river's brink, it sinks below the surface and swims rapidly towards its victim by powerful tail strokes. Then comes a sudden snap of the jaws and a lash of the tail, and the prey is captured, to be held under water until drowned if too large to be swallowed. The powerful teeth of the crocodile, like our own, are lodged in sockets in the jaws. Other crocodilian characters are the intromittent organ or penis of the male and the position of the internal openings of the nose (internal nares). The latter lie very far back in the mouth, and the top of the windpipe is drawn out into a projection wrapped round by protecting folds. The danger of water entering the lungs is thereby lessened.

Many other points in the anatomy of the crocodile present great interest. The body is not only protected by horny scales, of which those along the upper side of the tail form a saw-edged ridge, but is also defended by bony plates or scutes in the skin. The stomach is not unlike that of the bird, part of it being converted into a muscular gizzard, the crushing action of which is enhanced by stones and other hard objects, which are swallowed from time to time. The organs of circulation are of great interest, because the heart is four-chambered, as in mammals and birds, not three-chambered, as in other reptiles and amphibians. Pure and impure blood do not mix in the cavity of the heart, but, as such mixing takes place outside owing to imperfect separation of the great vessels, the net result is the same as in other reptiles. But crocodiles, we may say, are well on the way to becoming warm-blooded animals in respect to the structure of the heart, and they are more intelligent than other reptiles, owing no doubt to their larger and more complex brain. Alligators, which are confined to the New World, are distinguished from crocodiles by the sharp canine teeth of the lower jaw. These fit into depressions at the edges of the upper jaw.

A great variety of forms adapted to live under the most varied conditions are included in the *Chelonia*. Some are vegetarians, others flesh-eating ; but in all cases the teeth are replaced by a strong horny covering to the jaws, making up a kind of rounded beak, which is hooked in the carnivorous members of the order. The most characteristic feature of tortoises and turtles, however, is the remarkable defensive armour. The body is sheltered in a strong case consisting of an upper shield or *carapace*, which is more or less firmly united at its edges with a lower shield or *plastron*, making up a sort of box, into which the head, tail and limbs can be partially retracted. The outer layer of the case is composed of horny plates, which in certain marine species form the source of " tortoiseshell." Beneath these are bones, some of which are derived from the backbone and ribs.

The extremities of land tortoises are stumpy and clawed, being well suited to progression over firm surfaces. In marsh and fresh-water tortoises the limbs are more flattened and serve as paddles, a modification which is carried to its extreme in the marine members of the order, turtles, where the limbs are powerful flippers.

LESSON 28

Some Facts about Snakes and Lizards

O F the two remaining orders of the Reptilia, the *Lacertilia* and *Ophidia*, the first comprises lizards, which may be described as the most average of existing reptiles, and which have a very wide distribution. The sand lizard, *Lacerta agilis*, is native to our own country and may often be seen in summer basking in the sun on banks or scrubby slopes. While the animal remains motionless it easily escapes observation, because its mottled brown skin harmonizes well with the surroundings and affords a good example of protective coloration. The small creature is capable of exceedingly rapid movement, darting quickly upon the insects, worms, and other small animals which constitute its food.

The general shape of the lizard is not unlike that of the newt, from which it differs in one very important respect The body is clothed with horny scales derived from the upper layer (epidermis) of the skin, which is dry and devoid of glands. The scales are different from those of fishes, since these are derived from the deeper layers of the skin, or dermis. On the terminal digits the scales form horny claws. The limbs of the lizard we might describe as sprawling, and the body preserves its poise partly by means of a long tail, which is cylindrical, thick near the trunk, but gradually tapering towards its thin hinder extremity, and almost twice as long as head and trunk together.

In many instances the tail plays an important part in protecting the lizard from an untimely end, for when seized suddenly it readily snaps across and affords time for escape. This curious procedure is made possible by weak places in the backbone.

Other important reptilian features are met with in its skeleton. Ribs are carried by all vertebrae in front of those carrying the pelvic girdle. The foremost ones, belonging to the neck region, are short and, like those of the hinder part of the trunk, have free extremities. The ribs of the thorax are attached to the breastbone lying on the lower side of the body, a characteristic not evident in lower vertebrates. The skull forms a more complete roof to the brain than in amphibians, and articulates with the first vertebra of the backbone by a median condyle. The hinder part of the skull of vertebrates, which in development shows its primitive segmented nature, has encroached to a lesser or greater degree on the trunk. The extent of this encroachment, marked by the number of segments making up the hinder part of the skull or occipital region, is much greater in reptiles and higher vertebrates than in amphibians and fishes. The last nerve to emerge from the cranium in reptiles and higher types is the twelfth, while that in types lower than the reptiles is the tenth. At least two additional segments have been incorporated in the skull of reptiles.

In vertebrates higher in the scale of life than fishes, the vestiges of the gill arches, otherwise called the hyoid apparatus, form the basis of support for the tongue muscles. This hyoid skeleton supports a long protrusible tongue, which in lizards is forked at the tip. Respiration is by means of lungs, the skin having lost this function, and the manner of breathing shows another change from the amphibian condition. Instead of raising and lowering the floor of the mouth, the reptile pulls forward its ribs by means of muscles running obliquely between them. Before inspiration the ribs slope backwards, but when they are pulled forward the volume of the thoracic cavity is increased, with the result that air rushes into the lungs in an attempt to fill the partial vacuum between these organs and the wall of the thorax.

Slight advances are seen in respect of the circulatory system. The heart consists of the two auricles and single ventricle and the sinus venosus of the amphibian. The part of the ventral aorta nearest the heart (*truncus arteriosus*) is split into three—instead of being a single vessel with three pairs of branches as in the frog —so that the ventricle opens directly into three arteries. The upper two arteries are the right and left systemic arches, from one of which (the right) springs the carotid arch, while the lower is the pulmonary arch passing exclusively to the lungs, the branch to the skin having disappeared. The pulmonary circulation is thus rendered distinct. The ventricle is imperfectly divided into halves, but its spongy walls prevent complete admixture of pure and impure blood. The left systemic arch and the pulmonary arch open from the *right* side of the ventricle, and thus receive impure blood from the veins of the body after its passage through the right auricle. Pure blood passes along the right systemic arch, however, so that the carotid arches receive this for distribution to the brain. Right and left systemic arches unite to form a single dorsal aorta, which thus obtains mixed blood. Though the circulatory organs are modified with respect to those of the frog, the same result is obtained in the end.

Some tropical lizards, like the iguanas of America, attain a great size. The iguana, which is esteemed as food, may be as much as six feet in length, and is one of the climbing members of the Lacertilia, other examples being the geckos and chameleons of the Old World, both of which are animals of small size. Geckos have curious pads under their toes studded with hairs of peculiar shape, which enable these animals to scramble up smooth vertical surfaces with alacrity. The chameleon has hands and feet resembling sugar-tongs with hooked prongs, due to the digits being bound together into two groups, forming grasping organs of great efficiency. This reptile is also notable for the relatively enormous distance to which it can shoot out its adhesive club-shaped tongue. It is even proverbial for the way in which it can rapidly change its colour to suit various backgrounds, so as to harmonize with them. This variable coloration is protective, making the chameleon invisible to its foes, and also aggressive, as the insect prey of the little lizard are thereby lulled into a sense of false security, until they find themselves seized and transferred to the mouth of the chameleon in the twinkling of an eye.

Snakes. Among the reptiles, snakes are the most dominant existing members of their class and are closely related to the lizards. The shape of the body has undergone modification, having become extremely narrow, elongated and cylindrical, and well suited to a life spent in wriggling through undergrowths in forests. The limbs have almost entirely disappeared—the hinder ones of pythons, however, being represented by a pair of insignificant stumps, each of which terminates in a claw. In the absence of limbs the junction between trunk and tail regions is indicated solely by the opening of the cloaca.

Snakes are essentially carnivorous and, with a few degenerate burrowing exceptions, are able to swallow animals much larger than themselves. This is rendered possible by the distensible nature of the body, due in part to the absence of breast and shoulder bones. Further, the two bones of the lower jaw are not firmly united at their forward extremities, being only connected by an elastic ligament which stretches easily. To preclude the possibility of choking during swallowing the top of the wind-pipe is drawn out into a long cone, which temporarily protrudes from the side of the mouth.

On the lower surface of the snake's body are found a number of prominent horny shields arranged in a double series, and to the ends of these the ribs are attached. By means of appropriate muscles the ribs can be moved, so that the shields are carried forwards one after another, resulting in a rapid gliding mode of progression. We might almost say that the snake walks on the tips of its ribs. Accompanying this movement are undulations of the body from side to side, producing a writhing motion. Such movements are facilitated by an extremely flexible vertebral column, the vertebrae of which are provided with additional locking joints that guard against dislocation. The joints, which are confined to snakes and iguanas, consist of wedge-like out-growths of the fore face of one vertebrae (zygosphenes) and de-pressions of corresponding form on the hinder face of the vertebrae in front (zygantra).

Many snakes are non-poisonous and these possess numerous conical, backwardly projecting teeth on the jaw edges and on the roof of the mouth, which—though of no use for chewing—hold the prey firmly and prevent its escape. Our common grass-snake, *Tropidonotus*, is a good example of such forms. It is particularly fond of the neighbourhood of streams and is an expert swimmer. Its favourite food consists of frogs and fishes. Other examples of innocuous snakes are the boas and pythons of tropical America, which crush compara-tively large animals into shapeless masses, prior to lubricating them with abundant saliva and then swallowing them.

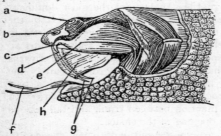

POISON APPARATUS OF RATTLESNAKE. a, eye; b, nasal opening; c, poison duct entering the poison fang at d; e, poison sac; f, tongue; g, opening of poison duct; h, pouch of mucous membrane enclosing poison fangs.

Venomous snakes possess glands opening into the mouth and secreting a poisonous fluid, which is introduced into the blood of the bitten victim. Vipers are the most specialized snakes, and in these creatures the teeth are reduced to a pair of hollow fangs in front of the upper jaw. On each side of the head is a large poison gland connected with the cavity of the fang by a narrow canal. When the mouth is closed the fangs are folded back against the roof of the mouth with their tips directed backwards, but when the snake opens its mouth and " strikes " the fangs are moved forwards and erected so that their sharp tips can be brought into action. Poison enters the wound made by the fang by a small opening near the tip of this structure.

Characteristics of the Adder. In conclusion we might indicate the general characters of England's only poisonous snake, the adder, which is common on sandy moorlands, on heaths, and in other dry or stony situations. It rarely exceeds two feet in length and can be distinguished from the grass snake by its broad triangular head and short tail. The colour is yellowish brown and a broad dark zigzag stripe is easily seen along the upper side of the body. We might also explode the myth that the forked tongue of the snake is a sting ; this it definitely is not, though it is a delicate organ of touch, used constantly for feeling over the surface of the ground. Finally the noises made by the snake do not usually issue from the mouth. The rattle of the rattlesnake is made by the tail, while the hiss of many different kinds of snakes is made by the nose.

LESSON 29

The Structure of Birds

(See plate 62)

SINCE feathers are distinctive of birds, we might define a bird as a feathered animal, and by so doing effectively separate it from all other kinds of living creatures. The zoologist would proceed a few steps further in referring to one of our feathered friends as a warm-blooded, egg-laying, bipedal vertebrate with not more than four toes and with forelimbs transformed into wings. This definition scarcely does justice to the attractive reality ; and instead of attempting to define birds, we shall do better to examine their characters in some detail, at the same time inquiring shortly whence they came.

With the problems of bird life is associated the question, how feathers came to be evolved—a question still shrouded in mystery.

There is some resemblance between the modes of development of feathers and reptilian scales, however. Both arise as outgrowths of the outer layer of the skin (epidermis) which become horny, and both lie partly buried in the deeper layers (dermis) which form a nutritive core. This would lead us to a correct conclusion, namely, that birds are but modified reptiles, but by erroneous inference. The scales of reptiles are never moulted completely as are feathers, and though the scales on the feet and elongated ankle bones of birds closely resemble reptilian scales, we do not know of any stage between the former and feathers.

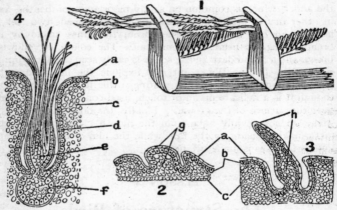

STRUCTURE AND DEVELOPMENT OF A FEATHER. 1. Small portion of feather with pieces of two barbs, each having to the left three distal barbules, and to the right a number of proximal barbules, many belonging to adjacent barbs. **2.** Early feather-papilla in its follicle. **3.** Feather-germ. **4.** Down-feather in its follicle. a, stratum corneum; b, stratum Malpighii; c, dermis; d, follicle of downfeather; e, calamus of down-feather; f, follicle of permanent feather; g, feather papilla; h, feather-germ.

The surface brought to bear against the air in flight is formed of the quill feathers of the wings, which together form an area of very large extent in proportion to the bulk of the bird. These feathers present the necessary combination of lightness and strength, together with the requisite flexibility. Examining one of them closely, we shall see that the hollow quill at the base is continued as an axis of an expanded vane, the numerous side branches (barbs) of which adhere closely together. The reason for this becomes apparent on looking at some barbs under the microscope, for these will be found to bear still smaller branches (barbules) beset with interlocking hooks. The loose texture of the plumes of the ostrich—not a flying but a running bird—is due to the lack of such hooks.

While in a bat the fingers are much elongated to support the flying membrane, the opposite is true of a bird, where firm support is required for the wing quills or *remiges* (rowing feathers). The bone corresponding to that of our upper arm (humerus) is short and strong, and is succeeded by two bones of the modified forearm (radius and ulna), of which one (the ulna) bears the so-called secondary quills. There is much fusion in the bones of the hand, which has only three digits. The first of these (or thumb) bears a tuft of feathers known as the bastard wing, which probably aids in the execution of turning movements, while the remaining two support the primary quills.

Mechanics of Flight. The motive power for the effective downstroke of the wings is supplied by very large muscles (pectorals), which make up the flesh of the breast. Here, also, we find the smaller and weaker muscles that raise the wings, the tendons of which pass over a sort of pulley formed by bones of the shoulder girdle, to be attached to the upper edge of the humerus. The wing is pulled down with its concave under surface sloping upwards and backwards, and part of the force expended goes to support the bird in the air, the other part being spent in propelling it forwards.

During the downward beat the wing quills are pressed together by an elastic band running unbrokenly along the entire wing and passing across their bases so as to offer a continuous surface. When the wing is raised, however, the individual feathers are slightly rotated, so that air is allowed to pass between them, owing to relaxation of this ligament. This automatic tightening of the ligament on the downstroke and relaxation on the upstroke, together with the resulting movement of the quills, enable the wing movements to be executed with the minimum expenditure of energy. The feathers of major importance in the stroke are the secondaries, which most effectively get a grip on the air. The primary feathers appear to be of great use in side steering— hence their great elongation in the insect-hunting swallows and swifts. The radiating quills attached to the stumpy tail are called, from their function, *rectrices*, or steering feathers. They appear to serve also as a brake in flight.

The character of flight depends on wing size, for the smaller the wings the oftener they must beat, and vice versa. The wings of the wild duck beat thrice as fast as those of the carrion crow, which beat twice as fast as those of the stork, while the wings of the common sparrow beat even faster. The bird can also use its wings as a parachute for gliding. When gulls or herons attain a certain speed in flight they are able to glide without wing strokes. The end of an unsuccessful swoop by a bird of prey like the hawk can be converted into an upward glide to a great height. Another kind of flight is sailing, seen in such birds as the albatross, which has a relatively large wing area. This is accomplished without assistance from air currents and without wing beats, though head, shoulder and tail movements occur. Other peculiar types of flight are seen in the owl, which flies with uncanny silence, and the penguin and cormorant, which, in effect, fly under water.

Skeletal Features. While the forelimbs of the bird have been sacrificed to flight, the skull has become modified into an efficient substitute for a hand, enabling its possessor to grasp objects reached from the ground, to preen its feathers, and to arrange the materials of its nest. The skull has been consolidated by a more complete welding of its individual bones, and so completely that in the woodpecker it serves as a hammer. Teeth have been discarded, but in their place a horny beak has been developed. The head has become exceedingly mobile, and can be turned through half a circle, largely owing to an elongation of the neck by multiplication of its vertebrae. These vertebrae have articular surfaces of a saddle shape, distinctive of birds.

The breastbone or sternum has been enormously enlarged for attachment of the great pectoral muscles which move with the wings. The ribs of the thorax comprise two parts : an upper vertebral part connected with the vertebral column, and a lower sternal part associated with the sternum, the two sets together forming a complete framework of the thorax. The vertebral and sternal ribs slope backwards from their point of union, making an angle between them behind. When this angle is reduced—as it is by contraction of muscles connecting the rib halves—the distance between the sternum and the vertebral column is increased ; in other words, the cavity of the thorax is enlarged. In this way air is drawn into the lungs, for these organs are firmly attached to the thorax wall.

STRUCTURE OF BIRDS

The lungs of the bird are small, indistensible bags curiously prolonged into a number of cavities, called air sacs. The windpipe, or trachea, which is supported in birds by bony (not cartilaginous) rings, divides on entering the thorax into two smaller tubes or bronchi. These divide into still smaller branches in a peculiar manner. A main branch passes through the lung and leads into an air sac in the abdomen, but gives off a branch on each side to similar sacs in the hinder part of the thorax. The remaining part of each bronchus forms a number of branches leading into air sacs in the front part of the thorax, in the neck, and between the forks of the merrythought or fused collar bones. The air sacs have thin walls lined with cilia, but with little vascularization. They are probably not respiratory in function, but, since they are connected with cavities in the spongy bones of the body, probably serve to render the body buoyant. Most birds consume large quantities of water, but give out only small quantities of urine ; and, further, since birds do not possess sweat glands, the air sacs are probably the seat of a peculiar form of heat and water loss known as internal perspiration.

The voice of birds is not produced by the larynx or voice box, as in mammals, but by a structure peculiar to birds, called the *syrinx*. This lies at the point at which the trachea divides into bronchi, and is really an enlargement of this junction, across the cavity of which accessory vocal cords are stretched. These structures vibrate, and in vibrating give rise to musical sounds, when air passes rapidly over them, as in expiration.

Owing to the conversion of the forelimbs into wings the hind limbs of the bird are set far forward, so that the body is more nicely poised , and for their support there are very long hip bones, united to a region of the backbone (*sacrum*) composed of a number of joints fused together. In order to further more rapid progression along the ground, the legs have been lengthened. Beginning at the upper extremity, there is a rather short thigh bone (*femur*), followed by a long shin bone, an elongated shank bone, and four toes, the small toe having been lost. The bird walks on its toes, and the ankle joint is, therefore, raised off the ground, and corresponds in position to the junction of shin and shank bones. No small irregular ankle bones (*tarsals*) are seen because, in the interests of firmness, half of those seen in the typical pentadactyl limb have united with the lower end of the shin bone (the *tibia* being here a *tibio-tarsus*), while half have fused with the bones of the sole of the foot (*meta-tarsals*) to form the single shank bone (*tarso-metatarsus*).

Birds are notoriously varied feeders, and so it is not surprising to find numerous modifications of feet and bill, as well as of the digestive apparatus. The crow has what we might call a generalized bill—strong, not too pointed, and suited to a variety of purposes. This type of bill is shortened, sharpened and curved in birds of prey, flattened and broadened in mud feeders like the duck, drawn out into a slender bill for capturing insects in warblers and wrens, or into a delicate probe for seeking nectar in humming-birds, and modified in a thousand and one ways for various feeding purposes. Feet mostly have to do with walking, running, perching or swimming, but may be concerned with the capture of food, as in eagles and ospreys. The eagle's foot, like that of most birds, has three toes directed forward and armed with powerful claws, the first toe being directed backward. Owls can bend the last toe backward beside the first. The parrot holds food to the mouth with its foot, which thus serves as a hand.

LESSON 30

Modern Birds and Their Ancestors

As an example of the internal digestive arrangements of birds which swallow hard food, we might conveniently take the domestic pigeon. Here the gullet is swollen into a large crop, the inflation of which gives the pouter its characteristic appearance. It is used for the temporary storage of food, and is not digestive. It leads into an oval stomach or proventriculus, from the lining of which digestive juices are poured out. A hinder division of this organ has thick muscular walls and a tough brown lining. This is a mechanical stomach or gizzard, which, containing stones and other hard objects swallowed periodically by the birds, churns up and triturates food particles and completely compensates for the absence of teeth in the jaws. If the pigeon is fed constantly on flesh instead of grain the brown lining is shed, and the gizzard becomes glandular and ceases its grinding work. Herring gulls may change the nature of the stomach lining twice in the course of a year, feeding on fish in winter but on grain in summer. Some flesh-eating birds, however, have as well-developed a gizzard as the pigeon, e.g. crows and kingfishers.

The gizzard is also a feature of the digestive tract of some reptiles. Another reptilian character is the cloaca, into which the final part of the alimentary canal (a long, coiled intestine) opens. In birds this chamber is partially divided into three smaller chambers, which lie in line one behind another. Into the first one (*coprodaeum*) opens the terminal part of the intestine, into the second (*urodaeum*) the urinary and reproductive ducts lead, while the last (*proctodaeum*) opens externally by an aperture through which sperms and eggs, urine and faecal matter must pass to the exterior.

With all the structural modifications of the bird's body we have insufficient space to deal, but must be content to mention only the most interesting and instructive ones. Of these one connected with the muscular system is important, and concerns certain muscles of the leg which go to form a curious perching mechanism. Most schoolboys who have treasured the foot of a fowl know that a pull upon a single tendon serves to bend all the toes. This tendon passes over the ankle joint. In the roosting bird the weight of the body, falling on the legs, tends to bend the shin bone (tibio-tarsus) more completely on the shank bone (tarso-metatarsus), which stretches the tendon. This results in the flexure of the toes, which thus grip the perch firmly. The grip is maintained while the bird is asleep by the weight of the body.

Warm-bloodedness is one of the distinctive features of bird biology. The temperature of the blood of birds is from 2 to 4 degrees Fahrenheit higher than that of the mammal's blood. This high body heat may be taken as an indication of the rapid rates of oxidation, that is to say, combustion, proceeding in the body. Birds show the type of heart structure met with in the crocodile, the ventricle being completely divided into two chambers, with elaboration of the arrangement of the arterial system. The aortic arch carrying blood to the head forms the dorsal aorta (that of the right side only persists in the adult), and this vessel thus conveys only arterial blood to the body. The improvement of the circulatory system in this way probably engendered corresponding improvement in vigour, and prepared the way for primitive efforts to fly.

Other changes in the circulatory system are important also. Owing to the very large size of the wing muscles (pectorals) the blood vessels carrying blood to them are correspondingly large. The main veins of the body are a single inferior and paired superior venae cavae, but the sinus venosus has disappeared. The renal portal system has also disappeared, so that blood from the hinder parts of the body passes directly into the inferior vena cava, but may travel by an alternative vein (the coccygeo-mesenteric) into the hepatic portal vein, and thence to the heart by way of the liver. This alternative vein is peculiar to birds. While discussing the vascular system, we may also mention a peculiarity of the blood corpuscles of birds. These bodies are biconvex and both larger and more numerous than in other vertebrates. The red blood corpuscles of the vulture are more than twice the diameter of our own, and while a cubic centimetre of our own blood contains about five million corpuscles (ten per cent less in women), a corresponding quantity of bird's blood contains about a million more. This feature is associated, no doubt, with the increased activity of life in birds.

Classification of Birds. We may now turn to the question of bird classification. The class *Aves* is divided into two sub-classes containing : (1) Old Birds (*Archaeornithes*) and (2) New Birds (*Neornithes*), of which the former includes only one genus, the extinct form known only by its fossil (*Archaeopteryx litho-graphica*). The fossilized remains of this remarkable creature, which was about the size of a rook and birdlike in its ways, were found in the Jurassic lithographic slates of Bavaria, at Solenhofen, and are shown in Volume 4, Plate 54. Though definitely birdlike, this animal showed certain reptilian characters, and may be regarded as a link between reptiles and birds.

The *Neornithes* contain three divisions : (1) *Palaeognathae*, or running birds ; (2) *Odontognathae*, or toothed birds ; and (3) *Neognathae*, or flying birds. In the course of animal evolution there seems to have been a frequent bifurcation into more active and more sluggish types, and there is no doubt that a cleavage of this sort occurred very early in the evolution of birds.

Running Birds. The Ratitae were established in Miocene times, if not in the Eocene, and became cosmopolitan, though never very successful. They are flightless birds, usually of large size, which differ from all other members of their class in many features. The breastbone or sternum, which in flying birds possesses a prominent keel or carina for attachment of the pectoral muscles, is keelless, or the keel is vestigial. The barbs of the feathers are disconnected, owing to the fact that the barbules lack hooks. The wings and wing muscles are greatly reduced in size, and there is no pygostyle or tail stump. The body is uniformly draped with plumage, except in naked patches on the extremities and on the head and neck, and definite feather tracts (*pterylae*) are lacking. There is no voice box or syrinx.

Existing Ratitae are represented by five genera : *Struthio*, the African ostrich : *Rhea*, the South American ostrich ; *Casuarius*, the Austro-Malayan cassowary ; *Dromaeus*, the Australian emu ; and *Apteryx*, the New Zealand kiwi. The giant *Aepyornis* of Madagascar has long since gone, and the giant moa (*Dinornis*) of New Zealand has also disappeared.

Toothed Birds. The Odontolcae include interesting fossil birds. We have already mentioned that *Archaeopteryx* flourished during Jurassic times. The first primitive birds appeared in the next succeeding geological period, the Cretaceous, in the form of the Odontolcae, which appear to be an offset of the main avian line of descent. They were flightless birds, and the skeleton shows, too, features of interest to us. The sternum lacked a keel, and the jaws held numerous teeth implanted in grooves. *Hesperornis* was about three feet in length, a highly developed diving bird related, perhaps, to the modern grebes and divers.

Flying Birds. The great majority of modern birds are included in the Carinatae, which possess a strongly keeled sternum and hooked barbules. W. P. Pycraft divides them into four legions : (1) *Colombomorphs*, including penguins, grebes, divers and petrels ; (2) *Pelargomorphs*, storks, herons, falcons, pelicans, cormorants and gannets ; (3) *Alectoromorphs* (the fowl tribe), together with gulls, pigeons, auks, cranes and plovers ; and (4) *Coraciomorphs*, a tremendous group, including swifts, owls, kingfishers, cuckoos, rollers, humming-birds and vast hosts of perching birds. A better idea of the characters of birds will be obtained, however, if we consider some 14 orders separately. The first of these consists of extinct creatures known only by their fossil remains, the *Ichthyornithes*, typified by *Ichthyornis*. This creature's remains are found in the same beds as those of *Hesperornis*. It was a more slightly built bird, about one foot tall, and a powerful flier. It had a relatively large head with a long pointed beak, had numerous teeth firmly implanted in sockets in the jaws, and pointing backwards. Remaining orders of the Carinatae are existing creatures, with which we deal in the next Lesson.

Modern Types of Flying Birds

THE archaic water birds, divers and grebes (*Colymbiformes*), occupy a rather isolated position in classification ; they have downy feathers in young and adult stages alike, the wings are generally short and narrow, the strong, sharp beak is flattened from side to side, the legs are set far back, and the toes are webbed (fringed with flaps of skin in grebes). These birds are well adapted to the pursuit of fish. The diver order (*Gaviiformes*) yields two common species, the great northern and the red throated divers. Divers are marine except at breeding time, when they ascend rivers and build their nests on moors. They are not gregarious unless forced to fly inland by gales or stormy weather. Two grebes commonly haunt our inland waters. *Podiceps cristatus* is the great crested grebe, *P. fluviatilis* is the little grebe or dabchick. The adults have a swift, direct flight with head and feet fully extended, but they are able to rise from the surface of water only with difficulty.

Penguins. This order of marine birds (*Spheniciformes*) is also found in the seas of the Antarctic, and is related to petrels on the one hand and divers on the other. They are flightless birds and their rudimentary quill-less wings are clothed with fine, scale-like feathers. When the birds are submerged during swimming operations, the wings are used as paddles, so that penguins may be said to fly under water. They progress on land by a curious waddling gait, are tame and fearless ashore and, when irritated, show great pugnacity. These creatures nest in holes in the ground, usually far from the sea, to which they make daily fishing excursions, a task which soon weeds out weak individuals. The eggs are preyed upon by other birds, and the young are helpless at birth, being fed for an exceptionally long period by the adults.

Petrels, Albatrosses and Fulmars. These are oceanic birds (*Procellariiformes*) with webbed feet (the great toe is missing) and remarkable powers of flight. The strong, somewhat hooked beak is well adapted for fish-eating, and the horny sheath or bill is composed of several pieces, in both upper and lower jaws. The wings are generally long, narrow and pointed. Many of the largest flying birds are included in this order, as also a few of the smallest, some petrels being scarcely larger than finches. Most species inhabit desolate tracts of ocean and islands in the southern hemisphere, but a few are common with us. The birds of this order show many differences, one of the most interesting being the way in which they take food. The albatross swoops down to the sea surface and takes food with outstretched wings ; the shearwaters drop to the surface with a great splash and disappear after the prey for a few moments ; while the diving petrels plunge to even greater depths than the shearwaters.

Gannets, Cormorants, Pelicans and Flamingoes. The order *Ciconiiformes* embraces both long- and short-legged water or marsh birds of fish-feeding habit with all four toes connected by webs. One family contains many greedy swimming birds like gannets, cormorants, pelicans and frigate birds, in which the wings are long and pointed and well developed. A second family includes the herons and bitterns, shy, solitary wading birds with a long neck and very long legs. These are frequently seen in lakes, fens and rivers, monotonously waiting for something to turn up. Occasionally they fly, at very high altitudes, to mud-flats near sandy shores. Another family contains equally shy and retiring birds, storks and ibises, which live in open country or in woods, sometimes in creeks or salt water pools. Flamingoes are included in yet another family. They are generally solitary, but may sometimes be seen in flocks flying in V-formation. Like herons, flamingoes have long necks and extremely slender legs. The bill, which is covered by soft skin, is bent down and has horny plates at the sides.

Swans, Ducks and Geese. The species of the large and cosmopolitan order *Anseriformes* are web-footed, aquatic birds, mostly with flattened bills covered with soft skin and edged above and below with horny plates. They are almost entirely vegetarian feeders. One extensive family includes swans, ducks and geese. Our wild duck, *Anas boschas*, which is the form from which domestic species have arisen, is a typical member of this family. Diving members of the family include the eider duck, one of our winter visitors ; the teal and the widgeon are non-divers and common objects of sport. Of geese indigenous to Britain the grey lag is perhaps best known, and the domestic goose is probably descended from it. Swans are also included in this order, the white species being common throughout Europe and extending to Asia and Africa. The black swan of Australia and the black-necked swan of South America are remarkable on account of their colour. Perhaps the most curious member of the order, however, is the chaka or crested screamer of Paraguay and Brazil. This bird has an extraordinarily pneumatic skeleton, the air cavities extending into the bones of wings and legs. It also possesses two sharp spurs on the wings, and has developed the curious habit of soaring almost out of sight in large spirals.

Vultures, Hawks and Eagles. The predaceous character of members of the order *Falconiformes* is clearly indicated by the strong, hooked beak and the powerful talons, admirably adapted for seizing prey. Members of this order are to be found the world over. One family includes vultures of the condor type, birds of immense size with a hooked but not sharp bill and with feet not suited to grasping. The head and neck of these birds may be bare or covered with a short stubble of down, and the naked skin is sometimes brightly coloured. They can sail at great heights and have an interesting form of sustained flight with little movement of the wings, as well as remarkably keen sight. The members of the falcon family, which includes also hawks, eagles, kites, buzzards and ospreys, possess the characters of the typical falconiform bird and are distinguished from vultures by the covering of feathers on head and neck. Another family includes the curious secretary bird, which stands with its extraordinarily long legs crossed. For this resemblance to the archer in its stance, the bird was called *Sagittarius* or archer, which name has been corrupted to *Secretarius*.

Tinamous. The terrestrial birds belonging to the order *Tinamiformes* are possessed of powerful flight and show characters similar to those of the *Ratitae*. Their appearance resembles that of the partridge, and they are ground birds which rarely perch. They resemble the running birds in special features of the skull and skeleton, but the sternum has a strong keel, as would be expected from the powerful flight. They reside in the New World, in Peru, Brazil, Bolivia and the Argentine.

Game Birds. These birds, the *Galliformes*, are also ground birds, with strong, blunt-clawed feet adapted for scratching up the ground in search of food. The family *Phasianidae* alone calls for comment, including as it does turkeys, fowl, grouse, and guinea-fowl, and also the peculiar hoatzin or stinking pheasant of the New World. Guinea-fowl have been derived from a West African species, turkeys from a North American form, while the red jungle fowl of south Asia (*Gallus bankiva*) is ancestral to domesticated fowls, and the peacock was originally native to the same region. The hoatzin is about the size of the pigeon and gets its common name from the strong musk odour it gives off.

Cranes and Bustards. These are long-legged birds (*Gruiformes*) living, for the most part, in marshes. They lack a crop. Members of the rail, coot and water hen family have flattened bodies, which facilitate movement through the dense undergrowth constituting their home. The crane family includes archaic forms bearing superficial resemblance to herons, being long-legged and having slender necks. Bustards, on the other hand, have a thick neck and a flat head.

Plovers, Snipe, Gulls and Pigeons. These birds belong to a mixed order, (*Charadriiformes*), containing marine, terrestrial and arboreal forms. The plover family are waders that fly well, but are not swimmers like the gull and skua family. Gulls are widely distributed sea birds with a staple diet of fish and other marine animals, though they migrate inland for feeding and breeding purposes. Our commonest forms are the common gull, the herring gull and the black-headed gull. Other relatives are the terns or sea-swallows, recognized by their pointed wings and tails. The chief British representatives of the auks are the razor-bill, the guillemot and the puffin or sea-parrot.

Parrots, Macaws and Cockatoos. In the members of the order *Cuculiformes* of arboreal birds the first and fourth toes are directed backwards, the last toe sometimes being reversible. One group is that to which the cuckoo belongs, characterized by a gently curving bill deeply cleft and long pointed wings. A sharply marked group is that including the parrot, with its strongly curved and hinged bill. Perhaps the most curious form is *Stringops*, the burrowing parrot, which is of owl-like appearance but has only slight powers of flight.

Owls, Swifts, Humming-Birds, Woodpeckers. The flying birds with short legs fall into several orders. To the *Coraciiformes* belong the beautifully coloured rollers and kingfishers, as well as bee-eaters, hoopoes and hornbills. In several other orders we find nocturnal creatures with forwardly directed eyes, such as owls

(*Strigiformes*) ; wide-mouthed nightjars (*Caprimulgiformes*) ; swifts and humming-birds (*Micropodiformes*), the latter the smallest of all birds which flit from flower to flower ; and wood-peckers (*Piciformes*). These last are powerfully built birds with an enormously elongated tongue, flat and horny claws, and a firm tail that is used as a prop during climbing activities. The toucan and wryneck are two more members of this last order.

Perching Birds. The order *Passeriformes* is a vast assemblage of some 5,500 species, including half the total number of known birds. The feet of such birds are specially modified for grasping and perching, and the vocal organs are well developed. Classification into families is especially difficult and is accomplished with respect to the arrangement of the syrinx muscles. The order includes such birds as thrushes, robins, wrens, hedge-sparrows, nightingales, blackbirds and whitethroats, as well as swallows and martins, crows and their beautiful relatives called birds of paradise : also magpies and jays, ravens, starlings, finches, and many other well-known birds not mentioned in connexion with other orders.

LESSON 32

Mammals and Their Classification

THE success of both birds and mammals in the struggle for existence is due primarily to the fact that their respiratory and circulatory organs have become extremely efficient. These two classes of vertebrates have succeeded in purifying the blood very thoroughly, and there is no mixing of pure and impure blood as in amphibians and most reptiles.

We might define the *Mammalia* shortly as vertebrates which breathe air, have warm blood, and are covered with epidermal outgrowths in the form of hairs. But to complete the definition we should need to add many other distinctive features. The skull has two condyles connecting it with the first vertebra, in distinction to the single condyle of the Sauropsida. Plates of gristle (epiphyses) are found at the ends of the vertebrae and long bones of the limbs of the growing animal. When growth ceases, these become bony. The lower jaw consists of a single bone on each side, and is joined to the skull by a bone called the squamosal, the quadrate bone found in birds and reptiles in an intermediate position having no relation to jaw suspension. Most mammals have two sets of teeth, forming the milk and permanent teeth respectively. The teeth are implanted in sockets and are of different shapes, being distinguished, for this reason, as incisors or cutting teeth, canine or tearing teeth, premolars and molars or grinding teeth. A muscular partition divides the body cavity into two parts, the thorax (which contains the heart and lungs) in front and the abdomen (which contains the digestive and reproductive organs) behind. The heart consists of two auricles and two ventricles, one of each of these cavities on either side being completely separated from its fellow of the opposite one. There is a single aortic arch, but this corresponds to the left arch of reptiles, not the right as in birds. The blood corpuscles are discoidal in form and lack nuclei.

Perhaps the most important advantage gained by mammals in the course of evolution has been the development of a relatively large brain, which is correlated with marked intelligence. This has been a leading factor in the struggle for existence and a good illustration of the principle that the race is not always to the swift nor the battle to the strong. Man himself is the most remarkable example of this, and owes his supremacy to a fine brain, an upright posture, together with stereoscopic vision and useful busy hands.

Most mammals are *viviparous*—that is to say, they bring their young into the world alive as miniatures of themselves. The unborn animal (foetus) obtains nourishment from the blood of its mother by means of a special organ (the placenta) which develops in the womb and becomes embedded in the womb wall. After birth the young animal receives nourishment from the secretion of milk or mammary glands. Exceptions to the first of these rules are found in the most primitive group of mammals, the *Monotremata*. These include *Echidna*, the spiny ant-eater, and *Ornithorhynchus*, the duck-billed platypus, both of which are found in Australia. Both are carnivores, though the prey are lowly creatures. The *Monotremata* are much more primitive in structure than any other existing mammals and present many points of resemblance to reptiles, but are well on the way to extinction.

The two other main groups of the Mammalia are the *Metatheria* and the *Eutheria*, of which the former are pouched mammals while the latter are mammals such as we see around us in this country. Excepting the American opossums, the members of the *Metatheria* are natives of the Australian regions, where, in the absence of competing types, they have acquired an amazing diversity of character, due to adaptation to most varied habits. The wolf (*Thylacinus*) is a flesh eater, the banded marsupial ant-eaters (*Myrmecobius*) are insectivores, the pouched mole (*Notoryctes*) feeds on various small creatures, the kangaroo (*Macropus*) is herbivorous, the wombat (*Phascolomys*) burrows after roots, and the phalangers (*Phalanger*) climb after fruit. Most of the types of mammals with which we are familiar in the northern hemisphere are paralleled in the southern hemisphere by

SOME PRIMITIVE MAMMALS. Upper left, the duck bill or duck-billed Platypus (Ornithorhynchus) is an Australian carnivore with several reptilian resemblances. Though oviparous, it feeds its young on exuded milk. Below is a spiny ant-eater (Echidna), another mammal of the Monotremata group. Right, a rock wallaby, a typical marsupial.

marsupials. The young marsupial is born in a very immature condition. At a very early stage of development it crawls into a sheltering pouch formed by a fold of skin on the underside of the mother's body.

Mammalian Orders. We will now glance at the most general characters of the eleven main orders of existing *Eutheria*

1. *Edentata* (toothless mammals). The chief living represent-atives of this decadent order are archaic forms found in South America and, to a small extent, in the Old World. Not all are toothless, as are the ant-eaters, which belong here. The leaf-eating arboreal sloths and the burrowing, mail-protected arm-adilloes possess teeth, but only primitive ones, which lack the enamel covering characteristic of mammals.

2. *Insectivora* (insect-eaters). The members of this large and ancient order are small creatures found in nearly all parts of the world. They are specially adapted to feed on insects and other small animals. The hedgehog, mole and shrew are British species.

3. *Chiroptera* (bats). These interesting animals are closely related to the *Insectivora*, but differ from them in possessing organs of flight. (The larger bats of the East Indies are fruit-eaters.) So complete is the adaptation of the limbs to flight that the animal is able only to shuffle along with difficulty.

4. *Rodentia* (gnawing mammals). This again is a large and ancient order of widely distributed animals that are mostly small and adapted for vegetarian life, though some are omnivorous. They possess four chisel-edged incisor teeth, which grow continuously throughout life and are kept permanently sharp. Of familiar British types, the rabbit, hare, squirrel, rat, mouse and vole may be taken to illustrate the wide variation in habit that characterizes the order.

5. *Hyracoidea* (conies). This order includes small animals, often confounded with rabbits, which inhabit African and Syrian deserts. The fore-foot has four toes, the hind-foot only three, and these are provided with small hoofs, with the exception of the inner toe of the hind limb, which is clawed. The upper incisors are somewhat like those of the rabbit, but the back teeth are very different from the rabbit's, being more like those of the rhinoceros.

6. *Ungulata* (hoofed mammals). This order includes most of the large herbivorous mammals, as well as a few omnivorous ones. The hoofed extremities are more or less perfectly adapted to swift progression on land. We distinguish between two ungulate types, odd-toed and even-toed respectively, terms that refer to the number of digits on the hind foot. Among odd-toed ungulates the pig-like tapirs of south-east Asia and tropical America possess four toes on the fore foot and three on the hind foot, while the rhinoceroses of Africa and south Asia have three toes on each foot. The horse and its allies have but a single toe, which is greatly enlarged, on each foot. Among even-toed ungulates, the omnivorous swine and the plant-eating hippopotamus do not chew the cud, and in this respect differ from ruminants like deer, oxen, goats, sheep, giraffes, llamas and camels.

7. *Proboscidea* (elephants). These huge plant eaters, which are native to Africa and south Asia, are simpler in many ways than

the members of the *Ungulata*. The teeth are much specialized, however, and the drawing out of the snout into a prehensile trunk is a notable peculiarity.

8. *Sirenia* (sea-cows). This is an order of plant-eating marine animals represented only by the manatee and the dugong, which inhabit the shores and estuaries of the South Atlantic and the Indian ocean respectively. The tail is flattened horizontally, the fore-limbs have become modified into flippers, while the hind limbs have disappeared.

9. *Cetacea* (whales and porpoises). These are even more completely adapted to aquatic life than the *Sirenia*. The whale-bone whale and its allies are entirely toothless, but the porpoise and the sperm-whale have numerous pointed conical teeth.

10. *Carnivora* (flesh-eating mammals). A great variety of predacious forms are included in this order, as well as the non-predacious pandas which, although they come between the raccoons and bears, are strictly vegetarian animals. The *Felidae* (cat family) embrace species best adapted to carnivorous life. To this family belong the lion and tiger, as well as civets and other cat-like creatures. The *Canidae* (dog family) include dogs, foxes, wolves and jackals, which are less specialized than members of the previous family. Another family is the *Mustelidae*, represented by badgers and small bloodthirsty forms like weasels and the fish-eating otters. Another family is the *Ursidae* or bear family, the members of which are omnivorous (with the exception of the polar bear) and less specialized than other flesh-eaters. The family of aquatic fish-eaters known as the *Pinnipedia* includes the walrus, sea-lion and seal, all of which are well adapted to marine life, as the form of the body and of the flipper-like extremities well testify.

11. *Primates* (men and monkeys). All the members of this order are possessed of relatively large brains. This affects the general form of the skull, and one result is the forwardly directed eyes. With the exception of Man and the gorilla these highest mammals are adapted to a climbing life in the tree tops, and the feet are efficient grasping organs. The types most closely approaching Man in structure are the man-like apes (*Anthropoidea*). Of these, the gorilla (which has cartilage nostril supports and an almost human external ear) and the chimpanzee are native to tropical Africa, while the orang utan belongs to Sumatra and Borneo, and the gibbons to south-east Asia.

Some Mammalian Pedigrees

THE search for the ancestral mammal takes us back to Permian times, when certain undoubted reptiles existed in which we discern rudimentary mammalian characters. These reptiles are called the *Theromorpha*. The most highly developed of them, the *Theriodonta*, possessed teeth firmly implanted in sockets and clearly differentiated into incisors, canines, premolars and molars. They had a pair of occipital condyles, and at the back of the mouth cavity hung a soft fold of skin (soft palate). The hips and shoulders were of mammalian type and the limbs lifted the body well off the ground. Such characters mark off the *Theromorpha* as " mammals in the making " and as the probable ancestors of the modern mammal.

We know that the evolution of mammals occurred about this time because in Triassic times fairly well advanced mammalian types existed, one of which (the *Multituberculata*) persisted until Tertiary times. In this type the lower jaw was formed largely of a single bone (dentary) and was suspended to the skull by the squamosal instead of the quadrate, as in reptiles. Thoracic and abdominal cavities were separated by a diaphragm, and the blood corpuscles had lost their nuclei. Side by side with such obvious mammalian characters as these persisted many reptilian ones, the best marked being the nature of the shoulder bones. Moreover, the organs of excretion and reproduction opened along with the rectum into a common cloaca, and the egg-laying habit persisted. It was at this stage that the Monotremata diverged from the main line to the realm of higher mammals, to progress so very slightly that we recognize the reptilian features in present-day forms like *Echidna* and *Ornithorhynchus*.

In the early part of the Tertiary epoch extensive tracts of marshy ground covered considerable areas in the land masses of the northern hemisphere, and here numerous primitive mammals lived. In Eocene times the Marsupials were distinct and roamed the entire earth. They failed, however, to compete successfully with the more efficient Placentalia and succumbed, except in the secure isolation of their present home. The placentals were well marked at the beginning of the Eocene period as small creatures with five fingers and toes and a flat-footed (plantigrade) gait. Unlike the *Multituberculata* (which had teeth with numerous cusps, as the name implies), these primitive mammals had teeth with three cusps and low crowns. Some (*Condylarthra*) lived for the most part on vegetable food, others (*Creodonta*) were carnivorous, while a few were insectivorous.

By late Eocene times, many orders of mammals existed. The creodonts became shaped into the *Carnivora*, which had already branched out into a dog-cat-bear group (*Fissipedia*) and a seal group (*Pinniepedia*). A stock of primitive mammals combining the characters of creodont and insectivore gave rise to the even-toed ungulates (*Artiodactyla*), while types combining the characters of the Condylarthra and the insectivores yielded the odd-toed ungulates (*Perissodactyla*). The even-toed forms became divided into camels, deer and cattle along one line, and hippos and pigs along another. Closely related to them are the conies and the elephant. The primitive insectivorous mammals gave rise to modern insectivores, rodents and edentates, as well as to the primates. Closely allied to the Insectivora are the bats (*Chiroptera*). Whales (*Cetacea*) are believed to have arisen from animals closely related to the creodonts, while sea-cows (*Sirenia*) are probably derived from the same ancestor as elephants.

We might consider briefly the changing background to these divergent lines in the evolution of the mammals. The swamps of the early part of the Tertiary epoch were to a large extent superseded by extensive plains covered with grass and other vegetation. With these changes primitive swamp-dwellers were giving way to hoofed animals and related forms suited to rapid progression on plains and adapted to feeding on vegetation which, being drier than the succulent vegetation of marshes and damp forests, was more difficult to chew and digest. It is intelligible that hoofed animals should become more speedy than their ancestors when we remember that the Carnivora began to evolve from the same stock contemporarily. The struggle for existence, under the influence of which no source of food remains neglected, was never keener than at these times, when some forms preyed on plants and others on plant-eaters.

The pedigrees of some of our swift runners, like the horse and deer, are well known from the fossil records preserved. The evolution of the horse from *Eohippus* of Eocene times, through

Miohippus (Miocene), *Pliohippus* (Pliocene), to the modern horse, *Equus*, is known with a probability that amounts to certainty. This gradual transition from a plantigrade swamp-dweller to a racehorse which runs on the tips of fingers and toes, was accompanied by modification of the bones of the limbs and of the teeth, as also by progressive increase in size.

		Characteristic Type	Fore Foot	Hind Foot		Teeth
QUATERNARY OR AGE OF MAN	Recent					Long Crowned, cement covered
	Pleistocene				One Toe (both feet)	
TERTIARY OR AGE OF MAMMALS	Pliocene					
	Miocene				Three Toes (both feet). Side Toes not touching ground	
	Oligocene				Three Toes (both feet) Side Toes touching ground	Short Crowned, without cement
	Eocene				Four Toes, front feet. Three Toes, hind feet. Side Toes touching ground	
AGE OF REPTILES	Cretaceous Jurassic Triassic	Hypothetical Ancestors with Five Toes on each Foot and Teeth like those of Monkeys				

EVOLUTION OF THE HORSE. This table shows how fossil skulls, toes and teeth enable us to trace the process by means of which through millions of years the three-toed Eohippus—about the size of a modern fox-terrier—of the Eocene period became the great hoofed- creature of today.

Courtesy of American Museum of Natural History

The two bones of the lower arm and leg (radius and ulna) tibia and fibula) became fused, the ankle and wrist came to move only in one plane, and the third digit alone of hand and foot persisted and became enormously enlarged. Its nail formed a hoof. The two " splint " bones found just below the knee of the modern horse are no other than the remains of the second and fourth digits, which have almost disappeared (*see* illus. in Volume 4, page 131). Hand and foot became greatly elongated, for the apparent knee of the horse is really its wrist, the hock corresponding to our ankle. The teeth became longer but lost their roots, and ridges which developed on the crowns of the molars provided a grinding mill adequate enough to allow the animal to feed on dry herbage.

One result of evolution in the direction of the Ungulata has been the abolition of the collar bones (clavicles), which are strut-like bones between the breast and shoulder bones. Since these elements are ill suited to resist sudden impacts (this bone is often broken in Man by a slight fall) they are only a source of weakness in swift running types, where the body is frequently brought down on the fore limbs suddenly. Many mammals possess these bones, but they are never developed in the Ungulata.

The hand of another odd-toed ungulate, the rhinoceros, is of interest in that the first and last digits alone have disappeared, the second and fourth being of equal standing with the third. The reduction of digits has not proceeded as far as in the horse.

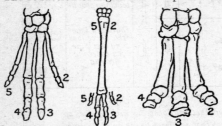

It will be noticed that in the limb of the odd-toed ungulate the plane of symmetry passes through the third digit. Not so in even-toed members of the order, where this p l a n e passes between the third and fourth digits, which have become more or less dominant together.

HANDS OF MAMMALS. Comparison of the hands of the pig (left), deer (centre) and rhinoceros (right). The digits are numbered.

Thus in the hand of the pig we notice that the thumb or first digit has disappeared, while the outer digits (2 and 5) are much smaller than the inner ones (3 and 4), which are the chief agents of progression. But as these animals have not fully emancipated themselves from the old swamp life, the outer digits are useful on soft ground to prevent sinking in too far.

Turning now to the deer, which is the embodiment of swift progression on land, we find the limbs greatly elongated and very slender, and the hand more specialized than that of the pig. The

only one or two function at any one time. As those in front of the jaw are worn down the ones behind move forwards and take their place. The elephant's trunk, which is no more than its drawn-out nose, enables its possessor to manipulate objects, and so adequately compensates for the sacrifice of arms and legs to the task of supporting the huge body. By its means tree-branches or herbage are easily secured as food.

Elephant history starts with a creature no larger than a pig, *Moeritherium*, in Eocene times. The molars of this animal (it possessed incisors, too) had only two transverse ridges. Later came *Palaeomastodon*, a larger animal with three-ridged molars, a rudimentary trunk, and two incisor teeth. The Pliocene form, *Tetrabelodon*, attained a larger size and had incisors modified into long tusks, with only two molars, each having six ridges. This primitive elephant showed the back-to-front tooth succession of the modern elephant.

Sea-cows, or *Sirenia*, are related to the *Proboscidea*, and at this point mention may be made of their special peculiarities. The dugong and manatee are regarded as ancient offshoots of the ungulate stock which have become adapted to aquatic vegetarian life, have simplified their teeth and have modified their fore limbs into efficient paddles, while losing the hind limbs. The integument is thick and wrinkled and may lack hair or possess a scanty covering of it. The snout is not elongated, as in the elephant, and the nostrils open on its upper surface. One gigantic toothless member of this order, *Rhytina*, formerly lived on the islands of the Bering Sea, but became extinct in the 18th century.

LESSON 34

Facts About the Teeth of Mammals

MANY mammals possess more or less efficient weapons which stand their owners in good stead in the event of attack. Some of these, like the sharp teeth and claws of the cat-like types, are primarily offensive in character, but serve equally well for defence. It is in vegetarian forms that we find a great variety of weapons which are primarily used in what may be termed active defence. A good example is afforded by the formidable tusks of the elephant and the wild boar. Antlers and horns come in this category also, and are found in greatest variety among the Ungulata. One type is that possessed by the Indian buffalo and the American bison, as well as by oxen, sheep, goats and antelopes. They are bony outgrowths from the top of the skull, covered by horny sheaths of varying shape.

The antlers of the deer, possessed only by the male (except in the reindeer), are bony outgrowths of the skull, but differ from horns in that they are shed annually and replaced by new growth. In many instances they become more complex each year, varying in the number of " points," thus serving as an index of age. Until their full size is attained they are covered with soft, hairy skin (the " velvet "), after which a projecting ridge (the " burr") grows out at the base of the antler and stops the circulation of the blood in the skin, so that the velvet dies and peels off while the antler becomes dead bone and is in time discarded.

Mammals often possess structures which, being used in passive defence, may be considered as " armour." The skin may be tough and thick, as in the elephant and rhinoceros, or the fur may be so dense as to be a protection. In several orders hairs are transformed into spines, which help to ward off attacks of enemies, as in the spiny ant-eater of Australia (*Echidna*), the hedgehog (*Erinaceus*), and the porcupine (*Hystrix*). Among mammals poor in teeth (*Edentata*) we find plate and scale armour. In the armadillos of South America, some of which are able to roll themselves up into balls like hedgehogs, bony plates in the skin serve to defend the body. In the pangolins of Africa and Asia the body covering is of horny overlapping scales.

Teeth are valuable weapons, and as they are important characters in diagnosing the various mammalian orders we must make special mention of them. The teeth of the primitive mammal were beset with sharp tubercles. Among the odd-toed Ungulata the tapir has ridged grinding teeth, which show a useful improvement upon projecting tubercles. The rhinoceros shows a step in advance of the tapir, its teeth being reduced in number and the crowns of the grinders having a more complex set of ridges, which make them very efficient masticators. Similar complex grinders are seen in the horse, ass and zebra. The elaborately ridged crowns of these teeth are obviously composed of three kinds of material, enamel, dentine and cement, which vary in degree of hardness and maintain the rough surface by unequal wearing. Canine teeth are practically absent, though often feebly represented in the stallion, and the incisors are provided with deep pits, which get filled up with food and show that practical guide to age, the black " mark " on the crown. Among even-toed ungulates, omnivorous swine and peccaries are primitive, as is shown by the full number of teeth together with the tubercles on the crowns of the grinders. The hippopotamus of Africa is practically an immense pig of vegetarian habit and with a somewhat specialized dentition.

The large order of g n a w i n g mammals (*Rodentia*), consisting of small and comparatively simply organized creatures with headquarters in South America, is represented in Britain by such familiar forms as the rabbit, hare, squirrel, rat and mouse. Taking the rabbit as a type, we find two chisel-edged incisors above and below, and a number of prismatic grinding teeth with transversely ridged crowns farther back. A wide space, or diastema, due to the lack of canines, separates the two kinds of teeth. Behind the upper incisors lies a second pair of minute teeth, which easily escape observation. All the teeth grow continuously throughout life. The incisors remain sharp because they are thickly coated in front with relatively hard enamel, but consist mostly of dentine or ivory (which is not so hard) behind. Hence they wear unequally and maintain a sharp edge. As the teeth are constantly growing, constant

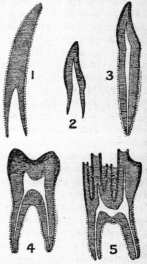

FORMS OF TEETH. Diagrammatic sections. **1.** Incisor or tusk of elephant with pulp-cavity persistently open at base. **2.** Human incisor during development, with root imperfectly formed and pulp-cavity widely open. **3.** Completely formed human incisor. **4.** Human molar with broad crown and two roots. **5.** Molar of the ox, with enamel covering of crown deeply folded and depressions filled with cement; the surface is worn by use. Enamel shown black, pulp white, dentine by horizontal shading and cement by dots.

gnawing is necessary to keep them worn down. A rodent which is so unfortunate as to happen to lose an incisor is handicapped by the unchecked growth of the opposing tooth, which attains an inordinate length and may even cause the death of its possessor.

Some of the small nocturnal animals which make up the order of insect-eaters (*Insectivora*) are to be found in all parts of the world except South America and Australia. A good type of this group, which is common in the Old World, is the familiar European hedgehog (*Erinaceus*). In accordance with the nature of its food, mostly consisting of worms, small insects and snails, the teeth of the hedgehog are sharply pointed, those at the back having their crowns provided with small cutting projections. Such teeth are eminently suitable for dealing with not only such small creatures as we have mentioned, but also snakes, frogs and even mice, none of which is despised as an article of food. The name hedgehog, by the way, is suggested by the shape of the snout, which is something like that of the pig, and is used in much the same way for grubbing in the ground.

Equally interesting are whales and porpoises (*Cetacea*), which have derived from terrestrial ancestors by a line of descent which is still somewhat doubtful. Some members of the order possess numerous sharp simple teeth, well suited for seizing and holding slippery fishes and cuttles. The common porpoise is one of the most familiar forms, but the huge sperm whale or cachalot is an example of a toothed cetacean on a large scale. It is noteworthy that the whalebone whales have no functional teeth, though in very early life these are to be found embedded in the gums they never penetrate. A notable peculiarity is met with in the Greenland whale in the form of numerous pairs of horny plates (baleen), frayed out at the edges and hanging down from the roof of the mouth. So-called whalebone was formerly derived from them. The whales of this group feed upon small animals which float in enormous numbers at or near the surface of the sea, making up what is technically called the " plankton." Moving along at some speed, the whale takes in large quantities of sea water, which is strained through the baleen, leaving behind in the mouth the swarms of minute creatures (largely copepods) it contains. Danger of choking during this process of feeding is obviated by the conelike top of the windpipe, which fits into the back of the nasal passages in such a way that water cannot find its way into the lungs.

The Carnivora have claws instead of hoofs, and possess teeth more or less perfectly adapted to flesh tearing and eating. The cat family (*Felidae*) includes beast of prey *par excellence*, such as the lion, tiger, leopard and cheetah of the Old World, and the puma and jaguar of the New. Examination of the lion's skull serves to show some of the specializations that exist in connexion with the carnivorous habit. The jaws are enormously strong, and the lower one is raised by powerful muscles inserted in prominent ridges seen on the skull. The canine teeth are sharp tusks used for seizing and holding prey, while the crowns of the back teeth are cutting blades of great efficiency. In carnivores of this family, as also of the dog family (*Canidae*), there is one tooth on each side of each jaw, which is enlarged and modified for tearing. This so-called carnassial tooth is the last premolar in the upper jaw and the first molar in the lower. The bear and the seal do not possess well-developed carnassial teeth.

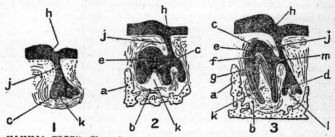

MAMMAL TEETH. Three stages in development: a, bone of alveolus; b, dental sac; c, enamel-membrane; d, enamel-membrane of permanent tooth; e, enamel-pulp; f, layer of enamel; g, dentine; h, dental groove; j, dental lamina; k, dental papilla; l, dental papilla of permanent tooth; m, neck connecting milk-tooth with lamina.

Bears (*Ursidae*), with the exception of the Polar bear, are omnivorous: and while the canines form prominent tusks, the back teeth are blunt-crowned grinders suitable for dealing with a miscellaneous diet. Seals are aquatic carnivores or Pinnipedia, to which order the walrus and the sea-lion also belong, distinguished by the possession of a thick coat of fat (blubber) beneath the skin. The walrus has paddle-like limbs and only a scanty covering of hair. The upper canines form large tusks used for grubbing up shellfish as food, while the grinders have blunt crowns well suited to crushing the bodies of these food animals. Sea-lions and seals have closely set fur, the former being sometimes known as eared seals on account of their minute external ears. Both types have narrow, sharply pointed back teeth.

It is fitting to conclude this Lesson with a brief account of the mode of development of the mammalian tooth, which is derived partly from the epidermis but partly from the deeper skin or dermis. Enamel is developed from the epidermis ; while the remainder of the tooth, consisting of dentine, cement and tooth pulp, is formed by the deeper layer. The tooth is therefore partly an ectodermal and partly an endodermal product.

The mouth ectoderm lying above the jaws of the embryo sinks below the general surface as a long band, the *dental lamina*, which follows the curve of the jaws. From this band minute tooth rudiments are produced as buds in two groups, one giving rise to the milk teeth, the other to the permanent teeth appearing by replacement later. The early tooth rudiment is a hollow cup formed of a double layer of cells, the *enamel organ*, which embraces a finger-like projection of the dermis or *dental papilla*. The cells of the inner layer of the enamel organ secrete enamel in the form of a thin continuous sheet, while the most super-ficial cells of the dental papilla or *odontoblasts* form successive layers of dentine (a system of delicate parallel tubes containing organic fibrils and impregnated with lime salts), of which the bulk of the tooth is composed. The inner cells of the dental papilla form tooth pulp, a loose reticulum of cells and fibrils containing blood vessels and minute nerves. The tissue surround-ing the tooth rudiment becomes vascular and encloses the entire structure in a *dental sac*, from which blood vessels pass into the developing pulp. As the rudiment enlarges, it projects from and eventually breaks through the epithelium of the mouth, when the outer layer of the enamel organ (or enamel membrane) is ruptured. The teeth of most mammals develop distinct roots, each with a minute aperture communicating with the pulp cavity, embedded in the bone of the alveolus or jaw.

LESSON 35

An Introduction to Zoogeography

CHARLES DARWIN laid the foundations of the study of animal geography by his observations and deductions regarding the total absence from oceanic islands of both mammals and amphibians, as also by his experiments and obser-vations on the methods of dispersal of organisms. Perhaps the first ideas about the distribution of animals came from the celebrated French biologist, Buffon, whose brilliant " Histoire Naturelle " (1777) was the first treatise on animal geography. Since Buffon's day, our knowledge of this subject has been greatly enriched by the labours of other distinguished zoologists, notably by Darwin, Wallace and Sclater.

First, let us state briefly some of the curious facts and apparent anomalies that have to be explained. Why, for instance, must we go to Africa to shoot a lion and to India to capture a tiger ? Why are camels found only in the great desert belt of north Africa and Central Asia, and their closest allies, llamas and alpacas, only in the southern Andes. Most extraordinary is the case of the curious tapirs, of which two or three species are found in tropical America, and the only other species (the Malayan tapir) in Borneo and the Malay peninsula. Among birds we have the humming-birds swarming all over America, but in no other part of the world. The equally beautiful birds of paradise, of which over fifty species are known, are found only in New Guinea and a few adjacent islands. Lastly, we have the great mammalian group of marsupials limited to Australia and nearby islands, except the opossum family, which abounds in South America and as far north as California.

We may look at these curiosities in another way, from the point of view of the similarities of animals in countries far apart and the diversity that is often found between those which are comparatively near together. An Englishman travelling to Japan will have gone nearly half round the globe to find forms of life closely similar to those of his native land. But if an Australian settler goes to New Zealand, a distance of about 1,300 miles, he finds himself in a country zoologically and botanically entirely unlike the country he has left. Even more remarkable is the case of two small islands, Bali and Lombok, in the Malay Archipelago. The islands are only fifteen miles apart, but their forms of life are strangely different. Their birds differ more than do the birds of Britain and Japan. Again, Borneo resembles Sumatra and the Malay peninsula in its mammals and birds to a greater extent than it resembles the much nearer island of Celebes, whose forms of life are more closely allied to those of India or Africa.

Those and most other peculiarities in the distribution of animals are rendered intelligible, sometimes directly explained, by the application of certain general principles which we must now examine. Before Darwin's " Origin of Species " appeared, the common belief was that almost all the islands scattered over the great oceans were the remnants of former continents, which had sunk beneath the waters, while existing continents rose up to take their place. This view was accepted almost as a matter of course, and seemed, at first sight, to be quite in accordance with the fact that most of the older rocks in all parts of the world were of marine origin. During the voyage of the " Beagle," however, Darwin was able to visit many of these islands to be greatly impressed by the poverty of their forms of life. He also noticed that they were of a volcanic or coral nature and never contained stratified rocks characteristic of continents, or of islands that once formed parts of continents. He concluded that they had all been formed in the ocean itself, though some of them appeared ancient.

The total absence of native land mammals was thus readily explained ; these animals, though often good swimmers, could never cross wide seas or oceans. He also showed by experiment that the eggs of frogs and newts, similarly lacking on such islands, are quickly killed by salt water. Wide seas like wide deserts or lofty mountains, form permanent obstacles to the dispersal of animals, and in zoogeography are called barriers.

If we look at a map of the world and consider the positions of the large land masses we find that they are connected in so remarkable a manner that it would be possible for a man to traverse all the continents, starting from Cape Horn, almost without going out of sight of land or requiring any vessel other than a small sailing boat. If our map shows the contour of the ocean floor we shall see that the beds of the great oceans do not form hills and valleys and mountain ranges, as was once supposed, but are really immense undulating plains at depths of from ten to thirty thousand feet, out of which the continents rise abruptly, so that the 100-fathom line lies close to their shores, while even the 1,000-fathom line leaves only a narrow selvage around them, which in no way alters their contours. If we take this 1,000-fathom line as roughly indicating the amount and extent of land during the whole Tertiary period of geology, we find all the continents united towards the north by wide stretches of land, which offer ample facilities for the migrations of land animals at successive subsequent epochs.

The distribution of animals depends in part upon their individual powers of locomotion, though this is by no means the only factor of importance in determining their habitations. In most continents, and many large countries and islands, birds show a similar restricted range to mammals, notwithstanding their very superior locomotory powers. Reptiles also show very little difference in this respect, but are more dependent on temperature ; they are scarce in temperate and almost absent from very cold countries. Amphibians are more restricted in their ranges than reptiles in some respects, but more extended in others. This is due to the fact that they can withstand a lower temperature, but are killed by salt water, for which reason they are absent from all true oceanic islands, such as the Azores, Madeira, St. Helena, Mauritius, and remoter islands of the Pacific.

We might now turn to some of the puzzles of distribution, taking first the case of the tapirs. Two common species of tapir inhabit tropical South America from Brazil to Paraguay and the Malay peninsula, Sumatra and Borneo. Three other species occur in tropical America, one in the Andes and two in central America from Panama to Mexico. But no tapirs exist either in Africa or continental India. This apparent anomaly was completely explained during last century. First, in 1825, Cuvier described the skeleton of *Palaeotherium* from the early Tertiary beds of Paris as being allied to living tapirs ; later, both in France and Germany, remains of true tapirs were found in Miocene and Pliocene strata, and fossil tapirs have also been found in China and America. These discoveries clearly indicate that many species of tapirs formerly inhabited warm and temperate Asia, Europe and North America in middle and late Tertiary times. During these epochs warm and even sub-tropical conditions prevailed in the northern hemisphere as far as the Arctic Circle, accompanied by luxuriant vegetation. These conditions were probably brought about in part by a greater extension of land in the North Atlantic, admitting of more or less easy communication between eastern and western hemispheres. The problem of the curious distribution of the tapir is thus solved.

The case of the camel is perhaps even more interesting than that of the tapirs, which it somewhat resembles. Camels are now inhabitants of the desert regions of western Asia and north Africa, and of no other part of the world. The related llamas and alpacas are found, however, in the Andes and temperate plains of South America. The two groups are almost as remote from one another as are the American and Malayan tapirs. The study of fossil forms has enabled the animal geographer to solve this problem of distribution. In all probability the camel and llama tribes originated in the central United States, where, towards the end of the Tertiary period, they became extinct. Previous to this catastrophe, however, some of the true camels migrated to the eastern hemisphere, probably by way of continuous land bridges in the North Pacific, and have left their survivors (camels and dromedaries) in the highlands and deserts of Asia. About the same time the llama group migrated southwards along the central mountain ranges into South America (driven, perhaps, by the adverse conditions which led to the extinction of many of their allies), where they found suitable conditions for survival south of the equator, in the high Andes and the arid Patagonian plains.

In order to describe and compare the distribution of the various species, genera and families of animals, it has been found necessary to mark out a certain number of extensive areas characterized by distinctive forms of animal life. The older naturalists usually adopted the great geographical and racial divisions—Europe, Asia, Africa, America (North and South) and Australia ; or the broader Arctic, temperate and tropical regions. They also used the general term " India or the Indies " for all Eastern tropical lands, sometimes including the tropics, as in our still common but misleading term " West Indies."

The first thoroughly scientific attempt to establish a series of regions that should accurately summarize the main facts for any extensive class of animals was made by Dr. P. L. Sclater, in 1857, for the class of birds, probably the best known of all the more extensive groups of animals. He was first to point out that Europe and Asia do not correspond to primary divisions of animal life, as shown by the striking similarity and considerable identity of both the birds and mammals across the whole of Europe and temperate Asia.

This formed his first great region, which he called the *Palae-arctic*, as including all Old World northern lands. Then came the tropical part of Asia, possessing hosts of peculiar species, genera and entire families of birds not known in the temperate zone. This he termed the *Indian* region, because India in a wide sense formed the bulk of it. Wallace altered this term in his " Geographical Distribution of Animals " (a classic which all interested in animal geography should read) to *Oriental* region, perhaps unnecessarily (as Wallace says), because it included Burma,

Siam and all the Malay islands, and this name has been widely adopted. It may be mentioned that the *Palaearctic* region also included north Africa as far as the Sahara, all its chief productions, both animals and plants, being closely allied to those of Europe or western Asia. The remainder of Africa, possessing a large proportion of peculiar types and being isolated from the rest of the world, constituted the *Ethiopian* region. The fourth region, or *Australian*, is perfectly characterized by its very distinctive marsupials, as well as an immense number of peculiar genera, and by several remarkable families of birds. The eastern half of the Malay Archipelago belongs to it, as do also New Zealand and most of the Pacific Islands. Then came South America, including the West Indies and Central America as far as Mexico, forming the *Neotropical* region, because it includes the whole tropics of the New World. Temperate and Arctic North America constitute the *Nearctic* region of Dr. Sclater, which has relations with both the Neotropical and Palaearctic regions, but has sufficient special features to be kept distinct. Madagascar is sometimes considered a distinct (Malagasy) region ; long isolation has allowed its fauna to differ strikingly from that of the African mainland. Lemurs abound, but neither anthropoid apes nor monkeys occur. Insectivores are numerous. These defenceless creatures thrive because the fauna of Madagascar lacks formidable carnivores.

LESSON 36

Further Study of Faunal Geography

(See Colour Frontispieces)

OUR last Lesson dealt with some of the facts connected with geographical distribution of animals. In this Lesson we shall follow up this study of *horizontal* distribution with a few selected facts and ideas concerning *vertical* or *bathymetric* distribution, that is to say, the distribution of animals at various depths in water and at various heights above the land.

Sea Fauna. Marine life is most abundant, both in numbers of genera or species and individuals, on the seashores in what is called the *littoral* region. Rocks exposed by the ebbing tide, rock-pools revealed at low water, and forests of seaweeds just below this mark, are situations in which animals of many different classes abound. Searching diligently, we should doubtless find sponges, hydroids, sea anemones and corals encrusting rocks and pebbles, turbellarians and nemertines sweeping gracefully over the ground, polychaete worms and Polyzoa peeping out of their protective tubes, and a great wealth of life wandering about and engaged in tasks of interest to the biologist. Here also we should find starfishes, brittlestars, sea-urchins and sea-cucumbers, as well as many kinds of Crustacea and Mollusca. Fishes also abound here ; and animals like seals, sea-cows and penguins may also be included.

Out in the oceans life is not so abundant, but here we recognize creatures which live near the surface or at slight depths, and forms which live only in the great depths of ocean. Of these, the former (or *pelagic* fauna) possesses the richer variety of types. In the pelagic fauna we should find (were we to tow fine silk or muslin nets through the appropriate regions of the sea) fora-minifera like *Globigerina*, radiolarians, many medusae of both Hydrozoa and Seyphozoa, numerous Siphonophora and Cteno-phora, crustaceans such as the Entomostraca, many gastropod, pteropod and cephalopod Mollusca, free-swimming Urochordata (commonly called salps), as well as abundant fishes and some aquatic mammals. The invertebrate section of the pelagic fauna is rendered inconspicuous by a glassy appearance, and the fishes and other vertebrates show less brilliant coloration than is met with in the littoral zone. Both invertebrate and vertebrate members of this fauna produce large numbers of eggs which, with the larvae of these animals, enrich the pelagic fauna temporarily at particular times of the year.

Animals of the deep sea, which constitute the *abyssal* fauna, though less abundant than their relatives nearer the surface and the shore, are more numerous than might be imagined when the physical condition under which they live (tremendous pressures, absence of light and lack of vegetation) is taken into account. Living in the mud of the plains forming the ocean beds at depths from 2,000 to 15,000 feet (consisting chiefly of Globigerina ooze) are the representatives of many animal groups. By dredging over the surface of the ocean floor we should capture some sponges, perhaps one of the elegant Hexactinellids, a few corals and medusae, many echinoderms but especially stalked crinoids and holothurians, prawn-like crustaceans and bony fishes. We should make only poor catches of crabs, molluscs and worms, because these animals are rare members of the abyssal fauna. We should encounter blind abyssal creatures, and many supplied with artificial lights of a phosphorescent character. Most forms would appear bizarre, the deep sea fishes having huge heads with gaping mouths and long needle-like teeth, and stomachs capable of accommodating fishes larger than their owners. The prawn-like crustaceans, we should find, are provided with enormously elongated legs, which enable them to walk as if on stilts over the soft ooze of the ocean bed.

The zoologist also arranges these aquatic animals in groups according to the nature of their movements. Types which drift interminably in the surface waters of the sea, among which are many medusae, siphonophores, sea-gooseberries and salps, constitute the drifting fauna of *plankton*. These creatures, like many invertebrate larval forms, can execute swimming movements but are swept along by ocean currents or drifts, against which their movements are of little avail. Distinct from planktonic types are animals with marked locomotory powers, among which we find bony and cartilaginous fishes, cuttlefishes and squids, as also a few crustaceans. These swimming animals constitute a second group, the *nekton*. Lastly we come to the types devoid of swimming organs, which creep over the sea floor or are permanently fixed to it. This group, the *benthos*, includes stalked crinoids, some starfishes and sea-cucumbers and a few worms.

Fresh-water Life. The animals living in fresh water, thus forming the *fresh-water fauna*, are conveniently divided into forms inhabiting lakes (*lacustrine* forms) and inhabitants of rivers and streams (*fluviatile* forms). Here we find many protozoa like amoebae, flagellates, sun animalcules and infusorians, but very few foraminifera and no radiolarians. There is but a single family of fresh-water sponges, the *Spongillidae*, and only a few genera of hydrozoa, of which *Hydra* is the most common. Actinozoa and Ctenophora are not represented in fresh water, and fresh-water starfish, sea-urchins and crinoids are unheard of. Many fresh-water worms are known, however, though bristle-worms are few. Turbellarians, nematodes and nemertines occur, as well as some aquatic relatives of the common earthworm.

Crustaceans are represented in fresh water by abundant Entomostraca, fresh-water shrimps and isopods, in addition to a few crabs and crayfishes. Bivalve and univalve molluscs are common in both lakes and rivers, but cuttlefishes, like salps, do not occur in fresh water. Many insects have larvae which inhabit fresh water, and a few spiders thrive in this medium. Fishes need no special mention except, perhaps, that elasmobranchs do not live in lakes and rivers, apart from the sting-rays of tropical American rivers. Among Amphibia, the Caducibranchiata and Perennibranchiata form conspicuous members of the fresh-water fauna, to which the related lung-fishes also belong. Sauropsidans are represented by the chelonians and crocodiles on the reptilian side, and by ducks and grebes on the avian side. Mammals like the duck-billed platypus, the hippopotamus and the otter also belong here. It might be mentioned, perhaps, that the fresh-water fauna may be divided, like the marine, into littoral, pelagic and deep-water forms, these last (like forms which live in subterranean caves, e.g. *Proteus*) being colourless and often blind.

Land Animals. Of members of the *terrestrial* fauna we have little to add to what has gone before. It is noteworthy that a land amoeba is known as the sole terrestrial protozoan apart from Mycetozoa. Sponges, coelenterates and echinoderms of dry land are unknown, but many crustaceans get along very well ashore. Of these, wood-lice, burrowing crayfish and land crabs are examples. *Peripatus* is a land animal, and myriapods, arachnids and many insects are typical land animals. The Pulmonata well represent the Mollusca on land, while some fishes (like the climbing perch, *Anabas*), many amphibians (frogs, apodans, toads and salamanders, for instance), abundant reptiles (lizards, snakes and tortoises), birds (especially the Ratitae) and the great majority of mammals are completely at home on land. Some terrestrial animals live in trees, and of these tree-kangaroos, monkeys and sloths are well known ; others spend their lives under stones or logs, like *Peripatus*, wood-lice and centipedes. The former are *arboreal* types, the latter *cryptozoic*.

Aerial Fauna. The zoologist lastly considers animals at home in the air, which form the *aerial* fauna. Of these, insects, many birds and bats are well-known examples. Other animals are able to propel themselves through the air for limited distances, or can glide from tree to tree over relatively great distances. Of such semi-aerial types we note the flying-fish (*Exocoetus*), flying dragon (*Draco*), a reptile, and the flying lemur (*Galeopithecus*), a mammal. Sometimes animals which live at high altitudes in the mountains are grouped together as the *alpine* fauna. The chamois, alpine hare and marmot occur in the Alps of Europe, while the yak, musk-deer and ibex characterize the Himalayas.

Scope of Ecology. Animal Ecology is the branch of Biology which deals with animals in their relation to their natural surroundings and to other living creatures, both animal and plant. The seashore, which we considered briefly as a single habitat, includes many regions showing wide differences. It may consist of limestone or granite, may be rocky headland, pebbly beach, shingle or sand, may be sheltered or exposed, and may be flooded by water from a river. Under such diverse conditions as these we cannot but expect wide differences in animal types and their relative abundance or scarcity. Few marine animals, for instance, can suffer exposure to heavy seas or high winds, though the opposite extreme of shelter may be equally hazardous. Sand and shingle beyond the reach of the waves form habitats for only a few animals.

The largest and most varied populations of the seashore are to be found where tidal action is moderate and where aerated water charged with numerous food organisms is manifest. The best opportunity to collect marine animals and plants of the littoral region is during the high-flowing spring tides.

The terrestrial region similarly includes many habitats, for animals and plants alike. Moorland and heath form the habitat of all our British reptiles, the lizard (*Lacerta*), the blind-worm (*Anguis*), the adder (*Pelias*) and the grass-snake finding conditions here much to their taste. Pastures and meadows form the homes of the skylark and corncrake, and here also we find field mice, voles and shrews, as well as moles, which, by devouring the larvae of many agricultural pests, earn for themselves the respect of the cultivator, though their burrows and mounds annoy the farmer. Woods and hedgerows form important habitats rich in number and variety of animal types, and even a single oak tree forms the home of over 200 insects, and may be considered as an important habitat by the entomologist. Such habitats as the ear of the field mouse or the food canal of the thrush are recognized by the ecologist, because each supports its own peculiar fauna.

Each individual animal lives in close relation to a peculiar set of associates, occupying a " niche " of its own. This term denotes the place of the animal in the society to which it belongs, its relation to food and shelter, friends and enemies. One niche is filled by birds of prey, which capture and devour mice and shrews. Kestrels fill this niche in open pastures, owls in oak woods. The ecologist prefers to regard the organism not as a unit, but as part of an assemblage or community, and visualizes an animal against a background of activities as well as objects. He thinks of the animal in terms of its niche.

LESSON 37

Animals in the Making

ALL living creatures have arisen from pre-existing living things and most animals are the products of that remarkable cell, the fertilized ovum, which results from the union of male and female reproductive cells or gametes. Some animals, it is true, are formed as buds from the parent's body and some eggs develop without having recourse to the process of fertilization. But with these comparatively rare exceptions we are not concerned in this Lesson.

The egg of *Amphioxus* is an appropriate subject for the study of early development, because it contains little yolk material, which, in the eggs of fishes, amphibians, reptiles and birds, by its abundance modifies early development in providing obstacles and mechanical difficulties. This egg, after fertilization, divides into two, four, eight, sixteen, thirty-two, sixty-four and larger number of cells, which arrange themselves in the form of a hollow ball or *blastula*. This division of the egg into cells is called *segmentation*. In *Amphioxus* the egg divides up completely, for which reason segmentation is said to be total or *holoblastic*. In the yolky eggs of fishes and birds abundant yolk prevents the formation of a simple blastula and, instead, a flat plate of cells is formed on the upper surface of the yolk. The generative protoplasm does not divide up completely, and segmentation is said to be partial or *meroblastic*.

One side of the blastula of *Amphioxus*, the future posterior side, becomes flattened. Here the cells are relatively large, and at one point they grow inwards towards the cells of the future dorsal surface, forming a lip which gradually extends completely round the flattened region. The tucking-in process is known as invagination, and the lip of the intucked region is the lip of an opening called the *blastopore*, the position of which marks the site of the future anus. In the region of the blastopore lip cells are multiplying rapidly and are growing over the posterior end of the embryo, a process (epiboly) which converts the simple blastula into a two-layered hemispherical cup. The cavity of the cup, which leads to the exterior by the blastopore, is the rudiment of the gut or *archenteron*, for the original cavity of the *blastula* (the *blastocoel*) has been obliterated between the two layers. Epiboly continues, resulting in an elongation of the embryo and a narrowing of the blastopore. The embryo at this stage is called a *gastrula*, its two layers of cells being ectoderm (outer) from which the nervous system, sense organs and epidermis will be formed, and endoderm (inner), which later forms the digestive canal and its derivatives like the liver and lungs. *Gastrulation*, therefore, results in the separation of two of the three germinal layers which characterize the triploblastic animal.

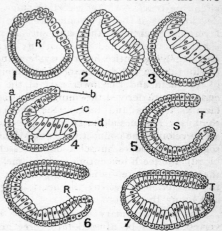

GASTRULATION IN AMPHIOXUS. Diagrams showing flattening (**1-2**) and infolding (invagination) (**3-5**) of the blastula, the blastocoel becoming obliterated and the archenteron established; (**6-7**) elongation of the gastrula and completion of gastrulation. a, ectoderm; b, dorsal lip of blastopore; c, endoderm; d, ventral lip of blastopore; R, blastocoel or segmentation cavity; S, archenteron; T, blastoporal opening.

Subsequent changes result in the separation from the endoderm of the third germinal layer (mesoderm) and the notochord. The latter is seen in the elongated gastrula as a strip of cells above the archenteron in the middle line, the mesoderm appearing as a wider strip on each side. Each mesoderm band develops a longitudinal groove open widely into the archenteron. As the groove deepens a pair of small pouches are cut off from it in front, their cavities being completely separated from the archenteron. The walls of the pouches form the first pair of somites, and behind these numerous other pairs are developed later. With the formation of the somites the three germ layers are initiated.

The details of germ layer formation vary in different members of the Vertebrata, but the general principles of early development are the same. The presence of yolk, or the development of the embryo within the body of the mother, results in modifications of the process of segmentation and gastrulation, often by a short circuiting process whereby certain stages are omitted. But the development of the embryonic structure from the three germinal layers is essentially the same in all vertebrates. From the ectoderm arise the epidermis (with its derivatives, scales, feathers and hairs), the entire nervous system and the sense organs, the lens of the eye, the membrane of the mouth and nose, the enamel of the teeth and the lower part of the digestive canal. From endoderm are derived the lining of the digestive canal (and of the larynx, trachea and lungs), the liver, pancreas, thyroid and thymus. The mesoderm supplies the raw materials from which are developed the connective tissues which bind the bodily parts together, the bones, muscles, blood vessels and heart (as also the blood), the teeth (excepting their enamel layer), the kidneys and their ducts, the reproductive organs, fat and bone marrow, and the membranes covering the heart, lungs and digestive viscera and lining the coelom.

This brief summary serves to show that the tissues of the vertebrate can be divided into three groups, according to the germ layers from which they are developed. Thus ectoderm gives rise to the most important nervous and sensory structures of the body, mesoderm to what are called the supporting tissues, and endoderm to the glandular tissues and the lining of the food canal. Ectoderm is all-important, and we might turn back to study briefly how this layer develops in the young gastrula. On one side of the elongated vertebrate embryo rather tall cells form a flat plate, the *neural* plate, the edges of which rise up as folds that meet in the middle line to form a hollow *neural tube*, the forerunner of the spinal cord and the brain. The first indication of brain development is a dilatation of the front end of the neural tube into three large vesicles, divisions marking out future fore-, mid-, and hind-brain. Eye rudiments appear as outpushings of the sides of the fore-brain, which form a cup (the optic cup) on each side of the embryo, connected with the fore-brain by a narrow stalk. The lens of the eye, however, forms as an ingrowth of superficial ectoderm towards the optic cup. As the ingrowth rounds itself off into a tiny vesicle it becomes associated with the optic cup (that part of the rudimentary eye which forms the retinal layer and the overlying pigment layer), with which it forms the eye. The ears develop as paired ingrowths of the ectoderm at the level of the hind-brain, the olfactory organs as similar pits situated just above the mouth.

We saw in previous Lessons that reptiles, birds and mammals are grouped together as *Amniota*, amphibians and fishes belonging to an alternative group of Chordata, the *Anamnia*. Amniota are so called on account of the protective fluid - filled membrane, the *amnion*, which envelops the developing embryo. This membrane is lacking in fishes and amphibians. The amnion arises in front of the head of the amniote embryo as an ectodermal

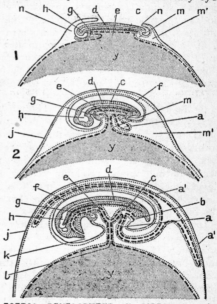

FOETAL DEVELOPMENT IN BIRDS. 1. early stage in the formation of the amnion; 2, stage with completed amnion and commencing allantois; 3, later stage. The outer line is the ectoderm; the endoderm is represented by a broken, the mesoderm by a dotted line. a, a', allantois; b, anus; c, notochord; d, spinal chord; e, archenteron; f, amnion; g, heart; h, brain; j, membrane; k, mouth; l, umbilical duct; m, m', coelom; n, amniotic fold; y, yolk-sac.

From Parker & Haswell, "Text-book of Zoology." Macmillan & Co.

fold, which grows backwards and soon covers the head. Up-growths on each side of the embryo continue amnion growth until this fold completely covers the embryo. Clear amniotic fluid fills the space between the embryo and the inner layer of the amnion folds (or true amnion), to serve as a water-cushion or shock absorber and prevent undue buffeting of the embryo. This membrane is sometimes imperfectly removed during human birth, when the individual is " born with a caul," and deemed lucky.

Another important accessory to embryonic development in higher vertebrates is the allantois. This appears in the chick embryo soon after amnion formation as a down-growth of the floor of the hind part of the archenteron. It is thus endodermal, but has an outer covering of mesoderm. It grows out into the extensive space between the true amnion and the fold outside this (the false amnion or chorion), which it soon completely fills. It thus comes to lie close beneath the porous egg shell, and being abundantly supplied with blood vessels, it is admirably fitted to function as a respiratory organ. This function of the allantois is of the greatest importance. Though the embryo has gill-slits closely resembling those of the fish, these are not functional breathing organs, so that respiratory exchanges effected during embryonic development depend upon this function of the allantois. But this embryonic organ serves another function, that of accumulating waste products during embryonic life. When development is complete the allantois is severed close to its connexion with the archenteron, the short stalk remaining to form the bladder of the new individual.

In the mammal embryo the allantois plays yet another part in the well-being of the embryo. At a very early time during pregnancy it establishes a connexion with the maternal tissues, and plays an important part in the transport of nourishment from the mother to the embryo. In this way the placenta is formed at the point where the allantois comes into contact with the wall of the womb. The minute blood capillaries of the allantois form a network in the substance of the placenta, so that the blood of the embryo is separated from that of the mother (circulating in the womb wall) only by the walls of these minute vessels. Interchange of nutrient and excretory substances is thus effected by diffusion without actual commingling of the two blood streams.

In studying animal development we are astonished to find similar organs developed in much the same manner, and to find structures like gill-clefts developed in the bird and mammal, as well as in the fish. Another feature which impresses the student of comparative embryology is the great similarity between embryos of vertebrates like the dogfish, lizard, chick and rabbit or Man during the early stages of development. During later development, however, such embryos tend to vary more and more, so that it becomes increasingly less difficult to distinguish between, say, the dogfish and chick embryos or the chick and the human embryo. These facts make it possible for us to detect closer or more distant relationship, because, in general, the more closely allied two animals happen to be, the longer do the embryonic resemblances persist. We have to wait longer to detect embryonic structural differences between Man and the anthropoid apes than to detect those between Man and the rabbit.

These facts are summarized in the so-called theory of recapitulation (the modern equivalent of Haeckel's Biogenetic Law), according to which the individual in its development to some extent repeats the history of the race to which it belongs. The embryos of the fowl and Man develop along the same general lines because the ancestors of both evolved along similar lines before finally diverging. Anthropoid ape and human embryos resemble one another for a longer period during development because these types diverged later in the evolutionary history of the Craniata. The theory is not to be accepted without reservations, for, as we have seen, mechanical difficulties may modify development. Also, embryonic organs do not necessarily appear in the same chronological order in different craniate types, nor in the order of their phylogenetic appearance ; the order of their development may vary, for reasons that are not quite clear. But the theory fits the most generalized facts, and provides the embryologist with a means of collaborating with the palaeontologist in deciphering problems of animal relationship.

LESSON 38

Growth in the Animal World

IN attempting to gain a few impressions of what is implied by the term " growth " we cannot do better than select the most familiar living organism, Man himself. Like other organisms, Man arises as the product of a single living cell, the fertilized ovum. This seemingly simple unit of living matter contains all his growth potentialities and, given suitable conditions for further development, holds within itself all the possibilities, hopes and aspirations of Nature's finest creation. Yet the ovum shows no trace of its inherent powers when viewed under the microscope. It is so small that if all the ova produced by a woman during her sexual life were laid in a row, this row would scarcely be one inch in length. It is apparently simpler than the lowly amoeba, but nevertheless embodies a fundamental and mysterious complexity, which has baffled the most original thinkers of this or any previous age.

Whilst travelling towards the womb, the fertilized ovum divides up to form a ball of cells or *blastocyst*, which is really a most efficient parasite. At this early stage, however, it is two-ended. One of its poles produces chemical substances which dissolve away the lining of the womb, so that the blastocyst sinks into it. The opposite pole closes the opening thus made after entry of the blastocyst. This two-endedness, or polarity, is the earliest sign of symmetry; it determines the position of the true embryonic rudiment and of the placenta. More than this we cannot say, because our concern is the subsequent enlargement or growth. From the stage mentioned to the completion of life before birth (pre-natal development), that is, for about forty weeks, the young human being remains an efficient parasite. In this short space of time the insignificant ovum grows and develops into a baby weighing about seven pounds and measuring about twenty inches.

The ovum is a simple spherical cell, but the baby's body is a vast community of billions of cells of diverse types and belonging to tissues like bone, nerve, muscle and blood. The cells resulting from division of the ovum have progressed along different lines to become fitted for a variety of tasks in the economy of the body after birth. They have, as we say, become *differentiated*. Growth, in the sense of size increase, has been accompanied by cell specialization or differentiation. Moreover, cells showing similar characters have been aggregated into tissues, and tissues of various kinds have been amalgamated into organ systems with special functions to perform. This unfolding of organs implies something over and above differentiation into cell types, and it is given the specific name *morphogenesis*.

It is better at this point to regard growth as mere enlargement, and if we do this we soon encounter a curious fact : the newly born infant has exhausted only about five per cent of the growth capacity of the fertilized ovum. If suitable conditions prevail after birth it can make use of the remaining capacity before growth finally ceases at maturity. There is a momentary cessation of growth at birth, while the newly born adjusts itself to a strange and new life, and when growth re-commences it is at a reduced rate. During the last month before birth the foetus increases its weight by one per cent each day. If such a percentage rate of growth continued after birth we should have to get used to seeing one-year-old infants as large as adults now, and youths larger than the sun. Such a phenomenally rapid percentage growth is impossible after birth, even in an expanding universe, and accordingly it is reduced.

Most parents have observed that a baby does not grow continuously in length, but grows by fits and starts. The first year after birth is one of relatively rapid growth, and it is followed by a longer period (until an age of five years is reached) of relatively slow growth. From five to seven comes a second phase of rapid growth, and this in turn is succeeded by slow growth until the eleventh or twelfth year is reached. At this time girls grow more rapidly than boys. A third period of fairly rapid growth follows, and wanes as puberty approaches. Biologists making a special study of infant growth refer to these alternating periods of rapid and slow growth in length as " springing-up " and " filling-out " periods respectively.

These rhythms mark important changes other than those of size. Rapid growth in height represents bone growth, which alternates with rapid growth of the teeth. And, as H. A. Harris has shown (in an article in " The Primary School "), the diseases and irregularities of childhood are peculiarly associated with the springing-up periods. These periods of rapid growth carry difficulties in their train and tax the resources of the infant to the utmost, so that the filling-out periods are of dire necessity in providing fresh resources for the next burst of growth.

Such rhythms of growth are not confined to Man, or to the mammalia, but characterize the growth period of most animals. Fishes like the plaice cease feeding about the end of November and fast throughout the winter, during which season growth is at a standstill. Since the growth rhythms here coincide with the seasons of the year they are termed *seasonal* growth cycles. This type of rhythm is common among marine creatures which depend for food on microscopic forms specially abundant in the sunlit months.

While the young animal is growing its proportions are subject to great change. The head of the newly born infant takes up about one-quarter of the entire length of the body. The head is well developed because it has followed the growth of the brain, which has an early start and a high initial growth rate, and attains one-fifth the weight of the adult brain at birth. The fore part of the body grows most rapidly at the outset, parts farther back growing progressively more slowly, thus we speak of an axial growth gradient with its high point in the head region.

The infant's body is relatively small at birth. It commences to grow later than the head and does not possess so high a growth rate. In order to attain normal adult proportions, therefore, it must grow more rapidly than the head after birth. The *sign* of the growth gradient must be reversed. The way in which the early growth advantage of the head is cancelled out after birth is readily seen by the fact that the body is four times the length of the head at birth, but eight times this length at maturity. The proportions of young animals are just as dissimilar from those of their parents. The calf and foal at birth have relatively huge heads and short, shallow bodies, poised on relatively long limbs.

Organs and parts which grow rapidly after birth are such as possessed slow growth rates before birth, and vice versa. All parts do not grow uniformly, nor do all organ systems. The skeleton grows at the same rate as the entire body and determines stature, though all parts of the skeleton do not grow at the same rate, the most interesting exceptions being adjacent bones. Thus, while the bone of the upper arm grows in length during six consecutive months of the year, the bones of the lower arm are increasing in girth ; and during the next six months these growth conditions are reversed.

Besides *skeletal* growth, several other types of growth are shown. The first or *neural* type is that of the brain, which develops precociously and grows rapidly in very early life, but progressively more slowly, until growth finally ceases. By the time an infant is two years old the brain has attained three-fifths of adult size, so that growth can afford to be more leisurely hereafter. Glands like the thymus and tonsils grow fairly rapidly during childhood, more slowly towards puberty, and not at all in adult life, sometimes losing weight instead. And the reproductive organs grow slowly in infancy, remain stationary from two to ten years of age, and grow very rapidly just prior to maturity.

GROWTH IN THE ANIMAL WORLD

Growth of the bodily organs involves continuous competition between various parts. It may be likened to a long-distance race, in which some competitors start well but lack staying power, some pursue an even course, and some start badly but end with a flourish. Unlike the competitors in such a race, however, the parts of the body all finish simultaneously, so to speak.

Every fertilized egg is a potential adult, but before it can realize this potentiality certain directive agencies located in the egg must meet with suitable conditions essential to normal development. The directive agencies still have an air of mystery around them, but are believed to be resident in the genes, which make up the chromosomes of the egg nucleus in much the same way as individual beads are strung together to make a necklace. Genes represent the physical basis of heredity, being the elements handed on from one generation to the next. By the interaction of genes with food materials present in the egg, as well as materials to be obtained by various means in later development, chains of chemical reactions occur, and result in successions of complex syntheses, cell divisions and arrangements, which culminate in the production of an organism .resembling its parents.

Food is obviously an important factor in growth and development, for without food there is no source of energy to feed the flame of life and no building material to assemble in the body of the growing animal. The nutritional value of the various food substances and the rôle played by the vitamins are fully dealt with in Lessons 12–14 in our Course in Physiology (Volume 3).

Other important agencies in growth are the secretions of the ductless glands or endocrines, especially the thyroid and the pituitary body. Remove the thyroid of the frog tadpole and it fails to change into a frog, unless it is provided with thyroid secretion or minced thyroid gland, when metamorphosis occurs quickly. The iodine feeding of tadpoles yields the same result as the feeding of thyroid gland, for the potency of the gland is correlated with its iodine content, and this structure is really an effective iodine trap. Lack of the iodine-containing principle (thyroxine) secreted by the thyroid leads to that peculiar dwarfed human condition known as cretinism, in which there is disproportionate growth of certain organs and parts of the body. Thyroid or thyroxine feeding restores growth to its normal relative rates. The pituitary gland is linked with the thyroid in its working.

LESSON 39

Philosophy of Zoology

I N foregoing Lessons of this Course we have referred not infrequently to various topics of a general nature, such as evolution and variation, which include not only the concrete facts of Zoology, but also abstract generalizations deduced from these facts ; these topics form the subject matter of the philosophy of Zoology. We have observed that an animal has a certain structure and shows affinities with other animals, that it develops in a certain manner, and is found only in certain geographical and geological situations. There is only one satisfactory explanation of these facts. Animals, like plants, have come to be what they are by a slow process of evolution, which has gone on through geological ages from an early period in the earth's history to the present day. We have already seen numerous evidences supporting this doctrine of evolution in previous Lessons in this Course and in the Course in Biology, and can be content here to summarize the four principal types of evidence.

The first is *morphological*, and includes the common structural plan of series of animals like fishes, amphibians, reptiles, birds and mammals. Any other view put on the facts would fail to explain why we see the same bony elements in such apparently different structures as the wing of the bat and the bird, the foreleg of the horse and the tapir, the arm of Man and the flipper of the whale. Vestigial structures like the vermiform appendix of Man and the splint bones of the horse's leg, which are functional and important in one animal and useless and redundant in another, would be equally difficult to explain apart from this doctrine. The second type of evidence is *embryological*, and includes the fact that allied animals of one phylum or class have similar embryonic forms, more similar the more closely allied the adults appear to be. Sometimes structures seen during development are permanent and functional in animals lower in the scale of life, as are the gill clefts of the Amniota. The biogenetic law demands an evolutionary doctrine to explain the many facts it covers.

(636)

PHILOSOPHY OF ZOOLOGY

Embryology is supported by palaeontology, which supplies the third type of evidence, *palaeontological*. Imperfect as is the fossil record of life on the earth, it shows how life has progressed from the apparently simple to the more complex by numerous experiments (some of which failed, however) spread over millions of years. Thus we speak of the Age of Fishes or that of Reptiles—and in this order—before we come chronologically to the Age of Mammals. The history of some modern forms, like the horse, elephant and camel, has been worked out in great detail from the fossil record, with confirmation of the so-called evolution theory.

The last type of evidence, geographical, includes the peculiarities of geographical distribution of types like the camels and the llamas (see Lesson 35, page 616) radiating from centres which, perhaps, have proved entirely unsuitable to some of their unsuccessful allies and yet find themselves restricted in their choice of a suitable habitat by geographical barriers.

Problem of Evolution. Controversy among biologists at the present time centres around the way in which evolution has occurred. In 1809 Lamarck made the first noteworthy contribution to this problem in his "Philosophie Zoologique." He inclined to the view that evolution is attributable to the action of the environment, or the conditions of life, on the organism, and, particularly, to the use and disuse of parts and organs. The giraffe made continuous efforts to reach higher and higher for the leaves which formed its food, and this, continued through many generations, resulted in the production of the animal's long neck. The disappearance of the hind limbs of snakes or cetaceans he explained by progressive diminution through countless generations as a result of disuse. This question of the "inheritance of acquired characteristics" is not in favour with zoologists at the present time. Even if it does take place, which they consider extremely doubtful, it is difficult to see how it could account for the evolution of the many groups of animals known to Zoology. Weissman convinced zoologists that while there is no single instance in which the effects of use and disuse have been proved to be transmitted, there is abundant proof that they are not.

Darwin's important contribution to this question is well known as the theory of Natural Selection, with its buttresses, the biological phenomena equally well known as the "struggle for existence " and " variation." An indubitable struggle for existence is enforced early in the lives of some animals, like fishes and marine invertebrates, which produce tremendous numbers of eggs mostly to form food for other creatures. The struggle among the larval forms met with in the sea is especially keen, and is accompanied by the destruction of immense numbers of potential adult individuals. On land the struggle is keen between different animals and animals of the same kind alike, though keenest between the most closely allied species, which may share the same food and physical conditions of life. Between carnivores and their herbivorous prey we see sharp rivalry ; the claws and teeth of the oppressor are opposed by swiftness and camouflage of the oppressed.

Awareness of the enacting of the struggle for existence led Darwin to formulate his principle of Natural Selection to account for evolution. He took into account also the fact that no two individuals of the same species, or even born of the same mother, are ever exactly alike, and that the differences they show are often inheritable—that is, he took into account variation. Darwin had great faith in the importance of inborn variations, and believed the characters of a species to be in a state of constant change, making it possible by selecting in certain directions to preserve new variations. Species, he considered, were formed by the accumulation of variations in one direction—a slow process, but one spread over vast periods of time. Thus he maintained that the numerous varieties of pigeons known to fanciers as carriers, fantails, pouters, tumblers and others, which differ greatly from the wild rock pigeon interbreed freely with this latter type and have undoubtedly been derived from it. If Man during his brief reign can produce forms as different as these, is there any process of selection operative in Nature that during much vaster periods of time can cause offspring of the same ancestor to differ as markedly as existing species do ?

The main point of Darwin's " Origin of Species " is that such a process of Natural Selection does operate. Members of a species which are best fitted to conquer adversity (enemies, food scarcity, extremes of temperature and the like) will survive to perpetuate their line, an ever-increasing standard of fitness being held out to successive generations. When conditions change for part of a species (due, let us say, to migration into a new environment) a new standard will be set up, and individuals varying in characters which confer advantage on them in the struggle will tend to survive at the expense of individuals lacking advantageous variations. By continued selection of variations in this or similar ways numerous classes, orders, families and genera, as well as species, within a phylum will arise.

A third theory of evolution is well known as the theory of development in straight lines or *orthogenesis*. The classical example chosen to illustrate this theory is the horse. The progressive evolution of the horse, however, does not require the theory, since it can be explained according to the theory of Natural Selection without involving any new principle. Moreover, the theory of orthogenesis is altogether insufficient to explain how diverse animals like invertebrates and vertebrates arose. By straight line evolution we cannot conceive of the development of a ventral nerve or a compound eye in any vertebrate.

All variations are not inheritable ones, and the ones which are not inherited are sometimes spoken of as *modifications*, as distinct from inherited ones or *mutations* (what Darwin called ' single variations "). A mutation is a novelty of sudden appearance. Darwin cited the case of a peculiar ram with a long body and short legs which suddenly appeared amid sheep of ordinary strain and transmitted its special characters to its offspring. From this type of sheep breeds have been produced, one virtue of which is an inability to jump walls and fences. It must not be supposed, however, that mutations are necessarily due to changes undergone by the chromosomes (the physical basis of the inheritance) during maturation of the germ cells, since they have been known to appear in forms which reproduce asexually, as well as in forms in which chromosomes have not been demonstrated, e.g. bacteria.

Mendelism and Evolution. The discoveries of the Austrian abbot, Mendel, greatly enriched our knowledge of the science of heredity. (*See* Biology, Lessons 14, 15, 16, 17.) The results of Mendel's researches led to the formulation of two important principles, the so-called *law of segregation* and that of the *independent recombination of units*, which teach us much about the relation the hereditary constitution of an organism bears to that of its parents. The units of the hereditary constitution, which, together with the interplay of environmental factors, determine the characters of an organism, are conceived as self-producing particles of a chemical nature (genes) which collectively build up the chromosomes. The genes (sometimes loosely called factors) occur in pairs, except prior to gamete formation, when individual units separate to yield one type of unit to each gamete. This is the implication of Mendel's first principle. The second principle indicates that different kinds of genes behave independently—i.e. each kind of unit follows the first principle as though others did not exist.

We can turn directly to the possibility of Mendel's principles as a cause of evolution. An important point in this respect is that mutations are inherited according to such principles. Moreover, because of the Mendelian mechanism of sexual reproduction they occur in new chromosomal combinations. New characters may originate, therefore, as a result of mutation and recombination, varying animals showing new variations, some at least of which are inherited. If an inheritable variation is one that confers an advantage on its possessor in the struggle for existence it will tend to persist, owing to survival of its possessor, while a non-advantageous inheritable variation will tend to be lost through the failure of its possessor in the struggle. Modern zoologists incline to this modified form of the theory of Natural Selection, and regard it as a most important factor in the production of adaptive change, and in the evolution of new forms. Non-inheritable variations can be given fuller expression in the individual by optimum conditions of life, but cannot lead to the production of new life forms.

Books Recommended for Further Study. " Text-book of Zoology," Sedgewick (Geo. Allen and Unwin) ; " Biology of Birds," Sir J. A. Thomson (Sidgwick and Jackson) ; " The Social Insects," W. M. Wheeler (Kegan Paul) ; " Embryology and Evolution," G. R. de Beer (O.U.P.) ; " Animal Biology," J. B. S. Haldane and J. Huxley ; " Vertebrate Morphology," G. R. de Beer (Sidgwick and Jackson) ; " Biological Principles," J. H. Woodger (Kegan Paul) ; " Experimental Embryology," G. R. de Beer (O.U.P.) ; " Evolution," Sir J. A. Thomson and Sir P. Geddes (Home University Library ; Thornton Butterworth) ; " Text-book of Entomology," Imms (Methuen) ; " Evolution of Man," G. Elliot Smith (O.U.P.) ; " Animal Ecology," C. S. Elton (Sidgwick and Jackson).

This Lesson concludes our Course in Zoology.

END OF VOLUME SIX